rilsk

Anadyr

Petropavlovsk
Kamchatsky

Okha

Komsomolsk-na-Amure

Yuzhno-
Sakhalinsk

Bratsk

Khabarovsk

Blagoveshchensk

Irkutsk

Vladivostok

Past, Present & Future

OIL OF Russia

Also by Vagit Alekperov

Russian Vertically Integrated Oil Companies
Russian Oil: A Top Manager's View

Edited by Vagit Alekperov

The Eve of the Petroleum Era
Soviet Union's Oil
New Russia's Oil

Vagit Alekperov

Past, Present & Future

OIL OF Russia

East View Press
Minneapolis

OIL OF RUSSIA: PAST, PRESENT AND FUTURE

Translated from the Russian by
Paul B. Gallagher and Thomas D. Hedden
Assisted by Todd Jackson
pbg translations, inc.
Edited by Alex Lane and Laurence Bogoslaw
Managing Editor Ana K. Niedermaier

Cover Design by OROPACK Design Bureau

Library of Congress Cataloging-in-Publication Data

Alekperov, V. IU. (Vagit IUsufovich), 1950-
 Oil of Russia : past, present, and future / Vagit Alekperov ; translated from
the Russian by Paul B. Gallagher and Thomas D. Hedden. -- 1st ed.
   p. cm.
 Includes bibliographical references and index.
 ISBN 978-1-879944-07-7 (hardcover)
 1. Petroleum industry and trade--Russia (Federation)--History. 2. Lukoil
(Firm)--History. I. Title.
 HD9575.R82A6194 2011
 338.2'7280947--dc22

                            2010040119

Published by East View Press,
an imprint of East View Information Services, Inc.
Minneapolis

Printed in the United States of America

First Edition 2011

1 3 5 7 9 10 8 6 4 2

CONTENTS

Note to Readers

Vagit Alekperov needs no introduction to anyone in the oil business. As president of LUKOIL, Russia's largest non-state-owned oil and gas company, he is well known for his business acumen, inexhaustible vigor, and genuine charm. Even if your life is only slightly affected by petroleum (and I am willing to bet that if you are holding this book—it is), you are probably familiar with his name.

It may be less well known that Vagit is also a member of the Russian Academy of Natural Sciences. Over the past decade, Academician Alekperov has led a team of researchers seeking to salvage the history of the Russian oil industry from the oubliette of tsarist and communist-era archives. On reflection, this distraction from the demands of business reveals itself as a wise investment. In an industry where project-planning horizons are decades long and global in scope and where quotidian acts often reach historic proportions, a keen appreciation of history is not just a reward but a prerequisite for success. We can be grateful that Vagit is sharing his insights into a subject that has long suffered from regrettable obscurity and lack of access.

Russia's oil industry has always been important to Russia and to the global energy supply system as a whole. Its image, however, has so often been distorted by a combination of ideology, fear, and romance that many promising commercial opportunities have withered or failed to materialize in the resulting atmosphere of uncertainty and mistrust. My personal and business experience in Russia has been decidedly positive. I credit this in no small part to my relationship with Vagit and his company. Thus, it is a special pleasure to see his unfiltered account of the Russian oil industry make its debut in English. I am hopeful that the understanding it fosters will strengthen and multiply constructive cooperation with our Russian partners and help promote global energy and environmental security.

Oil of Russia: Past, Present and Future is both a result and a welcome symbol of Russia's increasing openness and renewed engagement in the world.

Jim Mulva
Chairman and Chief Executive Officer
ConocoPhillips
December, 2010

Foreword

In the early 21st century, mankind has encountered serious global problems that pose considerable complications for the further development of civilization. Who can forget the major climate changes that produced heavy snowfalls in various European countries this past winter and brought snow even to New Zealand in October 2009? Over the past 30 years, the world's average temperature has risen 1.1°F. Meanwhile, a more arid climate has already shortened the growing season in the Sahel region of sub-Saharan Africa, fueling ongoing armed conflicts in a region already suffering from a shortage of water and foodstuffs. And in Central America, stronger hurricanes threaten to seriously undermine the economy of developing countries and destabilize the political system, thereby encouraging a new flow of migrants.

Here we should also include the visible consequences of biosphere degradation: in the last two centuries, the world has lost two-thirds of its forests, two-thirds of its arable land, and seen its ocean, sea, and river bioresources seriously depleted. The Earth's biodiversity is threatened—110 vertebrate species have already completely disappeared. Mankind is beginning to experience a shortage of drinking water and nearly 1.2 billion of the Earth's population now suffer from a shortage of water resources, while 2.6 billion have no access to elementary sewage systems.

These alarming trends are precisely why the Millennium Declaration, adopted by the UN in 2000 and approved by all its members, identified the assurance of sustainable environmental development and the formation of a global development partnership as its principal goals.

At present, the ever-faster globalization of the world economy due to objective factors in the development of modern civilization requires further and further extension of the international division of labor and economic specialization at the national level, acceleration of scientific and technical progress, computerization, enhancement of the roles of financing and services in all commercial fields (especially in transportation and communications), and reduction in the economic distance between countries to bring them closer together and unite them. Literally before the eyes of a single generation, enormous new regions in the former stagnant periphery and areas of human activity have been introduced into the world economy. The Internet and mobile telephone communications have destroyed the mental boundaries between countries, bringing hundreds of millions of people of various nationalities and faiths together to share common human values and scientific advances. It is this very rapprochement and unification of countries and ethnic groups that reveals globalization's most important economic essence: globalization as a worldwide process of growing economic interdependence among all the world's countries, with a tendency toward a gradual transition toward the development of those countries based on a higher principle, that of economic complementarity.

Yet, despite the benefits of a more interconnected world economy, this new era of globalization and development is not without its own consequences. In particular, the current state of the world's energy industry and the prospects for its development give great cause for concern. World energy consumption is growing rapidly, by an average of 20% per decade over the past 30 years. Added to this is the fact that the first eight years of the new century were marked by both a deepening of old factors and the appearance of many new ones and trends in the world energy markets and in international relations, primarily on the oil and gas issue, which require thorough analysis and day-to-day observation for the adoption of decisions at the international level.

An additional cause for serious concern came in 2009 from the results of the first comprehensive study by the World Energy Agency (WEA); this study verified the status of more than 800 oil fields in various parts of the world, which account for some 75% of the world's total "black gold" reserves. The study found that most of these oil fields had already passed their production peak and production was now falling nearly twice as fast as forecast just two years before. According to WEA data, world oil production is declining 6.7% annually, while a similar study in 2007 showed a decline of only 3.7% annually.

The WEA reviews of recent years have consistently raised the question of the serious imbalance of world energy generation in the long-term future. If current world economic trends continue, a possible physical shortage of oil production in 2030 is forecast, amounting to 12.5 million barrels a day (with a demand of 116 million barrels). That is, the oil deficit could exceed 10%. In turn, according to data from the Russian Institute of Energy and Finances, demand for primary energy resources in 2015–2030 will grow at rates that could create difficulties with supply, with a baseline scenario for world economic development that is unsustainable from the standpoint of ensuring energy supply in future decades.

Indeed, the latest WEA study warns that if governments continue present policies, global energy demand in 2030 will be 50% higher than it is today. Developing economies will account for 74% of the growth in demand, with China and India together accounting for 45%. Furthermore, the world's growing population, which by 2030 will reach 8 billion, will play a considerable role in this process, with developing nations accounting for 97% of population growth.

Such trends will have a substantial economic impact, with the world community having to spend considerable additional financial resources in the foreseeable future to address the problems brought on by declining production and increasing demand. By the most optimistic estimates, energy development through 2030 will cost $22 trillion—more than 1% of the total world GDP over that period.

According to most leading experts, the continuation of current trends in world economics and energy policy, combined with a failure to take proactive steps to improve energy efficiency, could have critical consequences. Furthermore, neither advances in renewable forms of energy nor the revival of nuclear power or a coal renaissance alone can solve the problem of the growing unsustainability of energy markets and the energy deficit.

Thus, the priority for the immediately foreseeable future continues to be the production and discovery of conventional types of hydrocarbon resources: oil, coal, and especially gas.

Yet this is not without its own unique challenges. The effect of nonlinear globalization processes is that at its current stage of development, the world energy market is encountering a whole series of problems, the most important of which are high, unstable oil prices, the growing dependence of many countries on energy exports, the depletion of major hydrocarbon fields, and a lack of investment resources to develop hard-to-reach crude hydrocarbon reserves and other unconventional fuel sources.

At present, the instability of the global oil market is a direct threat to the economy of most countries of the world and the world economy as a whole—and this is why, as the G-8 leaders have repeatedly stressed, the problem of ensuring global energy security is at the top of the world community's agenda. It is in this respect that mankind now badly needs breakthrough ideas capable of setting a basic course of action into the future in order to outline at least intermediate phases and criteria for assessing this complex process. Several years ago, Russia advanced a real plan for energy security, intended to combine the interests of producers, consumers, and transit states. Like any call for reconciliation, the plan was built on compromise, and strove to ensure transparency, stability, and predictability of national oil and gas market regulation systems. However, there are now serious obstacles on the path to realization of this plan, which unfortunately remain strong in world trade, undermining the principles of globalization.

The leading nations of the world have recently begun actively implementing new energy strategies, which are primarily aimed at protecting national interests and limiting the scale of external impacts. In other words, energy protectionism and nationalism have become the main theme of many countries' political policy, despite declarations and professed understanding of the need to solve global energy problems together.

The appearance of such attitudes inevitably exacerbates the situation in international relations, forming new international blocs and reinforcing existing ones on whose basis energy interests rest or are integrated. Ideas and plans for "energy alternatives" can often be found in the press and in statements by various political figures. But these proposals are generally unconstructive due to the one-sidedness of the proposed initiatives and sometimes are simply downright utopian.

Today, special responsibility for the world's fate rests with the Russian Federation, which not only produces a large share of the world's energy, but also participates actively in international energy cooperation and thereby makes a substantial contribution to ensuring global energy security. Russia currently produces 10.5% of the world's primary energy and exports about half of its own fuel production.

What is more, our country continues to hold first place in the world in oil production, with 9.91 million barrels a day in July 2009, which incidentally is a record for the past decade.

As a major player on the world oil and gas markets, Russia occupies a key position in the international energy security system. For example, annual deliveries of Russian energy resources to the European Union are equivalent to more than 440 million tons of oil, or nearly a third of EU energy consumption.

Russia's geographic position, energy potential, and powerful oil and gas transportation system enable it to develop cooperation both with traditional partners in the West and with the countries of central Asia and the Far East, as well as the US and Canada.

It is not a stretch to say that Russia's transit potential plays an important role in shaping the world's energy architecture. Today, our country's trunk pipelines extend nearly 139,000 miles, including 29,000 miles of oil pipelines, 97,500 miles of gas pipelines, and 12,000 miles of petroleum products pipelines. The trunk pipeline system carries 100% of Russia's produced gas, 99% of its produced oil, and over 50% of its refined petroleum products. The trunk oil pipeline system includes 387 pumping stations, and the petroleum products pipeline system has 100.

At present, deliveries of crude hydrocarbons to Europe and the Central Asian and Caspian regions all pass through Russian territory. Our country is essentially becoming a unique locomotive of the world energy market and a backbone for further development of the global economy and adherence to the principle of sustainable development throughout the world.

We should note that Russia's growing prestige today in the world arena is due primarily to well-considered policy, domestic political and social stability, and good opportunities for growth of the country's economic potential.

However, like most of the world, the consequences of the present global financial crisis have subjected the Russian economy to a very serious strength test. Yet, beginning in March 2009, clear signs of economic and financial stabilization have become apparent.

In late July 2009, the Russian government approved the basic outlines of national budget policy for 2010–2012. In this plan, the successful realization of the "Strategy for Development of the Russian Federation Through 2020" will guarantee that our country will overcome the consequences of the world crisis and soon adopt a path of sustainable development. Essentially, unlike a purely technocratic approach concentrating solely on questions of scientific and technical development and economic efficiency, the innovative strategy through 2020 aspires to a fundamentally new type of development. It is decisively based on a transition from a raw-material economy to an innovation-based economy, with comprehensive stimulation of innovation. Russia's strategy for developing innovation also relies on one of our main competitive advantages—the realization of human potential, the most effective use of our people's knowledge and skills, to continuously improve technology, economic performance, and our society's life as a whole. This is a crucial breakthrough strategy that Russian society must implement with updated "human capital."

It is a well-known truth that in order to move forward it is necessary to look to the past. The book you hold in your hands—*Oil of Russia: Past, Present and Future*—does just that. It presents a comprehensive history of the origins and development of the Russian oil industry, a history that is being made available in English for the first time. It is my belief that the numerous examples and experiences of Russia's oil pioneers contained in this text will no doubt prove instructive for today's readers and industry leaders.

And if, as I genuinely hope, the reader of this book manages to gain an understanding of the role that historical forces have played in the Russian oil and gas industry and in turn the enormous responsibility this industry bears to the world community, the author will consider his modest mission to have been accomplished.

Vagit Alekperov
President
LUKOIL Oil Company
December, 2010

Chapter ONE

The Russian Empire's "Black Gold"

Oil on the Tablets of Ancient History

The ancients called oil "the blood of the earth." It seeped up from cracks in the ground, floated on streams, spread pungent aromas and sometimes spontaneously combusted, attracting the brave and the curious with its power and fascinating character. The modern Russian word for petroleum—*neft*—is derived from the word *nafata*, which came into Greek from an Old Persian word meaning "to seep, to ooze." As civilized technology evolved, oil continued to reward its investigators with rich fruits from its inexhaustible potential.

Oil has been known to humanity since remote antiquity. Archeologists have found that it was extracted and used as early as the sixth or fifth millennium before the Common Era. The oldest known fields are in the area of the Dead Sea, on the banks of the Euphrates River, on the Kerch Peninsula in the Black Sea, and in China's Szechuan Province, some of the earliest sites of civilization.

Oil or its various naturally occurring forms are mentioned in many ancient writings. According to biblical tradition, Noah smeared his ark inside and out with tar for impermeability to save his family from the Great Flood. The Bible also relates that during the construction of the Tower of Babel, pitch was used as a cementing material: "They said to each other: 'Come, let's make bricks and bake them thoroughly.' They used brick instead of stone, and tar [*chemar*] for mortar."[1] *Chemar*, a Hebrew word commonly translated as tar or bitumen, is the highly viscous bituminous material remaining from the weathering of petroleum. Similar material was also used in the construction of the Great Wall of China and the Hanging Gardens of Babylon. Tar was also used for waterproofing the ancient dams on the Euphrates River.

Many historians support the view that the area of the Dead Sea was once the site of 13 ancient cities, dominated by the city of Sodom, all of which were destroyed by the pressure of ground water mixed with petroleum and by explosions of gas contained therein.

There is evidence that the ancient Egyptians obtained oil from the Dead Sea and used it for mummification, as well as for various medicinal purposes. In particular, tar ointments were used to treat scabies and boils, and long "baths" in petroleum pools were used to ease joint pain.

According to the Greek historian Xenophon (ca. 430–355/354 BCE), the ruins of ancient Babylon show that heated asphalt was used in building the temples of the Hanging Gardens. The grandiose mosaic roadways

1

and magnificent inscribed plates in the garden palaces of Babylon were cemented with asphalt. Residents of Babylon smeared wooden walls and doors with rock tar to protect against adverse climatic conditions. Archeologists also have found an asphalt floor in the ruins of ancient Kassan (near modern Baghdad, Iraq). Petroleum for these purposes would have been supplied from sources near a tributary of the Euphrates, 120 miles from Babylon.

The *Arthasastra* of the Indian thinker Chanakya (Kautilya), who lived in the fourth and third centuries BCE, provides reports of experiments with "flammable oil." And an enormous basin, the bottom and sides of which were covered with a layer of bituminous material, was found in the ruins of the ancient Indian city of Mohenjo-Daro.

The ancient Greek medic and scholar Hippocrates (fifth to fourth centuries BCE) gave a series of medicinal recipes employing petroleum for the treatment of skin diseases. The works of Herodotus, the so-called father of history (490/480–ca. 425 BCE), mentioned oil sources on Zante, an island in the Ionian Sea, while another scholar of antiquity, Plutarch (ca. 45–ca. 127 CE), gave a description of a continuously burning source near the Median capital of Ecbatana (modern Hamadan, Iran). Plutarch noted that the origin of the oil was unknown, but speculates that "the liquid substance that feeds the flame… proceeds from a soil that is unctuous and productive of fire."

Mentions of petroleum continue in the works of Roman historians from the periods of the Republic and early Empire. Pliny the Elder (Gaius Plinius Secundus, 23/24–79 CE) wrote in his *Natural Histories* that petroleum had qualities similar to those of sulfur, and that the mythical enchantress Medea allegedly smeared her rival's crown with it so that, during a sacrificial offering, the crown caught fire and her rival was burned alive. In another work, he praised petroleum's wondrous curative properties: "And this substance heals cataracts, stops bleeding, relieves toothache, and even promotes eyelash growth."

The Roman physician Pedanius Dioscorides (first century CE) mentions lamps burning a "Sicilian oil" that came from sources near Agrigento. In the ancient encyclopedia attributed to Bishop Julius Africanus (ca. 224 CE), we can find a recipe for self-igniting flame, which also includes liquid natural asphalt.

Texts from the early days of alchemy, the so-called Alexandrian epoch of the fourth and fifth centuries CE, promoted improvements of the oil distillation process and a certain modernization of laboratory equipment and apparatus.

When Aristotle taught that "nature does nothing in vain," he recognized that people will always search for the meaning and purpose of things. They found many uses for oil, adapting it to the needs and abilities of civilization, and its meaning evolved alongside.

The Secret of Greek Fire

It is also evident that petroleum was actively used in ancient military applications. The invention of "Greek fire" was a genuine military sensation in antiquity. This new type of weapon considerably strengthened the military might of countries possessing the secret of its preparation and military application.

Historians have yet to establish who invented the "napalm of antiquity." Some believe it was Byzantine alchemists, while others contend that the secret of its preparation was already known in Ancient Greece. Mentions of such an igneous material can also be found in Chinese chronicles.

Evidence of the use of Greek fire appears throughout the history of the Byzantine Empire. In the latter half of the seventh century, the Empire came under attack from a new threat—the Arab Caliphate, a powerful Arab state built on the tenets of the new religion of Islam, with its capital located at Medina. The Arab Caliphate began military actions against the Byzantine Empire, and in 655 Arab and Byzantine fleets met off the coast of Lycia. The imperial fleet, commanded by Emperor Constantine II, outnumbered the Arab fleet, but ultimately lost the battle. Fourteen years later, Arab ships reached the strategic Sea of Marmara, and in 670 they captured the city of Cyzicus on its coast, turning its port into a major base for their navy. At the same time, the Arab land army moved on Chalcedon (modern district of Kadikoy in Istanbul), and a strong detachment took the coastal area, effectively cutting the Byzantine capital of Constantinople off from the sea (and partly from the land as well) for nine years. Reprieve came only during the winter, when the Arabs would withdraw their navy to Cyzicus to protect it from winter storms.

In 672 Arab troops captured the strategic city of Smyrna down the Anatolian coast and substantially increased their naval strength. Then, beginning in 674, their assault on the Empire intensified. There no longer appeared to be any hope; Byzantium could only be saved by a miracle.

And such a miracle occurred. In a fortuitous turn of events, Byzantine Emperor Constantine IV Pogonatos (652–685) was unexpectedly informed that a certain Kallinikos, a refugee either from Baalbek, Syria, or from Heliopolis, was offering his services in the defense of Constantinople using a previously unknown and formidable weapon. (Incidentally, the name Kallinikos, translated from Greek, means "good victor.") The unusual incendiary compound and a unique device that enabled the compound to be thrown distances that were quite considerable for the time entered the arsenal of the Byzantine navy shortly thereafter. Once equipped with this new weapon, the imperial fleet was ordered to sail to Cyzicus and engage the Arabs.

Upon reaching the Arab fleet, the Byzantine sailors unleashed a furious attack using the unusual devices. The Arab ships were engulfed in

3

flames, and clouds of black smoke filled the sky. The very sea appeared to be on fire. The conflagration lasted over a day, consuming nearly the entire Arab fleet. The frightful material (at the time, the Byzantines called it "liquid fire") literally turned the Arab warships to ash, and their human losses were enormous. "The Greeks have a fire like lightning from the sky. They sent it at us and completely burned everything in their path, so we could not defeat them," said one surviving Arab in describing the sea battle with the Byzantines. Thus Greek fire came to play a pivotal role in preserving the empire of "the second Rome."

A hundred and fifty years after the battle, the Constantinople monk Theophan wrote in his chronicle, based on the reports of historians whose works have unfortunately not survived, that 30,000 men died at Cyzicus on that day. This may have been an exaggeration common for the time, but either way, it is clear that the Arab fleet never fully recovered from the defeat, while the Byzantine Empire continued to survive for nearly another seven centuries.

Modern researchers have repeatedly suggested that the secret of the successful battle application of Greek fire by the Byzantine military lay not only in its composition and the precise proportions of its ingredients, but in the method of its delivery. The ancient inventor Kallinikos likely installed boilers with siphons on the ships, thereby creating an effective means of delivering the incendiary mixture to the target. The jet of liquid flame, forced under pressure from a largely sealed boiler through a siphon tube, surpassed in weight and speed anything that could have been expected from the projectiles of the time. On reaching the target vessel, the fire immediately spread along the decks, making it impossible to fight.

The composition of "Greek fire" and the device for its use in battle were held in strictest secrecy in Byzantium. In his treatise *De Administrando Imperio* [*On the Governance of the Empire*], Constantine VII Porphyrogenitus (945–959), mentioned the nations whose ambassadors pestered him with "stupid and unworthy" requests to let them use "liquid fire." Advising his son how to reject barbarian requests diplomatically, Constantine VII writes: "You can object and refuse in these words: 'God revealed and taught this through an angel to the very first and great Christian emperor St. Constantine, and this angel gave him a great commandment: This fire must be made only by Christians and only in the city where they rule and nowhere else; and no other people must receive it or be trained in it.' "

In 957, Constantine VII took further measures to ensure Byzantium's monopoly on the use of this powerful weapon, not only proclaiming the method of its production a state secret, but also ordering a curse to be carved on church altars against anyone who dared to transmit it to foreigners—which in those times was equivalent to issuing a license to kill such transgressors.

For over a century, the Byzantines won many battles using their secret weapon, and it was not until the 12th century that Arab alchemists surmised the secret of Greek fire and used it against the crusaders. The historian Boga-Eddin relates that during the siege of Accons during the Third Crusade (1189–1192), "Petroleum and other materials were cooked in iron pots, and when the mixture turned to fireballs, were thrown at the siege towers of the Christian troops," which instantly exploded and burned. Jean de Joinville, an adviser to the French King Louis IX (later Saint Louis) and a participant in the Seventh Crusade (1248–1254), saw "liquid fire" in action and was so impressed that he included a description in his *Memoirs*. According to de Joinville, it was like a lightning-bearing flight of a "winged and long-tailed dragon with a body as thick as a barrel, accompanied by a thunderclap; a burst of flame, which threw back the darkness of night to a great distance."[2]

The Eternal Flames of the Absheron Peninsula

The Absheron Peninsula, which juts out into the Caspian Sea near modern-day Baku, Azerbaijan, has also been known for its petroleum since ancient times. The eternal flames that rose from its oil fields never failed to draw the attention of travelers. Thousands of pilgrims streamed to temples located on the peninsula to worship the sacred eternal flames. Historians recount how the Byzantine Emperor Heracles (575–640), while wintering at the mouth of the Kura River 18 miles west of Baku, destroyed the sacred altars, thereby striking a considerable blow against the cult of fire worshipers. However, the altars were soon rebuilt, and fire worshiping emerged anew.

Ancient authors noted that oil was exported from the Absheron Peninsula to Persia as far back as the beginning of the Common Era. Reports of oil production on the peninsula can be found in the manuscripts of many Arab and Persian historians of the Common Era: Ibn Miskawayh (10th cent.), Abu Dulaf (10th cent.), Yaqut al-Hamawi (13th cent.), Hamdullah al-Qazwini (14th cent.).

References to Absheron petroleum appear in numerous other records. The Arab scholar and geographer Abu al-Hasan Masudi (d. ca. 956), in chapter 14 of his treatise, *The Meadows of Gold and Mines of Gems*, wrote: "Ships... visit the coast of an area called Bakukh [Baku]; this is a field of white and variegated petroleum. Only Allah knows where else in the world besides this place there is white petroleum.[3] This is the coast of the nation of Shirvan. In this oil-bearing place is a volcano, which is one of the sources of flame. It is never calm at any time, and throws fire high into the air."

The famous Italian traveler Marco Polo (1254–1324) described how people in Baku used petroleum for medicinal purposes and religious ceremonies, while around 1320, the French missionary Jourdain Catalani de Severac wrote in his notes: "There is one place, called Baku, where they dig wells from which they recover and scoop up oil: it is called naphtha, and this oil is flammable, and medicinal, and burns well."

The Arab geographer Abd ar-Rashid ibn Salih al-Bakuwi asserted that the monthly production of Absheron crude in the early 15th century was 200 *khalvars* (about 66 barrels, or 10 tons[4]). Most of it was apparently shipped to Persia.

In the travelogue of Italian Giosafat Barbaro (written sometime between 1474 and 1479), one can find the following description: "In this part of the sea is another city, called Baka, from whence the name of the Baka Sea came, near which there is a mountain that spews out black oil, very malodorous, used at night in lamps and for rubbing camels twice a year, because if they are not rubbed, they contract mange."

The Turkish scholar and traveler of the second half of the 16th century Katip Celebi, also known as Haji Khalifa, wrote that "around the fort of Baku are about 500 wells, from which white and black petroleum oils are produced."

After his visit to Baku in 1568–1574, the French traveler Jeffrey Duckett wrote the following: "Near the city we observe a strange phenomenon—an amazing quantity of oil comes out of the ground here, for which people come from remote parts of Persia; it serves throughout the country for the lighting of homes. This oil is black and is called 'nefte.' It is transported throughout the country on mules and donkeys, which you often encounter in caravans of 400–500. There is also another type of oil near this city of Baku, white and very valuable, and I suppose this is the same as what we call petroleum."[5]

In the 17th century, Friedrich, Duke of Holstein, sent two embassies (1633–1635 and 1635–1639) to Muscovy and Persia to establish a trade route to Persia and acquaint themselves with the oil riches of the southern and western coasts of the Caspian. Adam Ölschläger (1599–1671), also known as Olearius, a member of these embassies, visited the Caspian coast in 1636. He wrote that "petroleum is a special oil that is scooped up in very large quantities from permanent wells around Baku and near the Barmakh mountain and is transported in wineskins in large cartloads, as we ourselves witnessed, for sale…. On March 2, we left the mountains and came to a plain a quarter of the way from the sea, passed the high mountain of Barmakh, and not far from the sea saw oil wells. These are various types of pits, numbering up to 30, nearly all located within one gunshot's range; these issue powerful springs of oil—oleum petroleum. Among these were three main wells, to which we had to descend to a depth of 14 feet, for which purpose several crossbeams were installed, which could be used as steps. From above, we could hear the springs burbling, as if boiling; their odor was fairly strong, and the white oil had a more pleasant smell than the brown oil. Here both brown and white oil could be extracted, but there was more of the former than the latter."[6]

Another detailed description of the Baku oil field was made by the secretary of the Swedish embassy to Persia, Engelbert Kämpfer (1651–1716), during his stay on the peninsula on January 6–8, 1683. He was struck by the "dusty steppe," which "presented a unique and beautiful sight, for some crevices burned with a large flame, while others emitted a quieter flame and permitted all to approach up close; still others emitted smoke, or in any event a barely noticeable vapor, that widely dispersed a very heavy stench of petroleum. This covered an area 88 paces in length and 26 paces in width." After describing the area of the temple of fire-worshippers at Surakhany with its eternal flames, the author reported the following: "A thousand paces to the northwest of the eternal flames is another wondrous thing, namely: sources of white petroleum."[7] Kämpfer describes oil production from deep wells using horses and its storage in special covered pools, and also includes drawings of the eternal flames, mud volcanoes, and oil wells.

Oil Springs of the Taman Peninsula

The story of Russian oil production occupies a special place in the pages of the world's petroleum annals. Rooted deep in antiquity, this history is inextricably linked to the Taman Peninsula and the numerous surface outcrops of oil-bearing rocks there.

From 389 BCE until 375 CE, this territory was part of the Bosporan Kingdom, the largest ancient state in the northern Black Sea region. The residents of this large ancient Greek (and later Roman) colony used petroleum for lighting and other household needs, and for creating the incendiary mixtures that came to be called Greek fire. Excavations by Soviet archeologists in the 1940s and 1950s revealed primitive oil lamps, as well as remnants of clay vessels for storing oil.

The Byzantine Emperor Constantine VII, already mentioned earlier, author of the treatise *De Administrando Imperio* (10th cent.), made mention of the Taman Peninsula's petroleum sources as follows: "[You] must know that beyond the city of Tamatarcha are many sources that discharge petroleum.... The oil from these nine sources is not uniform in color, but some of them are red, others yellow, still others nearly black."

In 965–966, after the victorious campaigns of the Russian forces commanded by the Kievan Prince Svyatoslav (942–971) and the crushing of the Khazar Khanate, this territory was renamed the Tmutarakan Principality, encompassing both the Taman Peninsula and the lower reaches of the Kuban River. As a military and trading outpost of Kievan

Rus, the city of Tmutarakan quickly became one of its biggest southern trading ports, gaining it a tenable position in the Black Sea region. At various times from 980 onward, it was ruled by Princes Oleg Svyatoslavovich, Mstislav Udaloy, and Rostislav Novgorodsky. The principality even had the right to coin its own money. Incidentally, the collection of the State Historical Museum in Moscow contains the only three surviving silver coins of the principality minted on a Byzantine pattern during the reign of Prince Oleg Svyatoslavovich.

Unfortunately, very little is known today about the history of this principality. Free peasants, or *smerds* as they were called in the ancient Russian state, may have worked at the petroleum sources. It is likely that, as before, the oil was shipped to various regions and countries, including Byzantium.

What is known, however, is that around 1111, the Tmutarakan Principality fell under attack by nomadic steppe hordes, the Polovtsy, who, as it turned out, had discovered the key to using Taman petroleum in warfare.

Khan Konchak's "Living Fire"

According to the Russian chronicles, Ancient Rus's perennial enemies, the Polovtsy, began actively using their new weapon, "living fire," made from oil produced from sources on the Taman Peninsula, in 12th-century battles. The *Hypatian Chronicle* describes the events of one battle of the allied forces of Russian princes in 1184: "The damned and godless and thrice-cursed Konchak with countless detachments of Polovtsy moved against Rus, hoping to capture and burn the Russian cities with fire, for he had found a certain infidel who shot with living fire…. Khan Konchak had a man who knew how to shoot fire and burn cities, who had self-firing bows so great that eight men could barely draw them, and they were mounted on a great carriage. With this, he could throw man-sized stones into the center of the city, and he had a special smaller but very cleverly made device to throw fire."

However, neither "living fire" nor the "countless" hordes of Khan Konchak could withstand the combined forces of the Russian knights, or their courage and valor. In this battle, the Russian warriors, led by the Kievan Prince Svyatoslav Vsevolodovich, won a brilliant victory: "But Konchak fled behind their back to the other side of the road, and [the Russians] only captured his concubine and the infidel who had the living fire. And he was brought to Svyatoslav with his entire apparatus, and their other warriors were either killed or taken into captivity."

It is possible that this was when the secret of "living fire" became known to Russian warriors, and one can find indirect evidence of this in several chronicles. Thus, when the Kama Bulgars captured the ancient Russian city of Ustyug, Prince Georgy of Vladimir sent his brother Svyatoslav along with a strong home guard to keep the captors in check. In 1219, Russian forces successfully attacked the Kama Bulgar city of Oshel (modern Ashli), and as one chronicler wrote, "In front marched infantry with fire and axes, followed by archers... they came to the city, ignited it from all sides, and a great storm and smoke drew on them."

Qizilbash Oil in Moscow

Medieval Russian written sources also contain the first mentions of the primitive production of oil on the territory of the Muscovite state. For example, the *Dvina Chronicle* (15th cent.) states that the tribe of Chudes, living on the banks of the Ukhta River in the north, collected oil from the river surface and used it for various household purposes.

However, the northern taiga wilderness could not be counted on to supply the regular oil deliveries required by the Russian capital during this period, so the eyes of domestic entrepreneurs turned to the south. Beginning in the 16th century, trading and customs books began to include records of petroleum from the Absheron peninsula, the so-called Qizilbash oil, which was brought to Moscow by traders from various lands. Thus, a section of the *Trading Book* [*Torgovaya kniga*] (1575–1610) entitled "Memoir on How to Sell Russian Goods to Foreigners" mentions that in the case of a successful trip to Shamakhy, Azerbaijan, the reader could contract to deliver more than 57 barrels of black oil to foreigners.

In those days, Shamakhy was the capital of the ancient feudal state of the Persian vassals known as Shirvanshahs. Shamakhy contained a Russian merchant colony that had existed since the 12th century and developed successful trade relations. The Russian merchants purchased oil in local containers—*tuluks* and *suleyas* (in leather bags with a capacity of about 36 pounds and bottles with a capacity of a little over 24 pounds, respectively)—and transported it by ship to Astrakhan. From Astrakhan, the oil was shipped up the Volga to the cities of Tsaritsyno, Nizhny Novgorod, Yaroslavl, and other major Volga trading centers. Oil reached the capital of Muscovy primarily from Nizhny Novgorod via the Oka and Moskva (Moscow) Rivers. It also reached Arkhangelsk by a northern route via Vologda, and from there ships carrying Russian goods by sea delivered the cargo to Europe.

Data have survived showing that in 1636, after an inventory of reserves in Moscow, the state treasury contained 20 barrels of Qizilbash oil. It should be noted that in Russia, oil traders who had left the Qizilbash tribe of Afshars were called *Qizilbashes*, literally "Red Heads," because they decorated their heads with enormous red-woven turbans.

The books of the Moscow trading house contain a record from 1694 of the shipment of oil from Baku and Astrakhan to Moscow by the Russian merchants Ivan Sveshnikov, Ivan Shaposhnikov, and Mikhail Pushnikov and the collection of duty on the goods.

Various Oil Projections

There is written evidence that petroleum was used again in warfare in Russia in the Middle Ages. The incendiary mixture for various weapons made by Russian masters at the Cannon and Grenade Works included not only sulfur, saltpeter, and camphor powder, but also turpentine, drying oil, pitch, linseed oil, and asphalt. These components were mixed with oil, yielding "fireballs" weighing about 1.8 pounds and arrows for destroying fortifications and burning ships, bridges, and siege towers. As for the quantity of "petroleum" munitions, it is possible to get a sense of the vast number of these weapons used by considering the inventory of remaining equipment of the Artillery Office following the Crimean campaign of 1689: 480 "fire lances," 2,400 "fire-shooting arrows with finned lances," and 100 "fireballs" in 1691.

In addition to armaments, oil was also used in Russia in the late 17th century to make compounds for firecrackers and fireworks for numerous secular holidays. Yet another application of oil can be found in the Russian medieval chronicles, in which the unique color and appearance of household objects of worship and Russian icons is attributed to the special composition of the paints used, which included petroleum. Icon painters were instructed to "make up any paint wax and apply drying oil and petroleum so that it will dry faster.... And when you apply drying oil to the icon and it becomes stiff, apply a little petroleum or turpentine with a finger and spread it. It will quickly adhere to the icon and will not run."

There is also evidence that petroleum and its derivatives were widely used in medieval Russia for therapeutic purposes. Russian physicians used oil as a medication for certain skin diseases, and for joint diseases and rheumatism. This is documented in the 16th- and 17th-century manuscripts *Book of Cures* [*Lechebnik*], *The Garden of Health Care* [*Sad zdravookhraneniya*], *The Home Pharmacopeia or Pharmacy* [*Farmakopeya ili apteka domashnyaya*], and *Stones and Herbs* [*O kamnyakh i travakh*]. The manuscript *Book of Cures* advises: "If you smear patients with oil, then the disease will be relieved. White oil relieves disease that comes from cold. But black oil, which is not very pleasant, relieves cough and intestinal colic." The same source recommends dripping oil into the eyes "of a person who has cataracts[8] or whose tears are running."

In 1692, the book *Noord Oost en Tartarye* [*North and East Tataria*], written by Nicolaes Witsen, who lived for three years as part of the Dutch embassy to the court of Tsar Aleksey Mikhaylovich, was published in Amsterdam. This book contains the following noteworthy information: "The Ukhta River is a day away from Pechora…. On this river, a mile and a half from the portage, is a small place where oil that is black petroleum separates from the water."

Leonty Kislyansky's Discovery

In the 17th century, the Russian state was governed through a growing network of offices. These included the Embassy Office, which managed relations with foreign states and trade with foreign merchants; the Treasury Office, in charge of treasury trade and industry; and the Weapons Board, which manufactured, procured, and stored weapons and palace utensils. In 1637, the government formed the Siberian Office, which combined administrative, judicial, and financial functions in the administration of the extensive Siberian territories.

The documents of the Siberian Office contain reports that the local residents collected "Siberian rock oil" on the Yenisey and along the banks of Lake Baikal. It flowed out of the rocky river banks, floated on Baikal, and was thrown up on its shores by the wind. Siberian rock oil was used as an ointment against rheumatic diseases and for healing wounds. It was even shipped to Moscow, as recorded in the entry for 1650 in a customs book: "The Ustyi native Roman Yevdeyev came from Siberia on someone else's ship… in addition to soft materials, he brought half a pound of rock oil." Incidentally, we know from the archives that one pound of rock oil was worth 10 kopecks in Yeniseysk in 1649.

In 1684, the Siberian Office, on the basis of a decree by tsars Ivan Alekseyevich and Peter Alekseyevich, directed the chief administrator of Irkutsk, Leonty Kislyansky, to "question all ranks of people and taxpaying foreigners about gold and silver, and about copper and tin and lead ores, and about iron and about diamonds, and mica and dye, and about saltpeter, and about other resources."

Leonty Kislyansky had a very successful career in medieval Russia. He was born in Poland, entered Russian service in 1671 after adopting the Orthodox faith, and was granted perpetual citizenship by Tsar Aleksey Mikhaylovich. He served from 1671 to 1677 in the Embassy Office and the Weapons Board as a master of painting, where he first encountered the use of petroleum in iconography. In 1680, Kislyansky was assigned to serve in Yeniseysk, and then in 1683, he was sent to Irkutsk as an administrator.

At the time, the stockaded town of Irkutsk was relatively small. It was surrounded by a wooden wall with six towers and bridges, one of which contained a treasury barn, which held a copper cannon, rifles, and various ammunition. The town had only 40 farmsteads. The Russian ambassador to Beijing, Nikolay Sparafy, stopped at Irkutsk in 1675 and noted that there were no moorings at the mouth of the Angara, only cliffs and rocks, and "in a word, groves—exceedingly terrible, in particular to those who first of all had not been there, because everywhere around are very high snowy mountains and impassable forests and rocky cliffs."

Among Leonty Kislyansky's duties were: to collect "tributes"—sable, fox, and beaver pelts—from tributary local tribes; "not to be harsh, impudent, or offensive;" "to seek out new lands for the state's exalted hand;" and to trade with the Bukhars and other foreign merchants, "but to ensure that they did not carry off rifles, powder, and lead to their own lands." In addition, he was charged with the special mission of baptizing locals wishing to adopt the Orthodox faith, and "to disburse three rubles and one piece of fabric apiece" to each newly baptized person and "enlist them into service."[9]

In fulfilling the instructions of the Siberian Office, Leonty Kislyansky, with the assistance of service people, found mica in Siberia along the banks of the Ura and Angara Rivers and in the Baikal region, as well as graphite and lapis lazuli on the banks of the Vitim River, and was the first to report "oil shows," or visible indications of petroleum in Siberia.

This is reflected in his report to the Yenisey governor, Prince Konstantin Shcherbatov, dated 1684, and excerpted here: "But in the stockaded town of Irkutsk, the Irkut residents literally said in conversation before me: behind the stockaded Irkutskaya Creek, fire supposedly comes out of the mountain from who knows where, and in that place snow does not live in winter and grass does not grow in summer. And against their warnings, I went from Irkutsk not far, only a *verst* [0.93 miles][10] or less, and vapor came from the mountain, and if you put your hand on it, you cannot hold it for long, and from far off you sense the stench from this petroleum vapor, and when you approach this vapor and the well, there comes a direct stench of real petroleum from the well, and if you dig the hole a little deeper, a little more heat comes from the well, and then you know that there is real petroleum." Impressed by the abundant resources, Leonty Kislyansky began planning for the extraction of the petroleum, only hoping that, "God willing, there will be no trouble from the unfriendly Mongols and Chinese, and based on those supposed signs and rifts I will dig and earn a living with all solicitude."

After that, apparently, it was precisely his hostile "neighbors" that prevented the Irkutsk administrator from realizing his far-reaching plans. Somewhat later, he reported to Yeniseysk: "I have not dug any petroleum to date because I intend to produce it in great quantities, but I have yet to find the men to carry out the work."

Later Leonty Kislyansky, for his diligence in the service of the state, received the title of *stolnik*, and was appointed to a high post in Moscow, and we know of his participation in a series of Russian military campaigns. Unfortunately, at the time there was no one among his comrades-in-arms who could continue further exploration of surface oil shows, so the treasury of Siberian "black gold" remained untouched until the mid-20th century.

Peter the Great and Oil

For most Russian and foreign historians, the grand achievements in Russia in the early 18th century are seen as a period of great Petrovian reforms. It was in this century that, according to the noted foreign researcher J. Blum, Russian industrial development was equal to and sometimes even superior to that of the rest of Europe. Russian historian and Academician Yevgeny Tarle (1874–1955) even went so far as to deem the extensive vigor of Russian history in the late 18th century as one of the most important and great phenomena of world history.

Along with all the reforms and developments of this era, Emperor Peter I (Peter the Great, 1672–1725) was also responsible for the first attempts at the practical use of petroleum in Russia.

On August 24, 1700, a decree from the tsar founded the Mining Office, which came to supervise all activities in the development and exploitation of the Russian Empire's minerals. In another decree dated November 2, 1700, Peter the Great clearly defined the objectives of this state mining institution, which encompassed all phases of the prospecting, exploration, and development of mineral deposits.

Efforts to find ore riches were undertaken throughout Russia at Peter the Great's initiative. By January 2, 1703, the newspaper *Vedomosti* ["Gazette"], edited by the tsar himself, reported: "They write from Kazan that much oil has been found on the Sok River."

In 1713, Peter the Great wrote a letter to his closest associate, the diplomat Pavel Yaguzhinsky (1683–1736), demanding the procurement in Baku of 10 *vedros* (32.5 gallons; or about 101 kilograms)[11] of oil and the delivery of the same to St. Petersburg. When the oil was purchased, it became clear that the price of oil had risen considerably, reaching 30 kopecks a pound by 1713. After a thorough search, Yaguzhinsky managed to purchase 16 *vedros* (52 gallons; or about 164 kilograms) of oil at 25 kopecks a pound from the trader Ivan Fëdorovich of Syromyat Sloboda [Syromyat Free Settlement].

Faced with the high costs of importing oil to Russia, Peter the Great turned his attention to developing petroleum sources within the country, focusing on the potential oil-bearing lands between the Terek and Sunzha

Rivers. He ordered the preparation of an expedition to the region, but the expedition's departure was postponed due to the emperor's upcoming trip to Europe.

It was during this extended visit to Europe that Peter the Great met with eminent European scientists and miners. These meetings and his introduction to the state of affairs in Western economics led the tsar to certain conclusions on the necessity for prompt modernization in Russia, including the mining industry.

After his return home, Peter the Great signed a decree forming the Manufacturing and Mining Board,[12] and appointed his close associate Yakov Bryus [Jacob Bruce] (1670–1735), later given the title of count and the rank of general field marshal, to head it.

Meanwhile, the delayed expedition to prospect for oil-bearing lands in Russia took place in 1718, and at the tsar's order, court physician Gottlieb Schober was sent to the Terek-Sunzha region. Not far from a mineral hot spring, he discovered that "oil or petroleum flows from a certain mountain… no one collects it or uses it."[13]

At the direction of Peter the Great, the statesman and diplomat Artemy Volynsky (1689–1740) inspected the site of this same region. In a letter to the tsar, he conjectured that "this is a flow of true *balsam sulfuris*," which in this area "is called petroleum out of ignorance," and is used "instead of tar to lubricate carts, of which, Majesty, I expect you can get a *pood* [36 pounds] at 30 or more."[14]

As the number of Russian enterprises and mining operations grew sharply, it proved inconvenient to combine the management of mining plants and manufactories in one government agency. Peter the Great's decree of December 10, 1719, "On the Institution of the Mining Board for Allocation to It of Ore and Mineral Affairs," created a special institution, the Mining Board, with a diversified network of local institutions. In his decree, the tsar wrote: "Our Russian state is blessedly richer than many other lands in both required metals and minerals, which have remained unsought by any diligence until the present…. God's beneficence must not remain underground in vain."

On that same day in 1719, Peter the Great established the Mining Privilege, defining the government's policy in the mining industry for the next 88 years, until 1807. The Mining Privilege declared all minerals the property of the tsar, regardless of who owned the parcel of land. Landowners were granted the right of preferential development of minerals and construction of plants. The Mining Privilege established the right of hereditary ownership of plants, protected industrialists from interference by the local administration, guaranteed financial assistance in the construction of enterprises and the right of free sale of smelted metal, and set the amount of compensation for discovered ore. In 1739, the Mining Privilege was supplemented by a special Mining Regulation.

In addition to other issues, the Mining Board also addressed oil prospecting. In the spring of 1721, Mezen resident Grigory Cherepanov reported to the Mining Board that he had found an "oil spring" in Pustoye Ozero District of Arkhangelsk Province. Tsar Peter the Great, to whom this was reported, immediately directed a thorough investigation of the oil source, as well as the awarding to "ore expert" Cherepanov six rubles, "so that he would also have a desire to find more ore in the future."

Subsequently, the Russian emperor maintained an interest in petroleum and even ordered the assembly of knowledgeable people for discussion of the oil business. Several inspections of the Ukhta oil source were made, during which eight bottles of Ukhta oil were delivered to the capital in 1724.

Peter the Great's Caspian Campaign

In the first quarter of the 18th century, the Caspian region became an object of Emperor Peter the Great's constant attention. He regarded it as an important strategic springboard, both for the defense of the Empire and for the future development of Russian trade with the East.

Persia claimed the role of partner to the Russian Empire during that time, as it possessed considerable capabilities and, in turn, badly needed a strong ally capable of protecting it from claims by the militant Ottoman Empire in the west and restless Afghan tribes in the east.

The evolving situation and complication of conditions inside Persia forced Russia to act in various directions. The first step was the signing of a mutual trade treaty with Shah Soltan Hosayntan Hosayn in 1718, specifying certain actions by the Russians both to protect their own interests and to assist the legal Persian government if necessary.

A steady stream of alarming reports from Persia prompted the Russian government to consider a possible adverse scenario in the development of events, and Peter the Great began planning a Russian military campaign to the Caspian to preclude them.

Thorough preparations for this complex military operation required nearly three years. First, two Russian officers, Fëdor Soymonov and Karl von Werden, performed a thorough survey of the region in 1719, drawing up a detailed map of the Caspian Sea.

It was during this time that Fëdor Soymonov made a special visit to the oil fields on the Absheron Peninsula. It is clear that Emperor Peter the Great did not overlook his report, particularly its mention of the fact that, from 1716 onward, petroleum from the Baku oil wells—which were farmed[15] to a vassal of the Persian shah, Soltan Mohammad Hosayn Fetig 'Ali—earned the shah's court the Russian monetary equivalent of over 49,000 rubles annually. If we consider that the maintenance of a single

Russian army soldier cost about 1.5 kopecks per day, this sum would have been sufficient for the annual maintenance of a Russian army of nearly 10,000. Furthermore, Peter the Great's numerous notations on the reports of Fëdor Soymonov and Karl von Werden, and on the reports of the Russian envoy to Persia, Artemy Volynsky, convincingly show that petroleum had gained a firm grip on the emperor's attention.

In the winter of 1721–1722, armed units of militant Afghan tribes overthrew the Persian ruler, Shah Soltan Hosayn, and Prince Tahmasp, the lawful heir to the throne, was forced to flee and hide in the Trans-caspian regions of Persia. This gave Peter the Great a pretext to come to the defense of the lawful authority, and he personally led an army of 50,000 during the Persian (Caspian) campaign of 1722–1723.[16]

The beginning of May 1722 was the official start date of the "Caspian campaign." Admiral General Fëdor Apraksin (1661–1725) commanded the navy, and a flotilla of cargo ships (scows) was commanded by the aforementioned Lieutenant Captain Karl von Werden, who was thoroughly familiar with the region.

In August 1722, while Russian ships were en route to Derbent, Emperor Peter the Great and several fellow travelers went ashore near the town of Tarki [later Fort Petrovsk, modern Makhachkala] and set out on foot for the oil wells, which his majesty wished to see. On August 23, 1722, the authorities and people of Derbent met the Russian emperor with a most honorable reception. The city's *naib* (head of the city admin-istration) gave him the keys to the city gates. Peter the Great then returned to Astrakhan, turning command of the Russian troops over to Lieutenant General Mikhail Matyushkin (1676–1737).

In Astrakhan on November 4, 1722, Peter the Great wrote an instruction for the commander titled "What to Do When, God Willing, We Take Baku." Included in this instruction was the significant phrase, "Explore duties and revenues. And especially on petroleum and saffron. How much they were in good times and how much now, and how much went to the shah and how much went in pockets."

On August 18, 1723, on orders from Lieutenant General Matyush-kin, an "Inventory of Oil Wells and Vaults near Baku" was drawn up. According to this inventory, in the field, i.e., 6.6–13.2 miles from Baku, there were 66 operational wells and 16 storehouses; in a second field, 13.2 miles from the city, there were four wells with "white" petroleum; and outside the city gates were 14 storehouses containing oil and five empty storehouses.

In a second instruction dated September 9, 1723, Peter the Great ordered the retrieval of several dozen pounds of oil, which were delivered to St. Petersburg in eight bottles in early 1724.

The lawful government of Persia, in the person of the new Shah Tahmasp II, deemed the Russian troops' Caspian operation a mission of liberation. In gratitude for saving the country, Persia ceded western and southern parts of the Caspian coast, including the cities of Derbent and Baku, and the provinces of Gilan, Mazandaran, and Astarabad (now Gorgan) to Russia under the Petersburg Treaty, signed September 12, 1723.

Soon thereafter, in late September, General Matyushkin, then in Astrakhan, received a decree from Emperor Peter the Great, "On the Entry of His Imperial Majesty into Eternal Possession of the Cities of Derbent, Baku, and Other Provinces."

In May 1724, the emperor again ordered that "white oil, 1,000 *poods* [120 barrels] or as much as possible,"[17] be sent to him. Fulfilling this order, General Mikhail Matyukhin sent more than 18 barrels of "white" oil from Baku to Astrakhan in the summer of that year, which was later delivered to Moscow.

After the death of Peter the Great in February 1725, interest in the practical application of petroleum waned considerably, but archive documents imply that three barrels of oil were sent to the merchant Johann Lubs in Holland by decision of the Commerce Board in February 1726. The foreign middleman was asked to learn its real price and possible sales volumes. Judging by the Commerce Board report, demand for petroleum in Holland proved small, yet, despite the commercial inauspiciousness of the results, this exercise is significant in that it represents the first attempt, carried out more than 280 years ago, by a Russian government institution to undergo a marketing study of the foreign petroleum market.

Yakov Shakhanin, "Mineral Hunter"

The monarchical successors to Emperor Peter the Great in the following decade could not hold the Caspian additions to the Empire, including the oil fields on the Absheron Peninsula. The succession of palace coups during the time of "female rule" substantially weakened the Russian Empire's foreign policy positions. As a result, under the Treaty of Resht of 1732 and the Ganja Treaty of 1735, the Caspian regions were returned to Persia.

Thus, petroleum was once again an overseas good for Russians. In 1733, Dr. Johann Lerche, a member of the Russian embassy in Persia, visited the Absheron Peninsula. "On July 30, 1733," he wrote, "I rode five *versts* [3.3 miles] from the unquenchable flame to Balakhany, to the black petroleum springs.... Fifty-two of these wells were found during the times of the Persian shah; by means of these, great trade was carried on in those days, but now only 26 remain intact.... Wells 20 *sazhens* [140 feet] deep, of which one flows very strongly and delivers 500 *batmans* of oil per day (a *batman* is 15 pounds of Russian weight [13.5 lb. avdp.]); they boil strongly, so they can be heard."[18]

Additionally, Dr. Lerche noted one extremely interesting fact—namely, the distillation of petroleum as a well-known process. As he put it, "The oil does not catch fire quickly, it is dark brown in color, and when it is distilled, it becomes light yellow. The white oil is somewhat turbid, but distillation makes it as clear as alcohol, and this ignites very quickly."

However, despite the abundance and quality of Absheron Peninsula oil, the high price and difficulty of delivering Baku crude to Russia forced domestic entrepreneurs to finance oil prospecting directly in promising areas of the Russian Empire.

In 1735, the "mineral hunter" Yakov Shakhanin, under orders from the Mining Board, obtained the right to prospect for metal and mineral ores in all provinces and regions. His persistent prospecting quickly yielded positive results. He found sulfur and aluminous ores on the shores of the Volga, and even built a small processing mill, but could not take advantage of the fruits of his labors. As a result of a commercial conflict due to a disagreement with comrades (that is, with other participants who co-owned the enterprise), the Yaroslavl town hall turned Shakhanin over as a conscript, and he was sent to serve as a soldier to the 10th company of the Karelian Regiment.

Torn away from his favorite business of mineral prospecting by military service, Yakov Shakhanin decided in February 1738 to take a bold step: He submitted a report directly to the Cabinet of her Imperial Majesty Anna Ioannovna, asking that he be released from his conscript obligation and that the mineral fields he had discovered be used for the benefit of the state. In the report, he also informed the Empress of the oil fields and saltpeter deposits he had found in the Volga region: "There is more of my saltpeter and mineral petroleum mine, specifically along the Volga River below the city of Sibirsk near the city of Tetyushi, and also saltpeter in the Novodevichy Hills near the palace village of Zhegulikh, and 20 *versts* [13.2 miles] above the city of Syzran, in the hills near the village of Kostychey, saltpeter lies about two miles."

First Cabinet Minister Count Andrey Osterman (1686–1747), who received Yakov Shakhanin's appeal, imposed the following resolution: "Based on this report, transfer the hunter of the Military Board to the artillery, so that it may use him in those affairs, and so that it may order those saltpeter sites shown by him to be certified by knowledgeable masters."

Based on this directive, the Main Artillery Chancellery sent Yakov Shakhanin, the "mineral hunter," to the Samara sulfur and saltpeter mines located in a Sergiyev suburb, and ordered their director, Commissar Vasily Verkhovsky, to "travel to the saltpeter and petroleum sites indicated by Shakhanin and certify the same…. And those sites that are several *versts* [miles], describe in detail… take about ten pounds each at various sites for judgment of quality, and where there is petroleum in the hills." Thus, the leadership of the artillery chancellery was not only interested in saltpeter needed for the production of gunpowder, but also in petroleum, since their duties included the preparation of holiday light shows.

The expedition confirmed Shakhanin's information regarding the presence of petroleum on the high right bank of the Volga. An oil sample taken there in early 1741 by special courier Lieutenant Mikhail Lugovsky was delivered to Moscow, and then to St. Petersburg. On April 16, 1741, the Main Artillery Chancellery sent it to the Academy of Sciences for further study.

On April 23, 1741, in the laboratory of the St. Petersburg Academy of Sciences, Academician Johann Amman (1707–1741) completed his analysis of the sample oil from the Samara sulfur mills and observed: "The oil sent smells very bad, and it is thick, black, and very dirty. It does not burn, even if a lit match is held over it, or even if the match is dipped into the oil. But when a lit cotton paper wick is placed in the oil, it burns quietly and a small flame rises above it…. In my opinion, it is good for nothing other than for making grease, torches, and tar strings, as well as wicks where an unclear, weak flame is needed. In addition, it can be used in icon lamps in place of a wick if its finest and lightest particles are separated by distillation, then it will be nearly the same as simple Persian oil."

An American chemist, Yale University professor Benjamin Silliman, came to the same conclusion, that distillation of the petroleum could yield a quality lighting material, but that conclusion was drawn over a century later, in 1855. While his report played a decisive role in accelerating the development of the American oil industry in the latter half of the 19th century, the thorough findings of Academician Amman in 1741, alas, remained unnoticed in Russia.

As for the fate of the "mineral hunter" Yakov Shakhanin, he made an attempt to create a partnership to develop the Syzran oil fields and tar deposits, but failed for unexplained reasons.

Fëdor Pryadunov's Oil Works

Twenty years after the death of the first Russian Emperor, Peter the Great, the Mining Board once again returned to the issue of Russian oil produced in the Empire's North. The history of the North's development in this regard is tied to entrepreneur Fëdor Savelyevich Pryadunov (1696–1753), a pioneer of the domestic oil business, and the creation and operation of his oil works, the first such works in Russia.

The Russian State Archive of Ancient Acts in Moscow holds a document titled "Extract" that recounts the story of the first Russian oil enterprise belonging to Arkhangelsk resident Fëdor Pryadunov. Here are just a few lines: "In 1745, on the 18th day of November, by decision of the Mining Board, and by the report of the former Arkhangelsk Mining Office at the request of Arkhangelsk resident Fëdor Pryadunov, it was ordered that an oil works be started at an empty site on the small Ukhta River in Pustoye Ozero District in Arkhangelsk Province, and further that the plant be maintained with voluntary capital without stopping, and said oil be sold."

A detailed description of this field is given in K. Molchanov's book, *Description of Arkhangelsk Province, Its Cities, Monasteries, and Other Noteworthy Sites* [*Opisaniye Arkhangelskoy gubernii, yeya gorodov, monastyrey i drugikh dostoprimechatelnykh mest*] (1813): "In the neighborhood of Izhmyn, on the Ukhta River, there was an oil works, which consisted of the following structure: above the actual oil spring flowing in the middle was built a four-cornered frame 13 rows high, of which six rested on the bottom, and the rest on the ground surface. Inside the frame was a narrow-bottomed tub, which admitted the petroleum flowing out of the water through a hole in the bottom, protected from the fast-flowing water by a cutwater placed on one side." It is clear from this description that the author is speaking of a structure for gathering petroleum from the water's surface.

Other archival documents speak of how oil production on the Ukhta was begun in August 1746 by Pryadunov and his employees.

Another unique document on Ukhta petroleum has survived as well. This is a certificate dated May 6, 1747, written by two German researchers, D. M. Miller and M. D. Lossau. The document is an attachment to Fëdor Pryadunov's February Report No. 524 of 1749, wherein he states that "I took ordinary and distilled oil and sent it to Hamburg."

The Hamburg scientists diligently investigated the Ukhta oil, comparing it to Italian oil, and concluded that it could be used "in cold phlegms, in dislocations, in colds, in shivers, in enfeeblements, and in joint fractures, as rock oil will provide good external care."

The archival "File on Fëdor Pryadunov's Oil Works" contains information to the effect that Mining Lt. Christian Lehmann performed the first distillation of oil brought by Pryadunov to the Mining Board's laboratory in Moscow on October 10, 1748: "Of which three pounds were taken for rectification, which yielded two pounds of rectified pure oil." It is also specified that Fëdor Pryadunov had begun independent studies in that laboratory: "On October 19 of the same year, Pryadunov verbally informed the Mining Board that 40 *poods* [4.8 barrels] of Russian oil said to have been extracted by him, Pryadunov, by the first of May 1746 and 1747 in Pustoye Ozero District on Ukhta Creek, had been delivered to the laboratory of the Mining Board in Moscow, all of which Pryadunov was said to have rectified. And rectification yielded two-thirds pure oil weighing 26 *poods* 26 and a half pounds [962.5 pounds]."

Archive documents show that as a result of an unusual spring flood and the resulting destruction at the Ukhta field, oil production was suspended in 1748.

In 1749, only 216 pounds of oil were produced in the field, partly due to the fact that in August and September of that year, Fëdor Pryadunov was under arrest in Moscow on a complaint by the Main Medical Chancellery for failing to obey a prohibition and acting as a "vulgar uncertified healer treating all diseases of various types of people with rock oil."

On October 19, 1750, at the direction of the Mining Board, Fëdor S. Pryadunov's oil works was examined by a special commission consisting of Corporal Grigory Golenishchev and land burgomaster Fedot Rochev. Their report left a fairly detailed description of the Ukhta field, listing all facilities, including the following: "In the forest was a dilapidated yard, cleared canopy and roof, a new bathhouse in the yard, three overgrown lagoons and a half-barrel, and it contained a kneading trough, a bowl, a plate, and a petroleum scoop, as well as 55 logs, a new boat, and a petroleum tub."

From that time on, Fëdor Pryadunov suffered a series of ordeals, including further arrests for tax evasion, and then imprisonment for many months in the Moscow debtor's prison, where he passed away in March 1753.

After Fëdor S. Pryadunov's death, the oil works in Ukhta passed from one owner to another. Available archive data show that the Ukhta oil field operated from 1746 through 1786, i.e., for less than 40 years.

In subsequent years, the Mining Board undertook attempts to resume oil production in Pechora Territory. These included reviewing a request from Novoye Usolye resident Vasily Ratov and Moscow merchant Aleksandr Sobolev on the possibility of "permitting the production, along the Izhma and Posva Rivers... of petroleum, which is said to exist in significant quantities at those locations." In view of the bad experiences of their predecessors, including that of Fëdor Pryadunov, these entrepreneurs immediately made a request for concessional taxation, i.e., "release from payment of tithes for ten years—due to the newness of the plant, so that they could recoup the capital used in prospecting for the mineral."

It is noteworthy that this request contains the first proposal for protectionism: "Prohibit shipments of oil from other Baltic Sea locations, for they could satisfy all of Russia with petroleum from the locations sought out by them."

In the end, the Mining Board resolved to permit production by Vasily Ratov and Aleksandr Sobolev, but to deny tax relief, as there was no need for construction of a plant, because "petroleum is gathered from the water's surface." Unfortunately, historians have nothing further to say on the operations of this enterprise in subsequent years.

Nadyr Urazmetov: Oil Pioneer of the Volga Region

The first attempts to organize oil production in the Volga region were associated with the efforts of Major General Mikhail Opochinin, president of the Mining Board from 1753 to 1760. At that time a local entrepreneur, Nadyr Urazmetov, was granted a permit to open an oil field on the Sok River above Sergiyevsk.

In his letter to the Mining Board, Urazmetov wrote: "Last year, in 1752, we explored on our own serf land on the Kazan Road in the Ufa District along both sides of the Sok River above the town of Sergiyevsk upward, riding along the right side, near Mt. Sart-Ata, we found black petroleum in a small lake. Going further, above the Sergiyev line along a stream called Syrgut in Russian, or Kukorta in Tatar,… we also found petroleum.… And along the Sok and near Surshla and Usakla there is a lake and there is black petroleum in it, and above that lake atop the Sok River is the Choktemir Forest, and from that forest came a small spring containing black petroleum. From those sites we took about ten pounds or more of oil for a sample, and we ask the Mining Board to accept and test that black oil and give us permission to construct an oil works on the assigned proprietary land."

On February 21, 1754, mining chemist Christian Lehmann sent the Mining Board a report on the analysis of the petroleum found by Nadyr Urazmetov, in which he noted its suitability for various purposes. The analysis was thorough, inasmuch as it determined the ratio of drams in white and red parts, or in modern language, the ratio of various petroleum fractions.

On September 15, 1754, the Orenburg Province Chancellery reported receiving "Her Imperial Majesty's Decree 1132 of July 12 from the State Mining Board on the request of the Orenburg Province, Ufa District, Kazan Road, Nadyr District, Village of Nadyrova, foremen Nadyr Urazmetov, Yusup Nadyrov, and Aslyam da Khozi Mozyakovykh, acknowledging permission given them to build an oil works on their proprietary land in Ufa District, on Kazan Road, on Karmaly Creek and enjoining them from giving any offense to or imposing on or obstructing anyone in the construction of said plant and in the search for petroleum, both to members of other faiths and to other people of any title inhabiting their land."

Eight years later, in his *Topography of the Orenburg Province* [*Topografiya Orenburgskoy gubernii*], Pëtr Rychkov (1712–1777), a corresponding member of the St. Petersburg Academy of Sciences, wrote the following about Nadyr Urazmetov's enterprise: "There are petroleum springs in various places near the aforementioned Sergiyevsk, where there were oil works before this. By decision of the Mining Board on June 16, 1754, in response to the request of the Tatar foreman Nadyr Urazmetov, a decree was issued to this Nadyr and his son Yusup to start up a plant near the Zakamskaya Line on the Karamala Creek, for which they found four petroleum springs nearby and submitted samples of oil from them to the Board, which the Board's tests proved to be oil."

In early 1757, the Orenburg Mining Command sent a report to the Mining Board regarding certification of an oil works. The report stated that "on August 21, 1756, geodetic student Pavel Zubrinsky was [sent] from this command to perform the prescribed certification and description, and he certified and described and charted the site." The certification and description were then forwarded to the State Mining Board on December 19, 1756. It should be noted that Zubrinsky's chart of 1756 has survived and it is held in an archive in Moscow. Russian historians believe it is the first map of a major oil field of the Volga-Urals region.

Unfortunately, however, Nadyr Urazmetov was unable to complete the work he started. The "Report of the Orenburg Mining Command to the Mining Board," dated December 19, 1756, on the inspection of Urazmetov's oil works, states that "Nadyr Urazmetov, having received the Mining Board's order, came to his village and contracted a serious illness, for which he has still received no treatment. However, in the previous year 1755, at the site where the works was to be built, he did erect a barn for cooking at the first opportunity. But only due to that illness, he could not build a proper plant... nor properly start it. But a comrade of his son Yusup Nadyrov... wrote to his colleagues without his consent, and he, Yusup, does not wish to build the works. But he, Nadyr, when he is free of the illness, wishes to build the works according to his commitment." However, the Mining Board did not take Nadyr Urazmetov's illness into consideration, the bureaucrats would not wait for his recovery, and in late 1757 Urazmetov was removed from the list of works owners. To date, no further information on the fate of this pioneer of the Volga oil business has been found in the Russian archives.

Mikhail Lomonosov and Russian Oil

During the reign of Empress Catherine the Great [Yekaterina II] from 1762 to 1796, the Russian state gained a new impetus for its development. The Manifest of 1775 and the "Charter of Rights and Benefits for Russian Cities" opened up new prospects for development of industrial production and trade in the country.

The renowned natural scientist, experimenter, and Academician Mikhail Lomonosov (1711–1765) made a solid contribution to the development of the scientific and industrial potential of the Russian Empire. Among his many achievements, he was the first to formulate the universal principle of conservation of matter and motion, which formed the basis of physical chemistry.

In 1743, Lomonosov completed his manuscript, *First Principles of Metallurgy or Mining [Pervyye osnovaniya metallurgii, ili rudnykh del]*. In preparing the book for publication, he added a section, "On the Earth's Layers," which dwelled on the plant origin of petroleum, peat and coal. The book, which was published in 1763, contained a lot of new ideas on fossil fuels and their origins. For instance, in "On the Earth's Layers," the Russian scientist wrote that underground heat drives petroleum out of coal and peat, so that it "enters various dry and wet clefts."

In Lomonosov's opinion, petroleum could also form as a byproduct in the conversion of peat to coal. The talented scientist came to the following conclusion: strong underground fires produce thick, black tar such as asphalt or jet, while milder underground heat produces clear, light crude. Lomonosov supported the conclusion with the results of his observations on the distillation of "oily materials:" "when it is produced over a high flame, the oil comes out black and thick; conversely, a light flame makes it light and clear." As an adjunct to the physics class of the St. Petersburg Academy of Sciences, he carried out the distillation of petroleum under laboratory conditions a number of times in the course of his experiments. (It should be noted that the State Historical Museum in Moscow has preserved his laboratory.)

The scientist wrote that "the thinnest material from peat and from primary distillation oil, collected in some warm cavity, is redistilled by secondary actions, which chemists call 'rectification.' " Thus, Mikhail Lomonosov assumed the formation of petroleum through the prolonged action of mild heat and recognized its migration from its formation sites into porous layers.

According to his theory, plant and animal remains were petrified, and the partially burned bodies gave rise to peat, coal, and amber. Peat originates from swamp vegetation. The origins of coal could be attributed, he thought, to peat bogs via carburization in the absence of air under the influence of moisture, high temperature, and pressure. Lomonosov concluded that peat, coal, and petroleum were the products of the natural refinement of organic matter. "We can be confident that these hot underground materials originate from growing things because of their lightness, for all minerals sink in water, but petroleum floats on it, even though after being underground it has taken up some heavy rocky material."

Later, the respected Russian scientist and Academician Vladimir Vernadsky (1863–1945) praised Mikhail Lomonosov's theory, stating: "I don't know of a single 18th-century theory that could be compared to these views of Lomonosov." And even to this day, Lomonosov's theory of the origins of fossil fuels, developed in the latter half of the 18th century, continues to attract strong advocates and followers.

An illustration from the Madrid manuscript "History of the Byzantine Emperors" by John Skylitzes, demonstrating the use of "Greek fire" as an incendiary mixture in military applications.

The main component of the mixture is believed to have been oil with additives: probably various combinations and proportions of resin, saltpeter, sulfur and quicklime.

The flames intensified on contact with water.

An antique oil lamp.

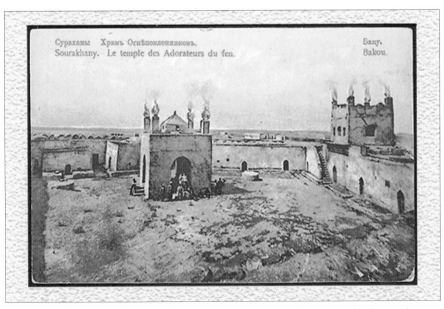

Postcard of "Surakhany. Temple of Fire-Worshippers. Baku." The Ateshgah (Zoroastrian temple) near Baku dates back to the 15th century. It was completed in its final form in the 17th-18th centuries. Historians believe this place was used for cult practices since ancient times. The temple was depicted in the symbol of the Nobel Brothers Petroleum Production Partnership. It is now the State Historical-Architectural Reserve of Azerbaijan.

Map of oil-bearing lands near the Sok River (middle 18th century).

Map of the Caspian Sea, drawn up on the personal orders of Peter I (early 18th century).

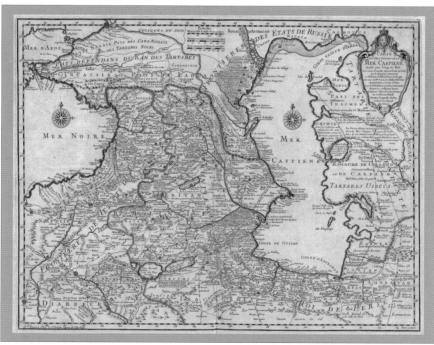

Map of the Caspian Sea and adjacent nations by French cartographer Guillaume de Lisle (Delisle), published in 1723. Following a 1717 meeting with Peter I at the Academy of Sciences in Paris, he radically revised a map he had made in 1700. Previously, the Caspian had been poorly understood in Europe and incorrectly depicted on maps as stretching from west to east.

Tsar (Emperor after 1721) Peter I (1672-1725) instigated the systematic investigation, description and inventory of the mineral deposits of the empire, ordering in 1700 the creation of a Mining Office, later renamed the Manufacturing and Mining Board. The first documented evidence of the discovery of oil deposits in Russia appeared three years later.

In 1702, Tsar Peter I issued a decree establishing the first periodical newspaper, *Vedomosti*. An article appeared in the inaugural issue, released in January 1703, about the discovery of oil in the Volga region: "They write from Kazan that much oil has been found on the Sok river."

The great Russian scholar and encyclopedist Mikhail Lomonosov (1711-1765) devoted considerable attention to the study of oil and laid the foundation for establishing the organic origin of oil.

Bust of Fëdor Pryadunov by Ukhta native Viktor Vasyakin.

After prospector Grigory Cherepanov reported in 1721 the discovery of oil in the Ukhta region to the Manufacturing and Mining Board, Arkhangelsk merchant Fëdor Pryadunov went to Ukhta in 1745 and established an oil works and a "mineral oil rectifier" (rectification of oil by passing it through a boiler with water).

M. V. Lomonosov's laboratory alembic used to distill Ukhta oil.

Russian Empress Catherine II (1729-1799). Her September 1773 decree laid the foundation for the formation of a system of higher mining engineering education in Russia.

С. Петербургъ
St.-Pétersbourg

Горный инотитутъ Императрицы Екатерины.
Institut des Mines.

The St. Petersburg Mining School (established in 1773). Many of its alumni contributed greatly to the development of the Russian oil industry.

Emperor Alexander I (1777-1825) in 1801 issued a decree to organize the "Main Expedition to Establish Mining Production in Georgia."

Russian Emperor Alexander II (1818-1881) liberated the Russian oil industry from the tax-farming system, a relic of feudalism.

Emperor Alexander III (1845-1894), the first Russian monarch to visit oil fields on the Absheron Peninsula in October 1888.

Russian Emperor Nicholas I (1796-1855) paid considerable attention to oil production on the Absheron Peninsula.

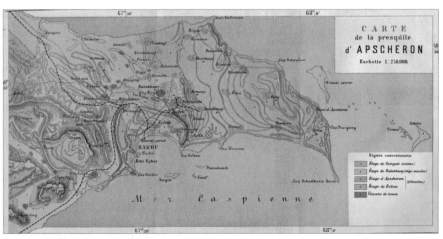

Map of oil fields on the Absheron Peninsula (late 19th century).

View of the Old City, Baku.

Bibiheybet oil field (Baku, 1905).

The First Expeditions of the Russian Academy of Sciences

During the reign of Empress Catherine the Great, the fields of mining and metallurgy continued to grow progressively in Russia, and many Russian scientists, following Lomonosov's footsteps, made solid contributions, primarily in the organization of the first scientific studies of the country's territory.

In 1762, Pëtr Rychkov (1712–1777), corresponding member of the St. Petersburg Academy of Sciences, presented one of the first descriptions of surface oil shows in the Volga region, near the Airyaka River, in his book, *Topography of the Orenburg Province* [*Topografiya Orenburgskoy gubernii*]: "Variegated oil shows can be seen, namely blue and yellow, white, black, and green, and on the water's surface we observe tar-like material that produces a very disgusting smell."

Johann Schlatter (1708–1768), president of the Mining Board, retired in 1767 for health reasons and his place was taken by Count Musin-Pushkin. Previously, the count had been a prosecutor, a member of the board of Main Mining Plants in Yekaterinburg, and vice president of the Mining Board. He was also known for having written the first domestic instruction manual on methods of extracting coal and of combating mine gases and shaft flooding during the tunneling process. At his direction, the natural scientist Stepan Vonevin was sent to the Caucasus region in 1768, where he compiled a map of the region's minerals, marking the location of petroleum springs near the Terek River.

In 1768–1769, the noted natural scientist Ivan Lepëkhin (1740–1802) included a detailed description of a series of Volga oil fields in his *Travelogue of a Doctor and Academy of Sciences Adjunct Through Various Provinces of the Russian State* [*Dnevnyye zapiski puteshestviya doktora i Akademii nauk adyunkta po raznym provintsiyam Rossiyskogo gosudarstva*]. Regarding surface oil shows in the area of Samarskaya Luka and the Sok River, he wrote: "Everything was already prepared for departure when the Tatars notified us that there was a petroleum spring some 15 *versts* [10 miles] from their village…. Sergeant Major Kravtsov, the Tatar escorting us, stated that the residents used it to lubricate wheels…. From the village of Yakushkina, directing our wagon train by ordinary road to Sergiyevsk with one student and escort Kravtsov, we went to the so-called petroleum lake, which was some four *versts* [2.6 miles] from Yakushkina, beyond Shungur."

Other Russian scientists also offered descriptions of surface oil shows in the Volga region. For instance, in a three-volume study produced after his 1768 expedition, Academician Pëtr Pallas (1741–1811) gave a detailed description of several petroleum springs around the city of Syzran and along the Shungut, Kamyshly, and Sok Rivers: "The waters of one spring empty into the Sok River. The entire low land around the lake consists of petroleum land, so that in summer, holes dug everywhere along the shore contain petroleum." As to the use of petroleum by the local population, he wrote: "Resident Chuvashes and Tatars not only use this tarry water for gargling and drinking when suffering from oral thrush or boils in the throat, but also zealously collect the petroleum and use it in many cases as a home remedy."

The report of a 1768–1774 expedition led by Academician Johann Falk also presents a description of petroleum sources in the area of the town of Tetyushi, comparing it to similar oil shows at other sites along the Volga.

Confidential adviser Mikhail Soymonov (1730–1804), a graduate of the Moscow Artillery School and participant in the Nercha Geologic Expedition, did much to advance the development of the Russian mining industry. Appointed in 1771 by the president of the Mining Board, he headed the mining institution for ten years and made immense contributions to the development of Russian industry.

Upon his initiative, Catherine the Great issued a decree on October 21, 1773. The decree established the St. Petersburg Mining School, which laid the foundation for the formation of a Russian system of higher mining engineering education, which in turn had a significant effect on the development of the domestic oil industry. This was Russia's first technical institution of higher education, and a true embodiment of the great reformer Peter the Great's idea to train domestic engineers to develop the mining and metallurgical industries.

In 1776, Soymonov was sent abroad "for medical treatment," and in 1781 he retired temporarily "to improve his health," and was replaced as president by the senator and confidential adviser Ivan Ryazanov. In 1781, pursuant to the "Institution for the Administration of Provinces of the All-Russian Empire" (1775), the administration of mining was transferred to the Treasury Boards under the control of the Expedition on State Revenue attached to the Governing Senate. In this new configuration, the Mining Board lost its previous importance, and in 1782 the Senate decreed "that the Treasury Boards should not send its revenues to the Mining Board." In the same year, Catherine the Great published her Manifesto, according to which rights to the land surface were identified with rights to the subsurface, i.e., the rights bestowed by Peter the Great in the Mining Privilege of 1719 were practically eliminated. Later, in 1783, Empress Catherine the Great abolished the Mining Board. This perilous state of affairs in the mining industry lasted 16 years. It is clear now that the decision to administer the mining department through the Treasury Boards was yet another unsuccessful government experiment, one that ultimately caused a decline in the industry.

This misguided experiment ended with Emperor Paul I [Pavel Petrovich] (1754–1801), who assumed the throne in November 1796.

With his decree of December 19, 1796, he reinstated the Mining Board, restoring the rights it had enjoyed before 1775, except for the advantages bestowed on nobles by the Noble Charter and Urban Statute. Under this decree, the Ural mining plants were placed under the Mining Board, and the Senate's Expedition on State Revenue and the Treasury Boards' Expedition for Mining Affairs were abolished.

Thus, the Mining Board resumed its activities. Actual State Councilor Andrey Nartov (1736–1813), a graduate of the cadet corps and one of the founders of the Free Economic Society, was appointed as its president. The task of "supervising the Mining Board as to mine plants and fields" was assigned to Actual Confidential Councilor and former Mining Board chief Mikhail Soymonov.

In 1798, Aleksandr Alyabyev, a skilled administrator and former Perm Province vice governor, was appointed to replace Andrey Nartov as president of the Mining Board. He tried to return to Ukhta oil fields. On August 2, 1801, the Mining Board reviewed a case concerning sparkling stones and oil fields found by collegiate assessor Pëtr Sumarokov. The grounds for this review was Sumarokov's letter, in which he wrote, after returning from a trip through Mezen District: "At various locations, I found fields rich in oil… we collected up to 80 *poods* [9.6 barrels] of oil from several excavated pits, but of that 58 *poods* [7 barrels] were kept and delivered in winter at my own expense to the city of Mezen, and from there brought to Arkhangelsk with the permission of his Excellency the Governor General Timofey Ivanovich Tugolmin, who was administering the post at the time and at whose directive the oil was tested and found to be of the highest quality…. Through wells, up to a thousand *poods* [120 barrels], possibly more, can be had from these sources."[19]

However, the Mining Board nevertheless limited its review of the matter to the finding of its president, Aleksandr Alyabyev, who proceeded solely from the economic assessment of the volume of oil imported into Russia: "As for oil fields on the left bank of the Ukhta River, I do not have detailed information on local conditions and cannot say how much oil production and transportation will cost, but I do not believe these fields will yield a large profit…. From the schedule compiled at the Mining Board for 1797, 1798, and 1799, which I obtained for communication of this subject, it is clear from the three-year total that only 45 *poods* 37½ pounds [1,657.5 pounds] of oil, worth 111 rubles 46 kopecks, is imported annually from foreign lands to Russia, which amounts to two rubles 59 kopecks for each *pood* [36 pounds] (although foreign oil is always refined and therefore of higher quality than that collected directly from sources). Such small imports demonstrate that it is little used."[20]

The Mining Department at the Start of the
Steam and Iron Age

At the beginning of the 19th century, coinciding with the ascension to the throne of the Emperor Alexander I (1777–1825), a new chapter opened in the history of Russia's oil industry, full of dramatic events involving many outstanding Russian entrepreneurs, engineers, and scientists.

On November 19, 1801, Emperor Alexander I issued a decree to organize the "Main Expedition to Establish Mining Production in Georgia," which was headed by Count Apollos Musin-Pushkin (1760–1805), a well-known figure active in Russian mining. An honorary member of the St. Petersburg Academy of Sciences and a member of the Royal Society of London, he also occupied the position of vice president of the Mining Board for a number of years. As early as June 15, 1797, he sent his "Opinion about the Mining Industry" to the Mining Board, the first analytic report about the state of mining in Russia. It noted the following: "The mining industry in Russia differs noticeably from that established in foreign countries. The reasons for this difference are numerous, and have to do with the climate, the population density, the political relationships of the economy and government trade, as well as the very decrees governing the European nations that have mining."

In November 1801, the Russian Emperor most graciously allowed Count Musin-Pushkin to set out, at his request, as a traveler to the Caucasus Mountains to prospect for ore deposits. The results of this expedition were used to compile the first mineralogical descriptions of the Caucasus and South Caucasus, which laid the foundation for widespread development of this land's natural resources.

In the fall of 1802, Emperor Alexander I issued a decree abolishing the boards founded under Peter, creating ministries in their place. Thus, a transition of the mining industry began from collegial administration to undivided administration.

In 1807, the Mining Board was replaced by the Mining Department, which at first was an organizational unit of the Ministry of Commerce. The first director of the Mining Department was Ural region native Gavriil Kachka (1740–1812). Under his authority, the Mining Department directed the Treasury's plants and mines through district-level governing bodies, controlled the activity of existing private mining and metallurgical enterprises, allocated land sites to new ones, and granted permission to carry out prospecting for mineral resources. At first, the department consisted of two subdivisions: the Mining Council, for preparation of legislation concerning the industry, and the Mining Expedition, whose authority included executive functions. The head of the Mining Expedition had extensive powers, while the Mining Council was a consultative body under the director of the department.

Government reform involved reexamination of the legal framework of mining. In 1804, the head of the Perm Works, Andrey Deryabin (1770–1820), delivered a report to the government in which he proposed to introduce hired labor in mining industry enterprises, restore the freedom of the mining industry, carry out a technical reconstruction of enterprises, and improve working conditions. This report was considered by a special commission chaired by Count Aleksey Vasilyev (1742–1807), minister of finance. A decision was made to write a new mining statute, and although not all of Deryabin's proposals were incorporated into the statute, this document, which was approved in 1806, became one of the most progressive regulations of the time in Russia. For example, it provided for the replacement of serfs with paid workers for auxiliary plant work. The statute also confirmed freedom of mining for treasury lands, and devoted attention to standardizing the working day of laborers and modernizing mining equipment.

In 1810, the Mining Department was incorporated into the Ministry of Finances and renamed the Department of Mining and Salt Works. An experienced specialist, Chief Mining Captain Andrey Deryabin, was appointed as its director.

Further significant changes were afoot for the Russian mining industry, in particular, the return of the Absheron Peninsula to Russia. The signing of the Treaty of Gulistan between Russia and Persia (1813) ended the Russo-Persian War of 1803–1813, and the agreement returned the territory of the Baku Khanate to the Russian Empire.

At that time, there were 116 hand-dug wells on the Absheron Peninsula producing "black" oil and one producing "white" oil. The total annual production was about 18,000 barrels. The means of oil production at that time were very primitive, with the local population drawing oil from open pits and shallow wells.

It should be noted that by this time a Russian military garrison had already been located in Baku for several years, and the oil fields were leased out to various people to be operated under a tax-farming arrangement. Here again, private initiative at the outset of development resulted in positive results. Evidence of this is provided by a report issued July 30, 1813, by General Nikolay Rtishchev, commander-in-chief of Russian forces in the Caucasus, to St. Petersburg: "Under the tax-farming arrangement for four years, this item, along with others that are very unimportant, at first brought a net sum of 450,000 rubles in banknotes, without any concerns or expenses on the part of the Treasury.... The Treasury income for this production can be considered certain only when an item rich in resources is under a tax-farming arrangement with honest persons.... But if these institutions are directly managed by the Treasury, then besides the necessity of establishing a special staff of civil servants for this and provide their salaries, workers and travel expenses must be supported. Everything will require significant expenses for the Treasury."[21]

According to archival sources, in 1813 the Russian government leased out the Baku oil wells under a tax-farming arrangement to Mark Tarumov, province secretary. A second agreement to turn the oil wells over to him from January 1, 1817 through January 1, 1821 was concluded in the summer of 1816.

General Anikita Yartsev (1737–1819), former head of the Ural mining plants, described the Baku fields in his manuscript, *History of Russian Mining* [*Rossiyskaya gornaya istoriya*] (1819): "Around Baku there is an unbelievable quantity of mineral oil or petroleum, for 12 *versts* [7.9 miles] from Baku several villages of the Balakhany neighborhood have 25 open hand-dug oil wells, although the oil springs often do dry up, which necessitates the digging of new wells; however, even the old ones are not quickly refilled, but are carefully left open for a certain time, since sometimes after several months the oil springs usually reappear in them.... The excess is transported to the city of Baku; although there are no special reserve storage depots there, outside the city 15 hand-dug wells have been set up and dug out into the hardest gypsum rock, and lined with stone. The reserve oil is poured into these wells, and kept until it is removed by sellers."

After the term of the agreement ended, a new tax-farming contract was signed with Tarumov on January 12, 1821 for the following four years, under the previous conditions, for an annual payment of 131,000 rubles. The agreement solidified Tarumov's right to a monopoly on the sale of this oil: "And if anyone should be discovered, then for a first offense, such a secret seller shall be forced to pay the Treasury 1,000 rubles in banknotes, and the entire quantity of oil shall be confiscated and given to the tax farmer, as property belonging to him. For a second and third secret sale of oil, in addition to such fines to the Treasury and the tax farmer, the secret seller shall be turned over to be dealt with according to the laws." In addition, the agreement provided the tax farmer with generous resources and rights, including "the work force to dig and repair wells, remove oil from them and transport it to reservoirs, and also the right to prospect for new sources of petroleum on the peninsula." There is also a very interesting point in the agreement that allowed Tarumov to engage in oil trading with Persia, without paying customs duty.

Despite such favorable conditions, however, his subsequent activity was apparently not profitable, and after his agreement expired not a single person could be found who was interested in or willing to take over the wells for a new term. Therefore, as there was no one who desired to run these fields for the next four years for the amount of the previous tax-farming arrangement, Count Yegor Kankrin (1774–1845), minister of finance, issued a directive placing them under the administration of the

Treasury starting January 1, 1825. In connection with this, the minister of finance issued an order creating two special posts: superintendent of oil fields and salt lakes located in Baku province, and an assistant from the ranks of mining civil servants.

The "Description of Treasury buildings located at hand-dug oil wells and cellars that fell under the purview of the Georgian Mining Expedition in January 1825," compiled by Chief Mining Captain Karpinsky in February 1825, gave precise information "about the condition of the hand-dug oil wells and cellars for the storage of oil; about the quantity of oil in them left by Mr. Tarumov in the fortress of Baku and in the settlements of Binagadi, Surakhany, and Beybati." In 1825 there were a total of 125 hand-dug oil wells, including: 82 wells of "black" petroleum and 12 Treasury cellars in Balakhany, 5 wells of "black" petroleum in Binagadi, 15 wells of "white" petroleum in Surakhany, and only 16 cellars for storage of "black" oil in Baku itself.

The natural scientist and traveler Karl Eduard von Eichwald (1795–1876) visited Baku that same year (1825). In his work *Reise auf dem Caspischen Meere und Caucasus* [*Trip to the Caspian Sea and Caucasus*], he gave a detailed description of the "eternal flames" and pointed out the properties of combustible gas mixed with air, and also described the hand-dug oil wells: "Wells producing 'white' oil are located to the northwest of the village of Surakhany, at a distance of approximately 1.5 *versts* [1 mile] from it. To recover oil, 16 wells have been set up; to improve their capacity, they are built broad inside, while at the top, on the contrary, they are narrow, not more than a foot in diameter. They are covered tightly with fitted caps, so as not to allow the oil to evaporate. Many hand-dug wells collect 'white' oil with water; every well gives an indefinite quantity of oil: more in summer and less in winter."

A detailed article by St. Petersburg Mining School graduate Nikolay Voskoboynikov, "Mineralogical Description of the Absheron Peninsula, Forming the Baku Khanate," which appeared in *Gorny zhurnal* ["Mining Journal"] (1827), provided the first classification of the various forms of Baku petroleum, explained the origin of the so-called "white" petroleum, provided a detailed description of the oil wells and pools (oil pits) in the Absheron Peninsula, and also described existing methods of storing oil and the technology of the work performed to set up oil wells. Voskoboynikov pointed out the following: "The rather thick, black petroleum is found predominantly in the areas of Bakhche and Shubany, where it accumulates in small pits, whose depth is from one-third to one *arshin* [9.3 to 28 inches]. It is also encountered close to the villages of Balakhany and Binagadi, close to oil wells. This petroleum is of poor quality, making it unusable for lighting without a significant admixture of greenish petroleum; very thick oil of this type is also used for caulking vessels."

He provides curious information about the sea oil field of local inhabitant Kasim-bek, which consisted of two hand-dug wells: "One of them was located at a distance of nine *sazhens* [63 feet] from the shore at a depth of one-quarter *sazhen* [1.75 feet], and the second 15 *sazhens* [105 feet] from the shore at the same depth. The wooden frameworks of the wells rose half a *sazhen* [three and a half feet] over the surface of the water."

Meanwhile, the performance of necessary well repair work, the establishment of a system to account for the oil produced, and a number of other accomplishments of Mining Expedition specialists increased production, and in 1825 more than 28,800 barrels of oil were produced. Despite the increased production, the Treasury received no more than 76,000 rubles for a year. After this, Count Yegor Kankrin, minister of finance, issued an order stating: "Experience with Treasury administration of the fields in 1825 showed that the profit received from them falls far short of the income the Treasury received during the period when they were run under a tax-farming arrangement."[22]

Therefore, when entrepreneurs who expressed the desire to run the aforementioned fields under a tax-farming arrangement were found, the oil wells were leased to them for two four-year terms (1826–1834).

However, after these eight years had passed, history again repeated itself: "As no one wanting to run these fields again was found, the fields came under Treasury administration for the following four-year period under a tax-farming arrangement, starting on January 1, 1834."[23]

The Projects of Mining Engineer Voskoboynikov

The next significant phase in the development of the oil fields in the Absheron Peninsula is inextricably connected with the fruitful activity of the talented mining engineer Nikolay Voskoboynikov (1803–1861).

Starting January 1, 1834, Emperor Nicholas I (1796–1855) issued a decree militarizing the Mining Department as the Corps of Mining Engineers. The Corps was headed by the minister of finance himself, Yegor Kankrin (1774–1845). It was at this time that the term "mining engineer" first appeared in Russia. Moreover, the post of chief of staff, responsible for daily operational management of the department, was created. The first person appointed chief of staff of the Corps of Mining Engineers was Major General Konstantin Chevkin (1802–1875).

On January 1, 1834, Corps of Mining Engineers Major Voskoboynikov was appointed director of the Baku and Shirvan oil and salt fields. An order of the Mining Department defined his responsibilities as seeing to it that the hand-dug oil wells were correctly run, and that the oil was produced and delivered to Baku and the near banks of the Kura River, the designated places for the sale of oil. With his new appointment, mining engineer Voskoboynikov was granted the opportunity to realize his innovative ideas concerning the development and improvement of the oil business.

First and foremost, his attention was focused on the technology of setting up hand-dug oil wells. At that time, the existing procedure for setting up oil wells involved first excavating a pit resembling an inverted cone all the way down to the oil stratum. At least 7 terraces averaging 31.5 feet in depth were made on the sides of the pit. The average volume of earth taken out of such a well was around 2,317 cubic feet. The walls of deep wells were reinforced from the very bottom to the surface by a wooden framework and boards. The lower courses of the well had openings made in them to allow the inflow of petroleum.

In an effort to increase the efficiency of the work, Major Voskoboynikov proposed that access be gained to the oil stratum by constructing shafts, instead of by digging a large-diameter pit on the surface. The shaft was divided in half by a partition. Over the head of the shaft, a raised tubular structure made of boards was set up on one side to increase the circulation of air in the shaft. This proposal significantly reduced the volume of earthmoving work required to set up oil wells.

Clogging presented a serious problem in operating oil wells. To clean a well, a man was lowered on a rope, and he collected dirt into a bucket using his hands. As a rule, the lack of air greatly limited the time a worker could remain in the well. In 1835, mining engineer Voskoboynikov proposed constructing a canvas ventilator to deliver fresh air into the oil well to facilitate cleaning and repair work. Later, he introduced an improved individual device: a breathing apparatus consisting of an artificial nose and a flexible tube fastened to it. Use of this apparatus allowed for the successful cleaning of a narrow and curved well known as "Ali-Bek," which had never been cleaned before.

The advancements made during Nikolay Voskoboynikov's initial period of work resulted in positive growth: in just the first two years of his management of the fields (1834–1835), oil production increased to 42,355 barrels (compared with 41,562 barrels in 1833).

However, storing, receiving, and delivering oil still presented an extremely acute problem in the fields. Storing oil in earthen cellars and open oil pits resulted in great losses as a consequence of significant evaporation, leakage through various openings in cellar and pit walls, and additional losses from bucket spillage when workers carried them by hand.

In 1836–1837, Nikolay Voskoboynikov reorganized the entire oil storage and delivery system in Baku and Balakhany on the basis of his own design. Five Balakhany oil cellars with a total capacity of more than 14,650 barrels were connected by inclined stone canals. On one side, a building was constructed to receive oil removed from the wells. Inside it, four stone reservoirs were set up, each with a capacity of three barrels, from which the oil was released along an inclined canal into a settling reservoir. Once the oil had settled, it was poured into an inclined canal, along which it flowed by gravity into cellars for storage or into a delivery reservoir. Stone reservoirs containing copper kettles having three or four openings were set up along the length of the canal opposite the cellars. When the copper kettles were turned, oil flowed through the openings along the branches of the canal into the cellar or into delivery reservoirs. The inclined stone canal around the oil delivery building ended in a copper pipe, through which oil flowed into a copper kettle. The copper kettle could be turned, and had a device that could direct oil among six pipes into wooden barrels having a capacity of 3.4 barrels each.

In the same way, inclined stone canals connected nine cellars in Baku with a total volume of more than 6,125 barrels. On one side of these cellars there was a building for receiving oil transported from the fields. This building housed copper reservoirs, each with a capacity of 3.4 barrels, and reservoirs for oil settling. After settling, the oil flowed along an inclined stone canal into storage cellars or to the building for wholesale and retail delivery. Wholesale delivery was carried out from three reservoirs, and retail delivery was carried out from one reservoir, which was equipped with copper faucets and held 72 barrels. The reorganization of the system for receiving, storing, and delivering oil significantly reduced oil losses and created an orderly system to account for and store it. The quantity of oil sold significantly increased, since it could be stored in special containers and delivered in any weather. For example, the amount of oil sold in Baku in December 1837 was 3,603 barrels, while around 1,200 barrels were sold per month before the reorganization of the oil facilities. In addition, there was a significant reduction in the number of workers, and the work of draining and filling oil was made easier.

Another bottleneck in the Baku fields was the process used to excavate the oil, which was done by hand in leather buckets, or by using horses for deep wells. Of course, such methods were not very productive. In 1839, the Main Administration of the South Caucasus considered Major Voskoboynikov's proposal to increase the production of oil from hand-dug oil wells by using pumps. However, this plan was not accepted, because piston devices of sufficient output were not yet available.

Yet another of the major's innovative proposals concerned the problem of shipping oil by sea. In order to load vessels transporting oil via the Caspian Sea, field director Voskoboynikov proposed building "a pier on piles" on the shore and running a "separable railway" to it from the Baku cellars. Setting up such an oil terminal would allow for quick loading of oil onto vessels. But the Caspian Treasury Office also found this plan hare-brained, and rejected it.

The First Refinery on the Absheron Peninsula

Starting in mid-1834, mining engineer Voskoboynikov began experiments involving the distillation of "light" Surakhany and "heavy" Balakhany oil, and the use of the resulting products for lighting. The resulting distillation products, a transparent and colorless oil essence and a greenish-yellow oil essence, burned without soot, and produced a light brighter than that of candles.

At the end of the summer of 1834, Nikolay Voskoboynikov submitted a report to General G. V. Rozen, head commander of affairs in Georgia, titled "Refinement of White Oil at the Baku and Shirvan Fields Using a Distillation Apparatus, and Preparation of Iron Drums for Storage of Same." He emphasized that "it would be useful to refine it by distillation on site, which would cost the Treasury very little, for the 'white' oil wells themselves have natural fires close to them; the advantage of the produced refined oil is that this oil can be sold at a high price and in large quantity."

The Scholarly Committee of the Mining Engineers Corps approved Major Voskoboynikov's report on November 14, 1834. Academician Germain Henri Hess, member of the Department of Manufacturing, likewise gave a positive review of Voskoboynikov's report, proposing that "1) Chemists separate both 'white' and 'black' petroleum, and determine the properties both of the components and of the fractions obtained from it, and publish such information. 2) At the same time, to accelerate development of its sale, determine if it could be used to prepare varnishes for cast iron and iron and, in general, for all needs for which turpentine is used, and also to produce the carbon black that is put into printing ink, and does 'black' petroleum differ from the tar produced from coal, and finally, is it possible to collect the soot coming from the natural petroleum fires, which could be used as a dye for tanneries."

Further instruction came on January 24, 1835 from an order signed by Count Yegor Kankrin, minister of finance, for Mining Engineer Voskoboynikov, Director of Baku and Shirvan oil and salt fields, regarding "the preparation at the Baku mineral fields of up to 1,000 *poods* [120 barrels] of refined oil, to be sent to Russia via Astrakhan… and to report to the Treasury Expedition about his actions in this case for its faster fulfillment, to have appropriate observation on his part."

The Georgian Treasury Expedition's Report No. 6849 of November 10, 1837, to the Department of Mining and Salt Works of the Ministry of Finance contains interesting details about the plan for the Balakhany factory. It also mentions Report No. 322 of June 12, 1837 by Mining Engineer Voskoboynikov, in which he states that, 1) Having finished his work setting up the Baku reservoirs, which required his continual presence in Baku, he would soon set off for the villages of Balakhany and Surakhany to set up distillation apparatus there to produce "white" oil from "black;" 2) All supplies necessary for this purpose—namely, 450 sheets of 56-inch iron weighing 5,789 pounds, 144 pounds of lead, 144 pounds of ammonium chloride, and 288 pounds of tin—had already been sent to him by Astrakhan second guild merchant Solodovnikov; 3) At his request Baku Commandant Lieutenant Colonel Luzanov had informed him of the assignment to him of one mechanic, two blacksmiths, and two furnace service people from Georgian Line Battalion No. 8 to set up the distillation apparatus, iron drums, and furnaces. He added that to produce "white" oil from "black" oil he had devised a new apparatus presenting all the benefits for protecting the remains of "black" oil from changes in its quality. Moreover, he had discovered natural fires around the village of Balakhany, which could be used to operate several pieces of distillation apparatus, significantly reducing expenses involved in distilling "white" oil; he would present a description and drawings of the newly devised distillation apparatus to bring them into operation on a larger scale.

Detailed information about the technical equipment and facilities at the Balakhany refinery is contained in the drawings and description preserved in the Russian State Historical Archive (RGIA) in St. Petersburg. They show that the refinery's main building contained quadrangular distillation kettles made of roofing iron. Each kettle consisted of two parts. The upper part of the kettle tightly capped the lower part and had two pipes attached to it to remove vapors to receiving vessels. Initially, water was poured into the kettle through a pipe inserted into an opening in the upper part of the kettle; afterward, oil was poured onto the surface of the water through the pipe. The kettles were supported by iron bars and were embedded in the furnace. Pipes passed through reservoirs containing cooling water. The receiving vessel for distilled oil was an iron cylinder immersed in a circular iron vat filled with water. The oil in the kettles was heated using natural gas drawn from nearby gas sources and collected in special reservoirs, and then fed through pipes to burners.

Incidentally, this was Russia's first experience with the industrial use of natural gas. The gas burner was made of an iron pipe with small openings on the top. The combustion products passed through a canal to a chimney, heating a water-filled copper tub along the way. Water from the tub was poured into the kettle to keep the oil from overheating.

At the refinery, the light Surakhany oil yielded 83.9% lighting distillate, 12.5% residue, and 3.6% was lost to evaporation. The heavy Balakhany oil yielded only 10% distillation product and 85% residue, and 5% was lost.

As it turned out, Voskoboynikov's Balakhany refinery was in operation for only a very short time: from November 1837 through August 1838. Over nine months, it produced more than 108 barrels of lamp oil, which was sent to Astrakhan. But since the oil distillation product did not initially undergo further chemical processing (refining), the petroleum acids present in the distillate caused corrosion of the walls of iron barrels when it was stored and transported, which in turn changed the product's color and significantly degraded its combustion properties. The large production expenses and high cost of transportation of the finished product made the refinery unprofitable. The refinery's numerous misfortunes also reflected the absence of Major Voskoboynikov, who was removed from his post without grounds and was under investigation after being denounced by adversaries.

The new director of the Absheron oil fields appointed by the Mining Department opted out of managing the oil distillation work, and by the beginning of 1839 the Balakhany refinery ceased to exist. However, the short-lived distillation work of the refinery was not in vain: the series of technical solutions devised by mining engineer Nikolay Voskoboynikov and put into practice at the refinery had a substantial influence on all subsequent developments in refining in Russia.

On Petroleum Quitrent

Along with the development of the fields on the Absheron Peninsula, signs of the emerging oil business also started to appear in the North Caucasus. One of the first to announce the presence of oil sources in the North Caucasus at the beginning of the 18th century was the Russian geographer and cartographer Ivan Kirillov (1689–1737). Author of the first systematic and economic geographical description of Russia, *The Flourishing Condition of the Russian State* [*Tsvetushcheye sostoyaniye Vserossiyskogo gosudarstva*] (1727), he reported that "between the small towns of Shadrino and Chervlenoe, on the other side of the Terek River, there are oil wells; however, there is no oil industry on them."

Russian archives contain documents suggesting that Cossacks and local inhabitants collected and used oil from the Braguny and Chervlenoe wells. For example, the description of the archive of the Kizlyar commandant mentions two files: "Delivery of Oil on Cossack *Kayuks*" (1743) and "Release of Cossacks to the Chervlenoe Wells to Collect Petroleum" (1756).

Russian researcher Stepan Vonevin's report of September 15, 1768 noted that: "It is possible to see the Braguny hot springs and the Chervlenoe hand-dug oil wells extending up to the edge of these mountain ranges, which begin almost from the mouth of the Sunzha River and bend to the west up along the Terek, almost parallel to it."

In 1770, the St. Petersburg Academy of Sciences had this region explored by aide-de-camp Johann Anton Güldenstädt (1745–1781), who later became president of the Free Economic Society (VEO). In his book

Reisen durch Russland [*Travels through Russia*], characterizing the territory located not far from the village of Mamakay-Yurt, he wrote: "Around 10 *versts* [6.6 miles] to the south of the Pavlovskaya greenhouse there is an oil spring... gushing out of the mountains lying opposite the greenhouse in two places at a distance of 100 paces; this so-called petroleum is a black, thick, and natural mineral oil, or mineral tar. In the first spring there is a little of this tar, and in the last two, several barrels of it are produced every year for lubricating wheels."

At the beginning of the 19th century these oil-bearing areas were the property of Prince Turlov, and in 1811 the Mozdok Cossack Regiment took control of these oil wells under a tax-farming arrangement. However, after the Grozny fortress was built (1818) and the Caucasus Cossack Line Forces were formed, the oil sources came to be administered by its leaders, who started to lease the wells out to various entrepreneurs under a tax-farming arrangement. Crude oil was used instead of tar; distilled oil was sold to pharmacies as a medicine, for cleaning clothing, and for producing waterproof fabrics.

The beginning of the 1820s was marked by a significant event that became an important landmark in the history of the domestic oil business. For more than two decades, primary processing of oil had been carried out in the North Caucasus by the brothers Vasily, Gerasim, and Makar Dubinin, who were serfs of Countess Panina from the village of Nizhny Landekh, Gorokhovets District, Vladimir Province. Their landowner had imposed on them the condition of paying a considerable monetary quitrent, so they arrived in this restless region in search of a source of funds.

At first they were engaged in small-scale trading. In 1823 they decided to apply their experience in tar distillation and turpentine production, so they built a one-still refinery in the region of the village of Akki-Yurt, not far from the city of Mozdok. Its construction involved using the schematic diagram of a furnace for production of pitch and turpentine. Using oil from the wells of the Voznesensk field as raw material, this refinery carried out the primary distillation of oil with a periodic cycle, producing "white" oil (unrefined kerosene distillate), which they offered as a therapeutic agent and also as one of the components of lighting material for street lights in Stavropol and other population centers of the North Caucasus.

A description of their refinery has survived: "An iron still is cemented in the top of a brick furnace, and 40 buckets of 'black' oil are poured into this still at a time. Once the 'black' oil has been poured into the still, a copper cover is put on it. A copper pipe passes from the cover through a wooden tub filled with water and makes one turn in the tub. The tub has a wooden bucket placed next to it against the pipe. The brick furnace is built with a windbox, and when it is fired at the base, oil from the still is drawn through the water into the pipe, where it is refined, producing 'white' oil, which flows out through the pipe into the bucket; 16 buckets of it is produced from 40 buckets of 'black' oil."

The family quitrent enterprise of the Dubinin brothers operated for more than 20 years. However, since they remained serfs and as such were required to pay their landowner a large monetary quitrent, they could not adequately develop their production. In addition, intensifying market competition exacerbated their financial situation.

On March 17, 1844, the Dubinin brothers sent a petition for consideration to Colonel Prints, head of the Pyatigorsk District. They wrote: "We take the liberty to explain to the high authorities that we wished to expand the oil industry and trade here and in Russia to a greater extent, but we do not have sufficient capital to do this. Therefore, we most humbly request, in reward of our 20 years of labor and in order to promote the development of domestic oil trade of Russian production, to allow the delivery to us of sixty barrels of black oil from Treasury sources located near the Grozny fortress, every year for five years, without monetary payment, with permission for us to export freely from the Caucasus and Russia and to sell, at an unrestricted price, both the processed white and black oil, which is the residue after it is boiled down. If it is impossible to deliver the oil to us without monetary payment, then we ask for monetary assistance from the Treasury in the amount of 7,000 rubles in silver."

Two years passed without a favorable response to their request, so on August 9, 1846 they sent a new petition to Count Mikhail Vorontsov, viceroy of the Caucasus: "Most Excellent Prince! In industrial matters, wide distribution and especially activity involving the manufacture of our own domestic products is a national treasure, which is the strength of the state, and examples convince us that in all actions, of whatever type they might be, incentives or rewards double the strength and spirit to overcome great new obstacles, and incentives revive tired labor.... We, the Dubinin family, have been producing oil for more than 20 years amid incessant danger from enemy attacks by mountain peoples, and have made continuous efforts to please the government."

The viceroy of the Caucasus awarded the head of the family, Vasily Dubinin, the medal "For usefulness" on a Vladimirov ribbon, but the brothers still did not receive financial support from the authorities. Shortly thereafter, a raid on Akki-Yurt by a detachment of mountain dwellers from the formations of Imam Shamil put a definitive end to the more than 20-year history of the Dubinin brothers' quitrent enterprise.

In their appeals to the authorities, the Dubinin family emphasized that: "We have discovered by our efforts a method of refining petroleum of natural black color into white. Before us, no one here knew such a method of refining, and we did not keep it secret for only our own benefit, but to promote the common good we quickly disclosed it to all inhabitants of the city of Mozdok, which is not far from where the sources are located, and selflessly taught it to other manufacturers."

Despite the end of the Dubinin brothers' enterprise, their example really did spread in the North Caucasus. The historical literature lists the names of entrepreneurs who followed their methods: N. Avdyunin, V. Shvetsov, and the merchant Sukhorukov, among others.

At the beginning of the 1830s, researcher Rikhard German (1805–1879), traveling all over the Caucasus to study the properties of mineral sources, wrote in his work "The Large Asphalt Stratum in Minor Chechnya" that "10 *versts* [6.6 miles] from the fortress rises a group of hills consisting of marl. In the basin located among these hills there is an oil source: this is a pit, faced on the inside with a wooden framework and filled with water; it contains parts of iron (II) sulfate and thick oil floats on top of this water; this liquid continually releases hydrocarbon gas. This source gives 20 buckets of oil per day, from which pure mineral oil is prepared in a building built close to the source. The asphalt remaining from distillation is used on site in place of fuel for the distillation apparatus."

It is possible that this refining company belonged to the partnership of Nikolay Avdyunin, a third guild merchant from Mozdok, who concluded a three-year tax-farming arrangement in 1833 on hand-dug oil wells close to the Grozny fortress. This company subsequently fell into other hands. Vasily Shvetsov, the new tax farmer, wrote the following in his petition: "General demand and high prices have made many, including Mozdok merchant Avdyukin, the former tax farmer, with his company, study the production of petroleum according to the method indicated by the Dubinins. When the sources came under my administration, I also paid attention to this branch of industry, acquired by the same method up to 1,000 *poods* [120 barrels] of 'white' oil and, in the hope of deriving significant benefits, sent the entire prepared quantity to Moscow in 1837, but found the prices of it were already from 24 to 27 rubles in banknotes."

Russia's First Asphalt Plant

Another region that provided a certain impetus to the development of the oil business in post-reform Russia was the Crimean Peninsula.

At the end of the 17th century, the Russian government, striving to ensure the safety of the southern areas and gain a window onto the Black Sea, began a struggle to take control of this strategic region. During the Russo-Turkish War of 1768–1774, Russian forces took control of the Crimea and under an agreement with Khan Sahib Giray (1772) and the Treaty of Kuchuk Kaynarca (1774), the Crimean Khanate was declared independent of Turkey and came under the protection of the Russian Empire.

In 1783 the Crimea was annexed to Russia and in 1797–1802 the territory of the peninsula became part of the Novorossiya Province. On October 8, 1802, Alexander I issued a decree dividing the Novorossiya Province into three Russian provinces: Nikolayev, Yekaterinoslav, and Tavrich. According to this decree, "Tavrich Province consists of seven districts, comprising: Simferopol, or Ak-Mechet, Perekop, the former Phanagoria, renamed Tmutarakan, which is the name that the island of Taman bore in Old Russia, and with the addition to the district of seven lands of the Black Sea force, Feodosiya (Kefiya) and Yevpatoriya (Kozlov), and finally, beyond Perekop, Dnepr and Melitopol Provinces. Simferopol is assigned the capital of this province."

The first geologic studies of the Crimean Peninsula territory were carried out in 1823 by the Russian surveyor Kozin. Among other things, he named and marked the basic sites of surface oil shows on the peninsula.

It is noteworthy that this is also exactly the same place where the first successful attempt was made in 1838 to set up domestic asphalt production in Russia. It was due to three persons: Mikhail Vorontsov, governor general of Novorossiya; Zakhar Kherkheulidze, town governor of Kerch; and Karl Byurno, colonel of engineers.

In 1823, Count Mikhail Vorontsov (1782–1856) was appointed governor general of Novorossiya and plenipotentiary viceroy of Bessarabia. His efforts to develop industry and agriculture and improve the cities of the region were highly valued by his contemporaries. Suffice to say that before his arrival in Odessa, the city had no paved roadways or sidewalks. His name is also associated with the establishment of domestic steam navigation on the Black Sea and the first experiments with municipal street lighting using illuminating gas.

Zakhar Kherkheulidze (1798–1856), town governor of Kerch, was also an extremely noteworthy person. On January 14, 1833, at the suggestion of Governor General Vorontsov, he was appointed town governor of Kerch and Yeni-Kale, and served as the head of the city for a full 17 years. This period became a sort of "Age of Kherkheulidze." In 1830–1840, a general plan for the construction of Kerch was completed, and the town governor was responsible for realizing the brilliant ideas of municipal architect Aleksandr Digbi, who built a whole series of marvelous buildings. During this period, the city center acquired its definitive form, the architectural highlight of which was Mount Mithridat. Many blocks of the city were also built, as well as a series of municipal squares. In addition, the Melek-Chesme River was straightened by a canal and the embankment was lined with stone; the slope of Mithridat had trees planted on it, forming a beautiful boulevard; the water supply system was improved, and new fountains were built. A series of industrial companies were also founded in the city. Based on his enthusiasm for improving the region's infrastructure, it is not surprising that Kherkheulidze gave his full support to Colonel Byurno's proposal to improve the city's streets and build the country's first asphalt plant.

A Frenchman by nationality, Karl Byurno (1796–1858) joined the Russian army in 1820 in the rank of second lieutenant of engineering forces. Over nine years of service, he was promoted to the rank of colonel of engineers, took part in the Russo-Turkish War of 1828–1829, and was awarded several medals. Starting in 1835, construction on the Black Sea coastline fortifications in the Caucasus began based on his plans. While this work was being done, he visited the Kerch Peninsula, where he was able to tour regions with surface oil shows and natural asphalt.

In the spring of 1838, Karl Byurno visited Paris, where he had the opportunity to familiarize himself with the city, including its experience in the use of asphalt in road construction. Since he directed the construction of defensive buildings, he was naturally aware of the high cost involved in shipping Seyssel asphalt from France to Russia, and instead proposed establishing domestic asphalt production.

His memorandum was fully endorsed by Governor General Mikhail Vorontsov, who instructed junior shift foreman Kulshin, a mining civil servant, to investigate petroleum and asphalt deposits in Kerch. The results of this expedition turned out to be promising, and in August 1838, Colonel Byurno was granted 12,000 rubles to build an asphalt plant close to the petroleum sources between Yeni-Kale and the Yeni-Kale lighthouse, with property rights to it for 12 years.

The construction work was performed in a rather short period of time. At the plant, one distillation still was set up with a capacity of 50 buckets. The processing of Kerch petroleum produced equal volumes of kerosene distillate and a thick residue called maltha. An apparatus was set up on the plant grounds to crush asphalt rock—so-called grease rock— which was screened and placed, along with the maltha, into two kettles, each having a capacity of 60 buckets. Gravel was then added to the heated asphalt compound. The asphalt concrete resulting from this process was poured using manual scoops into quadrangular cast iron molds lubricated with oil. The finished asphalt concrete slabs weighed around 72 pounds.

In 1839, under the supervision of Colonel Byurno, a number of streets and sidewalks in Odessa and Kerch were successfully paved with asphalt. Use of asphalt concrete to pave the terraces and landings of the stairs leading up Mount Mithridat turned out to be a successful solution.

The road improvement work had a substantial influence on the appearance of the cities of the Black Sea coastal region, and was given high marks by Governor General Mikhail Vorontsov and the local population.

In 1843, in connection with a new appointment, Colonel of Engineers Karl Byurno transferred management of the asphalt plant to the Kerch municipal authorities and left the peninsula. In 1844, he was promoted to major general and appointed inspector of engineering forces of the Caucasus Army.

The plant he had founded operated successfully for almost another twelve years, right to the beginning of the Crimean War. In 1854, it produced around 36 tons of asphalt concrete. However, during military operations it was destroyed by British artillery. Afterwards, for a variety of reasons, no real attempts were made to restore asphalt production on the Kerch Peninsula for several decades.

Entangled in the Tax-Farming System

Meanwhile, back on the Absheron Peninsula the scale of oil production in the final years of the first half of the 19th century can be judged on the basis of a memorandum written in 1842 by the Caspian Office of State Properties of the Ministry of State Properties. It indicated that there were 136 wells on the entire Absheron Peninsula, the annual production of which was up to 27,620 barrels of oil, and more of this oil was exported to Persia than to Russia.

Subsequently, a certain growth in the number of wells also increased annual oil production, up to the level of a maximum of 36,025 barrels. With small fluctuations, this level was maintained for 10 years, and then oil production began to fall starting in 1847, and in 1849 a total of only 30,682 barrels of oil were produced.

Striving to correct the situation, the administration of the South Caucasus attempted to introduce a new method of oil production by means of drilling wells. On April 30, 1845, Fëdor Vronchenko (1780–1854), minister of finance, directed the Caspian Treasury Office to grant 1,000 rubles in silver and commissioned Major of Mining Corps of Engineers Alekseyev, who was the director of the Baku and Shirvan oil and salt fields, to perform manual exploratory drilling for petroleum in the region of Bibiheybet. This work was carried out for several years; finally, on July 14, 1848, the most illustrious Prince Mikhail Vorontsov, viceroy of the Caucasus, reported to St. Petersburg that a well containing petroleum had been drilled at Bibiheybet. However, since the flow of petroleum was small and had no industrial value, this well was soon forgotten.

Such weak production and financial results of Treasury administration of the fields on the Absheron Peninsula prompted the Russian government to return to the tried and true method of tax farming to extract income from the oil industry. On June 9, 1849, at the initiative of Minister of Finance Fëdor Vronchenko, a decree was issued by the emperor ordering the return of oil field operations to a tax-farming arrangement.

Starting on April 15, 1850, taxation of the oil fields was farmed out to three entrepreneurs—Kukudzhanov, Babanosov, and Ter-Gukasov—who jointly undertook a series of measures to increase the number of wells to 218 over the next ten years.

It is very noteworthy that, in 1851, samples of "white" and "black" Absheron oil at the disposal of Prince Mikhail Vorontsov, viceroy of the Caucasus, were sent to the Great Exhibition in London, where they found a worthy place in the Russian section of the exhibit.

Nevertheless, by the 1860s it was already readily apparent that the tax-farming system of operating Treasury oil lands was both faulty and obsolete, and its elimination was called for by the interests of both the oil industry and the Treasury, which received unrealistically low income under the tax-farming system.

Speaking about the urgency of eliminating the tax-farming system, the renowned Russian scientist Dmitry Mendeleyev (1834–1907) wrote: "The obstacles to the oil business essentially involve the operation of oil sources. The petroleum sources of the Caucasus are given to tax farmers for petroleum. There is no advantage for them, having a short-term tax-farming arrangement, to engage in major and troublesome work, to spend capital on prospecting and exploratory drilling, to dig nine wells in order that the tenth would repay all their expenses. This tenth one might come at a time when the tax-farming arrangement ends, or when its holder is no longer able to enjoy the fruits of his entrepreneurship for a long time, given the certain degree of risk that is unavoidable in the oil business. The tax-farming system paralyzes oil development, and consequently the entire oil business."[24]

Pennsylvania Kerosene in Russia

The presence of the tax-farming system on Russian oil fields led to a paradoxical phenomenon: although the country had enormous hydrocarbon reserves, at the beginning of the 1860s the streets of St. Petersburg, Moscow, and other cities were illuminated by lamps that used kerosene from the US.

In 1862, the St. Petersburg City Council acknowledged that in light of the substantial financial costs, the existing alcohol and oil street lighting was unfavorable for the city, and announced a competition to install a new type of lighting.

Commercial proposals were soon received from three bidders: American citizen Laszlo Sandor, director of the Mineral Lighting Company, a merchant named Bregman, and the Noble & Co. trading house.

A commission of six members of the council was set up to perform tests. The tests began on January 10, 1863. Observation of the function of the new lamps continued until May 1 of the same year, when the city council announced the winner of the competition to be Laszlo Sandor, who incidentally had offered the lowest installation price: 34 rubles per large lamp and 29 rubles per small lamp.

A contract was signed with him to set up mineral oil lighting for two lighting periods: from August 1, 1863 to May 1, 1865. Installation of the new type of lighting did not cost much: The old hand carts with metal boxes, ladders and portable lanterns came under the control of the American entrepreneur and the oil and alcohol street lamps were converted into new ones. By the evening of August 1, 1863, 6,000 kerosene lamps were already burning in St. Petersburg, and soon their number reached 7,200.

In an attempt to keep up with the capital, in the autumn of 1863 the Moscow City Council also announced a competition for the installation of kerosene street lighting. The contract to install 2,200 kerosene lamps was won by F. Boital. By May 1, 1865, Moscow was lighted exclusively by kerosene. Before long, the number of kerosene lamps increased to 9,310; half-inch wicks were used in them at first, with one-inch wicks introduced later, in 1875.

The appearance and widespread use of kerosene as a new street-lighting material in both the capital and other Russian cities was due to a number of factors: it burned more brightly and evenly; its luminosity exceeded that of hempseed oil and of an alcohol/turpentine mixture; and above all, it was cheaper. A skillful marketing tactic by the American companies, initially involving giving customers low-priced kerosene lamps free of charge, also played an important role.

The recollections of 19th century contemporaries frequently mention the installation of kerosene street lighting with enthusiasm. For example, the popular writer Nikolay Davydov (1848–1920) reminisced that "Lighting with the new kerosene lamps seemed magnificent after oil lighting; without a doubt things became more lively on the streets, and the crowd itself dressed more colorfully and the clothes were better selected."

The example of the organization of kerosene lighting in the remote provincial city of Petrozavodsk is also instructive. In 1864, the Petrozavodsk City Council commissioned its members to find a master capable of converting 41 oil lamps "in order to light with kerosene," and also to fix "the ladders for lighting lamps." Master Popov did this work for 143 rubles, and from that time onward, kerosene lighting became customary for city-dwellers.

In addition to communal services, kerosene lighting became widespread in railroad and water transportation, at various cultural, educational, and medical institutions, and in small factories and workshops. It also played a key role in the development of telegraph communication in Russia in the 1850s and 1860s. In 1852, a telegraph line was run between St. Petersburg and Oranienbaum, and then between St. Petersburg and Moscow, followed by lines linking Moscow–Kiev–Odessa, St. Petersburg–Tallinn–Helsinki, and also from Kaunas to the Prussian border. After that, the construction of telegraph lines resumed to the west and the east. The normal work of telegraph station personnel, who work around the clock, would not have been possible without the high-quality lighting provided by kerosene lamps.

Lighting Oil of the Transcaspian Trading Partnership

For the oil fields of the Absheron Peninsula, the year 1859 was noteworthy for two events. First, the Ministry of Finance had concluded a new tax-farming agreement for oil wells with the entrepreneur Ter-Gukasov. And second, the refinery of the Transcaspian Trading Partnership, located in Surakhany (not far from the ancient temple of the fire worshippers), had begun production.

The principal credit for creating the Partnership and the refinery belonged to the entrepreneur Vasily Kokorev (1817–1889), who was drawn into the oil business as a result of the persistent efforts of the diplomat and lawyer Nikolay Tornau (1812–1882), an advocate of intensifying Russian influence in Persia through the broad development of economic ties. Baron Tornau was known in Russia as a brilliant Orientalist and was the author of a number of studies on the Islamic legal code, including the monograph *Muslim Law* [*Musulmanskoye pravo*] (1866). He subsequently became a senator and member of the State Council.

A letter dated August 30, 1857, from State Secretary Vladimir Butkov to Prince Baryatinsky, viceroy of the Caucasus, contains the following lines: "In the papers sent you will find a good thing: this is Kokorev's founding of a company to trade with Astarabad. I am sorry that we did not ask your opinion about this matter."

A letter dated November 16, 1857, from Count Dmitry Milyutin to Prince Baryatinsky, viceroy of the Caucasus, contains another reference to this company: "as for Kokorev's company, your Highness probably received the letter of Baron Tornau providing notification of the final organization of the management of this partnership."

Along with Vasily Kokorev and Nikolay Tornau, Actual State Councilor Nikolay Novoselsky and merchants Ivan Mamontov and Pëtr Medyntsev also became founders of the Transcaspian Trading Partnership. Afterward, they were joined by the Moscow entrepreneur Pëtr Gubonin (1825–1894).

To start with, the Partnership purchased 33 acres of land in Surakhany, near Baku. The initial idea of the founders was to construct a refinery to produce lighting material (photogen) made from *kir* (a mineral impregnated with weathered petroleum). The plan for this refinery was presented by Justus von Liebig (1803–1873), who was a professor at the University of Munich and a foreign corresponding member of the St. Petersburg Academy of Sciences. The necessary equipment was purchased in Germany, including cast iron retorts intended for dry distillation of *kir*, and spherical kettles having a capacity of 12 barrels each for secondary distillation of the distillate. They were assembled under the direction of German chemist E. Moldenhauer. However, the distillation technology for *kir*, which contained only up to 20% lamp oils, yielded very small volumes of finished product.

Vasily Kokorev had a good acquaintance, Mikhail Pogodin (1800–1875), an Academy member who had taught for a long time at Moscow University, from whom he learned about work on investigating organic substances being carried out by Vasily (Wilhelm) Eichler, a Master of Pharmacy of the university, and in 1860, Kokorev invited him to the Surakhany refinery to consult.

At first, the suggestions made by the chemist Eichler perplexed Vasily Kokorev, since Eichler was proposing some radical changes, namely: giving up the use of *kir* and switching immediately to the processing of crude oil, and making corresponding changes in the production process and equipment. These suggestions once again called for significant financial investments. All Kokorev's new business initiatives contained elements of significant risk, and the Surakhany refinery was no exception. Instead of German cast iron retorts, 17 iron batch-operation stills were set up, 12 of which had a capacity of 36 barrels each, and the remaining five of which had a capacity of 9.6 barrels each. The spherical kettles were replaced by cylindrical ones, which provided more uniform heating of the oil. The refinery was fueled by natural gas, of which there were oil shows right on the grounds of the refinery. For the first time, a production process employed an alkaline solution for refining lighting material. After these changes were made, the yield of finished product after distillation of Balakhany well oil was around 25–30% instead of the former 15%. Now 108 pounds of crude oil yielded 36 pounds of lighting material, which was given the new name "fotonaftil," or in a poetic translation into Russian: "petroleum light."

Despite the measures taken, the results of the production activity did not satisfy the founders. There was no way to make the refinery profitable, and the quality of the lighting material still left much to be desired. A new approach was needed to assess the state of refining and its prospects.

This time, Vasily Kokorev decided to turn for help to the scientific world of St. Petersburg, whose luminaries included the well-known chemists Aleksandr Voskresensky, Nikolay Zinin, Nikolay Sokolov, and Fëdor Ilish. Vasily Kokorev should be given credit for his intuition in taking the very unexpected step of inviting Dmitry Mendeleyev (1834–

1907), a private docent of chemistry at the St. Petersburg University, to Surakhany, even though this scholar was young (29 years of age) and had not yet even done any work in the area of petroleum research. All the same, he had already written a course called *Organic Chemistry [Organicheskaya khimiya]* (1861), received the Demidov Prize, and had successfully edited and translated Johannes Rudolf von Wagner's *Handbuch der chemischen Technologie [Handbook of Chemical Technology]*, or as contemporaries called it: "the first encyclopedia of chemical engineering."

Here is what the great scientist himself later wrote about this experience: "In 1863, V. A. Kokorev invited me, then serving as a senior lecturer at the St. Petersburg University, to travel to Baku and examine the entire operation and decide how to make the refinery profitable, and if that was not possible, then to close it.... At that time, in 1863, I was in Baku for the first time. This was how I first became familiar with the oil business."[25]

On August 20, 1863, the scientist left St. Petersburg, arriving in Baku at the beginning of September 1863. Dmitry Mendeleyev spent a total of only 20 days on the Absheron Peninsula, but these 20 days were truly decisive for the future destiny of the Russian oil industry.

Unfortunately, it has not yet been possible to reconstruct a full picture of these decisive days. Only a few later works of the great scientist contain isolated references to his work: about "appropriate changes" at the Surakhany refinery, about recommendations involving, "First of all, operating the distillation continuously and carefully producing enamel barrels," and "In 1863 I recommended to Mr. Kokorev that he set up such pipes as well as vessels with reservoirs and also set up a refinery around Nizhny."

The scientist's notebooks also preserve isolated fragments of his plans for work in Surakhany, including sketches of a drilling tool. However, the basic research work was aimed at improving the production process for distillation of oil. Over three and a half weeks, Mendeleyev and Eichler carried out a whole series of experimental distillations, including secondary distillation of the resulting distillates, with a separation of 50-degree fractions. The results obtained also allowed substantial changes to be made in the construction of distillation stills, as well as the introduction of continuous-flow condensers. This was the basis of Mendeleyev's subsequent scientific prediction about the possibility of the thorough refining of petroleum into various products.

The development of the technology for producing the fotonaftil lighting product became a very important scientific result of the joint work of chemists Mendeleyev and Eichler. After primary distillation of oil, the resulting product contained substances having an unpleasant odor, and the smoky, unsteady flame could not provide sufficient lighting. Initially, the scientists continued their experiments involving alkaline processing of kerosene, with subsequent acidification using hydrochloric acid to remove traces of alkali. After that, they studied the action of sulfuric acid on distillates with thorough mixing. They quickly obtained such impressive results that even ten years after completing this work Dmitry Mendeleyev wrote: "The oil processing techniques used in the past decade at the Baku refinery, obviously, not having been borrowed from anyone, could be instructive for many people."[26]

Later Dmitry Mendeleyev succinctly summarized his work on the Absheron Peninsula: "Some of these suggestions were immediately implemented, together with Mr. Eichler, which made the Surakhany refinery profitable, despite the fact that the price of kerosene had started to fall."[27]

Among Mendeleyev's many revolutionary ideas, his suggestion about the need to replace the digging of pits with the drilling of oil wells was immediately approved by Kokorev, who, in turn, was relying on his own experience in the salt industry.

Unfortunately, plans to introduce the drilling of oil wells on the Absheron Peninsula met fierce resistance from Ivan Mirzoyev, the new holder of the tax-farming arrangement on the fields. On November 10, 1865, the head of the Main Administration of the viceroy of the Caucasus received a letter from an authorized agent of Mirzoyev, who sharply objected to granting the Transcaspian Trading Partnership the right to drill on 462 acres located between the main sources and asked the Baku Treasury Office "to restore, on the basis of law, his rights, which had been violated, and to prevent the Trading Partnership from drilling oil wells within the boundary of the tax-farming line."

In 1862, the Transcaspian Trading Partnership participated for the first time in the London International Exhibition on Industry and Arts, where the fotonaftil from the Surakhany refinery received a silver medal for the high quality of its production.

In 1865 the refinery participated in the All-Russian Manufacturing Exhibition in Moscow and drew the attention of specialists and experts for the high quality of its production. The conclusion of the expert commission regarding fotonaftil was that "it is impossible not to notice how pure it is; it was white and more pure than the imported Pennsylvania oil, and when burned it did not have any odor."[28] It was fitting that the large silver medal that the jury awarded to the fotonaftil of the Transcaspian Trading Partnership became a worthy tribute to the creative research and initiative of Russian scientists and entrepreneurs.

On the Brink of the Big Oil of the Volga Region

The remoteness of the Absheron Peninsula and the complexity of delivering Baku oil to the country's industrial regions forced the Russian government to reconsider the question of managing petroleum prospecting in central Russia.

49

In the first half of the 19th century, reports about the presence of petroleum and sulfur on the territory of Kazan Province started to appear even in the local press. For example, I. Langel's detailed work, "A Brief Medicophysical and Topographic Survey of Kazan Province and Its Capital City Kazan, Composed by State Councilor and Knight I. Langel, Former Inspector of the Kazan Medical Authority and Member of Various Scholarly Societies" (1829), mentions caves with "curative" sulfur and petroleum springs. In particular, Doctor Langel wrote: "The city of Tetyushi lies on the right bank of the Volga, 160 *versts* [105.6 miles] from Kazan. It is located on a very high bank of this river, which has, located in several places along it, noteworthy caves containing curative sulfur and petroleum springs."

In 1830, the Mining Department sent its first expedition to prospect for useful minerals in the Volga region. Thus, the first special geologic (or, as it was called at that time, geognostic) study of the territory of the Volga region in the area of the village of Syukeyevo was carried out in that year by the geologists Nikolay Shirokshin and Aleksey Guryev. They published the results of their research in the article "Geognostic Survey of the Right Bank of the Volga River from the City of Samara to the City of Sviyazhsk," which appeared in *Gorny zhurnal* in 1831.

Analysis of this article shows that the geologists made a detailed study and description of rocks such as carbonates, which are widespread on the right bank of the Volga; clays, marls, and sandstones; and also Syukeyevo deposits of bitumen, sulfur, and other mineral formations: "Here, in the steep bank of the Volga, opposite the village of Syukeyevo, rocks are exposed in the following order: lowest of all is limestone, sometimes of a brown color due to the presence in it of petroleum and sulfur, for which reason rubbing it makes it gives off a strong odor that is character-istic of these substances; when it is permeated with a large quantity of petroleum, it can burn. Such strata usually have fine streams of petroleum seeping from them through cracks; this petroleum hardens in the air to form mineral tar."

The article goes on to advance a hypothesis about the formation of the Syukeyevo caves: "Flint, calcite, and gypsum are washed out by water, giving the limestone a porous appearance, sometimes leaving large voids, which are often filled with sulfur and petroleum deposits. Perhaps the caves, which are frequently encountered in this limestone, were originally formed from these same voids; the vaults of such caves are rounded by the action of water, which probably also widened them, washing out the concretions of gypsum, and perhaps also rock salt, for we have found grains of it in overlying gypsum. Both the vaults and the walls of the caves are covered with petroleum, sulfur, or calcareous nitrate, whose formation could also promote the widening of the caves.... The floors of the caves are often covered with water, for the Volga floods them in the springtime; aside from this, they have their own small springs with petroleum and sulfur." It also drew attention to the fact that "the lower layer of limestone, located almost on the Volga's summer water table, is the richest in such springs; whereas they are almost completely dried up in the upper strata, leaving behind a hardened mineral tar filling all the cracks and voids." The geologists also noted the primitive methods used by the local population to recover petroleum for household and medicinal purposes: "Such water, coming to the surface in springs, is used as medicinal water, for baths and to be taken internally. The inhabitants of the district collect petroleum for their own needs by digging out small holes in front of the source of a gushing spring; these holes fill with water, and petroleum floats on the surface; this petroleum is then removed."

Several years later, the Mining Department sent another expedition, this time with the specific goal of prospecting for bituminous minerals in the Volga region. In 1837, *Gorny zhurnal* published the "Report of Staff Captain Gerngros II on Prospecting Carried Out at the Direction of the Mining Authorities in the Sibir, Kazan, and Orenburg Regions to Discover Asphalt Deposits." In this work, mining engineer Aleksandr Gerngros described the deposits of useful minerals in the Volga region in detail. He gave a detailed description of the territories he had studied, their geologic structure, their nature and soils, as well as descriptions of the Zhiguli Mountains, the Syukeyevo cave (16.5 miles from the city of Tetyushi), and deposits of various useful minerals 6.6 miles from the city of Syzran, near the village of Karpara.

It should be noted that a large part of his report was also devoted to natural asphalt. He described deposits of asphalt near Kostichey in Pustylny Gorge, close to the city of Tetyushi, around the village of Pechorskoye, in the village of Troyekurovka, on the right bank of the Volga, at the point where the Syzranka River discharges into it, near the city of Syzran, etc. He performed mineralogical tests of the asphalt directly on site: "The tar's color is brown on the surface, black when fractured. It has a glassy luster and is extremely light and brittle. It melts and runs when exposed to fire, similar to pitch, giving of an odor of black sealing wax; it does not catch fire easily, and quickly goes out." About the product of another deposit he wrote: "Its entire mass is of a black color, together with a resinous odor similar to that of tar." Staff Captain Gerngros also noted a curious fact regarding the use of asphalt by the local population: "Near the village of Kostichey, where the viscous asphalt is encountered to a greater extent than elsewhere, blacksmiths use it for bluing iron products, which protects them from rust and gives them a more pleasant appearance." In his report, Gerngros also pointed out the location of a series of petroleum deposits: "Petroleum of various thickness and of a blackish-brown color was noted near the city of Tetyushi and the village of Sergiyevsk and 10 *versts* [6.6 miles] from the sulfur waters.

Between Tetyushi and Syukeyevo village, it comes out of rock faces and impregnates chalky marl.... But the most interesting petroleum deposit is located five *versts* [3.3 miles] from the village of Novoyakushkino, 200 *sazhens* [1,400 feet] from the mountain called Sarzhat. In a pit three feet deep and four feet wide, water is covered on the surface with black and very sticky petroleum, and although it is rather frequently skimmed off, within several days it accumulates again."

On the basis of his observations, mining engineer Gerngros drew important scientific and theoretical conclusions. In his report, he noted that "the asphalt sediments found in cracks of chalky marl, all the more so in its lower parts, suggest that at the present time they form from resinous particles that combine through some chemical process, and that the main deposit of it is hidden in the Earth's rocky crust." Thus, Aleksandr Gerngros simultaneously stated two very important theoretical principles. First, that the asphalt deposits in the Volga region are secondary and arose as a result of the migration of a more liquid product from the depths of the Earth to the surface layers. And second, that asphalt forms from more liquid resinous parts as a result of chemical processes—that is, as a result of petroleum oxidation. Even today, these principles formulated by mining engineer Gerngros coincide with the views of contemporary geology scholars regarding the formation of natural asphalt and petroleum deposits.

Unfortunately, Volga entrepreneurs did not make use of the impressive results of Staff Captain Gerngros's expedition to develop the oil business. However, 18 years later, when mining engineer Aleksandr Gerngros was appointed to the high post of director of the Department of Mining and Salt Works, he revisited the question of resuming petroleum prospecting in the Volga region.

This mission was assigned to the well-known Russian geologists Gennady Romanovsky and Pavel Yeremeyev, who were officers of the Corps of Mining Engineers. Over almost seven seasons (1863–1868), Corps of Mining Engineers Captain Gennady Romanovsky (1830–1906) made a detailed study of the sites of surface oil shows in the region of the Urals and the Volga, in the region of the cities of Buguruslan and Bugulma between the Sok and Kinel Rivers, and also in the regions lying south of Kinel. Having discovered oil shows at the Nizhnyaya Karmalskaya station in the Sheshma River valley, he drew the following conclusion: "There is no doubt that the rocks lying underwater contain cracks through which petroleum and gases escape." In the villages of Sarabikulovo and Shugurovo he found oil, where "certain waters containing drops of petroleum point, without any doubt, to the presence of liquid petroleum inside the strata." At the village of Staraya Semenkina mining engineer Romanovsky found sandstone that had previously been impregnated with petroleum, with a thick tar flowing out of the surface of the sandy sheets being heated by the sun. He also discovered petroleum at the village of Kamyshla. In this connection he wrote that "near the city of Tetyushi, around the source of the Cheremshana River, which flows into the Volga opposite the city of Singaleni, and also at the headwaters of the Sok River, close to the Sergiyevsk mineral waters, there are traces of petroleum sources." Concerning the origin of the petroleum deposits he had discovered, Corps of Mining Engineers Captain Romanovsky announced in quite definite terms: "The mineral oil of Samara Province flows out of layers of Devonian or Lower Carboniferous soil." In so doing, he made an important discovery that determined the future nature of prospecting in the region, as he had established that the petroleum contained in sediments of Permian age also served as a sign of "rich underground accumulations of it [mineral oil]." Developing this thought, he wrote: "I am completely certain that in Samara Province basins of liquid petroleum are definitely confined under Permian sandstones.... The petroleum must originate in Devonian sediments, and consequently at a depth of less than 100 *sazhens* [700 feet]."

The well-known geologist Pavel Yeremeyev (1830–1899), a professor at the Mining Institute, participated in the 1866 expedition to study the presence of oil in the Volga region. The first issue of *Gorny zhurnal* for 1867 published his extensive article "Research on Oil Fields in Kazan, Simbir, and Samara Provinces," in which he concluded that "despite the proven importance and universal significance of oil sandstone as an indicator of the presence of petroleum sources in Permian soil, the question of the reliability of oil fields in Kazan and Samara Provinces is still not resolved, and requires further elucidation."

This conclusion prompted mining engineer Gennady Romanovsky to take subsequent active measures. Defending his point of view and being an advocate of deep drilling, he insisted on constructing a deep well in the Volga region around the village of Batraki; this well was drilled using a steam engine. However, in 1869 a serious accident occurred while drilling at a depth of only around 16 feet, after which drilling work was suspended. Unfortunately, despite Gennady Romanovsky's insistent attempts, it was not possible to resume drilling work. Thus, the low quality of drilling techniques and tools prevented him from proving his theory to be correct and from subsequently producing Volga petroleum on an industrial scale.

The secondary nature of the petroleum in Permian rock of the Volga region was recognized at this time by other scholars as well, including Aleksandr Shtukenberg, a professor at Kazan University, and Aleksey Pavlov, a professor at Moscow University.

Some figures in the oil industry did attempt to verify the theoretical reasoning of these geology scholars, and began to carry out oil drilling work in the Volga region. However, these explorations did not produce any substantial results. Shallow wells showed only traces of petroleum, not industrial reserves. These failures contributed, to a certain extent, to the slowing of the large-scale exploration and prospecting work in the Ural and Volga regions that was intended to establish the regions' ability to produce industrial quantities of oil.

Transferring the Experience of Pennsylvania

Data from the Caspian Board of the Russian Ministry of State Property show there were 136 hand-dug wells on the Absheron Peninsula in 1842, which annually produced up to 27,620 barrels of oil. Archive documents clearly show that the Russian government at this time was beginning to think seriously about the low efficiency of the oil business, and also about the directions of oil exporting. Minister of Finance Mikhail Vronchenko, in a memorandum dated October 12, 1844 said: "In the eight-year period from 1836 through 1844, oil exports to Persia did not decline, but rose by 9,139 *poods* [1,097 barrels] as compared to the eight-year period from 1828 through 1836. The Treasury's three-year total net income (1840, 1841, and 1842) is now up to 109,000 rubles, and the last tax-farming payment was 91,000 rubles."

But in those days (the late 1850s), the United States of America was rapidly assuming the role of leader in oil production. Whereas that country produced only 2,000 barrels (350 tons) of oil in 1850, the picture had radically changed by the end of the decade. August 27, 1859 became a crucial starting point in the history of the US oil industry. That was the day the blacksmith William Smith obtained the first commercial inflow of oil (approximately 30 barrels a day) at a depth of 69.5 feet in a well drilled under contract to an entrepreneur, the former railroad conductor Edwin Drake. Edwin Drake's success attracted many fortune-seekers to Pennsylvania's Oil Creek Valley. The avalanche of Pennsylvania oil that poured onto the US domestic market promoted the rapid growth of the oil business. In 1861, a popular expression at the New York Stock Exchange was: "From now on, oil will be our king, not cotton!"

In turn, the low cost of American crude sharply increased the export possibilities for American kerosene. Beginning in 1860, it appeared in Europe, where the first 36 tons had been exported, while kerosene exports to Russia, which lagged behind the United States in oil production by a factor of 13 that year, began at the same time.

The rapid successes of the American oil industry in Russia did not go unnoticed, and Russians were compelled to analyze the cause of such a sharp swing in the industry's development, including trips abroad to witness US oil operations firsthand.

The first Russian mining engineer to visit the US oil fields was Corps of Mining Engineers Lt. Col. Gennady Romanovsky (1830–1906). In 1865, "by his Majesty's order," he was sent on a 10-month trip abroad to study the geologic nature of oil fields and methods of exploring and producing them. His route to the United States of America took him through Europe—specifically, through France and Great Britain.

In Paris, he met the noted French inventor Paul Destrem. Information collected in France on drilling technology and techniques later helped him work on a new type of drilling tool. He visited Great Britain briefly, and as he recollected, "found nothing remarkable or significant" for the Russian oil business.

The main purpose of Gennady Romanovsky's foreign trip was to study oil field development know-how in the American state of Pennsylvania. He spent nearly six months there, and saw with his own eyes the results achieved by the oil industry, which had developed in an environment of economic freedom and healthy competition, and he rated the activities of private companies at their true worth. In order to see the "petrol" fields personally, Romanovsky visited the cities of Pittsburgh, Harrisburg, Wheeling, Springfield, Columbus, and several other oil areas. In 1864, the US produced 2,497,700 barrels of oil, and rates of oil development and refining were steadily rising. The country was operating 194 refineries, which produced 28 million gallons of petroleum products. Incidentally, that same year the US exported 347,000 gallons of kerosene to Russia, which was used to light the streets of St. Petersburg.

Mining engineer Romanovsky personally attended the drilling of oil wells near the town of Parkersburg. The sight made a strong impression on him. Writing in his journal, he noted that: "When several sources of petroleum were discovered in Pennsylvania, it was ejected from the well along with mud and water, and sometimes with such force that it tore off the roofs of drilling sheds that were 50 to 70 feet high." He also noted a strong French influence on American drilling technology and techniques, which was especially noticeable in patents on a rotary drilling apparatus and a set of drilling tools obtained by the American Levi Dizbrow.

A critical event occurred during mining engineer Romanovsky's stay in the United States: the world's first "pipe line" (oil pipeline) was built and placed in service. That line was five miles long, and had a pipe diameter of two inches.

Gennady Romanovsky described the results of his trip in detail in his "Report of Lt. Colonel Romanovsky to the Mining Department on Drilling in Europe and on Lighting Materials," where he analyzed in detail the state of affairs in exploration, production, and refining of crude oil, or petroleum, which "in the United States provides considerable annual income both to the government and to private individuals." He also pointed out that in the US, the discovery and industrial-scale development of natural sources of petroleum (unlike in Russia) had been carried on for quite some time, due to the "convenience and cheapness of producing this lighting material." In North America, "petrol or crude oil is divided into two types: heavy for lubrication and light for lighting."

In an effort to bring the results of his trip to the attention of Russian mining engineers, Gennady Romanovsky published an article in the *Gorny zhurnal*, "On Petroleum Generally and North American Petrol in Particular" (1866), where he argued that the production and consumption of oil in Russia needed to be increased, even though "as a fuel it generally has not spread far and has not been adopted as boiler fuel on steamships and locomotives." In his opinion, the geologic research of mining engineer Friedrich von Koschkull, Lt. General Gregor von Helmersen, and Academician Otto Wilhelm Hermann von Abich demonstrated the presence of extensive undeveloped oil fields in the Caucasus, on the Absheron Peninsula, in the Transkuban Region, on the Taman Peninsula, and near Kerch. Therefore, decisive government participation was required.

Based on his thorough analysis of all that he had seen and understood on his trip, Gennady Romanovsky described the status of the US oil industry, setting guidelines for the practical use of American experience for further development of petroleum geology and improvement of drilling technology in Russia. Lt. Colonel Romanovsky also indicated steps that could be deemed necessary for the development of a Russian "petrol industry" and ways of exploring for petroleum. Based on the experience gained from his trip to the US, he thought it necessary to ban the leasing of land to foreign companies wishing to produce petroleum in Russia, and not to permit monopolies in the production of oil by Russian subjects. In his opinion, oil production and exploration had to be done by the state, at least at first. And only "under these conditions can Russian industry develop rapidly and benefit both the government and the people."

Russian Cossacks in the Oil Business

It is fitting that some of the most important developments in the chronicle of the 19th-century Russian oil business should occur on ancient land—the territory of the former Russian principality of Tmutarakan.

In the three decades following the end of the Russo-Turkish war of 1768–1774, the Russian Empire decisively fortified and consolidated its new southern borders. Soon, the long-awaited time came when Russians returned to the Taman Peninsula, the territory of the legendary outpost of 12th-century Kievan Rus.

On January 16, 1792, the commander-in-chief of hosts in the Caucasus and Kuban, General-in-Chief Ivan Gudovich (1741–1820), presented a plan to Empress Catherine the Great for establishing a Caucasian line, specifying construction of new forts and settlement of Cossack villages along the border, from Yekaterinograd village on the Malka River to the Kuban River and along the Kuban to the mouth of the Laba. He stressed that "this territory would be quieter if the entire border along the Kuban were occupied by the same Cossack hosts as along the Terek."

On June 30, 1792, Catherine signed an "Imperial Charter bestowed on the Black Sea Cossack Host," which stated: "The zealous and fervent service to Us of the Black Sea Host, proven... by feats on land and sea, their unbreakable faith... have drawn our special attention and mercy. We therefore, wishing to reward the Black Sea Host's services by affirming their permanent well-being... have granted them, in perpetuity, holdings consisting of the region of Tavrich Island of Phanagoria with all the land lying on the right side of the Kuban River from its mouth to the Ust-Labinsk redoubt, so that the Kuban River and the Azov Sea, to the city of Yeysk, serve as the boundaries of the host's land."

The first detachment of combat Cossacks under the command of Colonel Savva Bely arrived in Taman August 25, 1792 in rowing vessels. They were followed by new groups of Black Sea Cossacks. Commander [*ataman*] Zakhary Chepega, with his military staff, a wagon train and three 500-man cavalry and two 500-man infantry regiments, skirted the Azov Sea and arrived October 23, 1792 at Khan Town (now the city of Yeysk).

In 1794, Don Cossacks also began resettling in the Kuban region, founding six unit [*kuren*] settlements. Five Cossack districts were also formed that same year, on the lands settled by Cossacks.

In 1792, the Black Sea Cossack Host began to produce petroleum, and not just for its own needs. Persistent demand for oil deliveries had also arisen from the Black Sea Fleet. In 1793, naval commander Admiral Nikolay Mordvinov (1754–1845) wrote to Cossack Colonel Savva Bely: "The Sevastopol Fleet needs oil and since most of that Taman Island abounds in it, I have ordered Captain Mas, who is located in Kerch, to send the requisite number of workers there to collect and deliver it to Kerch. Please permit them to do this work."

In October 1832, the Caucasus Line Cossack Host was formed, and on November 19, 1860 it was divided into the Kuban Cossack Host and Tersk Cossack Host with the formation of the territorial administrative Kuban and Tersk Regions.

The lands of the right bank of the Kuban, settled by the Cossacks, and the trans-Kuban region with its long-resident mountain peoples, including the Adygeans, were placed in Kuban Region. The abolition of serfdom in the Russian Empire in 1861 and the end of hostilities in the North Caucasus opened extensive possibilities for settlement of the area by immigrants from other Russian provinces. Thousands of emancipated serfs from southern provinces of European Russia streamed into the

Kuban in search of free land and work. In a very short time, Kuban Region became a region of considerable growth in basic economic indicators. The opening and development of the Kuban oil fields played an important role in this.

In the early 1830s, the first geologic investigation of the Kuban region was carried out by specialists from the Georgian Mining Expedition, Nikolay Voskoboynikov and Aleksey Guryev. Their joint study appeared in the *Gorny zhurnal* for 1832 (Part 1) under the title, "Geognostic Description of the Taman Peninsula Belonging to the Land of the Black Sea Forces." They studied the peninsula's geologic structure, determined for the first time the age of the rocks comprising the Taman Peninsula and belonging to the Tertiary System, described all petroleum sources on the peninsula, and provided information on mud volcano eruptions in 1794, 1799, 1814, and 1822. The geologists concluded that "the original cause of both the Baku and Taman volcanoes was petroleum deposits."

In addition, they were the first to present information on the existence, in 1824, of the first refinery on the Taman Peninsula, belonging to the merchant Ledenev. The enterprise had operated for several years, and the finished "white" oil product was even sold in Kharkiv. Crude oil was produced in hand-dug wells on Kapustin Gorge near the village of Vyshe-Steblovskaya. The entrepreneur paid the Cossack Host 30 silver kopecks per 3.25 gallons of oil. Reports make it clear that in 1827 alone he collected 390 gallons of oil.

The encouraging results of the first regional studies by the geologists from the Georgian Mining Expedition nevertheless led to a certain change in the state of affairs. The first steps were taken in the Kuban to organize the oil business. In 1829, the Black Sea Cossack Host created the special rank of oil well inspector.

Later, at the initiative of the leader of the Black Sea Cossack Host, Major General Nikolay Zavadovsky, measures were undertaken to construct facilities at the oil fields. From June to August 1833, the extensive oil field areas, where there were 195 hand-dug wells in various states of repair, were inspected with the assistance of two Baku masters of oil well construction. These specialists determined that 12 of the wells contained "white" oil, the rest "black." The depths of the inspected wells ranged from 11.6 to 21 feet, with the well measuring 21 inches at the top, then broadening in the middle, and reaching 42 inches at the bottom. In addition, the masters constructed five new hand-dug wells, gave specific recommendations for further development of the fields, and trained the workers in well construction technology. Implementation of these recommendations enabled oil production to be increased somewhat.

In the summer of 1835, the Georgian Mining Expedition sent Senior Manager [*Oberhüttenverwalter*] Vollendorf to the Kuban. During his two-month stay, he performed a thorough study of the Taman, summarizing his results in a report dated January 14, 1836, titled "Description of the Taman Oil Fields."

Vollendorf divided the oil produced on the Taman Peninsula into three types: "Thick greenish, liquid greenish, and watery greenish." In addition to the digging of oil out of the wells, Senior Manager Vollendorf described the extraction of "thick greenish" oil from petroliferous sand found at depths of 49 feet. In all, 51 barrels of oil were produced from the Taman fields that year.

Vollendorf's report contained one more important fact: in the mid-1830s, the Kuban oilmen were using manual drilling in their prospecting work. According to his report: "When they want to dig a well at a new site, first they test the earth with an auger (they call it a sounding borer), sinking it…. When they want to reveal the presence of petroleum during testing, they pour more water into the drillhole and remove it more often, so the mud and oil no longer adhere to the auger…. They also learn of the presence of petroleum when the auger advances more easily, which indicates entry into a layer containing petroleum."

Senior Manager Vollendorf's trip to the Kuban yielded yet another noteworthy result: the appearance, in February 1836, of the first technical manual in the domestic oil business, *Rules for Guidance When Digging Oil Wells* [*Pravila dlya rukovodstovaniya pri kopanii neftyanykh kolodtsev*], with necessary drawings included in an appendix. The author systematized methods known at that time for constructing oil wells, proposed an optimal design, and specified necessary steps for well operation, including rudimentary safety measures for workers.

The need to increase oil production volumes in the region was also driven by the expansion of its areas of application. In his letter of August 1839 to the minister of finance, Count Yegor Kankrin, the commander-in-chief of the Civilian Unit in the Caucasus, noted that: "Black liquid oil is especially recommended as an excellent material for impregnating timber for construction of underwater parts, since it can replace natural drying of the wood and increase the strength of seagoing vessels. The latter fact, along with the introduction of 'black' oil for the lighting of beacons on the Caspian and Black Seas, deserves the government's full attention. This is particularly true in shipbuilding, for which required timber can be prepared sooner, and as petroleum protects against rapid rotting, this will be of considerable benefit, especially for the Black Sea Fleet, which has its own petroleum, probably of the same quality as that on the Taman Peninsula. The substitution of 'white' oil for turpentine and thick 'black' oil in place of tar offers an important benefit in preserving wood."

This proposal was accepted by the government, and imperial approval of the "Statute on the Black Sea Cossack Host," with a special chapter "On the Production of Oil and Sale of Same," followed on July 1, 1842. In accordance with the directive's provisions, all oil produced in the Kuban region was to enter the army stores for sale at a price approved by the commander of the Caucasus Line. The oil fields were to be managed by an official of the mining department, who supervised the Cossack squadron [*sotnya*], the commander of which held the position of oil well inspector. The Cossacks, in addition to free provisions, would be paid 10 silver kopecks per 3.25 gallons of crude. The mining official and oil well inspector reported to the board of the Black Sea Cossack Host, which in turn presented a petroleum report once a year to the Department of Military Settlements of the Ministry of War.

On the whole, however, there was still no substantial growth in oil production. This is clearly confirmed by indicators presented in the "Register of the Arrival and Disbursement of Oil Produced at Army Petroleum Institutions over 10 Years and Withholdings for Army Use from 1835 to 1844," prepared by the board of the Black Sea Cossack Host. During this period, only 970 barrels of "black" oil and 111 barrels of "white" oil were produced.

The unsatisfactory results from the Kuban oil fields were not overlooked by the government. Captain Anisimov of the Corps of Mining Engineers soon arrived to the Kuban and made a thorough study of the condition of the Taman fields with their "abundant signs of oil fields," which was reflected in his "Memorandum on the Inspection of Oil Facilities" (April 1845). He considered it possible to increase oil production to 232 barrels per year if existing wells were promptly repaired, if exploration was begun by manually drilling wildcat wells using a tool known as an exploratory drill, and if 50 new wells were constructed.

However, acting *ataman* Major General Rashpil and the board of the Cossack Host were of a different opinion: in view of the "small income… and to ease the Cossacks' internal service, all oil wells should be farmed out." Therefore, in December 1846, the Military Directorate of the Black Sea Cossack Host signed a four-year contract with the small business owner Yegor Cherkasov, granting him a monopoly on development of oil fields on army lands, as well as the sale, export, and import of oil, all for an annual fee of 380 silver rubles.

In 1848, the Black Sea Cossack Host reinstated the position of mining engineer at the oil fields, appointing to the post squadron leader Gavriil Litevsky, who attempted to introduce certain new oil well operation techniques into production. However, in 1853, oil production in the Kuban virtually ceased due to the onset of the Crimean War, and was not resumed until after hostilities ended. Unfortunately, most wells became inoperable due to the prolonged period of inactivity.

Colonel Novosiltsev's Oil Gusher

In early 1863, the Military Directorate of the Kuban Cossack Host entered into a tax-farming agreement for exploitation of Taman oil fields with the Kerch merchant Franz Kibler. The agreement was for a three year period at an annual fee of 135 rubles, to be paid to the army.

In July of the same year, Kibler assigned his tax-farming rights to Guards Colonel Ardalion Nikolayevich Novosiltsev (1816–1878). After familiarizing himself with the situation, Col. Novosiltsev contacted the Military Directorate and proposed extending the agreement through 1872, with monopoly rights to produce oil on the territory of the Taman peninsula and a simultaneous increase in the fee from 135 to 270 rubles per year. Col. Novosiltsev's offer was accepted, and the agreement was extended through May 1, 1872.

Col. Novosiltsev then contacted the Military Directorate and proposed that it grant him a series of Kuban Cossack Host lands lying beyond the Kuban river within the Natukhay District, declaring that "with its method of developing oil and with the establishment of refineries and plants for the manufacture of candles, paints, soap, and similar necessary household goods, the poorest of residents will have the opportunity to use and purchase what they need for housekeeping, and later deliver a profitable source of income to the populated territory."[29]

This proposal was likewise accepted, and under the second agreement Col. Novosiltsev gained monopoly rights to the land through May 1872 for an annual fee of 200 silver rubles. Additionally, he was required to annually provide 39 barrels of oil for the army's needs and 310 barrels to Cossack families. After the agreement expired, all facilities and structures he had erected would become the property of the army. Finally, under a third agreement, Ardalion Novosiltsev obtained the right to develop oil-bearing areas occupied by the Abinsk and Psekup Cossack Regiments on the banks of the Chiby, Sups, and Il Creeks through May 1872. In this manner, Col. Novosiltsev gained tax-farming rights to oil-bearing lands over a wide area, ranging from the shores of the Black and Azov Seas to the meridian of Yekaterinodar.

Naturally, work in this area required a fundamentally new approach to the organization of the business. A report by mining engineer Gennady Romanovsky indicates that a 7.4-horsepower mobile steam engine, a so-called locomobile, was being used in these fields. Col. Novosiltsev began drilling his first wells in 1864 at the sites of surface oil shows, initially near Anapa and then at the village of Staro-Titarovskaya and the town of Fontanovsky. The drilling was done by a crew of American specialists specially invited from the United States, headed by foreman G. Clay.

Russia's first oil exploration began with drillholes using mechanical percussion drilling and the casing of wells with metallic casing pipe.

However, these attempts at exploratory drilling by the conventional American method of "wildcatting" proved unsuccessful—all three holes were "dry." In addition, the excessive ambitions of the foreign specialists and their attempt to dictate unacceptable terms predictably forced Col. Novosiltsev to terminate their business relationship.

On the recommendation of mining engineer Friedrich von Koschkull, Col. Novosiltsev decided to concentrate exploratory work in the area of the Kudako, Psif, and Psebeps tributaries of the Kuban. On the advice of Lieutenant General Grigory Gelmersen, director of the St. Petersburg Mining Institute, he hired the Russian specialists Vladimir Peters, a mechanic who had proven himself an experienced driller of artesian wells, and Karl Sikorsky, who was qualified as an experienced pipe-fitter.

In August 1865, drilling of five wells began on the left bank of the Kudako River, 26 miles from Anapa. When oil inflows appeared at a depth of 40 feet, drilling was continued at even greater intensity. Finally, on February 3, 1866 (February 15, New Style),[30] at a depth of 123.5 feet, they struck Russia's first oil gusher in Well No. 1.

An archive document of February 5, 1866, "Report to the Commander of Adagum Regiment," contains the following description of the event: "Supplementing my Report 14 of November 18 in response to your Reply 6246 of November 5, please be advised that on my last trip to the Kudako area, after incredible efforts, this February 3rd we broke through a rock, and a strong jet of pure oil opened up with an extraordinary noise, yielding from 1,500 to 2,000 *vedros* [116 to 155 barrels] every 24 hours through pipes alone, without the assistance of the locomobile or any effort by the workers. I bring this to your attention for reporting to whomever you see fit. Vladimir Peters."[31]

The gusher from Well 1 continued unabated for 24 hours, after which the oil inflow decreased somewhat, but on April 14, when drilling reached 242 feet, an even more powerful gusher occurred, which continued for 28 days. The Kudako oil had a somewhat unusual greenish color and an acrid sulfurous odor. According to the calculations of mining engineer Friedrich von Koschkull, this first gusher in the Kudako River field yielded some 12,000 barrels of oil.

In the summer of 1868, mining engineer Gennady Romanovsky visited the oil field for the first time. He made a very detailed description, drew up a general plan, performed a feasibility study, and presented specific recommendations for further work. His status report on the Kudako field was published in the *Gorny zhurnal*. In his conclusion, he noted: "In speaking of the beginning of development and establishment of the oil business in Kuban Region we cannot overlook the services of Colonel Novosiltsev, who has surpassed many with his energy and labors."

Kuban oil became a major increment in fulfilling Russia's oil production objectives. Whereas Russia produced only 66,875 barrels of oil in 1865, its production volume more than tripled in 1870, to 204,685 barrels. In that year, Col. Novosiltsev's Kuban fields yielded 28,840 barrels, or 14% of Russia's total oil production volume.

The Tragedy of the "Russian Oil Craze"

Ardalion Novosiltsev's mighty oil gusher in the Kuban and his subsequent energetic activities were widely covered in the Russian press, with many newspapers even dubbing the phenomenon the "Russian Oil Craze."

In order to refine the massive amounts of oil produced by the gusher, Col. Novosiltsev built the biggest refinery of the day, with an annual capacity of up to 61,891 barrels of kerosene, on the grounds of the old fort of Phanagoria on the shore of the Kerch Strait in 1869. The refinery's equipment was made in factories in Glasgow (Great Britain) and incorporated state of the art technology for that time. The refinery had 20 steel distilling vats for oil, each with a volume of 4,881 gallons. The vats were surrounded by a cooling system with helical tubes seven inches in diameter. Crude oil was pumped into two tanks mounted on towers, where it was allowed to settle. It then flowed by gravity into the distilling vats. After distillation, the petroleum products were sent to a separating department, where the finished products were graded by specific gravity and distributed to corresponding underground tanks, from which they were pumped to purifiers. Mixers in the purifiers were driven by a 40-horsepower steam engine.

In 1876, Professor Konon Lisenko of the St. Petersburg Mining Institute visited the refinery and, in an article in *Zapiski Imperatorskogo Russkogo tekhnicheskogo obshchestva* ["Transactions of the Imperial Russian Technical Society"], observed: "With its location on the shores of a strait connecting the two seas that wash the shores of Southern Russia, and its proximity to the Kuban oil fields, Mr. Novosiltsev's Phanagoria Refinery has no equal in terms of its advantageous industrial conditions. But it also differs from all refineries I have seen in: 1) its distillation system; 2) the special arrangement of certain parts of the refinery; and 3) the elegance and high-quality finishing of all individual devices.... It seems to me that in some respects it could serve as a model for refineries in the Baku area."

The sophistication of the technological process at the Phanagoria Refinery was also noted by the respected specialist and production engineer Aleksandr Letny: "Oil produced in the Northwest Caucasus was refined by Mr. Novosiltsev's Taman refinery. In its time, this refinery performed distillation with superheated steam and produced petroleum ether and light and heavy lamp oils." In 1870, mining engineer Gennady

Romanovsky also visited the enterprise and wrote: "Order, cleanliness, and activity characterize the entire refinery."[32] In 1871, the refinery produced 612 barrels of "petroleum" (heavy kerosene), 632 barrels of photogen, 323 barrels of ligroin, and 3.6 barrels of gasoline, and earned 44,072 rubles from the sale of its petroleum products.

At the 1870 All-Russian Manufacturing Fair in St. Petersburg, Col. Novosiltsev presented the results of his labor to the general public for the first and only time. The fair catalog gave a brief description of the refinery: "The refinery was founded in 1868. Distillation is carried out with superheated steam in 20 vats with capacities of 1,500 *vedros* [4,881 gallons] each. Mixers and pumps are driven by a 40-horsepower steam engine, and water is lifted by a special 10-horsepower steam engine. Up to 60 people work at the refinery." The refinery's booth exhibited "crude oil and tar, mineral oil, photogen, petroleum, ligroin, gasoline, heavy oil, carriage grease, and lubricants."

However, the close of 1870 was marked by a serious setback for Ardalion Novosiltsev. On December 27, the first oilfield fire in Russian history broke out at his field in the Natukhay District. While drilling a well at 123 feet, workers struck a gusher of gassy oil. The firebox of a steam locomobile operating near the rig ignited a huge fire, causing human casualties and considerable material losses.

The approaching expiration of the tax-farming agreement in 1872 and a serious deterioration in Col. Novosiltsev's financial position left no room for the realization of his expansive plans for development of the oil business in the Kuban. First he was denied a contract to lease oil-bearing lands near Maykop, and then the land of his main field was transferred by "Imperial Grant" to the "Subjugator of the Caucasus," Infantry General Nikolay Yevdokimov, beginning in 1872.

A great struggle began over the right to continue the oil business, which completely absorbed all of Ardalion Novosiltsev's energy. Petitioning the government, he wrote: "After expending considerable capital on preliminary surveys, I have become convinced that an enormous quantity of oil can be produced there via artesian wells. Experience on the Kudako River has brilliantly justified my hopes. There, a continuous stream of petroleum erupts to a height three *sazhens* [21 feet] above the ground's surface from an artesian well 40 *sazhens* [280 feet] deep, which produces up to 10,000 *poods* [1,200 barrels] per day. I am proud that after expending much energy, labor, and money, I have been lucky enough to find such government riches, which will shortly constitute a new and very important source of state revenue. I have no doubt of success, but a shortage of funds could hinder me. The whole business rests on me alone, and the public is observing the business closely, seeing all its enormity, but has still not decided to help develop it."[33]

In response to his request, a Senate decree arrived in May 1871 entrusting Col. Novosiltsev's business to a special agency, a Trusteeship consisting of representatives of the Ministries of Finance and Internal Affairs, as well as creditors. The Trusteeship established relations with the Kuban Host by executing a 10-year contract, good through May 1, 1882, for monopoly rights to develop oil fields on the Taman and other lands previously allocated to Novosiltsev. Thus, Novosiltsev found himself removed from the everyday management of the considerable oil holding. In July 1876, the Board of the Kuban Cossack Host, in describing the Phanagoria Refinery, declared it Host property.

Through difficult negotiations, Col. Novosiltsev and officials of the chancellery of the governor general of the Caucasus in Tiflis (Tbilisi) managed to suspend this decision. Novosiltsev then began desperate attempts to win at least one more deferral of a debt repayment due by January 1, 1879. In an appeal to Emperor Alexander II dated October 30, 1878, Ardalion Novosiltsev wrote: "In striving to develop such an important domestic industry as the oil business, I have sacrificed not only my own fortune, but diverted considerable capital of private individuals, and even dared to resort to the august support of Your Imperial Majesty. The satisfaction of this obligation, sacred to the honor of a nobleman, has been the goal of my entire life, but now this business, brought to a productive end by many years of great sacrifice, could completely collapse."[34]

However, a brief deferral of payment by "Imperial mercy" proved unable to save him, and the business tragically unraveled. On December 6, 1878, in Simferopol, Ardalion Novosiltsev passed away unexpectedly. He was later buried at the cemetery of the Alexander Nevsky Monastery in St. Petersburg.

The First Oil Well in the Russian North

Widespread coverage of the Kuban oil gusher and the exploitation of resources in that region created a sensation throughout the Russian business community. However, oil prospecting in the resource-rich Ukhta District would not begin in earnest for another 20 years. Leading this new phase of the development of the Russian oil industry was Mikhail K. Sidorov (1823–1887), a trailblazing and devoted proponent of the exploration of the Russian North.

Mikhail Sidorov's diverse capabilities and long history of devoted work earned him a worthy place among leading entrepreneurs of Krasnoyarsk and Yenisey Province. In 1859, he outfitted an expedition to the Turukhan Territory, where he discovered the first Siberian graphite deposit near the Kureyka River. Together with Vasily Latkin, he founded

65

the Pechora Company to carry out field production and commercial operations in the Russian North. In 1860, his expedition discovered gold placers near the Shchugor River.

The productive operations of the Pechora Company were very evident to the residents of the territory. In 1864, forest Warden P. F. Gladyshev wrote a letter to Sidorov informing him of surface petroleum outcrops found in the Mezen District, Arkhangelsk Province. That same year, Mikhail Sidorov undertook a trip to the area and, together with local surveyors, he inspected the prospect parcels near the Ukhta River. The results of the trip were encouraging.

Incidentally, it is quite possible that Sidorov was also aware of the results of an expedition 20 years earlier to the Ukhta. In 1843, a geologic and geographic expedition consisting of geologist Alexander Keyserling (1815–1891) and researcher Paul Krusenstern (1809–1881) operated in the Pechora Territory. Over a period of six months, they traveled more than 4,620 miles from the headwaters of the Pechora to its mouth, performing various scientific studies. The result was the first geologic map of the Timan Mountain Range. Summarizing the results of the expedition, Keyserling published the book *Wissenschaftliche Beobachtungen auf einer Reise in das Petschora-Land, im Jahre 1843* [*Scientific Observations on a Trip to the Pechora Region in 1843*] (1846), which contained numerous references to Ukhta petroleum.

After his visit and inspection of this oil-bearing area, Sidorov sent an application for three oil-bearing parcels with the hope that "the government will not deny the first applicant its sympathy for his laborious undertaking in this harsh, uninhabited, and roadless land." But yet again, the hopes of an entrepreneur were dashed. Officials at all levels created all manner of impediments to his request, sometimes rationalizing their denials with the most ludicrous excuses. For instance, correspondence from the Arkhangelsk Province administration stated that: "Based on the Mining Charter now in effect, prospecting for gold, silver, and copper is permitted in the Olonets Province and Arkhangelsk Province (Articles 2253–2257); but regarding other minerals such as oil shale and petroleum, the Mining Charter contains no legal provisions or regulations."

Meanwhile, following his return from a trip to the United States, mining engineer Gennady Romanovsky made a report to a general meeting of the Mineralogical Society in St. Petersburg in 1866, in which he expressed the very perspicacious supposition that the geologic structure of the main American oil-bearing area in Pennsylvania was similar to that of the Ukhta District, and that there might be large reserves of "black gold" there.

This news from the capital and Sidorov's unquenchable insistence on obtaining land parcels on the Ukhta elicited interest among officials in developing the North's oil industry. In particular, Arkhangelsk Governor

Prince Gagarin had a great desire to gain the laurels of the first discoverer of an oil field in the North. To this end, he decided to form a provincial company to investigate natural riches and allocated 1,000 rubles for various types of oil exploration work. In the summer of 1867, under the observation of the commission's members, Arkhangelsk Statistical Committee secretary Pavel Chubinsky, and Arkhangelsk high school natural sciences teacher Fëdor Belinsky, a well 232 feet deep was drilled by manual rotary means from a wooden platform located 28 miles from the mouth of the Ukhta River. This well showed only signs of the presence of petroleum. Then a second well was drilled in rocks on the banks of the Chut River, 1.9 miles from where it empties into the Ukhta; again, only showing traces of petroleum. The drilling results, presented in the commission's report, disappointed the governor. Convinced of the poor prospects of further exploration, he lost interest in petroleum.

The chief impediment having apparently been removed, Mikhail Sidorov gained the long-awaited permit on August 9, 1867: "As a consequence of the Minister's assent, the clarification of the Temporary Section's proposal 8153 of June 20, and the Governor's message 3084 of July 26, the State Property Administration authorizes you to develop petroleum and oil shale in the Mezen District, at the location you specified, 40 *versts* [26.4 miles] from the mouth of the Ukhta River where it empties into the Izhma River, for a 20-year period, in exchange for payment, for each *desyatina* [2.75 acres] of land occupied, of quitrent in the amount of the mean per-*desyatina* [per-2.75 acres] fee prevailing in the Arkhangelsk Province." However, it took almost another year to overcome bureaucratic inertia and indifference and for work to begin on the allocated oil-bearing parcels. In the mid-summer of 1868, a crew outfitted by Mikhail Sidorov, led by experienced miner P. A. Lopatin, began development operations on the left bank of the Ukhta River opposite the mouth of its Neft-Yol River tributary, and within several months it had already drilled the first productive oil well in the Russian North.

The archives of the Russian Academy of Sciences contain two documents: "Daily Journal of Development and Deepening of an Oil Well on the Ukhta River by M. K. Sidorov in the Summer of 1868" and "Journal of the Success of Exploratory Drilling of M. K. Sidorov's Well in 1872." These documentary sources precisely define the duration of all phases of drilling on the Ukhta. Preliminary work to organize the drilling was begun in July 1868, and a well 16.5 feet deep was opened in August. Then the crew began manual well drilling using the rotary method with an eight-inch pyramidal bit. The rock cuttings were removed from the hole by a bailer, which was lifted by a hand crank. When a layer of hard rock was reached, the bit had to be changed every two hours. Beginning at a depth of 32 feet, traces of petroleum were noted on the drill pipe when the drilling tool was raised. Once the bit had reached a depth of 40 feet, a small stream of oil flowed from the hole to the surface, amounting to about 4.9 gallons per day. However, further drilling in beds of even harder rock caused the bit to break. There was no other tool in the field, and work was suspended for an extended period. In 1868, Mikhail Sidorov published an article titled "Petroleum in the Pechora Territory" in the *Tekhnichesky sbornik* ["Technical Collection"], in which he provided a detailed explanation of the progress of drilling on the Ukhta and the basic causes of the temporary suspension. At the same time, the first analyses of Ukhta oil, performed at the chemical laboratory of St. Petersburg Technological Institute by production engineer Eduard Wroblewski, confirmed the real possibility of its successful subsequent refinement.

After the departure of the experienced foreman Lopatin, Sidorov placed serf Aleksey Lebedev, who had been a member of the crew as a simple laborer until then, in charge of further work at the Ukhta field. With his stubbornness and natural talent, Lebedev managed to master the secrets of drilling despite a lack of specialized education. The archives of the Russian Academy of Sciences have preserved his designs of the bit, drill pipe, and temper screw, and today we can give due credit to the original drilling tool design developed by a simple Russian serf in 1871. Drilling operations resumed in June 1872 after the tools had been fabricated at a plant in St. Petersburg and delivered to the field. At first, drilling was done by manual rotary means, then by percussion on continuous pipes screwed to the bit. The drillers began using the cable method by the time the well reached a depth of 64 feet. In early September of that same year, Mikhail Sidorov brought to the field the noted German geologist Hans von Höfer, later a professor at the Mining Academy and author of the popular textbook *Das Erdöl (Petroleum) und seine Verwandten* [*Petroleum and Its Relatives*]. The prestigious scientist thoroughly familiarized himself with the results of the work at the field, and hypothesized the presence of a rich oil pool. He also praised work supervisor Aleksey Lebedev, noting that he had duly managed affairs at the Ukhta field at the level of an experienced mining engineer.

By late September 1872, the well had been drilled to a depth of 173.5 feet, after which a weak inflow of petroleum appeared on the surface. This was the long-awaited oil of the Russian North, obtained from a well despite the pessimistic forecasts of many skeptics. In all, the Ukhta well yielded over about 240 barrels of oil. Sidorov exhibited samples of Ukhta oil at the All-Russian Manufacturing Fair in St. Petersburg in 1870, at the Polytechnic Fair in Moscow in 1872, and at three World's Fairs: in Vienna in 1873, Philadelphia in 1876, and Paris in 1878.

At that time, however, industrial quantities of oil could not be produced from Sidorov's wells for a variety of reasons. Due to the absence of data on the geologic structure of the Ukhta petroliferous area, wells were drilled only at fairly depleted sites of surface oil shows. At the same time, the manual method of drilling in hard rock did not permit workers to reach the main oil pay zones, which lay more than 325 feet underground.

Of course, Mikhail Sidorov fully understood the need for further oil field development, geologic exploration, and use of power drilling, but the small quantities of oil produced could not pay for the considerable capital he had invested in the Ukhta oil field. He saw a spark of hope from the sale of 720 barrels of Ukhta oil shale (*domanik*) in France, but for a number of reasons, this sale led nowhere. In addition, Sidorov's first success in the oil business spurred a new wave of furious opposition on the part of the governor, Prince Gagarin, and local bureaucrats. As Sidorov wrote bitterly, "At this point, I should have halted work, because the new difficulties and new constraints imposed by the administration have placed me in such a position that I could not manage the parcel allocated to me as I saw fit, and where there is no right or freedom of action and everything depends on the administration's whim, all industry is unthinkable."

Understanding that he was inevitably doomed to failure on his own, Sidorov began working actively to pool the efforts of all entrepreneurs involved in the development of the natural minerals of the North. Leading a group of entrepreneurs, he appealed to the Russian government: "Based on our experience, our petroleum enterprises, on which we have labored since 1864, are proving nearly impossible to realize under the existing rules, which do not provide us any firm guarantees of compensation for our efforts and expenses. Even so, the development of the oil industry in the North and the construction of refineries will certainly bring tremendous benefit both to domestic industry in general and to the Pechora Territory in particular, because they will help reduce the price and expand the usage of oil, this necessary product in the northern Russian provinces, and settlement of the deserted margins of the North." Unfortunately, the government departments did not heed the voice of the Russian entrepreneurs, and their appeal remained on the shelf.

Sidorov's financial situation did not permit him to resume his oil business on the Ukhta until 1881. Prior to this, Sidorov had visited the Baku oil fields, familiarizing himself in detail with the organization of oil production, refining, and storage. At his request, the noted chemist Gustav Schmidt tested various schemes for distilling Ukhta crude at the Konstantinovka Refinery laboratory in Yaroslavl Province. In 1882, Sidorov invited a group of qualified mining specialists from Baku to continue the work, defined a plan for development of the Ukhta oil field, and drew up a list of necessary equipment. He placed a large order in Moscow with Gustav List's machine factory, which worked for nearly two years—from 1883 to 1885—to fabricate two steam boilers, a drilling rig, a steam engine with forward and reverse gears, a steam pump, drill bits, pipes, reamers, bailers, temper screws, a "free-fall" Fabian system, and other tools for percussion drilling, as well as metal tanks for the oil. This equipment was initially delivered from Moscow by water to Cherdyn, so that it could be shipped from there via the Kolva and Pechora Rives to the site of the field on the Ukhta. Due to certain difficulties that arose during transportation of these oversize cargoes, much of the equipment was never delivered to the field and was simply left at a wide variety of locations along the way.

Mikhail Sidorov's sudden passing on July 12, 1887 at the age of 64 halted his ambitious and well-planned initiative to develop the Ukhta oil field. He was buried in the Lazarus Cemetery in St. Petersburg, not far from the tomb of his esteemed countryman Academician Mikhail Lomonosov.

The Caucasian Saga of the Siemens Brothers

The successful operations of the German electrical engineering firm Siemens & Halske in the 19th century are fairly well-known. But few are aware that the Siemens brothers were also present at the birth of the Russian oil business.

In 1882, the newspaper *Kavkaz* ["Caucasus"] published a detailed article by production engineer Stepan Gulishambarov, "Oil Fields in the Empire, Georgia, Guria, Ossetia, Karalini, and Kakheti," focusing especially on the oil operations of the "Siemens brothers, Prussian nationals whose company is better known in the world for its successes in setting up telegraph communications and manufacturing electrical hardware."

The six Siemens brothers—Werner, Wilhelm, Friedrich, Karl, Walter, and Otto—had each received a technical education and were successful entrepreneurs. The operations of Siemens & Halske were inextricably linked with Russia from the company's earliest years. The Siemens brothers began establishing the first business contacts as early as 1851, only four years after they founded the company. Collaboration began with the delivery of 75 recoding telegraphs for Russia's first telegraph line, which ran from Finland through St. Petersburg, Moscow, and Kyiv to Odessa and the Crimea. For a company that had begun with a small production facility and 10 workers, this was a very important order. A year later, Werner Siemens, full of ambitious plans, came to St. Petersburg. His great expectations were completely justified, and his company was immediately supplied with enough orders to keep it busy for the next 15 years.

Siemens & Halske's Russian expansion compelled the company's managers to open their own representative office in St. Petersburg in 1855, headed by Werner's younger brother, the 24-year-old Karl Siemens. He quickly learned Russian and began studying the Russian way of life and Russian customs with great interest. Soon Karl married a Russian girl, and began to be called Karl Fëdorovich.[35]

By 1867, the Siemens brothers had become tax farmers for cobalt and iron ore mines in Kedabeg (Tiflis Province), and also leased the Mirzan, Shirak, and Eldar oil wells in Georgia for 4,500 rubles a year. By the time they began operating, the annual tax-farming fee had grown steadily: 1,000 rubles from 1848 to 1858, 2,800 rubles from 1858 to 1862, and 3,100 rubles from 1862 to 1866. Still, the volume of oil production from sources at the disposal of the Transcaucasus Treasury Board was very meager—according to the Learned Mining Committee, these wells yielded only 775 barrels in 1865.

Initially, the organization of oil production at the fields at Imperial Springs [*Tsarskiye istochniki*] rested on the shoulders of Walter Siemens (1833–1868), the acting consul of the North German Alliance in Tiflis. Residing in the Caucasus from 1865 on, he contributed much in the initial stages for the development and launching of many of the firm's commercial projects, including the production of oil. However, an unfortunate fall from a horse proved fatal, and he was buried in the Tiflis city cemetery on June 12, 1868. His short obituary in the *Kavkaz* described him as "someone whose individuality set him apart from most ordinary people."

Otto Siemens, who took over as acting consul of the North German Alliance in Tiflis, continued Siemens & Halske's Caucasian oil project. His brilliant abilities as a businessman, engineer, and production organizer were on full display at the Imperial Springs fields. State of the art foreign methods and equipment were employed to organize the first oil production there. Following the construction of new, deeper wells at sites of obvious surface oil shows, the first three new wells were started in 1869, and a refinery was built. According to data from the Caucasus Bureau of Mines, in 1870, the Siemens Brothers oil field contained 80 hand-dug wells and seven drilled wells whose combined oil production was 7,015 barrels. The refinery had four distillation vats with volumes of 325 to 390 gallons, four air coolers, three rinsing tubs, and eight basins for storing crude and residual oil. The produced crude was refined into 1,550 barrels of photogen, 124 barrels of gasoline, 217 barrels of heavy oil, and 4,035 barrels of residual oil.

In July 1868, the Imperial Russian Technical Society (IRTS) established a Caucasian Division in Tiflis. Otto Siemens was elected as a candidate for membership in the new engineering society and regularly took a very active role in discussions on important technical issues associated with the oil industry. One such issue involved the problem of using residual oil as fuel for the smelting of copper ore. Otto Siemens was one of the first in the Caucasus to find an effective way to resolve this problem. At the March 13, 1871 meeting of the Caucasian Division of the IRTS, he presented diagrams of two "regenerative apparatuses for the combustion of residual oil," one of them designed by Friedrich Siemens and the other by his own hand.

Vladimir Bogachev, a member of the IRTS Caucasian Division, evaluated the apparatuses, observing: "The idea on which the design of the aforementioned devices is based is extremely clever; but how practical the latter will be can only be decided by an experiment that Mr. Siemens intends to perform at one of his factories."

Otto Siemens can also be considered one of the pioneers in the asphalt paving of roads in the Caucasus. The production of road asphalt was soon under way at an Imperial Springs plant, and the asphalt was used successfully in the construction of Russian bathhouses in Tiflis, among other projects. In addition, Otto Siemens proposed installing asphalt sidewalks for less than 3 rubles per square foot to Tiflis Governor K. I. Orlovsky, but the conservative governor opted instead for cobblestone pavers.

Nevertheless, the company's contribution to the development of Russian industry, as well as the Siemens brothers' fruitful activities in Russia over the past 16 years, did not go unrecognized. Great success awaited the Siemens & Halske Company at the 1870 National Manufacturers' Exhibition in St. Petersburg, where it immediately won two medals, the gold and the silver.

Unfortunately, Otto Siemens was unable to bring all his creative ideas to fruition. He died in the fall of 1871, during a cholera epidemic in Tiflis. The *Kavkaz* published a report announcing that the Imperial German Consul, Dr. Otto Siemens, had passed away on September 23, 1871, and offering the paper's condolences to the Siemens trading house.

At the October 11, 1871 meeting of the Caucasus Division of the IRTS in Tiflis, mining engineer Ivan Shteyman, head of the Bureau of Mines of Caucasian Province, read out the obituary for Otto Siemens, which emphasized that his activities "in the mining industry have earned him a place of honor in the history of the Transcaucasus Territory."

After Otto's death, Karl Siemens took over management of the Caucasian oil project. In the summer of 1872, Siemens & Halske participated in a Polytechnic Fair held in Moscow. Vasily Minin, a reviewer for a Moscow newspaper, wrote: "The physics section got many interesting devices from Siemens & Halske in Berlin, including an electromagnetic range-finder, an electric pyrometer, and an apparatus for detonating mines.... Meanwhile, the Caucasian Territory's exhibit featured, alongside 'historical Petrovian artifacts,' a mineralogical collection that contained items from the Kedabeg copper smelter and products from their refinery." On the same topic, *Russkiye vedomosti* ["Russian Gazette"] noted: "The Caucasus exhibit revealed a great many riches that Russia has yet to start using."

On display in Pavilion 14 of the Caucasus section were samples of oil and petroleum products from the Siemens Brothers photogen refinery at Imperial Springs, the full list of which included products entirely new to Russia, such as gasoline (specific gravity 0.682); ligroin (0.692); "separated" gasoline (0.716); light oil (0.760); straight-run gasoline (0.725); photogen (0.820); doubly-rectified photogen (0.818); solar oil for burning in lamps (0.867); heavy fuel oil for furnaces (0.875); vulcan oil for lubricating machinery (0.935); petroleum tar (0.968); oil tar for marine use; skin ointment; liquid cleanser for removing grease stains; bituminous varnish for iron and wood; and asphalt.

The long list of displays at the Siemens Brothers refinery exhibit demonstrated their wide range of expertise and showed that the first practical application of the deep refining of oil in Russia occurred at their refinery. An expert jury rated Siemens & Halske's contribution to the development of Russian industry very highly. Werner, Wilhelm, and Karl Siemens were awarded a Certificate of Merit (First Class) for their "many practical applications of electric current," and a Grand Gold Medal for their "collection of crude oil and petroleum products." Friedrich Siemens also received a separate Grand Gold Medal for "perfecting regenerators for glassmaking and steelmaking furnaces." In addition, the director of the company's refinery, Karl Masing, was awarded the Polytechnic Fair jury's written commendation "for his diagram of the regenerative apparatuses for the combustion of residual oil, which are converted into steam and gas."

After the Polytechnic Fair, the Siemens brothers' oil business continued to grow. By 1875, according to data from the Learned Mining Committee, Tiflis Province already had 101 drilled wells in production, including 72 wells in the Mirzan, Shirak, and Eldar districts, and 29 wells in the Nabamberi area, and just 14 hand-dug wells

In addition, two refineries were already operating in the area of these fields: one belonging to the Siemens brothers, and the other belonging to Karl Masing, their former manager, who had started his own business. In 1875, the Siemens Brothers refinery produced 3,138 barrels of photogen (lamp oil) and 3,741 barrels of other products, while Karl Masing's refinery, which had just begun production, turned out 30 barrels and 13 barrels, respectively.

In 1878, the tax-farming system for Tiflis Province oil fields was replaced by a leasing arrangement, with an annual fee of 10 rubles per 2.75 acres paid directly into the treasury. Initially, this spurred the development of oil production in the region. By 1880, according to data from the Learned Mining Committee, Tiflis Province had only 51 drilled wells, producing 8,608 barrels of crude; this was refined into 4,069 barrels of lamp oils and lubricants.

However, subsequent operations at the Siemens Brothers oil field were not very successful. In 1882, their 41 wells produced only 4,508 barrels of crude, while the refinery turned out just 1,724 barrels of kerosene and 895 barrels of lubricants. It became clear that additional financial investments would be needed to recapture their former position in oil production and modernize the refinery.

At the same time, the accelerated development of the oil business on the Absheron Peninsula and completion of a railroad linking Baku and Tiflis opened the way for delivery of cheap Baku crude to Georgia, and the more expensive Imperial Springs oil could no longer compete. In the second half of 1883, the Siemens brothers decided to focus all future development on electrical manufacturing and sell off their oil business.

The Fight to Abolish Oil Tax Farming

The year 1861 marked a turning point for Russia. With the abolition of serfdom and the beginning of the period of "Great Reforms" initiated by Emperor Alexander II, Russia embarked upon a path of accelerated modernization. The old administrative system of feudal serfdom faded into the past, and a new epoch of economic development began. The socioeconomic progress of the Russian Empire required the achievement of a higher-quality national economy and industry, as well as substantial growth in gross indicators of industrial production.

Despite the dramatic changes taking place in Russia at this time, the tax-farming system, a rudiment of the feudal economy, continued to dominate Russian oil fields. The brothers Ludwig and Stanislav Perschke, noted researchers in the economics of the Russian oil industry, remarked: "The tax farmer, and equally the treasury, being interested during their brief administration only in the ephemeral present-moment maximum gain from the business, have absolutely neglected all considerations of strategic sense, and have not concerned themselves with improving methods of oil production or retaining obsolete oil wells and backward equipment and technology."

Another aspect of the tax-farming system that exerted a stagnating effect on the Russian oil business was that the tax farmer, holding a monopoly, could dictate price terms to producers; under these conditions, most independent oil producers, who generally used credits granted by the tax farmer, were forced by economic pressure to sell crude to the farmer at his dictated price.

Beginning in 1862, the Absheron fields were farmed by Ivan Mirzoyev, a well-known entrepreneur in the Caucasus, who had entered into a corresponding agreement on December 18, 1862. For a term of four years, until January 1, 1867, he gained control over oil and salt fields located in Baku Province (the Baku, Shamakhy, Lankaran, and Nuxa Districts and most of the Shusha District), Derbent Town (in full) and the Kitag-Tabasaran and Zaqatala Districts (in full).

According to the agreement, Mirzoyev had at his disposal "all property at springs and lakes, as well as warehouses." He was required not only to maintain "everything in a serviceable condition, but to strive to improve it, if possible, by increasing the production of oil and salt and making production more convenient, by preventing wells from clogging, and clearing them of *kir* and water." If he "wished to open exploratory shafts, new oil wells, or basins in these forms, he was required to notify the Treasury Board, and if he so wished, or the importance of the work required it, a mining engineer could be appointed at the tax farmer's expense."

Ivan Mirzoyev's tax-farming terms consisted of the following: an annual payment of 162,200 silver rubles. A mandatory price was set, at which he was required to sell oil and salt. He could open new permanent warehouses and stores only within the limits of his farm. He was given the right of unrestricted export to Persia at reduced prices, but for domestic customers, he was permitted to reduce prices only for the first three years of the agreement. Violation of this obligation would subject him to a fine equal to twice the difference between "the lawfully established price and the willfully established one," and he would be taken to court for theft of treasury property.

The agreement also established a relationship between the tax farmer and local residents. Oil from the Baku and Surakhany hand-dug wells was produced by residents of Balakhany, who were assigned to the Balakhany oil field. They were required to carry oil on their oxcarts to Balakhany storage cellars and thence to Baku tax-farm stores for the duration of the first quitrent year. For production and carriage, Mirzoyev paid these residents at a rate approved by the governor general of the Caucasus. Other work was outside the scope of the residents' obligation and was paid by voluntary agreement. Upon expiration of the mandatory obligation to produce (for a six-month term) and carry (for a one-year term), Mirzoyev organized the work through hiring at will. It is curious that tax-farmer Mirzoyev maintained a guard of 12 policemen at his own expense to maintain order in the fields.

It 1863, during his first year as a tax farmer, Mirzoyev increased oil production to 40,830 barrels of crude, and thereafter increased oil production steadily, to 88,350 barrels in 1868, and then more than doubling that figure in 1869, to 202,350 barrels. Overall, taking the January 1, 1863 production of 28,820 barrels at the Absheron oil fields as a baseline, he increased oil production by nearly sevenfold, to 184,455 barrels, in the ten years ending January 1, 1873.

While expanding his operations on the Absheron Peninsula, Ivan Mirzoyev simultaneously turned his attention to the promising Grozny

District. In early 1864, using a design of the Baku inventor Dzhevat Melikov, he built a small refinery in Grozny Gorge. Yevgeny Yushkin described the enterprise in his book, *Beginning of the Grozny Oil Industry in Sketches* [*Nachalo Groznenskoy neftepromyshlennosti v ocherkakh*]: "Fifty *sazhens* [350 feet] from the wells there were two small buildings with distilling vats and condensers, operated using oil and water from wells. Oil was piped from the wells into a 3,000-*pood* [360-barrel] covered rock basin for settling; the oil was pumped by hand to a 900-*pood* [108-barrel] covered wooden tub for final settling, after which it flowed by gravity to a refinery having seven stills with a total capacity of 1,880 *vedros* [6,118 gallons] in its two buildings, in a batch with a total volume of up to 1,335 *vedros* [4,344 gallons]." Some 4,325 barrels of crude were refined every month at the refinery. Photogen and kerosene were subsequently delivered to customers on oxcarts in plane tree barrels.

The following year, Mirzoyev expanded his tax farm by acquiring the Grozny, Mamakayev, and Karabulak oil springs from the Tersk Cossack Host effective June 15, 1865, for a ten-year term at an annual fee of 13,615 rubles.

According to an inventory drawn up that same year, there were 16 hand-dug wells on the bottom and eastern side of Grozny Gorge, nine of which had cribbing, while the remaining seven had one empty barrel each to prevent clogging by dirt embankments. The hand-dug wells produced about one barrel daily. Using a primitive gate driven by human muscle, the oil was hauled out of the wells in leather buckets called *kops* or *kaps*, which were leather bags of 180-pound capacity on iron hoops with a load weight on one side, giving the bucket the tilt necessary to excavate the oil.

The expansion of Ivan Mirzoyev's oil production in Baku and Grozny was due primarily to an increase in the number of oil wells. Whereas there were 218 wells on the Absheron Peninsula in the first half of the 1860s—broken down by oilfield district as follows: Balakhany 102, Binagadi 65, Bibiheybet 27, Surakhany 19, and Bakhchi 5—by 1871 this figure had reached 239 wells.

Yet, despite efforts to expand oil production and the modest successes of entrepreneurs such as Ivan Mirzoyev, the stifling effect of the tax-farming system on the Russian oil business meant that in 1871, the United States accounted for nearly 81% of world oil production, producing 36 times more oil than Russia, which lagged far behind.

Leading Russian industrialists, including Vasily Kokorev, Pëtr Gubonin, and Gadzhi Tagiyev, joined in an active struggle to abolish tax farming, along with major government figures and officials, such as Nikolay Romanovsky, Gertsog Leykhtenbergsky, Caucasus Governor General Grand Prince Mikhail Romanov, and Minister Mikhail Ostrovsky, as well as many leading scientists and members of the technical elite.

Table 1. Russian Oil Production, 1863–1872
(in barrels and tons)

	Oil Production in Barrels	Oil Production in Tons
1863	40,830	6,140
1864	64,723	9,730
1865	66,564	10,010
1866	83,079	12,490
1867	119,957	18,030
1868	88,284	13,280
1869	202,736	30,420
1870	204,685	30,780
1871	165,184	24,835
1872	183,252	27,735

Source: Stanislav and Ludwig Perschke, *The Russian Oil Industry, Its Development and Current Status in Statistical Data* [*Russkaya neftyanaya promyshlennost, yeyë razvitiye i sovremennoye polozheniye v statisticheskikh dannykh*]. Tiflis (Tbilisi), 1913, pp. 4, 5.

In 1867, the governor general of the Caucasus, Grand Prince Mikhail Romanov, ordered the formation of a special commission to address this problem, and mining engineer Ivan Shteyman, head of the Bureau of Mines of the Caucasus and Transcaucasus Territory, was made its chairman. State Property Minister Mikhail Ostrovsky later remarked: "In 1867, the Caucasus governor general and grand prince charged a special commission with collecting detailed information on oil fields and presenting ideas for eliminating the tax-farming system and replacing it with another method of development more appropriate to the benefit of the treasury and industry." The commission's materials and conclusions were set forth in a document entitled, "Ideas of the Commission, Instituted with Permission of His Imperial Majesty the Governor General of the Caucasus, for Discussion of Issues Concerning the Development of the Oil Industry in Caucasus and Transcaucasus Territory," which would later form the basis of legislation abolishing oil tax farming.

The commission noted: "The most important causes of the unsatisfactory condition involve the absence of legal provisions appropriate for the development of a private oil industry and in the widespread application of the tax-farming system to the production and sale of oil." The commission concluded that "by eliminating tax farming, the government will open up an enormous profitable field for honest industry. The most important thing should be the government's duty, and that is: only the removal of all economic obstacles on the path to development of any industry whatsoever. The rest will depend on the skill of private individuals to look after their business and their entrepreneurship.... The tax-farming system has forced the oil industry into a closed cycle in which the privileges granted to tax farmers to maintain revenue have prevented the entry of anyone else's entrepreneurship, free competition in trade, and even conditions favorable for the discovery of new sources."

The commission's conclusions were approved by the capital government, but it would not be until February 1, 1872, almost five years later, that "supreme" [i.e., imperial] approval was obtained for the two government documents abolishing the tax-farming system on the Absheron Peninsula: "Rules of the Oil Industry and Excise Tax on Photogen Production," and then on February 17, 1872, "Rules on the Cession into Private Hands of Treasury Oil Fields of Caucasus and Transcaucasus Territory, Now Subject to Tax Farming."

The First Auctions on the Absheron Peninsula

Under the new 1872 Rules, the system of ceding oil fields to tax farming was abolished effective January 1, 1873. And that meant only one thing: the oil business, which until then had been strongly associated with progress the world over yet had pulsated fitfully in the snares of the feudal system only in Russia, would henceforth follow the capitalist track in Russia as well.

The principal feature of the 1872 Rules was the following: Effective January 1, 1873, the system of ceding oil fields to tax farming was abolished, and oil-bearing parcels of land were transferred to private hands at public auction for a one-time fee. The first paragraph of the Rules determined that "Chief oversight of private oil fields throughout the Empire shall be within the jurisdiction of departments of the Ministry of Finance and shall be concentrated in the Mining Department. The duties of the local mining administration shall include: a) observation of the adoption of steps undertaken in the performance of work to protect the health of workers, and also to prevent explosions, fires, collapses, and destruction; b) observation of the conduct of underground work plans and the extraction of only oil and *kir* on oil industry parcels; c) collection of statistical information on oil industry performance."

The Rules permitted unhindered oil prospecting on all free treasury lands of the Caucasus by "persons of any status, both Russian subjects and foreigners." Applicants were permitted to lease no fewer than 2.75 acres and no farther than 560 feet around the application post. As stipulated in the lease, an industrialist was required to begin oil development within two years of receiving the deed to the area. For the use of such leases, the industrialist was required to pay rent of 10 rubles per 2.75 acres. The maximum lease term was set at 24 years.

Soon after receiving the text of the "Rules of the Oil Industry," the Main Administration of the Caucasus Governor's Office formed a special commission in Tiflis to handle the first oil auctions on the Absheron Peninsula.

Four auctions were held during December 1872. Entrepreneurs Vasily Kokorev and Pëtr Gubonin acquired six parcels (165 acres) in Balakhany containing 48 hand-dug oil wells for 1,323,328 rubles (with an opening bid of 365,296 rubles). Former tax farmer Ivan Mirzoyev acquired four parcels (110 acres) in Balakhany containing 30 hand-dug oil wells for 1,222,000 rubles (with an opening bid of 134,791 rubles). In addition, three parcels (82.5 acres) in Balakhany containing 18 hand-dug oil wells went to the entrepreneurs Benkendorf and Muromtsev for 120,834 rubles (with an opening bid of 17,040 rubles). Entrepreneur Stepan Lianozov acquired one parcel (27.5 acres) in Balakhany containing six hand-dug oil wells for 26,220 rubles (with an opening bid of 1,310 rubles). One parcel in Surakhany containing 21 hand-dug oil wells went to entrepreneur Ivan Ter-Akopov for 22,950 rubles (with an opening bid of 2,290 rubles). Finally, the two entrepreneurial teams of Tagiyev and Sarkisov and Zubalov and Dzhakeli acquired one parcel each in Bibiheybet containing 18 and 9 hand-dug oil wells, respectively, for 9,095 and 18,950 rubles, respectively.

From an economic standpoint, the results of the first auction demonstrated the correctness of the chosen policy for the Russian government. Whereas the state budget had collected a total of 5,966,000 rubles over the first 51 years of oil field exploitation, the treasury immediately received 2,980,307 rubles, half of the collected amount, from the first auction and was assured of a stable source of income in the future.

However, at the same time, the Russian government, having abolished the feudal oil tax-farming system, had simultaneously imposed a burdensome excise tax on lighting materials, i.e., it had enacted a time-tested indirect tax on a consumer good, kerosene.

Furthermore, it should be noted that the tax-farming system in oil fields of the Russian Empire was not abolished at a single point in time, but over the course of a complex process that lasted for more than 20 years. The jurisdiction of the 1872 Rules covered only the Caucasus and Transcaucasus, while the tax-farming system in Turkestan Territory was not abolished until a decree of June 10, 1892, "On the Application of Rules on Private Industry in Free Treasury Regions to the Transcaucasus Region." And finally, in 1894, Emperor Alexander III (1845–1896) approved "Rules on Oil Fields on the Lands of the Kuban and Tersk Cossack Hosts."

On the Way to Real Entrepreneurship

As a result of the first auctions in December 1872 on the Absheron Peninsula, at the beginning of 1873 an active process of converting

Russian oil fields from a semifeudal state to a capitalist form of industrial development was launched.

In that year of 1873, which was so noteworthy for the Russian oil industry, intensive drilling of oil wells began on the Absheron Peninsula, and their number grew rapidly. Whereas there had been only one drilled well in 1872, there were 17 in 1873 and 50 in 1874.

These early days have been dubbed "the great oil fever." According to eyewitness accounts of the events, areas of oil production became completely unrecognizable. Seemingly overnight, a forest of derricks sprouted from the earth, the land whined with steam engines, and everything around was transformed.

In June 1873, in an area belonging to the Khalafi Partnership, a gusher occurred from a depth of 98 feet, erupting continuously for four months, and no one knew how to quell it. Several oil lakes formed around the gusher (named the Vermishev gusher, in honor of one of the founders of the partnership). The gusher's appearance served as a concrete demonstration of the colossal riches of the Baku lands.

Oil production on the Absheron Peninsula was further increased as a result of a new method of well bailing. This new kind of bailer was a tub used originally to produce oil from hand-dug wells, but more elongated, with a considerably smaller diameter than when used previously in hand-dug wells, so that it could pass through the bore of a well casing with a bottomhole valve that opened inside. As the bailer was lowered into the well, the valve opened and the bailer filled with oil, but as it was raised, the valve fell, closing the opening, and the oil was raised to the surface.

By the spring of 1873, more than 80 refineries had been built around Baku, and by the end of the 1870s, their number had jumped to 200. The Baku sky, despite endless winds, turned black with soot, because the countless large and small refineries used the same crude as fuel when distilling oil, and they burned it in the same primitive way, on a furnace bottom. In the Black City outside Baku, an eyewitness wrote: "a continuous rain of black soot impregnated the soil, all buildings, and even darkened the southern sun."

As proponents of abolishing the tax-farming system (including Dmitry Mendeleyev) had predicted, the oil industry's conversion to new market conditions caused a substantial rise in the volume of crude hydrocarbon production and considerable development of the refining sector. In the first year following the new legislation, oil production rose by a factor of 2.6 over the previous year, reaching over 475,000 barrels.

The data presented below convincingly show that in the first five years following the abolition of the tax-farming system on the Absheron Peninsula, the Russian oil industry was able to achieve unheard-of rates of oil production under conditions of free enterprise, with Russian oil production nearly quadrupling from 1873 to 1877.

Monument to the Dubinin brothers in Mozdok.

In 1823, the Dubinin brothers - Vasily, Gerasim and Makar - built the first coal oil refinery in the world to distill "white" oil, refining oil from the Voznesensk field, near the Grozny fortress.

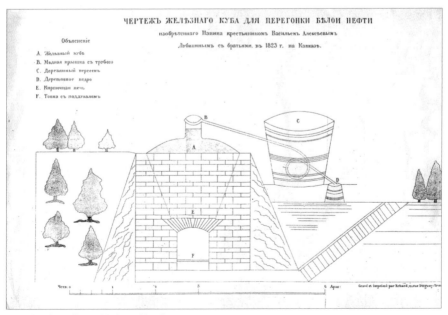

ЧЕРТЕЖЪ ЖЕЛѢЗНАГО КУБА ДЛЯ ПЕРЕГОНКИ БѢЛОЙ НЕФТИ
изобрѣтеннаго Панина крестьяниномъ Васильемъ Алексѣевымъ
Дубининымъ съ братьями, въ 1823 г. на Кавказъ.

Объясненіе

A. Желѣзный кубъ
B. Мѣдная крышка съ трубою
C. Деревянный пересѣкъ
D. Деревянное ведро
E. Кирпичная печь
F. Топка съ поддуваломъ

Sketch of Vasily Dubinin's oil refinery.
The Dubinin brothers created a process of distilling kerosene from oil that served as the basis for all boiler-based oil refineries constructed prior to the 1880s. The product obtained by distillation was first called "white" oil, then coal oil and finally kerosene.

Oil well in the United States, drilled in 1859 by Edwin Drake in Pennsylvania.

A. Konshin's mining engineering book *Description of the Development of Oil Deposits in North America* (1896).

The Drake Well Museum (Pennsylvania, USA).

Commercial Adviser Vasily Kokorev
(1817-1889).

State Councilor Pëtr Gubonin
(1825-1894).

In 1874, noted entrepreneur Pëtr Gubonin,
together with Vasily Kokorev, founded
Russia's first vertically integrated oil
company, the Baku Oil Company.

Panorama of oil fields on the Absheron Peninsula; shown in 1891
at a French exhibit in Moscow.

W. Simpson. *Petroleum wells of Baku on the Caspian* (1886).

Robert Nobel (1829-1896) ventured into the oil industry in 1875 after a happenstance trip to Baku. After persuading his brothers to join him, he became a founding member, with them, of the Nobel Brothers Petroleum Production Partnership in 1879. He was an excellent chemist and managed to achieve more highly refined oil than his competitors.

Alfred Nobel (1833-1896), a founder of the Nobel Brothers Petroleum Production Partnership, actively participated in the development of the oil business in Russia.

He bequeathed his fortune to a special fund, the earnings from which he annually awarded to leading scientists and cultural figures responsible for outstanding contributions to the development of humanity. The award is called the Nobel Prize in his honor.

Ludvig Nobel (1831-1888) was the largest shareholder of Russia's second vertically integrated oil company, the Nobel Brothers Petroleum Production Partnership. He organized the Russian Technical Society, which, after his death, established a prize in his name that served as the prototype of the Swedish Nobel Prize.

Product sample from the Nobel Brothers Petroleum Production Partnership.

A 250-ruble share of stock in the Nobel Brothers Petroleum Production Partnership.

Nobel Brothers Petroleum Production Partnership business report (1905).

Обшій видъ заводовъ Товаришества въ Черномъ городѣ.

A view of one of the refineries of the Nobel Brothers Petroleum Production Partnership (late 19th century).

Plaque commemorating 1 billion *poods* [120 million barrels] of production realized by the
Nobel Brothers Petroleum Production Partnership from 1879 to 1906.

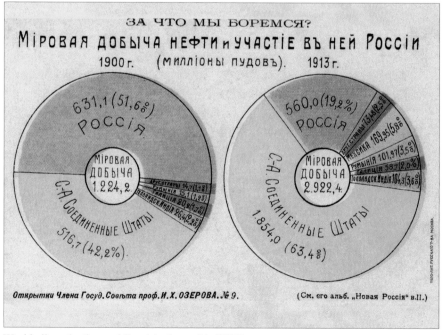

World oil production and Russia's share of it (1913).

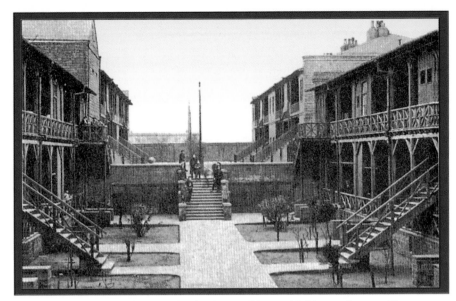

The Nobel Brothers Petroleum Production Partnership provided its employees with comfortable conditions, accommodations and food. Nobel settlement "on the mountain" (Sabunchi, Baku, 1910).

Вилла петролеа Бр Нобель.
Villa Pétroléa Nobel frères.

Баку.
Васоп.

Villa Petrolea, a settlement for employees of the Nobel Brothers Petroleum Production Partnership in the Black City, Baku. The beauty, cleanliness and facilities of the "Nobel Towns" are still legendary.

Table 2. *Russian Oil Production, 1873–1877*
(in barrels and tons)

	Oil Production in Barrels	Oil Production in Tons
1873	477,710	71,880
1874	595,635	89,560
1875	707,320	106,350
1876	1,452,000	218,300
1877	1,861,500	279,900

Source: Stanislav and Ludwig Perschke, *The Russian Oil Industry, Its Development and Current Status in Statistical Data* [*Russkaya neftyanaya promyshlennost, yeyë razvitiye i sovremennoye polozheniye v statisticheskikh dannykh*]. Tiflis (Tbilisi), 1913, pp. 4, 5.

As for exports, the main foreign destination for Russian crude oil and petroleum products in those days was Persia. In 1880, Russia exported 21,579 barrels of crude oil and petroleum products to that country from Baku, including: 6,953 barrels of kerosene, 6,480 barrels of residual oil, and 8,142 barrels of crude oil.

The First Vertically Integrated Oil Company

The abolition of the tax-farming system and the promotion of individual and group entrepreneurship paved the way for the development of joint-stock companies in the Russian oil industry. The strong inflow of private capital into the industry created unprecedented competition. The forms of business organization that existed at the time—individual and family businesses, full and trust partnerships—were not well-suited to the changing economic environment. They could not adequately respond to rapidly changing competition in the emerging national kerosene market, nor could they fully support the growth of petroleum product production or overcome the technological gap between the Russian and US oil industries.

After witnessing the results of the first year of escalated competition among oil industrialists on the Absheron Peninsula, entrepreneurs Vasily Kokorev (1817–1889) and Pëtr Gubonin (1825–1894) decided to create a large joint-stock company capable of performing the full spectrum of oil production, petroleum products manufacture, and sales.

In late 1873, they began organizing this first joint-stock oil company in earnest. Explaining his position to prospective stockholders, Vasily Kokorev issued a brochure, "Explanatory Note on the Charter of the Baku Oil Company" (St. Petersburg, 1874), in which he convincingly justified the advantages of concentrating capital within a single company for successful industrial oil production, as well as the manufacture and sale of petroleum products.

The most salient arguments for creating such a company were: 1) the need to radically change the Russian oil business to satisfy mass demand for petroleum products and to displace American kerosene from the Russian market; 2) the geographic remoteness of domestic oil production on the Absheron Peninsula from the bulk of customers in Central Russia and the rest of the Russian Empire, which demanded the creation, under market conditions, of an effective business structure to manufacture and sell petroleum products; 3) the real ability of a vertically integrated structure to substantially accelerate the entire cycle of capital turnover and cost payback and to maximize the growth in the size and rate of return by reducing unit costs throughout the production chain in view of the concentration of capital and the availability of a unified infrastructure and controlled sources of raw materials.

The founding of the Baku Oil Company (BOC), the Russian oil industry's first joint-stock company, on January 18, 1874 can properly be considered a milestone in Russian history. However, even from the start there were difficulties securing financing as the oil business was still a decidedly risky venture for the average (patriarchal) Russian entrepreneur. Yet these initial difficulties only encouraged the founders, and on July 9, 1874 the company began operating officially. According to the second paragraph of its charter, "The company shall gain lawful title to certain works, lands, ships, oil wells, basements, and warehouses, both belonging personally to business councilor Kokorev and also belonging to him jointly with state councilor Gubonin, by joint agreement of the owners and the company, according to an inventory to be presented at the first general stockholders meeting." At the outset, the BOC's fixed capital was 2.5 million rubles, and was backed by the issue of 20,000 shares having a par value of 125 rubles.

The BOC's first report, for the period from July 1, 1874 through April 1, 1875, described all the company's assets in detail. The oil production sector included: "Six groups in Balakhany, in an area of some 60 *desyatinas* [165 acres] with drillholes and hand-dug oil wells. Lands in Sabunchu, with an area of about 22 *desyatinas* [60.5 acres] with hand-dug wells and a basin. Oil basins and other buildings under construction by July 1, 1874." By 1875, the BOC owned 10 drilled wells at the Balakhany oil field that were 161 to 245 feet deep with daily flows of 72 to 1,200 barrels.

The refining sector included: "A refinery with all accessory buildings, apparatus, machinery, and combustible gas coming from the land, valued at 1.2 million rubles. The value of the new division currently under construction and supplies on hand is taken as 13,669 rubles."

The BOC's transportation sector included a small fleet based at Zykh wharf, consisting of six schooners, the steamer *Artelshchik*, and five barges. It also had its own anchorage at Baku, with a sailing schooner and barge for carrying residual oil. In 1875, BOC built the sailing schooner

Vasily, a ferry boat, and five barges at Tsaritsyn, and purchased the steam schooner *Transzund*.

The company's sales sector was comprised of a Baku office, 11 agencies, and four commission offices. The agencies, along with the major buildings and warehouse facilities, were located in Moscow, Saratov, Samara, Tsaritsyn, Kazan, Simbirsk, Sarapul, Perm, Nizhny Novgorod, Yaroslavl, and Astrakhan. The BOC's commission offices were operated out of Rybinsk, Penza, Vologda, and Vyatka. In Moscow alone, the BOC built six warehouses on leased land with an area of 5.5 acres 4,900 square feet and a total capacity of 423,500 gallons. In addition, the Moscow agency operated a retail petroleum products store that was very popular among Muscovites.

The company's board was located in St. Petersburg. It was headed by the proactive manager Nikolay Ignatyevsky, and it included the financial and mining specialists R. Kraft, I. Milyutin, and K. Gusev. Later, I. Gorbov and D. Polivanov joined the board.

The BOC managed to achieve impressive results after only three years, and the company soon became the leader of the Russian oil industry. Whereas in 1874/1875, the company reported production of 115,969 barrels of crude oil and 35,702 barrels of kerosene, it reported respective figures of 285,749 barrels and 62,482 barrels in 1875/1876, and 450,690 barrels and 108,475 barrels in 1876/1877.

In the spring of 1876, the noted Russian scientist Professor Konon Lisenko, of the Mining Institute, visited the Baku Oil Company's fields and refinery and soon became a scientific and technical consultant to the BOC.

After touring the Baku Oil Company's facilities, Professor Lisenko noted that the Baku Oil Company's Surakhany refinery had 25 stills holding 2,017 to 2,148 gallons each and five stills holding 677 gallons each; the former were designed for processing lighting gas, and the latter were for lubricants. Combustible material in the form of gas was collected in 44 iron cisterns and fed from there into pipes marked with a dotted red line that were routed through the refinery's various buildings. The refinery had a large cooper's shop, metal shop, and blacksmith's shop. In addition, the Baku Oil Company had a cooper's plant near Baku itself.

An important phase in the company's development took place at this very same refinery, with the organization of lubricant production. This development was primarily due to the work of mining engineer Aleksey Doroshenko, the manager of the Surakhany Refinery. The refinery installed a process line for making lubricants from residual oil, which had previously been regarded as waste and was usually simply burned. The production process for making lubricants at Surakhany Refinery consisted of the following: residual oil was heated to 572°F, after which superheated steam was passed through it, entraining the oil fractions in flow through a metal pipe into a condenser, where they separated from the water. Later, mining engineer Semën Kvitka remarked: "Generally speaking, while the oil industry is forever indebted to R. I. Ragozin for organizing the production of lubricants, Aleksey Semënovich Doroshenko earned his share of respect and gratitude from Baku residents for organizing the business in Baku."[36]

The expansion of oil production and increases in petroleum product refining volumes required BOC management to continually take steps to further improve production, develop infrastructure, and introduce modern equipment and new process solutions.

On February 17, 1879, the BOC placed in service a kerosene pipeline from Surakhany Refinery to Zykh dock. The company then built the tanker *Surakhany* in Sweden at Crichton Yard (Abo), designed to carry 5,500 tons of kerosene worth $75,000 (approximately 94,000 silver rubles). All this had a substantial effect on improving the efficiency of the company's transportation sector and its successful sale of petroleum products, both in Russia and abroad.

The company's investments in infrastructure and equipment paid off and by 1888 the BOC was producing more than 1.3 million barrels of crude oil. A year later, it produced 1.7 million barrels. However, starting in 1890, the BOC slipped to second place in Russia in terms of oil production volume, behind the Nobel Brothers Petroleum Production Partnership.

On the whole, however, the BOC's successful operation as the first vertically integrated company became a convincing example for many Russian oil industrialists. Moreover, it was this initial phase of joint-stock creation in the oil industry (1874–1879) that laid the groundwork for the future development of the industry, including the monopolies that emerged during the late 19th century.

The Nobel Brothers' Big Risk

As mentioned above, the Russian oil industry underwent a changing of the guard by 1890, with the BOC passing on its title of the number-one oil producer in Russia. Part of this was due to circumstances within the Baku Oil Company, including the death of Vasily Kokorev in 1889. But equally important was the initiative and actions of the ambitious Nobel Brothers Petroleum Production Partnership.

The initial phase of the company's formation was described in the Nobel Brothers Petroleum Production Partnership brochure, published in June 1882 in St. Petersburg: "The eldest brother, Robert E. Nobel, went to the Caucasus to fulfill a special assignment from his second brother [Ludvig], the St. Petersburg mechanical factory owner. In 1874 he began prospecting for oil, both on the Absheron Peninsula and on Cheleken Island. Upon discovering abundant sources in both places, he immediately began building a refinery, which he placed in service in 1875."

The "special assignment" Ludvig entrusted to his brother Robert in March 1873 was to purchase massive quantities of walnut wood for the manufacture of gun stocks at the Izhevsk Works. Robert was ultimately unable to make this purchase but, by a twist of fate, he instead found himself on the Absheron Peninsula, where his gaze fell upon the various petroleum and photogen (kerosene) enterprises. He already had some experience trading kerosene in Finland, and decided to take a risk. He spent all 25,000 rubles of his "walnut" money to purchase a small parcel of oil-bearing land and a photogen refinery with eight "Tatar" vertical stills, each having a capacity of 9.6–10.2 barrels, from the Dutch De Boor brothers. The new business, Robert thought, had decent prospects, since the Russian market was still largely dominated by foreign-made petroleum products. American kerosene imported to Russia in 1872 alone totaled 215,318 barrels, while Russian kerosene production was at the unacceptably low level of some 48,000 barrels per year.

In her monograph, *The Nobel Corporation in Russia* [*Nobelevskaya korporatsiya v Rossii*] (Moscow, 1970), the noted Russian historian and Doctor of History Irina Dyakonova notes that the abolition of the tax-farming system in Absheron Peninsula oil fields on January 1, 1873 established a favorable environment for the development of an oil business, and the Nobel Brothers took full advantage of it.

Mining Institute Professor Konon Lisenko, who visited the Absheron Peninsula in the spring of 1876, also reflected on this in his "Review of the Current State of Oil Production and the Use of Oil as a Fuel," writing: "The method of drilling wildcat wells used by Mr. Robert Nobel with great success deserves special attention... its advantage lies in the speed of work and the ability to drill a small-diameter hole to a comparatively greater depth.... Baku has several factory owners who want to develop oil processing on a rational basis. Among these I would include Robert Nobel, who hopes to introduce full processing of oil at a refinery that was under construction, but commissioned after my visit, with the inclusion of paraffin production from materials containing it in sufficient quantity." Further evidence of Robert Nobel's innovative activities include the Department of Trade and Manufactures of the Russian Ministry of Finance's decision in 1875 to grant him proprietary rights to the original design of a free-falling drilling tool with extensible cutters and a method of removing cuttings using water injected under pressure into the hole.

In December 1875, in a letter to his younger brother Alfred, Ludvig wrote: "Robert has returned to Baku from the east coast of the Caspian Sea. He found marvelous oil on Cheleken, lying at a depth of 10 *sazhens* [70 feet]. Now he has the crude material he needs.... His future successes depend on it. For my part, I did what I could in the sense of financial aid and technical support.... The main thing now is to conduct the business sensibly, on a large scale."

The first step in expanding operations at the Nobel Brothers' refinery was to install two additional distilling vats and introduce kerosene purification technology. In another letter to Alfred, Ludvig wrote: "The refinery is finally complete and has begun operating. Its production is significant, comprising 0.5 million *poods* [60,044 barrels] a year in its current form. If we double the amount of equipment (the equipment is inexpensive), then we will be able to double or even quadruple that figure once production lines are completed. Almost any way things turn out, we will be able to produce 2 million *poods* [240,175 barrels] of kerosene per year—everything relies on transportation and warehouses. But this is where the big problem lies. As for quality, we have achieved marvelous results: while only 30% of heavy and low-grade kerosene can usually be made from Baku crude, we can make 40% light kerosene from the same crude, on a par with the best American samples. We will be able to enter the market with a product that will give our company a shining reputation."

In July 1876, based on the results of a trip to the Absheron Peninsula, Ludvig Nobel began working on an analytical memorandum, "A Look at the Baku Oil Industry and Its Future." Essentially, the memorandum contained a comprehensive program for radically transforming the Russian oil business. Ludvig Nobel began by considering the experience of the US oil industry, stressing that it was "the production of lamp oils [that] nevertheless proved a tremendous use of the wealth for America, yielding more than $100 million in net revenue." He tried to identify the peculiarities and differences in oil production in the United States and Russia, and broke the entire industry down clearly into its major components: "Crude oil here is given out nearly free of charge, as it was temporarily in America, too.... Everyone understands that the business must have a tremendous future, but with the shortage of transportation routes holding back the entire business and in the absence of capital, enterprise, and skill to establish the business, I cannot foresee when the development of the Baku oil industry will actually begin." Ludvig Nobel's main proposals called for abandoning the use of animal-drawn vehicles to transport oil (it was stored in wineskins and drawn on ox-carts) and instead constructing oil pipelines from fields to refineries; constructing iron tanks for storing crude oil and petroleum products; more widely using residual oil (*mazut*) for heating and gas production; radically improving the quality of kerosene; introducing bulk carriage of oil in railroad tank cars and on inland and seagoing ships; and creating a diversified structure for storing and selling petroleum products in Russia. This program was received by most Russian oil industrialists with a fair amount of skepticism and excessive caution, so Ludvig Nobel decided to carry it out himself.

In the fall of 1878, Ludvig contracted Bari, Sytenko & Co. to build Russia's first oil pipeline on the Absheron Peninsula for his enterprise. It was 5.6 miles long, with a pipe diameter of three inches and a capacity of 9,607 barrels of oil per day. By the end of 1878, only 101,012 barrels of oil had been pumped through the pipeline, but in 1879, it carried 670,451 barrels.

The installation of the pipeline had a drastic effect on the Nobel Brothers' business: Whereas the company exported 750 barrels of kerosene from Baku in 1876, by 1879 the figures were 66,220 barrels of kerosene and 56,042 barrels of residual oil.

The Nobels also turned their attention to the technical modernization of the refinery as well. In 1877, they installed the first steam pumps for moving crude and residual oil to pressurized tanks that fed the distillation vats, and introduced the technique of cooling hot residual oil in the still using a cold-oil circulation system. This allowed the number of distillation cycles to be increased to 6–10 per day. In 1878, the refinery installed a large tube-type residual oil cooler, enclosed in a 2,400-barrel tank, which the workers nicknamed "Ivan the Great."

However, the tremendous yield of crude oil and petroleum products could not be delivered to the domestic Russian market by sea or inland waterway in barrels. And here, Ludvig turned to the experience of the Astrakhan merchants, the Artemyev brothers, who had reconfigured their wooden sailing ship the *Aleksandr* in 1875 to deliver bulk oil along the Volga. In January 1878, Nobel contracted with Sven Almquist, director of the Motala Shipyard in Sweden, to construct the world's first steam-powered oil tanker, the *Zoroastr*, named after the Persian philosopher Zarathustra. The *Zoroastr* had a load capacity of 4,083 barrels of kerosene stored in eight holds, and the ship's engines were rated at 290 horsepower. In late 1878, it completed its maiden voyage on the Caspian Sea under a Russian flag.

Ludvig Nobel also looked to the experience of the Baku Oil Company and soon followed their lead in creating his own joint-stock company. On May 18, 1879, the family business obtained imperial approval of the charter of the Nobel Brothers Petroleum Production Partnership, which created a joint-stock partnership with fixed capital of 3 million rubles. The capital was distributed as follows: Ludvig Nobel 1.61 million rubles, Alfred Nobel 115,000 rubles, Robert Nobel 100,000 rubles, Peter Bilder-ling 930,000 rubles, Alexander Bilderling 50,000 rubles, Ivan Zabelsky 135,000 rubles, Fritz Blumberg 25,000 rubles, Mikhail Belyamin 25,000 rubles, A. Sandren 5,000 rubles, and Benno Banderlich 5,000 rubles.

A fundamentally new phase in the history of the Nobel Brothers Partnership and the activities of Ludvig Nobel began soon thereafter.

Ludvig was tasked with achieving a leading position in the Russian oil business and turning the company into a vertically integrated enterprise, extending its activities from the oil well to the sale of end products to consumers.

The Executive Board's report to the April 1883 general stockholders meeting of the Partnership stressed: "The Partnership's objective was first, to displace American kerosene from Russia, and then to begin exporting kerosene abroad. The entire enterprise was organized in full accordance with the requirements of that objective.... The Partnership's industrial operations to date have been accompanied by ever-greater successes. Sales have grown increasingly every year. The high quality of the Partnership's products, and the reputation it has earned as a result, command high prices compared to those of similar products from other Baku entrepreneurs."[37]

As for oil field development, the Nobel Brothers Petroleum Production Partnership bet on the development of machine drilling. Whereas Robert Nobel drilled the first well manually at Sabunchu in April 1876, by 1878 the company had seven wells, all drilled mechanically. By 1882, of the 271 drilled wells in all of Russia, the Partnership had 25 of them. The company's first gusher was drilled in mid-1879, and others followed in 1880 and 1881.

Each year, the Nobel Brothers Petroleum Production Partnership continued to consolidate its position as a leader in the domestic oil industry. In just a short time, the company managed to turn itself into the leading Russian enterprise in the new field. Whereas in 1879 the company produced 38,548 barrels of proprietary crude and made 37,227 barrels of kerosene (including from purchased crude), by 1888, proprietary production had risen by more than 80 times, to 3.1 million barrels (13.4% of total Russian production), and kerosene production had grown by more than 40 times, to 1.5 million barrels.

Laszlo Sandor's Shugurovo Failure

News of the oil riches of the Absheron Peninsula continued to inspire fortune seekers, even those located in the very center of the Russian Empire. Thus, when encouraging information about petroleum reserves in the Volga region surfaced, it attracted the attention not only of Russian business people, but also certain foreign entrepreneurs who sought the petroleum "bird of happiness." Notable among these was a US citizen of Hungarian descent, Laszlo Sandor. He had previously acquired a respectable amount of capital supplying Pennsylvania kerosene to light St. Petersburg, which allowed him to prospect for oil in 1870 by drilling wells on the territory of the Bugulma–Belebey Rise. And, unlike the cautious Volga entrepreneurs, Laszlo Sandor was prospecting for oil on a large scale.

Hoping to attract the necessary funding to continue his work, he published a book in London in 1873 with the intriguing title *The Sandor Petroleum Regions of the Center of European Russia* [*Shandorovskiye neftyanyye rayony tsentra Yevropeyskoy Rossii*], in which he pointed out that competition against American oil—at the time American kerosene still dominated the Russian oil market—would benefit the Russian oil industry, but only once a deposit close to the main regions of Russian domestic consumption and convenient water arteries was brought into operation.

On the basis of work already done by Russian geologists, Laszlo Sandor concluded that such a deposit might exist in a completely new oil-bearing province, which he had earlier given the grandiloquent name of "Sandor" and which was located along the Volga only about 62 miles from the Kama River: "I cannot be absolutely, precisely certain of the ultimate success of the matter, but the first results have exceeded my most optimistic expectations," he wrote in his book.

Laszlo Sandor proposed that this oil-bearing province could be expected to play a much larger role for the Russian Empire than the traditional Absheron Peninsula region. His visit to the Baku oil fields gave him the impression that they were almost as rich in petroleum as the American oil fields in Pennsylvania. However, Sandor noted in his book: "Transportation between Baku and the capital of the Russian Empire is very difficult and unreliable, since the route from Baku to Astrakhan, which passes, in particular, across the mouth of the Volga, frequently dries up almost completely, and transportation from Astrakhan to Saratov involves similar complications." As such, transportation of oil up the Volga from Baku was a very expensive undertaking: significant amounts of steam and horse power were required, and *burlaks*[38] as well. He felt that the route from Saratov to St. Petersburg was easier.

Laszlo Sandor believed that a serious obstacle to efficient and profitable oil production on the Absheron Peninsula was the lack of sufficient construction timber in the South of the Russian Empire. Wood was required both for drilling derricks and for producing oil barrels, and was readily available in the Saratov, Samara, and Kazan provinces, from which large quantities were exported, especially to England. Sandor also thought that shipping the iron barrel hoops, potash, and sulfuric acid required for oil production down the Volga to Baku was overly expensive. In contrast, the bold American entrepreneur felt that the "Sandor petroleum province" did not suffer any of these shortcomings.

Sandor rented around 350,000 acres of land from various private landowners and serf communes for his oil prospecting work, which began in the valleys of the Sheshma and Sok Rivers. At the village of Shugurovo in the Bugulma District (the former Nadyr *Volost*), on the right bank of the Sheshma River, two wells were drilled 1,400 feet apart on a line parallel to the course of the river on the slope of the bank (close to the location of a present-day petroleum bitumen plant). The wellheads were located 119 feet above the Sheshma water level—Well 1 was 833 feet deep, and Well 2 went down 140 feet. In Sarabikulovo, Sandor located a well on a shelf, in an area reminiscent of a spacious terrace artificially constructed for this purpose. This well reached a depth of 669 feet. Wells were also drilled in the Sok River Valley (two wells on the right bank of the Volga, opposite Samara). In order to bring his exploration to a definitive result, Laszlo Sandor ordered one of the wells drilled as deep as possible. The well selected for this purpose was Shugurovo Well 1, in which work continued until April 1877. A weak emission of gas began at a depth of 797 feet and the cuttings removed from the well were saturated with oil. However, when the well was deepened to 833 feet, gas emission intensified, accompanied by a loud noise. Concerned that oil might explode in a gusher, Laszlo Sandor stopped further drilling.

At the end of his report to the Mining Department in April 1877 on the results of his oil prospecting, Laszlo Sandor wrote: "All my investigations were crowned with complete success.… Rich, inexhaustible underground basins of liquid petroleum are contained in the valleys of the Sok and Sheshma Rivers, to the northeast of Samara, and also in the Samara and Bugulma Districts. There are huge numbers of fields of oil-saturated earth at the villages of Shugurovo and Sarabikulovo."

After studying Sandor's report, Fëdor Raselli, director of the Mining Department, sent mining engineer Yakov Weitzenbreyer and engineer Aleksey Sivkov to the region to study the issue firsthand. In their report of June 4, 1877, they confirmed the signs of oil in the region where Sandor's work had been carried out: "We feel that the sulfur gases that come out in many places here, as well as the seepage of petroleum onto the ground surface and the large deposits of asphalt encountered everywhere here, serve as reliable signs that these places are an area of rich underground oil basins."

Unfortunately, Sandor's work was not continued: a shortage of funding prevented him from drilling to a greater depth and reaching the desired deposits of Devonian petroleum. However, despite the ultimate failure of his undertaking, Laszlo Sandor's undeniable achievements include the first wide-scale deep exploratory drilling in the Volga–Urals region and his identification of the region as promising for the industrial production of oil. He should also be credited with substantially expanding the production of bituminous rocks close to Shugurovo and even establishing a tar factory that was rather large-scale for its time and whose production was in demand by the local population.

The Fight against the Kerosene Excise Tax

By the mid-1870s, it was clear that the quantity of oil produced exceeded the capability of Russia's domestic market to absorb it—or in terms of economic theory, supply began to outpace demand. Many economists attributed this to the system of excise taxation of kerosene production, introduced at the same time the tax-farming system was abolished, on January 1, 1873.

The kerosene excise tax was not very effective and suffered from numerous imperfections from the very beginning. It was not just complicated, but artificially overcomplicated, which made it inconvenient for both the tax agencies and the oil industry. Worse, the kerosene excise tax brought little revenue to the Russian imperial treasury. During the five years it remained in effect, it provided the treasury with only 1,246,000 [rubles], while leasing of oil and gas sections on the Absheron Peninsula and the customs duty imposed on American kerosene totaled 20,879,000 [rubles], i.e., almost 17 times more.

The amount of excise tax depended on the capacity of the distilling vat. It initially seemed to government bureaucrats that such a method of calculating the quantity of kerosene would simplify the tax, as vats with capacities of up to 677 gallons were taxed at 4 kopecks per 3.3 gallons [per day], while larger vats were taxed at 10 rubles per vat per day. It was believed that oil distillation in vats with capacities of 9.6–12 barrels should take 30 hours, of which oil filling and distillation would take 17 hours and cooling 13 hours. Oil distillation in vats with capacity over 12 barrels would take several days. The kerosene yield was determined to be 40% of the volume of oil.

It was soon discovered, however, that the excise tax bureaucrats had misjudged the length of a complete oil distillation cycle. The kerosene yield from oil did not exceed 30%, and the production cycle in small vats did not match those of the large vats.

It also turned out that the refiners, in their natural desire to pay less excise tax, tried to distill as much kerosene per day as possible. This practice could not help but affect quality, as it pushed the production process outside its normal sphere of operations. Distilling vats at most refining stills were small, with capacities of 12–24 barrels of crude, while the refineries themselves consisted of three sections: distilling, cooling and purifying. The vat itself was cemented into a base in which a furnace was constructed, and workers added buckets of oil from time to time. The resulting kerosene was drained off into containers and transported to the port. With such technology, the Baku kerosene was not of high quality. It burned poorly and produced a lot of soot, so housewives, especially those in the cities, preferred American kerosene.

But even such a primitive kerosene production "process" was very often violated. Once factory owners understood the flaws of excise taxation, oil distillation was accelerated in an attempt to outperform the excise tax standard and thus remain profitable, but in so doing an even lower quality of kerosene was produced. Owners contrived to carry out four to 10 cycles per day. Under forced distillation, vats often overheated, so that heavy fractions were distilled while the light ones could not be captured in the condenser and escaped into the air. Frequent explosions and fires also resulted, from which the workers suffered the most, and corruption among excise tax bureaucrats was rampant. Ultimately, the Russian oil industry was driven into a corner, and the flawed kerosene excise tax became a quagmire preventing its further development.

At the suggestion of Actual State Councilor Staroselsky, the governor of Baku, people working in the oil industry elected a committee to prepare specific proposals for overcoming the industry's stagnation. As a result, the committee pointed out that one of the key reasons for the crisis was the unequal distribution of excise tax among refiners, noting in particular that the existing system made any technical improvements in refining equipment impossible and reduced kerosene production. The committee's main conclusion was that the excise tax on produced kerosene had to be eliminated for the industry to develop.

In turn, the Imperial Russian Technical Society (IRTS) took up this most important cause. On January 21, 1876, the IRTS established a committee "On the Oil Excise Tax and Development of the Oil Industry" under the chairmanship of Prince Nikolay Romanovsky, honorary chairman of the IRTS. This committee, which included prominent Russian scientists and industrialists, contributed significantly to the development of the domestic oil business. At the committee's February 11, 1876 meeting, during a discussion of the report by IRTS secretary Fëdor Lvov, Baku Oil Company founder Vasily Kokorev declared: "The liberation of the oil industry from the excise tax and from any constraint connected with it is a step that could really promote its development and one to which the oil industry has a right."[39] Then he stated his profound views regarding the need for complete refining of oil and its residues: "The oil question is an issue of state importance: in addition to photogen used for lighting, oil provides lubricants and dense, so-called residual oil. An enormous fortune's worth of lubricants are now being imported from abroad, whereas our manufacture of them should be an extension of photogen production, utilizing everything that can be recovered from the primary material—that is, crude oil—and it would be completely unjust to impose an excise tax on this byproduct."

In May 1876, the IRTS board sent Professor Dmitry Mendeleyev of St. Petersburg University on a trip to the International Exhibition of Arts, Manufactures and Products of the Soil and Mines in Philadelphia with the specific task of studying the state of affairs in the American oil industry, including finances, and of objectively determining once more the cause of the oil business crisis in Russia. Konon Lisenko, a professor from the Mining Institute, was likewise sent to the Absheron Peninsula for an on-site study of the "grave consequences of the oil excise tax."

Professor Lisenko observed that Baku refiners saddled with the excise tax were unconcerned with either improving oil distillation units or developing other valuable petroleum products on a par with kerosene (e.g., asphalt made of *kir*). He came to the firm conclusion that the photogen excise tax in the form that it was imposed by the February 1, 1872 regulations was a millstone around the neck of the nascent oil industry.

In his turn, Professor Mendeleyev in the United States focused particularly on the taxation system in the American oil industry. An excise tax had also been introduced there from 1862 through 1869, both on crude oil and petroleum products. This was done to cover some of the colossal expenses of the American Civil War. The oil excise tax did provide the US government with an impressive total of $9,000,000 per year, but despite that the country's leadership abolished the excise tax first on exported kerosene, and then on all petroleum products. Moreover, the government began to protect the export of kerosene by returning the customs duties collected on the tin cans in which the kerosene was exported abroad and not collecting customs duties on iron cans (barrels) that were reimported to the United States. The oil excise tax was totally repealed in 1868, during the Reconstruction period.

After returning from America, Mendeleyev compiled a detailed report on his business trip in the form of a corresponding memorandum, which he laid on the desk of Finance Minister Mikhail Reytern. Then, on December 18, 1876, he gave a detailed report at the general meeting of the Imperial Russian Technical Society.

On the whole, both scientists handled their tasks brilliantly, and their books—D. I. Mendeleyev's *The Oil Industry in the American State of Pennsylvania and in the Caucasus* [*Neftyanaya promyshlennost v Severo-Amerikanskom shtate Pensilvaniya i na Kavkaze*] and K. I. Lisenko's *Oil Production* [*Neftyanoye proizvodstvo*]—provided convincing arguments for repealing the excise tax.

The IRTS committee concluded that the most important way to help the Russian oil industry would be to "liberate it from any excise tax for at least 10 years." The Russian government understood this constructive viewpoint and based on the decision of the State Council dated June 6, 1877, which was approved by Emperor Alexander III on the same day, photogen products were exempted from excise and other taxes throughout the Russian Empire effective September 1, 1877.

This meant first of all, a victory for progressive public opinion in the battle against the fetters of excise taxation, and second—and this was more important—freedom for the oil industry from any taxes that would otherwise prevent it from growing stronger and moving forward along the path of free enterprise and fair market competition.

The Russian Oil Business Becomes Competitive

The repeal of the Russian excise tax on photogen (kerosene) production provided a powerful impetus to oil production across all key sectors. While oil production did increase during the five-year period of the excise tax, the accelerated development of the Russian oil industry began in earnest in 1877, with advancements in methods of oil production, transportation, refining and marketing.

Production and technical indicators also show significant progress in the Russian oil industry. The average depth of Baku oil wells doubled from 1878 through 1886, from 301 to 609 feet, with wells being drilled to depths up to 1,120 feet. Another telling sign of the industry's growth was the eight-fold increase in the variety of petroleum products available on the market.

Table 3. Russian Oil Production, 1878–1888
(in barrels and tons)

	Oil Production in Barrels	Oil Production in Tons
1878	2,479,000	372,790
1879	2,829,000	425,415
1880	2,978,000	447,800
1881	4,914,000	738,860
1882	6,202,000	932,545
1883	7,181,000	1,080,000
1884	10,688,000	1,607,000
1885	13,810,000	2,077,000
1886	14,831,000	2,230,000
1887	19,214,000	2,889,000
1888	21,856,000	3,286,000

Source: Stanislav and Ludwig Perschke, *The Russian Oil Industry, Its Development and Current Status in Statistical Data* [*Russkaya neftyanaya promyshlennost, yeyë razvitiye i sovremennoye polozheniye v statisticheskikh dannykh*]. Tiflis (Tbilisi), 1913, pp. 4, 5.

During the excise-free decade, the selling price of domestic kerosene dropped nearly 80%. The price of kerosene on the Tsaritsyn market (which was used to equalize prices elsewhere on the domestic Russian market) was 2.25 rubles per 36 pounds in 1877, dropping to 56 kopecks per 36 pounds in 1885 and 40 kopecks per 36 pounds in 1886. The reduction in the price of kerosene and its distribution throughout virtually all of Russia made it accessible to even the poorest families, who were able to replace the traditional kindling wood with convenient kerosene lamps.

By successfully competing with American kerosene, Russian kerosene began to dominate more and more new foreign markets each year and was readily purchased, both in Europe and Asia. Whereas exports in 1877 totaled only 552,404 barrels, subsequent years saw a steady rise in export shipments, and within 10 years more than 3 million barrels of Russian kerosene were being exported.

This decade of "oil freedom" in Russia was also marked by the emergence of a number of joint-stock oil companies, most of which had previously operated as trust partnerships. This led in turn to stronger competition not only in the oil industry as a whole, but in each of its sectors, i.e., the production, refining, and sale of petroleum products.

Thus, the S. & I. Jakeli & Co. Petroleum Industry and Trading Partnership was founded on July 11, 1880, with a fixed capital of 500,000 rubles, and it soon assumed a deserved place among the leading oil production companies on the Absheron Peninsula.

On July 1, 1883, Emperor Alexander III issued his approval of the bylaws of the Batumi Oil Industrial and Trading Company (BOITC). The founders of this company were the enterprising railroad engineers Sergey Palashkovsky and Andrey Bunge, construction supervisors of the new Baku–Tiflis–Batumi railroad line. Having the foresight to realize that the transportation of oil and petroleum products was the key link in sales operations, they focused their efforts on creating a fleet of railroad tank cars capable of transporting large volumes of Absheron oil from the fields to the seaports. The company's success during its first years of operation demonstrated the wisdom of this decision. In 1884, BOITC handled 200,547 barrels of crude oil and petroleum products, or 44.5% of the total volume of 449,850 barrels exported from Batumi. Such success spurred the founders to go beyond transportation and participate directly in oil production and refining. They leased two parcels in Balakhany, on oil-bearing land belonging to Count Lazarev and Princess Gagarina, and commenced drilling operations. They built four 1,590-ton iron tanks in Batumi: two to store kerosene and one each for lubricants and residual oil (*mazut*). In short order, the company built a well-equipped enterprise for mass production of packaging for petroleum products, with a daily output of 12,000 tin cans. All of this required considerable resources, so the founders urgently appealed to St. Petersburg. On November 16, 1884, Emperor Alexander III issued his approval "On Permitting the Batumi Oil Industrial and Trading Company to Issue Bonds."

Another vertically integrated oil company also appeared during this time. On October 2, 1883 imperial approval was issued for the bylaws of the Neft Petroleum Products Production, Transportation, Storage and

Trading Partnership, having an equity of 2 million rubles. Founded in part by the well-known Russian industrialist Pëtr Gubonin (1825–1894), the company's bylaws outlined its main areas of activity, including "acquiring, establishing, and leasing of refineries, oil pipelines, tanks, moorings, and warehouses for storing petroleum products; acquiring and leasing railroad tank cars, as well as seagoing and inland ships for bulk transportation of petroleum products; trading in petroleum products, and supplying them to steam engines on railroads, steamship lines, and to factories and other trade and industrial enterprises; and opening of offices and agencies everywhere to market petroleum products." Within its first three years of operation, Neft enjoyed robust results: it received 483,000,746 rubles just for the use of its fleet of 1,050 tanker cars for transporting oil and petroleum products, and in 1886 the company recorded a net profit of 60,000,616 rubles.

The activity of the Caspian Partnership Oil Industrial and Trade Company is another example of successful oil entrepreneurship. The company, founded by Pavel Gukasov (1858–1930), along with his brothers Akop, Arshak and Abram, began operations on January 1, 1887, with a fixed capital of 2.5 million rubles. Coming from a Tiflis merchant's family, the Gukasovs had all received a very good education (Pavel, for example, had graduated from the Moscow Commercial Academy and then the Dresden University of Technology).

The Caspian Partnership had started out as a trust with a small refinery in Baku. However, a decisive turn towards modern methods of production control and management, as well as the introduction of advanced equipment, soon brought tangible results for the Partnership. Within five years, the company was operating at three oil fields on the Absheron Peninsula, and by 1891 it was operating 18 wells in Balakhany, along with 18 steam engines (total power 236 horsepower) and 14 steam pumps, producing a total of 556,127 barrels of oil that year. At Sabunchu, the Caspian Partnership had 15 productive wells and was drilling six more, and was operating 21 steam engines with a total power of 295 horsepower, along with 28 steam pumps, all told producing a total of 2,127,839 barrels of oil that year. Also in 1891, a total of 6,897 barrels of oil were produced by a single drilled well operated at Romanino field. Overall, the company produced 2,690,883 barrels of oil in 1891, or 7.7% of the total oil production of the Absheron Peninsula. The company's refinery also produced 652,078 barrels of lighting oils (various types of kerosene), amounting to 6.7% of the total production of kerosene at Baku refineries. This level of output was sustained over the next decade: in 1900 the Caspian Partnership produced 4,517,229 barrels of oil, amounting to 6.2% of the entire oil production of the Absheron Peninsula.

In addition to the aforementioned companies, other entrepreneurs made significant contributions to the development of the oil industry on the

Absheron Peninsula, thus helping to secure Russia's competitive position in world markets. These included such major companies as Mirzoyev Bros. & Co. Partnership, G. M. Lianozov & Sons Oil Production Partnership, Pitoyev & Co. Partnership, I. A. Yegiazarov & Co. Oil Industry Company, A. I. Mantashev & Co. Oil Industrial and Trading Company, Aramazd Petroleum Industry and Trading Company, Aral-Caspian Company, and the Ararat, Massi, Astkhik, and Syunik partnerships.

Russian Oil in the Eyes of a Briton

Oil producers around the world could not help but react to Russia's appearance among the leading players on the European and world markets in the last quarter of the 19th century. Some companies, such as the American transnational Standard Oil Company, recognized Russia as a real threat to their monopoly on the world kerosene market and reacted immediately with strong competitive countermeasures, making use of all possible means and methods.

At the same time, there were also consistent proponents of mutually advantageous business cooperation with Russia, one of whom was the renowned British columnist Charles Thomas Marvin (1854–1890), a native of the city of Plumstead, Kent, who lived a short but rich life. As a correspondent for *The Globe*, he visited Russia several times, including its oil regions, went to Central Asia, became acquainted with the prominent Russian military figures General Mikhail Skobelev (1843–1882) and General Nikolay Ignatyev (1832–1908), and was a well-known expert on Russian-British relations.

Charles Marvin was also a prolific writer and his literary work was widely known. In 1878 he published the book *Our Public Offices, Embodying an Account of the Disclosure of the Anglo-Russian Treaty of 31 May*. During the Russo-Turkish War of 1877–1878 he published 20 pamphlets of various kinds, and in 1880 he published a book on Russo-Indian relations, *The Eye-witnesses' Account of the Disastrous Campaign against Akhal Tekke Turcomans*, which was even recommended in Russia for military libraries, and had commentaries written about it by General Mikhail Skobelev himself.

Charles Marvin's first study on oil, *The Region of Eternal Fire: an Account of a Journey to Petroleum Region of the Caspian*, came out in 1884. In subsequent years he wrote several books on the problems of the Caspian and Central Asian regions. His most famous work, *The Russians at the Gate of Herat*, was written in 1885 and published soon thereafter with a total print run exceeding 65,000 copies.

The London *Evening News* wrote the following about him: "Charles Marvin has already published 12 books and pamphlets on Central Asia containing 300 printed sheets and over 100 maps and illustrations. This is not bad for an author who is only 30 years old, especially if you note that all of his books have come out since 1879, and that during this time he made four trips to Russia and also wrote hundreds of articles." The Russian newspaper *Kavkaz* (Tiflis) echoed the British publication: "Charles Marvin is a remarkable traveler and a great writer on issues of the policy of Russia and England in the East."

Charles Marvin made his first visit to the oil-bearing regions of the Transcaucasus for in 1883. His first impression was fairly reserved: "The train landed us at a demolished, small shanty station in the middle of the desert, placing us with our great apprehensions in the hands of a Tatar, the driver of a phaeton." But his pessimism soon gave way to positive impressions and surprises: "Baku in fact literally enchanted me." In subsequent books, he continually noted how Baku had grown and become more attractive. He called it the "oil breadbasket of Europe," due to the active development of the oil fields. Charles Marvin naturally compared the volumes of production of Baku oil fields with Great Britain's indicators, in particular, on the recovery of whale oil. The Briton stated with surprise that in the entire 1886 season, 44 whaling ships had recovered 20,307 barrels of whale oil, yet this "quantity corresponds to the entire daily standard output of just one oil well in Baku." The British columnist also cited the words of a certain Captain Grey, who—no longer seeing the possibility of the return of advantageous prices for whale oil—was ready to "set up transporting bulk petrol."[40]

Marvin was astonished by the growing volume of oil production in the region and indicated that even the oil-bearing regions of the United States could not compete with the Baku oil fields. As if foreseeing the future oil triumph of Russia, he commented that "America's song is sung. It has nothing in this regard that could parallel the current productivity of Russia. The wells of the brothers Nobel and Company have yielded enormous quantities of oil. Many of these wells have been closed down so as not to give away the oil, which is currently very cheap."[41]

Incidentally, the British consul in Batumi also shared his impressions of Baku at that time: "The amount of oil wealth near the Caspian is so great, and the wells yield so much, that Baku merchants are capable of working and sending raw material to the market, and the issue of depletion should not create fear among people directly or indirectly involved in the Baku oil industry, at least not for many years to come. It is almost painful to observe the total lack of British merchants in Baku."[42]

And here Marvin was in total agreement, calling upon his compatriots to take a more active part in the development of Russia's oil industry. The columnist stressed: "Currently the attention of all the European countries is focused on Baku. If England does not show rapid energy, then not only the Baku, but all oil trade in general will pass right through its hands."[43]

Marvin was especially interested in issues of transporting Russian petroleum products and oil. "The factor that has the most important impact on the past, present and future of the Caspian oil industry is the issue of transportation," the British columnist stressed. The rapidly growing volume of oil and petroleum product exports from the Baku oil fields had already forced the Russian Empire to look for new means of transportation, and he thought that it was precisely in this area that England could become a major supplier to Russia of requisite equipment and transportation services.

To start with, Marvin urged the British companies to participate in the competition announced by the Russian government to build an oil pipeline 600 miles long, a massive endeavor for the time. The enterprise promised significant financial gains since the oil pipeline, whose capacity was to be 160 million gallons per year, was to be licensed under concession for 20 years. Considering that priority in this matter was given to European companies, England stood a good chance, especially given the prior experience of British firms in building pipelines in Russia.

Next, Marvin pushed for British companies to invest in the railroad sector. In one of his works, the British writer indicated that "what is really necessary for expansion of this export is an increase in the quantity of railroad rolling stock." Moreover, the Russian government was already planning to build a 10-million-ruble tunnel through the Surami mountain pass to reduce transportation distance and lower its cost.

Finally, he argued that England should take an active part in creating a tanker fleet. The columnist noted that in 1885, ships had hauled 87 million gallons of kerosene, 33,433,220 gallons of oils, 115 million gallons of oil residue, 9 million gallons of crude oil, and 90,000 gallons of gasoline. Marvin believed the primary obstacle to exporting kerosene from Batumi was the rate of tanker vessel construction, which lagged behind oil production.

Citing the successful experience of the Caspian tanker fleet (by the mid-1880s, 100 tankers were already operating in the Caspian Sea), the columnist argued that this type of oil transportation also had a great future in the oceans. Transportation of bulk kerosene on European waters was soon made possible by the Black Sea Steamship Line Company. In June 1886, after surviving a storm in the Bay of Biscay, the Swedish-built steamship *Svet* delivered 1,875 tons of kerosene to the very heart of the British Empire, London. Charles Marvin wrote in this regard: "The arrival of the steamship with a cargo of over half a million gallons of kerosene stored in tanks, not in barrels… silenced those who doubted the possibility of carrying out this task."[44]

Marvin was likewise interested in the issue of the status and sales prospects of Russian petroleum products in Europe. In 1883, after displacing American kerosene in the domestic market, Russian kerosene gradually began to gain European and world market share. Charles Marvin was one of the active proponents of importing shipments of Russian petroleum products to the British Empire instead of American ones. He emphasized that the Baku "refineries produce the best lamp kerosene for only 3 farthings per gallon instead of a wholesale price of over 6 pence (eight times higher) for the same quantity of American kerosene in London!"[45] In addition, he lauded the Russian kerosene's superior physical properties: it was essentially odorless, with a very clear color and higher ignition temperature (which was especially important for the British Crown Indian territories, with their hot climate).

"The highest grades of Russian kerosene have become famous so quickly that in the near future they will be valued above the American," wrote Charles Marvin. "There is no place in Europe to which Russian kerosene could not be transported today."[46] He urged British plants (in Birmingham, in particular) to produce lamps for Russian kerosene, since most lamps adapted for the transoceanic product were not suitable for use with the denser Russian counterpart.

The columnist also focused on the excellent properties of Russian lubricants, which were superior in quality to American and Scottish products. To confirm this, Charles Marvin cited the assessment of the prominent chemist, Boverton Redwood (1846–1919): "Russian lubricating oil is characterized by considerable fluidity compared to its specific weight; it does not thicken at low temperature and does not precipitate paraffin wax."

He was also very impressed by Russia's active use of residual oil or *mazut* as liquid fuel. This effective replacement for coal was used at that time by 250 bulk and passenger steamships, several hundred locomotives and more than 1,000 steam stationary engines.

In summarizing his discussions regarding the future of Russia's oil regions, Charles Marvin wrote: "The obstacles that hampered the oil business and held up the striving of petroleum products to leave the Caspian coast are breaking apart, and the time is not far off when all of Europe will be flooded with cheap Baku kerosene." The Briton, looking forward to the unlimited horizons of oil cooperation between England and Russia, stressed in particular that "a vast field is opening up for trade in supplying an enormous region with lamps, kerosene kitchens, oil pipelines, every manner of portable mechanisms, as well as bulk tank cars and tanks for storing kerosene and other objects, the need for which is caused by the developing oil field," and that "England should not miss the chance to seize at least some of the trade sectors that will result from oil industry development in Baku."[47]

The appeals of Charles Marvin and his like-minded supporters for the active development of an Anglo-Russian energy dialogue did not fall on deaf ears within the government of Great Britain or among entrepreneurs in both countries, and by the beginning of the 20th century Great Britain had taken over first place on the export list of Russian oil industrialists.

Viktor Ragozin's Oleonaphthas

The frenzied development of Russian industry, as well as railway, river, and sea transportation, required not only fuel, but also large quantities of quality lubricants. As a rule, foreign lubricants imported into Russia were of low quality and were actually made from substitutes. At best, they consisted of petroleum material mixed with vegetable oils and animal fat with gutta-percha added.

Russian engineers and entrepreneurs soon began to search for alternatives to foreign lubricants and throughout the country—in the Kuban, in the Crimea, in a series of provinces of central Russia—efforts were undertaken to create high-quality lubricants. Despite these efforts, however, production volumes remained relatively small, and it soon became clear that a fundamentally new approach was needed.

Such a breakthrough in the manufacturing technology of oils occurred in the center of Russia, in Nizhny Novgorod Province, when the Russian entrepreneur Viktor Ragozin (1833–1901) began producing lubricants on an industrial scale. A graduate of Moscow University, Ragozin began his first experiments in 1873 in a laboratory set up in his apartment in Nizhny Novgorod. The results of his work decomposing oil residue over the course of the two years gave him the knowledge and confidence to take his research to the next level.

In early 1874, Viktor Ragozin wrote a letter to Russian Finance Minister Mikhail Reytern, in which he laid out his plans for experimental research on obtaining lubricating oil under factory conditions using a new type of equipment. The matter reached Alexander II, and on November 6, 1874, the emperor issued his "Highest Order on the Performance of Experiments at Retooled Photogen Refineries," which stated the following: "According to the most humble report of the minister of finance on the petition of Nizhny Novgorod merchant Ragozin to give him permission to build a temporary photogen refinery that would not have any distillation stills at all, but instead would have chambers of a special type in which oil would decompose from the action of heat; where the goal of this is to test a new method of preparing kerosene, in particular, lubricating oil from petroleum."

In 1875, Viktor Ragozin built a pilot refinery in Nizhny Novgorod, located on the bank of the Volga beyond the steamship landing. It was here that he definitively developed the technology of preparing lubricating oil from residual oil (*mazut*) using superheated steam. At the end of the same year, he received a favorable review concerning the quality of his lubricants from the well-known Russian chemist Professor Fëdor Beilstein. This prompted him to set up a modern new refinery for large-scale industrial production of lubricants in the small city of Balakhna located 25 miles from Nizhny Novgorod.

The Balakhna refinery, put into operation at the beginning of 1878, was producing at least 12,000 barrels of lubricants a year using a technological process that was completely new at that time. The process involved first heating the residual oil to 572°F, then passing superheated steam through it; this steam carried the oil fractions with it into a condenser, where they separated from the water.

The lubricants produced using this method—Viktor Ragozin's "oleonaphthas"—were exhibited at the 1878 Exposition Universelle de Paris, where they met with great success, winning a gold medal.

In the same year, large batches of Russian "oleonaphthas" were delivered to France for more than 700,000 francs. Just two years later, practically the entire French navy had switched to the exclusive use of Ragozin's "petroleum oils."

In Russia itself, these lubricants were evaluated for use on railway transportation. A commission led by the well-known tribologist Professor Nikolay Petrov gave them high marks. The use of the Balakhna "oil tar" reduced the consumption of coal by one-third, and increased the operating distance of railroad car axles by a factor of eight.

The growing demand for lubricants prompted Viktor Ragozin to expand his production facilities. In 1879, a new, large-scale refinery was put into operation in the village of Konstantinovo near Yaroslavl. In its first year of operation, it produced 68,450 barrels of spindle, machine, and railroad car oil along with a wide assortment of kerosene and other refined products. Initially, the V. I. Ragozin & Co. Partnership's refineries produced four grades of lubricant: spindle, machine, and winter and summer variants of railway car oil. The list of finished products was soon expanded to include other grades of oil: cylinder oil, diesel fuel, etc. In 1879, the Konstantinovo refinery was producing 68,450 barrels of product worth 1.4 million rubles.

The V. I. Ragozin & Co. Partnership, which was formed in 1880, had scientific research laboratories in Moscow, Paris, and London, where chemical specialists carried out experiments and tested heavy refining products. Viktor Ragozin explained that: "Once I had set up the new processing of oil, I wanted to give my work a scientific foundation and consulted Russian and foreign chemists. I had Mendeleyev, Markovnikov, and Schulenberg from the College de France working in my laboratories. This work lasted for years."

For Viktor Ragozin's services to the domestic oil industry, the Scholarly Council of the St. Petersburg Technological Institute bestowed the honorary title of production engineer on him in 1888.

The Russian newspaper *Neftyanoye delo* ["The Oil Business"] wrote that "the Konstantinovo refinery occupies first place, in terms of both the quantity of refined product and the character of the fractionated distillates." The influential American publication *Engineering* seemed to echo the Russian press indirectly when it said that "concerning lubricating oils, there cannot be any doubt that the Russian product has enormous advantages over the American one.... Russian oils withstand the very strictest tests and have remarkably high viscosity relative to their specific gravity." Perhaps the highest form of praise came from the American oil industry's use of the slogan "just like Russian lubricants" on the packaging of their products.

The success of Viktor Ragozin's operations was very inspiring for other Russian industrialists as well. New refineries began to appear in Russia that were oriented toward the output of lubricants. In 1879, Russia had 19 such specialized refineries. All of this allowed a sharp increase in the export of lubricants. For instance, in 1881, exports to France alone amounted to 3.7 million francs, or five times more than just three years earlier.

By 1884, Russia was producing 407,098 barrels of lubricants from oil residues. Such an increase in domestic production had a dramatic effect in monetary terms as well: from 1864–1872, Russia spent 35 million rubles on imports of lubricating oil, while in 1897 alone the value of Russian exports of lubricants totaled well over 45 million rubles.

Unfortunately, due to growing competition on the Russian market for lubricants, Viktor Ragozin struggled to stay on top, making serious financial and credit policy miscalculations that led to a sharp deterioration in the company's financial condition, which in turn prompted the company's shareholders to remove him from leadership of the company. Subsequently, he went to work for the S. I. Shibayev & Co. Partnership for Production of Russian Mineral Oils and Other Chemical Products, where he found success in organizing efficient production of high-quality lubricants at a refinery in Baku. His Baku product went on to receive high awards at all-Russian and international exhibitions on more than one occasion.

The First Oil Exhibition

The results achieved in Russia by the end of the decade of "oil freedom" were very impressive and beneficial for the government, the scientific community, and Russian society as a whole. The country's production of oil grew nearly eight-fold, from 2.5 million barrels in 1878 to 19 million barrels in 1887.

Thus, it was quite natural that an important event in the history of the Russian oil industry would occur in early 1888: The first international Exhibition of Lighting and Oil Production.

Organized by the Imperial Russian Technical Society, the exhibition's Organizing Committee was headed by Actual State Councilor Pëtr Kochubey (1825–1892), who was also the chairman of the IRTS. The exhibition's opening ceremony took place on January 21, 1888 at the Society's exhibition complex on Panteleymonovskaya Street in Solyanoy gorodok, a part of what is now St. Petersburg. According to the Organizing Committee's records, the ceremony was attended by most of the exhibition's 540 participants, who had come from 40 different countries.

At that time there were no exhibitions anywhere in the world like the St. Petersburg Exhibition of Lighting and Oil Production. It was laid out in several well-designed and clearly organized halls, and consisted of three different parts, all united by the theme of light in the daily life of people.

The inscription outside the exhibit halls reads: "Fire is one of the oldest achievements in mankind's heritage. Starting at the beginning of his conscious existence, having barely begun the struggle for survival, mankind noticed fire in nature and was able to take control of it for his own purposes."

The historical exposition in the first exhibition hall presented methods of lighting from all countries, times, and peoples: from the lamps of Ancient Rome and the tar torches of the French Middle Ages, all the way to an electric lighthouse in New York—the Statue of Liberty—which had opened a year before the exhibition.

A St. Petersburg newspaper described the beginning of this exposition in very picturesque terms: "Before us, a fire-breathing mountain, a forest fire, peat burning within the earth, columns of flaming oil gushing out of the earth in a fountain; these gave the primitive savage the idea of the power of fire, which crushes the darkness of night, filling the cave, ravine, dugout, or hut where he lives and works with light that would replace the Sun, Moon, and stars."[48]

A prominent place in the displays was given to Ancient Roman lamps made of fired clay with images of Jupiter, Juno, Eros, and Mars, which were found in excavations close to Rome on the Appian Way and Via Latina, in Ostia, Pompeii, and elsewhere. These were followed by a sanctuary lamp with a monogram of Christ (a copy of a specimen surviving in the Vatican), dated to the first centuries of the Christian Era. An observer from one St. Petersburg publication noted with delight: "The exhibition, which is technical both in name and in content, has become an attraction for everyone interested in the history of human civilization. The organizers have made an attempt, completely in the spirit of Jules Verne, to present the path of development of lighting objects in visual terms, beginning with the pre-Christian Era."[49]

The exposition would not have been complete without Russian antiquities of the 15th–17th centuries. These included the Korsun chandelier: the Candle of Veliky Novgorod (a copy of an original surviving in the vestry of Saint Sophia Cathedral in Novgorod), and a copper chandelier in the shape of a cross from Mount Athos.

Literally two steps away from the Russian exhibit, visitors were transported to the world of Central Asia. This exhibit presented a candle holder made of fired clay, which had been found in excavated ruins of buildings from the epoch of Timur in Samarkand, and *charakhs* (lamps) from Khujand and Samarkand made of cast iron and clay and covered with green glaze. A bronze candlestick with an ornamental design and a relief image of dragons was brought from China, and another was brought from Japan in the shape of a crane on a tortoise, along with picturesque silk lanterns and wax candles with a relief pattern.

The organizers of the exhibition understood that a demonstration of the importance of light in the history of mankind should not be limited to just exhibits, no matter how unique they might be. Thus, they commissioned the artist Pavel Grigoryev to paint pictures exclusively for the exhibition, illustrating key moments in the history of lighting based on documents surviving in the Imperial Public Library. Visitors were presented with a series of majestic canvases whose subjects included fire worshippers in Baku in 500 years BCE; vestal virgins (protectors of the fire) in Ancient Rome; Kamchadals starting fire by rubbing wood; the Colossus of Rhodes; and a night patrol with a lantern in Ancient Egypt.

The second section of the exhibition had a clear scientific and educational orientation, one aimed at making the technology behind various lighting methods accessible to the general public. Educational exhibits from Russia's higher and secondary educational institutions invariably attracted the attention of visitors. The organizers also commissioned educational exhibits expressly for the exhibition: lamps of the French inventors Argand, Carcel, and Franchot, housed in glass shells to demonstrate their internal structure: one depicting the constant flow of lighting oil and a circular burner (end of the 18th century); one with a clock mechanism and a pump (19th century); and a moderator lamp with a spiral spring and an equalizing moving flow tube (19th century). Each exhibit was also accompanied by a large-scale sketch of the lamp to explain the various parts of the design.

The third section of the exhibition was devoted to the commercial and industrial sector, and provided an opportunity for Russian and foreign entrepreneurs to promote their companies and products. Competition among the exhibitors was fierce, with each company presenting various collections of petroleum and products made from it, pointing out in detail their consumer and technical characteristics, e.g., specific gravity, flash point and ignition temperature, color, rate of outflow, the results of fractional distillation, specimens of waste, etc.

For example, the V. I. Ragozin & Co. Partnership presented lubricants of excellent quality, as well as kerosene and products of heavy refining, including oil and gas tar. The refining plant of the Russian-American Petroleum Production Partnership (Kuskovo, Moscow Province) presented their crude oil and an assortment of products refined from it: gasoline, kerosene (American and Russian); oils of various thicknesses: lubricants, perfume oil, gas oil; oil residues, tar, artificial asphalt, sulfuric acid, and much more.

An expert committee headed by production engineer Stepan Gulishambarov felt that the most successful exposition at the exhibition was that of the Administration for Mining in the Caucasus, which presented information on the potential for the oil industry in the entire region. Their display included a geologic collection of rocks forming the Absheron Peninsula, samples of oil from the North Caucasus, a structural model of a well, geologic maps and drawings, and photographs of gushers on the fields of the Nobel Brothers Petroleum Production Partnership.

Also included at the exhibition was a separate building for kerosene lamps, including a special section for filling them with kerosene. Special attention was devoted to showing the latest designs of portable kerosene lanterns for agriculture. An important requirement placed on all designs by the exhibition jury concerned safety from fire, including the design's reliability and absence of cinder, soot, and unpleasant odors when burning. Another big draw at the exhibition were displays concerning lighthouses, which were considered the latest manifestation of progress in lighting technologies at that time.

Military visitors were invariably attracted to the displays of instruments from the Main Hydrographic Administration of the Maritime Ministry. In particular, the optical apparatus with gasoline burners for lighting buoys, a lamp with pressure pistons, Argand lamps, Captain Seleznëv's differential regulating apparatus, the beacon apparatus of the Upper Nikolayevsky lighthouse in Kronstadt, and the best spherical reflector of its time.

A section that was very popular with the public was the one presenting machines and mechanisms intended to produce and use electricity: dynamo machines (designed by Siemens & Halske, Schuckert, and the Bogdanov and Kon electrical shop), gas, kerosene, and oil engines, tachometers, and a rheostat. A novelty was the Otto system's two-cylinder gas engine, especially equipped for electrical lighting.

As for Russian and foreign specialists, there were many new products and ideas for them to discover at the various exhibits, particularly those featuring equipment for producing crude oil and petroleum products and new drilling instruments. Booths were also available for comparative testing of lubricants and other objects of oil production. Furthermore, the exhibition opened up numerous new possibilities for Russian industrialists to learn more about the European oil market and petroleum products.

Overall, the Exhibition was deemed a great success and was discussed for several years in the Russian scientific and engineering community after the closing ceremony on April 13, 1888. Commenting on its results in an article in the journal *Zapiski Imperatorskogo Russkogo tekhnicheskogo obshchestva* ["Transactions of the Imperial Russian Technical Society"], Pëtr Kochubey, chairman of the Society's governing board, noted that: "It is difficult to assess the importance of this exhibition, which without doubt went beyond the merely scientific or industrial. Russian industry demonstrated to the whole world its readiness to cooperate, its readiness to adopt all the best achievements. One would like to hope that Russia will soon be able to occupy its deserved place among the advanced powers producing and trading products of oil production."

Likewise, leading scientific and technical publications concluded that, at the 1888 St. Petersburg Fair, Russian industry was able to demonstrate not only its high potential in the world's oil contingent, but also its leading role in several technical and technological advancements in the industry. By all accounts, this exhibition should be considered one of the outstanding events in the development of world petroleum science and technology of the last quarter of the 19th century.

Medals from Two Emperors

In terms of domestic production, one company in particular took the lead both in terms of technical achievements and sheer output—the Nobel Brothers Petroleum Production Partnership. While inspecting the Absheron Peninsula in October 1888, Emperor Alexander III visited Nobel Brothers' fields and was greatly impressed by the scope of the operations and by the exemplary organization of oil production. It was not on a whim that he expressed certainty that the company would soon make itself known in other countries as well, and a month later, the head of the company, Emanuel Nobel, was awarded a high medal: the order of St. Stanislav, 3rd degree.

Further acknowledgment of the company's growing authority in the industry came during the 1889 World's Fair in Paris, where the Nobel Brothers Petroleum Production Partnership was awarded not one, but two of the highest medals—the Grand Prix. The Nobel Brothers Partnership became the only Russian company to receive two medals: one in class 41, "Mining and Metallurgy," and one in class 45, "Chemical and Pharmaceutical Products."

As head of the company, Emanuel Nobel set himself the goal of following the course set by his father, which was aimed at doing everything possible to consolidate the company's position inside the country and to gain a solid position on the world market. First, to silence critics who thought of him as a "representative of foreign capital," he became a Russian citizen in 1889. Yet, the first two years of his leadership were still a serious challenge for Nobel. He was judged by everyone, and was constantly compared to his father. But soon the company's personnel, which numbered many thousands, came to feel that the helm was in good hands. Further evidence of the growing trust in Emanuel's abilities is provided in a 1890 letter from his Uncle Alfred, "the dynamite king," who, after having assessed the results of the first two years of Emanuel's activity, exclaimed that: "I do not like compliments, but I must say that I am struck by how you have managed to cope with the most important matters. Well done, my nephew!"

Emanuel truly was worthy of such compliments. A talented manager who carried on his father's work, he did all he could not only to turn the Nobel Brothers Petroleum Production Partnership into a leader in the Russian oil industry, but also to bring it onto the world market, where it would compete with such companies as America's Standard Oil.

The company's output likewise speaks to Emanuel's success as a manager. In 1890, the Nobel Brothers Petroleum Production Partnership produced 5.4 million barrels of oil and refined 2 million barrels of kerosene, of which it exported more than 1 million barrels of kerosene, or more than 2.5 times more than in 1887 (408,300 barrels).

Table 4. Russian Oil Production, 1889–1892
(in barrels and tons)

	Oil Production in Barrels	Oil Production in Tons
1889	23,057,000	3,467,000
1890	27,140,000	4,081,000
1891	32,904,000	4,950,000
1892	34,405,000	5,169,000

Source: Stanislav and Ludwig Perschke, *The Russian Oil Industry, Its Development and Current Status in Statistical Data* [*Russkaya neftyanaya promyshlennost, yeyё razvitiye i sovremennoye polozheniye v statisticheskikh dannykh*]. Tiflis (Tbilisi), 1913, pp. 4, 5.

In 1893, the company participated in the Chicago World's Columbian Exposition, dedicated to the 400th anniversary of the discovery of America by Christopher Columbus. In the US, the Nobel company was awarded an honorary diploma and a bronze medal at the Columbus fair. The Nobel Brothers Petroleum Production Partnership also received high awards at international exhibitions in Lyon (1894) and Antwerp (1894).

The company's achievements were also given significant recognition at the All-Russia Industrial and Art Exhibition in Nizhny Novgorod in 1896. The Nobel Brothers Partnership was awarded the highest medal at the Exhibition, giving it the right to depict the state coat of arms "for exemplary plant organization, constant striving to perfect the production of excellent-quality petroleum products on an extremely large scale, using all materials and waste, introducing safe kerosene, organizing transportation and sale inside the Empire and in other countries, and caring for employees and workers."[50] Moreover, the Ludvig Nobel machine-building plant was awarded this same high medal "for extensive and good organization of work, perfecting implements for burning oil, the high quality of machines, and a considerate relationship with workers."[51] Incidentally, the machine-building plant's exhibit also presented wind engines of an original design, along with other machines and equipment. The operations and production of the Nobel Brothers Partnership impressed a correspondent for the journal *Tekhnicheskoye obrazovaniye* ["Technical Education"] so much that in June 1896 he wrote that the company's activity "clearly stood out as a bright spot against the solid dark background of our plant and industrial life."

On July 18, 1896, Emperor Nicholas II visited the company's pavilion and examined the extensive exhibit. The monarch's delight with what he had seen in the company's pavilion was soon embodied in the lines of an imperial decree. For his great contribution to the development of domestic production, Emanuel Nobel was awarded the high rank of councilor of commerce, which gave him the right to wear a special uniform and sword.

In 1899, the Nobel Brothers Partnership reached the height of its oil production; more than 11.2 million barrels, or around 18% of total Russian production and 8.6% of world production. By this time, the company had 135 shareholders, 1,300 field workers operating 304 wells, 195 steam engines, 220 pumps, and five pipelines extending 38 miles. Its average output per well was 65,568 barrels, compared with the national average of 46,474 barrels. The company exported 2,201,933 barrels of kerosene, amounting to 26.6% of total Russian exports. The company's share of total domestic Russian kerosene consumption was 50.1%. In 1899, it produced 23,177 barrels of gasoline, more than all other producers combined. The Nobel Brothers Partnership operated 105 oil storage facilities with 482 tanks between them having a total capacity of around 507,000 tons, and also had 1,237 railroad tank cars at its disposal, and a fleet of 21 tankers and 47 tank barges.

At the turn of the century, the Nobel Brothers Petroleum Production Partnership participated in the 1900 Exposition Universelle de Paris. The company's separate pavilion in Trocadéro Park became one of the Exposition's main attractions, exhibiting the Russian oil industry leader's major achievements over the past 20 years.

The company's technical and technological novelties were lauded in issue no. 5 of the journal *Trudy Bakinskogo otdeleniya IRTO* ["Working

Papers of the Baku Department of the IRTS"] for 1900: "The Nobel Brothers Petroleum Production Partnership was able to give a very clear picture of the oil industry, not only in Baku, but in the world. Next to an excellent map of the temple of fire worshippers in Surakhany is a one-eighth-scale derrick, whose entire mechanism is put into motion by hand. A collection of drilling samples illustrates the strata in the Baku oil region, and an extensive series of glass cylinders containing various products shows the scope of the oil industry. The network of apparatus and the model of a loading schooner are very carefully made. Numerous photos, tables, books, and brochures illustrate the company's numerous successes."

Naturally, the achievements of the Nobel Brothers Petroleum Production Partnership were singled out with the award of the main medal, the Grand Prix of the 1900 Exposition Universelle.

The Nobel Brothers Petroleum Production Partnership's title as leader of the Russian oil industry was solidified by its impressive results in the following years. In 1901, the company produced over 9.6 million barrels of oil in its fields and refined 2.5 million barrels of kerosene, of which 1.5 million barrels were exported.

The Rothschilds and the Russian Oil Business

Russian industry continued to make great strides, and in the last quarter of the 19th century, the output of industrial production grew at a mean annual rate of 8%. In addition, the opening in 1883 of the Transcaucasus Railway, connecting the Baku oil region with the Black Sea port of Batumi, created the shortest and cheapest possible route for Russian petroleum products to reach foreign markets. In light of such developments, Russia started to present significant interest for foreign investors. It was at this time that a company belonging to the Paris banking house of the powerful Rothschild family began to play an important role in the development of oil exports in Russia.

As fate would have it, the main placement of a bond issue for the Russian Batumi Oil Industrial and Trading Company (BOITC) was taking place in France. Before long, practically all of these bonds were under the control of the Paris banking house of the Rothschild family, which at that time was already weighing its options regarding entry into the Russian oil business.

At that time, Baron Alphonse James de Rothschild (1827–1905) had been heading the banking house for 16 years. He was a major financier who played an important role in French and world politics. It was he, for example, who organized the payment of France's reparations after its 1871 defeat in the Franco-Prussian War, thereby keeping the government of Adolphe Thiers in power.

A growing sales crisis in the Russian oil industry facilitated implementation of a strategic plan developed in Paris to strengthen the bank's positions in the Russian market. The bank instructed its authorized representative in Russia to take active steps to broaden the production and sales capabilities of the Batumi Oil Industrial and Trading Company and appointed French managers to take the helm.

On July 18, 1885, Emperor Alexander III approved a Committee of Ministers resolution "On Increasing the Fixed Capital of the Batumi Oil Industrial and Trading Company and Renaming It as the Caspian and Black Sea Oil Industrial and Trading Company (*KChNTO*)." The new *KChNTO* inherited a large fleet of railroad tank cars, four iron tanks having a holding capacity of 9,607,038 barrels each in Batumi, a plant that produced tin plate linings for wooden crates and wooden crates for filling and capping kerosene and gasoline in Batumi, a small refinery in Baku, and four operating wells in Balakhany having a mean daily output of around 600,450 barrels.

In government circles, the activity and growing influence of *KChNTO* raised concern. On April 10, 1889, Mikhail Ostrovsky, minister of state properties, wrote a letter to Minister of Finance Ivan Vyshnegradsky, in which he noted that: "Rothschild has had a steadily growing influence on the oil industry in the Absheron Peninsula, influence which has given him almost monopoly control over its future, and he holds many local people working in the oil industry in his powerful hands."

Nevertheless, Rothschild's presence in the Russian oil industry was seen by many as a welcome benefit. For instance, *A Survey of Factories and Plants in the Baku Province* [*Obzor fabrik i zavodov Bakinskoy gubernii*], published in Tiflis in 1890, contained a diametrically opposed assessment of the Rothschild family's Paris banking house's first years: "Many people were impatiently looking forward to Rothschild joining the Baku oil industry, in hopes that, with his capital, he would give a stronger impetus to the entire oil business. At the time, Rothschild's capital was very tempting to many people.... And the appearance of this trading house really did significantly enliven the oil industry. By making broad credit in the tens and hundreds of thousands of rubles available to many entrepreneurs, he helped them out of an extremely difficult situation, and he even saved several from complete ruin."

The clear organization of the production and sales cycle at the Caspian and Black Sea Oil Industrial and Trading Company allowed its foreign exports of kerosene in 1888 to reach 1,921,408 barrels, accounting for 58.6% of all Russian exports. The retooling of the company's refining enterprise with modern equipment likewise led to an increase in its output. In 1888, its refinery produced 300,220 barrels of kerosene, while in 1890, 564,413 barrels of kerosene were being produced there, amounting to 10.8% of the total volume of production on the Absheron Peninsula.

At the end of the 19th century, the company's fixed assets included 99 drilled wells, 130 steam engines, 78 boilers, 84 steam pumps, 28 iron tanks having a total volume of 19.7 million cubic feet, and a six-inch oil pipeline 5.3 miles long, through which more than 3,362,463 barrels of oil was pumped every year. Its fleet of railroad tank cars numbered 100 units. In 1899, the company's fields produced 3,905,982 barrels of oil. Its refinery in Keshle (near Baku) refined 950,256 barrels of kerosene and 2,053,504 barrels of residual oil. In addition to the Absheron Peninsula, the company began to operate on oil-bearing lands in Terek Province and the Kuban.

During this period, the post of chairman of the Board of Directors of *KChNTO* was held by Maurice Ephrussi. The company's directors included: mining engineer Konstantin Skalkovsky (1891–1896), former director of the Mining Department, Prince Georgy Gruzinsky, and financier Arnold Feigl. For a long time, the company's technical director in Baku was production engineer David Landau, father of the 1962 Nobel Physics Laureate Lev Landau (1908–1968), and a member of the USSR Academy of Sciences.

The turn of the century was also marked by all-Russian and international recognition of the Caspian and Black Sea Oil Industrial and Trading Company. It received a gold medal at the 1889 Exposition Universelle de Paris. In 1896, at the All-Russian Industrial and Art Fair in Nizhny Novgorod, the company was awarded a gold medal for "production of petroleum products of very good quality on an extensive scale, and for organizing trade in them on Russian markets." Finally, the company's exhibit at the 1900 Exposition Universelle de Paris received the highest award: the Grand Prix.

The company also took steps to increase the efficiency and influence of its business in the Russian domestic market. To this end, the Rothschild family's Paris banking house joined with the St. Petersburg International Bank to create a new Russian subsidiary—the Mazut Company.

In a letter of June 26, 1897 to the Department of Trade and Manufacturing of the Russian Ministry of Finance, the St. Petersburg International Bank identified the following goals for the new company: "The Mazut Company proposes continuing the work of the Polyak and Sons house involving the transportation, storage, and sale of acquired oil and petroleum products. Moreover, this company plans to expand this line of work, both by enhancing its means of transportation and by setting up its own refineries for refining oil. In the future, the founders also foresee that developing the work of the companies might, depending on the state of the oil market, necessitate expanding the area of operations, without, however, going outside the borders of the Russian Empire."

On March 3, 1898, the charter of the Mazut Petroleum Industry and Trading Company received imperial approval, and the company soon became one of the key players transporting and selling crude oil and petroleum products on the Russian domestic market. In the Caspian Sea alone, it was operating 13 of its own high-speed tankers, and a large fleet of steam tugboats and oil tank barges delivered kerosene and residual oil along the Volga. In short order, Mazut opened offices along the Volga in Nizhny Novgorod, Samara, Tsaritsyn (Volgograd), and Astrakhan, and also in the Baltic States, Belarus, and Poland. In 1903, just five years after it was formed, the Mazut Company concluded an agreement with the Nobel Brothers Petroleum Production Partnership, the leader of the Russian oil industry, and did so on an equal footing. This agreement, which was given the name "Nobmazut" (and, incidentally, bore clear-cut traits of a cartel), was intended to carry out a coordinated trade policy on the country's domestic markets. This soon resulted in a sharp increase in the cartel's share of sales of petroleum products in Russian regions.

The First Grozny Oil Gusher

In addition to developing oil production on the Absheron Peninsula, the Russian government also undertook a series of measures to organize oil prospecting in other regions of the country. Systematic geologic study of the Grozny region in the North Caucasus was begun in the spring of 1890 by mining engineer Afanasy Konshin, who pointed out in his report: "In the Grozny petroleum area it is already now possible to mark several dozen points to start drilling where reliable oil strata should be encountered at a moderate depth." Deposits that he pointed out as promising for industrial development included Grozny, Mamakayev, Benoyev, Dylymov, Chanty-Argun, Isti-Suy, Voznesensk, Bragun, and others.

Geologist Konshin's encouraging forecasts did not escape the attention of several entrepreneurs. In 1892, a drilling crew hired by retired Lieutenant Colonel Aleksandr Rusanovsky began hand drilling an initial well with a diameter of 9 inches, and went down to a depth of 209 feet. However, the drill site had been poorly chosen, without consulting specialists, and the well turned out to be a dry hole. A second well, with a diameter of 2.5 inches and a depth of 342 feet, produced the same disappointing results.

Despite these inauspicious beginnings, the Grozny region did prove to be a boon for the Russian oil industry. The accelerated development of the oil business in Grozny was associated in large part with the activities of Ivan Akhverdov (1850–1902), an entrepreneur from Vladikavkaz who had purchased the right to run oil-bearing lands on a tax-farming basis at the beginning of 1893. From the very first days at his Alkhan-Yurtovsky (Yermolovsky) site, he strove to make maximum use of the lessons learned from developing oil fields on the Absheron Peninsula.

Having visited this field, production engineer Konstantin Tumsky noted in his book *The Grozny Oil Business* [*Groznenskoye neftyanoe delo*] that: "In July 1893, we had an opportunity to familiarize ourselves with the situation of the Grozny oil business, thanks to the kindness of the owner of the fields, Mr. Akhverdov, the director Mr. Gankin, and the engineer [Lev] Baskakov. Travel from the Grozny station of the Petrovskaya branch of the Vladikavkaz Railroad to the oil fields (lying at 43°22' north latitude and 63°10' east longitude) is easy and takes only one hour. Drilling was subcontracted to Mr. Muravyëv, a drilling master from Baku. For drilling a 35-*sazhen* [245-foot] well at the site using his own pipes, tools, machines, and workers, it was agreed that he would receive 11,000 rubles. Further deepening requires new efforts. Percussion-rod drilling is used, as is usual in Baku. The company I. A. Akhverdov & Co. started the first drilled well No. 1 at an unnumbered site at the Alkhan-Yurtovsky (Yermolovsky) village, and steam-powered drilling was begun on June 28, 1893. The well was begun with 14-inch pipes. Below 47 *sazhens* [329 feet], water and petroleum gases began to appear, and from a depth of 61.5 *sazhens* [430.5 feet] signs of petroleum appeared from Karagan sandstone."

Finally, on October 6, 1893, the long-awaited event occurred: from a depth of 430 feet, the well produced the first gusher in the Grozny fields. According to eyewitness accounts: "Once the fountain had quieted down, it gushed 10 *sazhens* [70 feet] above the top of the pipes, with some interruptions." Mining engineer Lev Baskakov immediately sent a telegram to Ivan Akhverdov in Vladikavkaz with only one word: "GUSHER." The first flowing well in Grozny was exploited for almost two decades, until 1902, and it produced a total of around 89,000 tons of oil.

The news of the first Grozny gusher was pivotal in spurring the government to abolish the feudal tax-farming system at the fields of Tersk Region. On May 22, 1894, the "Rules for Oil Fields on the Lands of the Kuban and Tersk Cossack Hosts" were approved. These rules created reasonable terms for the development of oil entrepreneurship on a competitive basis.

On the threshold of this, retired Lieutenant Colonel Aleksandr Rusanovsky founded the first joint-stock company in the Grozny District, the Grozny Petroleum Industry Company, whose charter received imperial approval on January 25, 1894. The company's fixed capital was 800,000 rubles, and it began operations on September 24, 1894.

On August 27, 1895, Well 7 on Parcel 977, which was leased by the merchant Ivan Akhverdov, produced a powerful new gusher at a depth of 462 feet; for the first three days, it produced 120,088 barrels of oil per day. According to eyewitness accounts: "The gusher was of such fearsome force that the roar could be heard and odor of gases could be smelled at a distance of 15 *versts* [9.9 miles]. A column of oil gushed from the twelve-inch pipe to a height of up to 30 *sazhens* [210 feet]. The lack of storage facilities to collect the oil led to the flooding of an enormous territory, including pastures and approach roads, and the formation of large lakes of oil. The derricks of Wells 3 and 6 were hidden under the level of the petroleum." A correspondent of the newspaper *Terskiye vedomosti* ["Tersk Gazette"] described the event as follows: "By September 6, the dam no longer held and crumbled. The oil gushed through the two-*sazhen*-wide [14-foot-wide] breach that formed, and flowed rapidly across the steppe to the Neftyanka River, threatening to go out into the Sunzha River and spoil the water.... The breach in the dam was closed and major reinforcements were made to the embankment; the work involved 200 carts and 400 workers." The newspaper *Kaspiy* ["Caspian"] provided further details of the event: "The height of the dam had already reached 4 *sazhens* [28 feet] and its strength decreased in proportion to the increase in height. On the day before the catastrophe, ominous signs had already appeared in the form of small streams seeping through it, and on September 5, at about 3:30 in the afternoon, the embankment gave way and an enormous stream of oil gushed through the breach that had formed; an enormous waterfall of oil raged, forming a rare sight.... The noise close to the oil fall was so loud that one had to shout to be heard. The oil fall flowed for five hours, weakening slowly."

Nevertheless, despite these formidable consequences, the gusher became a symbolic event for the promising oil-producing region. Mining engineer Yevgeny Yushkin, who was an eyewitness to the event, wrote: "August 27, 1895 was the beginning of an era for the Grozny fields. The gusher in Akhverdov's Well 7 demolished all recent doubts about the vitality of the Grozny oil business." Well 7 continued to flow uncontrollably until the end of 1898, and over three years produced up to 7,205,279 barrels of oil (around 1.1 million tons).

These successes allowed entrepreneur Ivan Akhverdov to take his business to the next level. On April 12, 1896, the charter of the joint-stock company I. A. Akhverdov & Co. Grozny Oil Industrial Company was approved and its fixed capital was 8,812,500 rubles. The new company leased an additional 82.5 acres on the land of Alkhan-Yurtovsky (Yermolovsky) village for a term of 24 years. By the end of 1896, the company was producing nearly 68% of all Grozny oil.

News about the mighty Grozny oil gusher quickly spread through the country. And an ever-increasing number of new joint-stock companies and partnerships quickly began to form in Tersk Region to develop oil fields.

Even the Ukrainian entrepreneurs I. Mantsev, B. Veyser, and D. Margolin decided to try their luck at producing "black gold" on the shores of the Terek River, and in June 1895 they founded the Grozny-

Dnepr Oil Industrial Company, based in downtown Kyiv. The company's fixed capital was 375,000 rubles. According to the results for 1896, 67.9% of Grozny oil was produced by the I. A. Akhverdov & Co. Grozny Oil Industrial Company, 17.9% was produced by the Grozny Petroleum Industry Company, and 1.2% was produced by the Grozny-Dnepr Oil Industrial Company. In 1897, Grozny had three refineries, and in that year they produced petroleum products valued at 750,000 rubles.

The large quantity of Grozny oil being produced demanded prompt resolution of the urgent problem of transporting oil from the oil fields. In September 1895, the first oil pipeline was put into operation at the Grozny fields; it had a diameter of 5 inches and was 7.9 miles long. By January 1898, the fields of Zavodskoy District were connected by five oil pipelines. The Vladikavkaz Railroad Company owned two pipelines with diameters of 5 and 7 inches and a daily capacity of 6,000 and 12,000 barrels, respectively. The I. A. Akhverdov & Co. Grozny Oil Industrial Company had a 9-inch diameter oil pipeline capable of transporting 18,000 barrels daily. One of the remaining two oil pipelines, which had a diameter of 5 inches and a daily capacity of 9,000 barrels, belonged to the partnership A. R. & Co., and the other, which had a diameter of 8 inches and a daily capacity of 18,000 barrels, belonged to the Moscow Oil Industrial Company. The annual combined capacity of the five oil pipelines was estimated at 23 million barrels.

The increased volume of oil production likewise accelerated the development of the refining sector in the Grozny region. On November 10, 1895, a refinery of the I. A. Akhverdov & Co. Grozny Oil Industrial Company was put into operation; it had been built by specialists from the British company Steward Ltd. The refinery comprised five kerosene stills having a volume of 720 barrels, and refined 2,400 barrels of oil per year. In addition, there were two gasoline stills, a pumping station, nine metal tanks, and a generating station on the refinery grounds.

In December 1895, the Uspekh partnership, headed by Grozny merchant Nikolayev, put into operation a refinery designed by engineer A. I. Isakovich. Incidentally, in 1897 this refinery became the first to carry out secondary distillation of the gasoline fraction.

The Vladikavkaz Railroad Company put a refinery into operation in the second half of 1896. It had been designed by the talented inventor Feliks Inchik using the principles of heat regeneration. After visiting the refinery in 1897, Moscow University professor Vladimir Markovnikov made the following assessment: "There is nothing like it in Russia, and such will hardly be found even in foreign countries. It gives the impression of an elegant mechanical toy: Once the spring is wound up, it does everything itself, and it is remarkably regular." Shortly after the refinery was put into operation, it opened the first analytical laboratory in the region and the outstanding scholar Konstantin Kharichkov (1865–1921) was invited from Baku to serve as its director. Kharichkov, a candidate of natural sciences from St. Petersburg University, worked in Grozny for over 13 years, and during this time was able to convert the small laboratory into one of the leading Russian scientific research centers in the field of refining.

In 1901, the Kazbek Syndicate Company put the Nadezhda Refinery into operation. Four years later, Grozny refineries were refining a combined total of more than 3.6 million barrels of oil annually (more than 540,000 tons).

Springheads of Sakhalin Oil

Around the turn of the 20th century, the island of Sakhalin, off the Pacific coast of Siberia, attracted domestic and international attention after explorers regularly stumbled on oil.

The earliest official Russian record of Sakhalin oil dates back to June 6, 1880, when an affluent merchant named Ivanov petitioned the military governor of the Amur Region for the right to develop an oil spring he discovered: "I traced the flow of oil to the tip of North Sakhalin Island where the eastern shore projects into the Sea of Okhotsk. The source is between two mountains, the right called Uragan and the left—Murgun. The small river lying between the mountains is the Okha. These names were learned from indigenous travelers on the island." An official inspecting Ivanov's source in 1886 wrote that "there is an abundance of petroleum... around 25 *versts* [16.5 miles] north of the Nivkh village of Pomor as the crow flies." Dutifully, the official sent several dozen pounds of oil to the Imperial Russian Technical Society in St. Petersburg. Ivanov's heirs received the right to develop what would eventually become the Okhinskoye oil field, but they never broke ground.

Scientists finally peeked under Sakhalin's frozen crust in 1889. Mining engineer Leopold Batsevich (1850–1905) prospected the eastern shore and drilled some shallow exploratory wells first at Ivanov's field and later near the Nogliki settlement and Nabilsky Bay in north central Sakhalin. Since he did not reach below 70 feet, he did not hit oil, but saw enough signs pointing to significant oil fields to encourage a retired naval lieutenant, Grigory Zotov, to found the G. I. Zotov & Co. Sakhalin Oil Industrial Partnership, the first such company on the island. Zotov & Co. set out to develop mineral oil on the roughly 2,750 acres of land it leased about 29 miles from the village of Lyangri in the north of the island. However, due to financial difficulties, G. I. Zotov & Co. ceased to exist by the mid 1890s.

Nevertheless, oil's northeastern frontier continued to inspire explorers with dreams of prosperity to come and engineers kept arriving with longer and longer drills. In 1892 and 1893, an engineer named Maslennikov led deeper exploration in news areas. His several wells, about 96 meters [315 feet] deep, found more oil but did not produce commercial flows. Russian prospectors were eventually joined by their international colleagues. In 1898, the German engineer Klee drilled the regions of Nutovo and Boatasyn Rivers. He was financed by the Sakhalin and Amur Petroleum Mining Syndicate, which was organized in London with generous initial capital of £1 million (about £90 million today).

Yet Sakhalin tantalized its would-be conquerors almost to the point of despair. The 1899 edition of the journal *Sovremennaya tekhnika* ["Modern Technology"] somberly summed up the results of the concluding decade: "We have known for several years now that the northern and eastern shores of Sakhalin Island have oil fields that extend for almost 400 *versts* [264 miles] to the north. However, our explorations have not been particularly successful. Thus far, oil produced from test pits and drill holes (down to 462 feet) has been meager in quantity and mediocre in quality."

With the arrival of the new century, Sakhalin seemed to have finally yielded. On March 3, 1900, the Russian newspaper *Neftyanoye delo* glowingly announced "the discovery of rich oil fields on the island of Sakhalin. The prospecting was done by a foreign mining engineer, who is currently applying to the government for the right to exploit the fields." In 1903, a well-equipped expedition of the British geologist Dr. William Norman-Bott performed further research and was able to vindicate Batsevich's prediction: "The oil fields of Sakhalin are sufficiently dependable to justify large-scale drilling." By the following year, the Russian Sakhalin Petroleum Company was created in Kharkiv with ambitions for large-scale development of the island's oil. The company's advertising brochure boasted of Sakhalin's "petroleum reserves whose quantity exceeds that of all American deposits combined." Meanwhile, members of the imperial family invested in the First Sakhalin Syndicate founded in St. Petersburg. The rush to unearth Sakhalin's treasures was on.

After the end of the 1905 Russo-Japanese War, Russian Emperor Nicholas II retained the northern part of Sakhalin in the Treaty of Portsmouth, with the southern portion becoming a Japanese prefecture of Karafuto. The increased strategic and economic importance of the island and its resources lead the Russian state to assist in broadening and intensifying the development of the island. To do its part, the Geologic Committee of Russia performed a comprehensive study of Sakhalin's oil fields between 1906 and 1909. The first expedition, headed by the Committee's mining engineer Konstantin Tulchinsky, noted numerous oil shows in its book, *Sketches of Minerals of Russian Sakhalin* [*Ocherki poleznykh iskopayemykh russkogo Sakhalina*] (1907). Next year's expedition, led by mining engineer Eduard Ahnert (1865–1946), made thorough topographical surveys of the island's biggest river, Tym, and several northeastern bays. Ahnert's test drilling increased the number of known oil fields from five to 18. The expedition's findings supported an even broader drilling program undertaken the following year by the expedition of Nikolay Tikhonovich (1872–1952), a geologist of the Geologic Committee, which included a crew headed by mining engineer Pëtr Polevoy (1873–1936). The 1908 expedition remapped the entire Russian Sakhalin in great detail, identifying numerous uncharted rivers, mountains and dozens of new mineral deposits. On May 24, 1909, Pëtr Polevoy's presentation of the results of the prospecting work received high marks from the Geologic Committee in St. Petersburg.

After thirteen years on the island, the Sakhalin and Amur Syndicate hit the jackpot in Nutovo River. Started on April 27, 1911, the Syndicate's 12-inch riverbank well produced 180 pounds per day at a depth of 60 feet. When the depth reached 100 feet, the output reached 6 barrels per day. The Syndicate's success attracted a new surge of entrepreneurs from the mainland. In 1912 alone, domestic and foreign companies submitted a total of 174 requests for allotment of petroleum production sites on Sakhalin.

However, after the outbreak of World War I in August 1914, all foreign companies soon left the island, and attempts of Russian entrepreneurs to begin further large-scale development of Sakhalin's oil fields likewise came to a halt.

The First Trunk Petroleum Product Pipeline

One of the bottlenecks in the Russian oil industry was the lack of a developed pipeline infrastructure. This created serious obstacles to organizing the broader sale of petroleum products within Russia and in foreign countries.

Taking its cue from the positive results of American oil industrialists, who had put the first oil pipeline into operation in 1865, Russia constructed its first oil pipeline in 1878, five years after the abolition of the tax-farming system in the Transcaucasus.

The oil pipeline—built on the Absheron Peninsula by Bari, Sytenko & Co. for the Nobel Brothers' company—was 5.6 miles long, had a pipe diameter of 8 inches, and could transport a daily capacity of 9,600 barrels. In its first few months of operation, 101,012 barrels were pumped through the pipeline; in 1879 the volume increased to an impressive 600,510 barrels.

The Nobel Brothers' example was followed by the well-known entrepreneur Vasily Kokorev, one of the founders of the Baku Oil Company, for which Bari, Sytenko & Co. built a kerosene pipeline from the BOC refinery in Surakhany to the Zıkh pier on the Caspian Sea.

It soon became apparent to other Russian entrepreneurs that pumping crude oil and petroleum products through pipelines cost less than half of what it cost to transport them by rail. Nevertheless, construction of the Transcaucasian Railway had been completed by 1883. On the whole, this did lead to an increase in the export of petroleum products to other countries, from 15,400 tons in 1882 to 940,000 tons in 1891. However, a large part of the profit from these exports went to the railroad's owners. For example, out of a total of 15 million rubles earned in 1892 from the sale of Russian petroleum products, 11.2 million went to the board of the Transcaucasian Railway, while only 3.8 million rubles went to oil industrialists. This unprofitable scenario provided all the more reason for Russian oil industrialists to turn their attention to pumping oil through pipelines

The difficult operating conditions of the Transcaucasian Railway through the Surami Pass and railway's limited capacity likewise prompted oil industrialists to look for other means of transporting their products. In 1893, nearly 11 million barrels of kerosene were stockpiled in Baku, waiting to be transported. In October 1895, the railroad track and several bridges on the Transcaucasian Railway were damaged by the flooding of the Kura River. Shipments of petroleum products were stopped for two months, resulting in large losses for oil industrialists.

Oil entrepreneurs, along with support from the scientific and engineering community, made numerous appeals to the Russian government regarding the need for an alternative to rail transport. They argued that pumping crude oil to Batumi and refining it there would promote "deeper" use of this raw material, i.e., production not only of more kerosene and residual oil, but also mineral oil and other valuable products. Their appeals were taken into consideration and on May 23, 1896, the Russian Imperial State Council decided to build a trunk kerosene pipeline from Baku to Batumi, to pass along the existing railroad route.

Playing an important role in this was the eminent Russian political figure Sergey Witte (1849–1915), minister of finance, who had earlier occupied the post of minister of railroads. Witte was a firm supporter of developing the domestic oil industry in every possible way. For example, the "Instructions on Producing an Attestation of the Testing of Oil and Refined Petroleum Products," approved by him on February 6, 1896, did much to improve the quality of domestic petroleum products and make them more competitive on the world market.

Management of the design and construction of the Baku–Batumi kerosene pipeline was assigned to the Engineering Council of the Ministry of Railroads, with design development headed by Nikolay Shchukin (1848–1924), professor at the St. Petersburg Technological Institute.

Before work began on the pipeline, the Russian Ministry of Railroads first sent him and production engineer L. Wartenburg to the US in the summer of 1896 to familiarize themselves with the state of American pipeline transportation and the various techniques for building oil pipelines.

After Shchukin and Wartenburg returned to Russia, they began to develop the design for the Baku–Batumi kerosene pipeline. At the time, nobody knew how to construct a kerosene pipeline of such significant length (more than 545 miles), much less how to construct one along a railroad route. After all, kerosene is very prone to leakage and evaporation, which makes it challenging, and dangerous, to pump, especially near passenger railcars and petroleum product tank cars, not to mention in the vicinity of numerous tunnels, bridges, and other railroad structures.

One of the most complex parts of the project was the design of the first section of the kerosene pipeline from Mikhaylovo to Batumi, on the western mountain segment of the route, which was the most difficult for transporting tank cars with petroleum products.

Nevertheless, Nikolay Shchukin was able to develop a very careful hydraulic calculation for the pipeline, as well as instructions that set forth very strict requirements regarding the quality of the pipes and their junctions.

The design was discussed by many major scholars of mechanics and hydrodynamics, members of the Engineering Council, and invited specialists. These included the engineer Nikolay Sytenko, who authored a book about calculating the strength of bridges and viaducts; transportation engineer Genrikh Merching, who wrote a book about the movement of kerosene and oil through pipes; Aleksandr Bari, who was head of the engineering company Engineer A. V. Bari Construction Office; Mikhail Lazarev, representing the Congress of Oil Industrialists in St. Petersburg; and many others.

The government decided that the pipes would be fabricated only at Russian plants located in Mariupol, Sosnovitsy, and Yekaterinoslavl. Pipes having a minimum length of 15 feet were accepted from the plants. At their ends, they had a V-thread that tapered toward the end. This type of thread, which assures sealing of pipe junctions, was borrowed from American analogs. Steel flange joints were also provided for a series of pipeline sections.

Preliminary work on building the first section of the kerosene pipeline—from Mikhaylovo to Batumi (141 miles)—began in September 1896. Drawings of the railroad route and bridges indicating pipe placement were carefully prepared, and designs for the boiler and pumping stations were completed. In the summer of 1898, pipes began to arrive along the route and the pace of work significantly accelerated. Whereas only 27 miles of pipe had been laid from September 1898 to February 1899, by June 1899, 89 miles had been laid. Over 31 miles of this route, pipes had been screwed together and lowered into the ground, while over the remaining 58-mile section, they had been screwed together and left on the surface. By July of the same year, earth-moving work had ended, and the construction of boiler stations and buildings for service personnel had been completed. In November, the last batch of pipes was received.

Pumps for the pumping stations were provided by the Worthington Company (US). They were piston-operated, direct-acting pumps with a compound-type steam engine having valve steam distribution and double steam expansion. Two 110-kilowatt operating pumps and one backup pump were installed at every Mikhaylovo–Batumi kerosene pipeline station. In addition, tanks holding 8,125 tons of kerosene each were installed at the Samtredi and Kobuleti stations. A 1,080-ton tank was built for unloading kerosene from the tank cars at the Mikhaylovo station, along with a 10,800-ton storage tank; and a 15,300-ton tank was built at Batumi.

To avoid large kerosene leaks in case of an accident, the pipeline was outfitted with check valves every one to two miles along the pipeline. If the pipeline pressure dropped by 15%, an automatic device shut off the pumps.

March 14, 1900 is a special date in the history of the Russian oil industry. On that date, the first (and most important) section of the Russian Baku–Batumi trunk kerosene pipeline was completed, after a construction period of more than three years. A ceremony was held at Mikhaylovo Station on July 15, 1900 to celebrate the commissioning of this kerosene pipeline section. The ceremony was attended by Infantry General Grigory Golitsyn, head commander of civilian affairs in the Caucasus; Colonel Ivan Svechin, governor of Tiflis; Ludwig Perschke, director of the Excise Tax Administration of the Transcaucasus; transportation engineer Yevgeny Vedeneyev, head of the Transcaucasian Railway and kerosene pipeline construction manager, and other officials.

On June 12, 1901, Emperor Nicholas II approved the decision to completely finish construction of the Baku–Batumi kerosene pipeline. On June 16, 1901, the Ministry of Railroads decided to build the next section of the kerosene pipeline from the Ag-Taglya station (13 miles from Tiflis in the direction toward Baku) to the Mikhaylovo station, a distance of 87 miles. Directed by transportation engineer Aleksandr Dombrovsky, the construction work was finished within three years, and on December 30, 1904, this section of the kerosene pipeline was put into operation.

Construction of the final and longest (319 miles) section of the kerosene pipeline, between Baku and Ag-Taglya, was directed by the engineer A. Pavlichinsky. Here, the extensive experience acquired over the past seven years of construction was put to full use. Most of the equipment installed at pumping stations in this section of the kerosene pipeline was produced by Russian companies. A 110-kilowatt two-cylinder diesel engine was set up at each of the four kerosene pipeline stations located in areas without water. Operating the pumps with diesel engines turned out to be much less expensive than using steam engines, since the efficiency of the former was 28%, whereas the latter only had an efficiency of 10%.

By the beginning of the summer of 1907, all major work had been completed and the entire 547-mile length of the Baku–Batumi kerosene pipeline, with its 16 pumping stations, was triumphantly put into operation on June 21, 1907. From its inception, the operation of the Transcaucasian kerosene pipeline was entirely stable and by the end of 1907, more than 1.1 million tons of kerosene had been pumped through it.

Russia's investment in this massive addition to the infrastructure of the oil industry turned out to be a wise decision. While the construction of the Baku–Batumi trunk kerosene pipeline cost the Russian government over 21 million rubles, within its first five years of operation, the project not only completely paid for itself, but even generated a net profit of 6.5 million rubles.

Russia at the First International Petroleum Congress

By the end of the 19th century, the rapidly growing oil industry had captured the rapt attention of the world's scientific community. Gradually, the sensationalized reports of mighty oil gushers that appeared on the pages of scientific periodicals gave way to the appearance of a series of significant technical works that would later form the basis for the field of petroleum science.

Specialized forums devoted to the issue of petroleum and its related products soon began to appear. The International Geologic Congress, which began meeting regularly since 1878, focused on the genesis of petroleum and the organization of efficient hydrocarbon prospecting.

In turn, the creation in 1882 in Russia of a specialized institution, the Geologic Committee of the Mining Department, gave a powerful impetus to the development of the scientific study of the country's rich mineral resources. Research by the accomplished Russian geologists Grigory Gelmersen (1803–1885), Nikolay Koshkarov (1818–1892), Vasily Yerofeyev (1822–1884), and Aleksandr Karpinsky (1846–1936) generated keen interest from many scientific and engineering organizations around the world. In just its first ten years (1882–1891), the Geologic Committee had established an exchange of publications with 196 foreign geologic institutions and scientific societies, including organizations in Africa, Australia, South America, and other countries.

Recognition of the Geologic Committee's fruitful activity is evidenced by awards received at various international exhibitions: the Chicago World's Columbian Exposition of 1893, the Exposition Internationale de Bruxelles of 1897, and the Exposition Universelle de Paris of 1900, where the committee's geologic maps and publications won certificates of merit and gold medals.

An important step in the development of Russian and world geologic science was the 7th session of the International Geologic Congress, which took place in St. Petersburg in August 1897. After the Congress ended, some of attending delegates visited the fields of the Absheron Peninsula, and obtained convincing proof of the enormous scale of the Russian oil business.

Starting in 1894, issues involving the study of crude oil and petroleum products were also being discussed at meetings and international congresses in applied chemistry. In Russia, the US, Great Britain, and Austria-Hungary, national public organizations were working to combine the creative efforts of their best scientists and engineers to develop the oil industry.

However, at this point in time there was not yet a worldwide representative organization capable of comprehensively examining all of the numerous facets of the industry—from prospecting and recovery to refining and sales. Without such an organization in place, specialists had significantly different interpretations of national legal frameworks and processes for oil production. For instance, there was no unified approach to petroleum product analysis and certification methods, which inevitably produced a great variety of obstacles on the road to the successful development of international trade.

One person who could not resign himself to this state of affairs was Pavel Dvorkovich (1857–1929), a talented Russian petroleum chemist. At the time, he was working at the Petroleum Storage Tanks and Transportation Co. Ltd., a British company, and was simultaneously the publisher of the *Petroleum Review*, a London newspaper. By the second half of 1899, he had published a series of articles in this publication justifying the urgent necessity of an international oil forum as part of the upcoming Exposition Universelle de Paris.

As arguments, Pavel Dvorkovich cited historical chronicles of the 18th century, mentioning that it was France that had been the first European country to become aware of the nascent oil industry. In 1745, King Louis XV had given a concession to the nobleman de la Sablonnière to develop the oil-bearing territory Pechelbronn in the province of Alsace. This successful entrepreneur drilled several productive oil wells and built a small refinery, which continued to operate until 1785. Broad recognition was also achieved by French mining specialists for their significant contribution to the development of drilling equipment and procedures. Their fruitful activities are associated with the appearance of the freefall drilling tool invented by the engineers Kind and Fabian. To increase the efficiency of percussion rod drilling, in 1845 the engineer Favelle first applied the principle of circulating liquid through the pipe's internal cavity to remove cuttings through the annulus. Rodolphe Leschot's invention started the spread of diamond core drilling.

The widespread discussion on the pages of the *Petroleum Review* about the possibility of holding the first Petroleum Congress bore fruit. Each month, support for this initiative came from more and more people in various countries who worked in the oil business. The president of the Galician Petroleum Association, Baron von Gorayski, offered to head its delegation, and the Society of Drilling Engineers in Vienna and the California Petroleum Association both confirmed their desire to participate in the Congress. Pavel Dvorkovich soon received a letter from William Moore, director of the French subsidiary of the well-known American Worthington Pump Company, expressing his willingness to provide a meeting hall in its corporate pavilion at the Paris exhibition to hold meetings of the Petroleum Congress from August 16–28, 1900.

On May 14, 1900, encouraged by his success, Pavel Dvorkovich sent a letter to the renowned Russian scientist Dmitry Mendeleyev. In that letter, Dvorkovich wrote: "Knowing what deep interest you have shown over the past 30 years in the success of the oil industry, I am certain that you will be glad to learn that the first International Petroleum Congress will take place in Paris in August. My colleagues and I would be extremely flattered if you would agree to accept the title of honorary chairman of this Congress. It is scheduled for August 16–28, so we hope that this time will be convenient for you to be present in person at the opening of the Congress."[52]

As it turned out, Dmitry Mendeleyev was already in Paris and, as the director of the Bureau of Weights and Measures, had already been actively participating in the work of the Exposition Universelle de Paris, at the request of Finance Minister Sergey Witte. However, he was forced to return to Russia for family reasons and was unable to participate personally in the work of the first Petroleum Congress.

The first world forum of oil industry professionals opened on August 17, 1900 in Paris. The first meeting was attended by 59 delegates from 20 countries. Senator Michel Lesueur was elected president of the Congress and Pavel Dvorkovich was elected secretary. The congress delegates unanimously elected Dmitry Mendeleyev honorary president of the Congress, and sent a salutatory telegram to him in St. Petersburg.

A large part of the forum was taken up by discussion of the state of affairs in the principal world centers of oil production. In addition, much attention was given to the broader issues of petroleum geology, including a lecture by Carl Engler, professor of Germany's Karlsruhe Institute of Technology, on the chemistry and formation of petroleum.

The delegates also paid particular attention to talks concerning applied chemistry as it relates to the oil industry. Subjects of these talks included the chemistry of Russian petroleum, the composition of

American petroleum, the variation of the characteristics of crude oils from Pennsylvania and Ohio, and the chemistry of Japanese petroleum. A presentation on the use of petroleum for air navigation proved to be a prophetic prologue for the coming innovations of the 20th century.

The delegates also unanimously supported one of the key talks, "On the Uniformity of Methods of Investigating Crude Oil and Petroleum Products," given by the well-known British petrochemist Boverton Redwood.

The Russian delegation was at the center of attention at the Congress. In the lobby, the Russian delegation's director, State Adviser Aleksandr Ivanov, gladly answered numerous questions about the prospects for development of the oil business in Russia, while mining engineer Nikolay Lebedev, an employee of the Caucasus Mining Administration, repeatedly displayed a geologic map of the Caucasus Territory that he had drawn up to serve as proof of Russia's vast resources and potential.

Between meeting sessions of the Congress, the delegates familiarized themselves with the Exposition's extensive exhibits, and their attention was drawn above all to the Russian exhibit. Russia was represented by more than 2,500 exhibitors housed in an area of 258,000 square feet. Prince Vyacheslav Tenishev (1845–1903), a well-known figure in the industry, served as general commissioner of the Russian section.

Prior to the opening of the Fair, the Russian Ministry of Finance had published a comprehensive book, *Russia at the End of the 19th Century* [*Rossiya v kontse XIX veka*], edited by V. I. Kovalevsky, that contained a detailed analysis of Russian economic, scientific, and cultural developments of the previous century. Chapter 3 of the book, "The Chemical and Oil Industry," was written by Dmitry Mendeleyev and said, in part: "Owing to the measures insistently carried out by the government, Russia, which as late as 1876 had been ordering 55,000–66,000 tons of petroleum products per year from America, began to increase its production and refining of oil from the Caucasus; reduced the price of kerosene (lighting oil, oil) and other petroleum products to the lowest ever in the world; saturated the domestic market; began to provide the treasury up to 30 million rubles of revenue in the form of an excise tax on kerosene used by the country; and began to export, predominantly from Batumi, up to 990,000 tons (1898) of kerosene alone, not counting lubricants (more than 160,000 tons in 1898) and residual oil (around 55,000 tons in 1898)."

In the exhibit hall, the Russian oil industry was very heavily represented in the "Mining and Metallurgy" and "Chemical Production" groups. Mining engineer Ivan Lebëdkin, head of the Russian section, willingly gave explanations on the extensive exhibit to the delegates of the Congress.

The Nobel Brothers Petroleum Production Partnership, which was the standard bearer of the Russian oil industry, occupied a separate exhibition pavilion and presented an extensive exhibit of Russian petroleum, petroleum products, and oilfield equipment. Its exhibits included samples of Balakhany, Sabunchu, Romanian, Surakhany, Bibiheybet, and Cheleken crudes, natural gas condensate, three grades of gasoline, kerosene, gas oil, diesel oil, spindle oil, cylinder oil, viscosin, vaseline oil, solid oil, paraffin, residual oil, etc.

On August 18, 1900, the results of the international jury's voting were announced, and it was no surprise that the highest award, the Grand Prix, was given to the two leading Russian companies, the Nobel Brothers Petroleum Production Partnership and the Caspian and Black Sea Oil Industrial and Trading Company, as well as to the Geologic Committee of Russia. A gold medal was also awarded to the Baku Oil Company, a pioneer of the Russian oil business.

In addition, exhibition gold medals were awarded to mining engineer Sigismund Wojslaw, Vladimir Shukhov, geologist Sergey Nikitin, and many other Russian exhibitors. In all, Russian participants at the 1900 Exposition Universelle de Paris received a total of 1,589 awards: 212 Grand Prix, 370 gold medals, 436 silver medals, 347 bronze medals, and 224 honorable mentions.

On August 28, 1900, the last day of the first International Petroleum Congress, resolutions were adopted on the basic directions of development of the industry, and a committee was selected to prepare for the next forum. The gold medal of the Congress was unanimously awarded to Pavel Dvorkovich for his contribution to organizing the forum of oil industry professionals and for his memorable scientific talk. Michel Lesueur, Congress president, gave a brilliant closing address, expressing the hope for future fruitful cooperation and the active exchange of scientific and technical ideas.

It is believed that this first forum of oil industry professionals gave a green light to the beginning of the gasoline era, and all the substantial developments in industrialized society that came along with it.

In the following years, Russian scientists and engineers continued their active participation at the International Petroleum Congresses in Liege (1905), Bucharest (1907), and Lviv (1910), which did a great deal to promote the development of petroleum science. In July 1905, at the second International Petroleum Congress in Liege (Belgium), audiences were very interested in talks given by the Russian delegates on petroleum and its products in world industry and trade, and on establishing uniform methods of analyzing petroleum products. In September 1907, at the third International Petroleum Congress in Bucharest, a lecture on the rightful place of chemistry and petroleum geology in the natural sciences was a true revelation for many delegates. At the fourth International Petroleum Congress (Lvov, 1910) a decision was adopted to create a special international committee to establish uniform methods of analyzing petroleum products. This committee met for the first time in Vienna on January 17–20, 1912, drawing up a document that established common international techniques for analyzing and determining petroleum product properties. During the course of its work, the commission came to be known informally as the "International Petroleum Commission," and included a large contingent of Russian scientists.

At the Focal Point of the Kerosene Wars

The end of the 19th century was marked by many striking events that would have a fundamental influence on the state of the world economy in the new century. In 1898, the Russian Empire surpassed the US for the first time in volume of oil produced, producing 75.8 million barrels of oil, which represented 51.6% of world production. In contrast, the volume of oil produced in the US was 62 million barrels.

In the following year (1899), there were 10 oil-producing countries in the world, and their total production was 19,492,000 tons of oil, as opposed to 13,259,000 tons in 1894. Russia now occupied the leading position in world volume of oil production, with a share of 9,957,000 tons (51.1%); the US came in second with 8,308,000 tons (42.6%), followed by the Netherlands (461,000 tons on the island of Borneo), Austria-Hungary (356,000 tons), and Romania (118,000 tons).

On the roads of the US and Europe, automobiles were no longer a sensation. Meanwhile, seas and inland waterways were furrowed by vessels equipped with oil heating systems, the precursors to the powerful fleets created in the 20th century.

Russia strove not to fall behind in this respect. The first domestic automobile was unveiled at the All-Russia Industrial and Art Exhibition in Nizhny Novgorod in 1896. In 1899, a factory in Riga began serial assembly of "self-propelled carriages" under the sonorous name "Rossiya" [Russia].

It was during this period that a sharp rivalry began between Russia and the US for control of the world oil market. This dramatic stage in the relationship between the two powers is covered in detail in Professor Aleksandr Vasilenko's work, entitled "The Petroleum Factor in Geopolitics at the Turn of the 19th-20th Centuries," which is included in the anthology *The Eve of the Petroleum Era* [*Predvestiye ery nefti*].

For John D. Rockefeller and his Standard Oil Company, the beginning of the 1880s did not presage any special concerns for its monopoly position in the area of trade in petroleum products. In Europe, Russian kerosene first appeared in small volumes in 1882, and American experts evaluated it as a very timid attempt by Russian companies to enter the European market. Data from the Mining Department indicated that in

128

1882, Russia exported 31,450 barrels of crude oil, 3,360 barrels of mineral oil and vaseline, 27,260 barrels of kerosene, 84,420 barrels of lubricants, and 12,000 barrels of residual oil. In the same year, the US exported 559,955,000 gallons of various petroleum products. If we consider that 1 barrel = 42 gallons, we may calculate that Russian exports amounted to a pitiful 1% of American exports.

However, if the managers of Standard Oil had been privy to the content of the Nobel Brothers Petroleum Production Partnership's general shareholders' meeting in April 1883, they may have found their self-confidence seriously shaken. In its address to the shareholders, the Partnership's Board said, in part: "Having on its side the undoubted advantage of the Baku oil sources over American ones... Russian kerosene has a broad field for distribution in countries bordering Russia.... The company's goal was first to displace American kerosene from Russia, and then begin to export kerosene to other countries.... American kerosene has now been completely displaced from Russian markets, and in the past year the company had already begun to export its products to Austria and Germany."[53]

Production data from this period show that Russian entrepreneurs were already making great strides to change the existing state of affairs on the European oil product market. In 1884, the port of Batumi exported 449,808 barrels of crude oil and petroleum products, including 330,621 barrels of kerosene, 76,210 barrels of lubricants, 42,325 barrels of residual oil, and 652 barrels of crude oil. At the same time, deliveries to the Russian Black Sea ports of Odessa, Sevastopol, Kerch, and Kherson for domestic consumption comprised 209,138 barrels of crude oil and petroleum products, including 183,560 barrels of kerosene.

In the same year, 21,628 barrels of crude oil and petroleum products were exported from Baku directly to Persia, including: 14,014 barrels of kerosene, 1,008 barrels of residual oil, and 6,617 barrels of crude oil.

On October 31, 1886, Baku oil industrialists wrote a letter to Prince Aleksandr Dondukov-Korsakov, head commander of civilian affairs in the Caucasus, stating: "The Baku oil industry has reached such a degree of development that it could easily supply not only all of Russia, but also a large part of Europe with lighting and lubricating materials in the quantity that they need."

This assertion proved true in the coming years. In 1890, Russia exported 4.9 million barrels, including 3.5 million barrels of Russian kerosene sold on the European market. At the same time, US exports were 523,295,000 gallons of kerosene, including 343,078,000 gallons to Europe. Simple conversion shows that in 1890, Russian exports already amounted to 41.1% of total American exports, and 43.9% of exports to the European market.

Not surprisingly, the American government was quite concerned about the increasing activity of Russian oil companies in Europe. Therefore, the government gave Standard Oil management its blessing to take extremely tough action against Russian companies in all aspects of sales activity, using the most diverse means, including unfair methods of competition.

To this end, the American company began creating a wide network of subsidiaries around the world. In Great Britain, it formed the Anglo-American Oil Company in London on April 24, 1888 with a fixed capital of £500,000. Trading of American kerosene in Germany passed into the hands of the company *Deutsch-Amerikanische Petroleum Gesellschaft*, founded on February 22, 1890 with capital of 9 million marks (40% of whose shares belonged to Rockefeller and his partners). On March 10, 1891, the American Petroleum Company was founded in Rotterdam, with a capital of 5 million florins, to trade kerosene in the Netherlands, Belgium, and Luxembourg; 51% of its shares were owned by Americans. Sale of American kerosene in Italy and Switzerland was carried out by the *Società Italo-Americana del Petrolio* company, founded in Venice on May 16, 1891 with a capital of 2.5 million lire, 60% of whose shares belonged to the Standard Oil Company.

In the face of such tough competitive countermeasures by the US, the rate of growth of Russian exports to Europe soon slowed. In 1892, Russia delivered 3.5 million barrels of kerosene to Europe, i.e., over four years, growth in exports to Europe expressed in absolute figures amounted to 384,282 barrels (or 10.8%).

The Standard Oil Company's ongoing actions clearly worked toward the realization of its strategy to displace Russia completely, especially from the European kerosene market. Whereas in 1890 Great Britain imported 787,529 barrels of kerosene from Russia and 1,357,122 barrels from the US, by 1893 American imports had grown 60% to 2,209,619 barrels, while Russian imports, by contrast, fell 5.6% to 743,094 barrels.

It's no wonder, then, that at the end of the 19th century Russia's focus turned toward exporting kerosene to the Far East. However, as was the case in Europe, this region was already well-supplied by US companies. In 1887, official data provided evidence of the dominant market position of the US: its kerosene deliveries to the Far East were 9,782,459 crates, while those of Russia were only 899,903 crates. If we take into account the weight difference between the kerosene in a Russian crate (74 pounds) and that in an American crate (65 pounds), it turns out that in 1887 the US delivered 635,859,830 pounds to the Far East, and Russia delivered 66,592,822 pounds. Thus, in 1887 American kerosene exports exceeded Russian exports by a factor of 9.5.

Nonetheless, by 1888, Russia was already delivering 1.1 million barrels of Russian kerosene to the region, and by 1892 this figure jumped to 2.4 million barrels. In other words, over the course of just four years the increase in Eastern exports amounted to 1.3 million barrels expressed in absolute terms, or a 55% increase.

This trend is also confirmed by analysis of data on deliveries to the Pacific coast; in 1892, the US delivered 11,253,699 crates of kerosene there, while Russia delivered 8,647,683 crates. If these figures are compared on the basis of weight, it turns out that the US delivered 731,490,430 pounds, and Russia delivered 639,928,540 pounds. Thus, the Russian share of the total volume of kerosene deliveries to the Far East region reached the substantial value of 46.7%.

We should note that while deliveries to Europe in 1893 were 2.6 million barrels of kerosene, deliveries to the Far East were 3.4 million barrels.

To summarize the above discussion, it can be noted that over a rather short period the Russian oil industry made a dramatic breakthrough, and became a serious competitor to the US, both in the markets of Europe and in those of the Far East.

The increasing activity of Russian companies in the Far East did not go unnoticed in the US. In relation to the Eastern market, John D. Rockefeller's strategy was spelled out quite frankly by one of his confidants: "Beginning today, a struggle must begin with the Russian rivalry in the Eastern hemisphere.... This matter must be addressed energetically and with unlimited capital; otherwise, our foreign business, amounting to an annual figure of 50 million, will be very strongly affected. If this business had been left to people with unlimited power or combined efforts, Russia would now be master of all Eastern markets. Without a system of oil pipelines, cheap shipping, and an improvement in production, we would not have been able to hold the European and Asian markets against Russia, not even for one year."

The active measures undertaken by Standard Oil in the Eastern market yielded the desired results. By 1893, the US had delivered 18,674,661 crates of kerosene to the Far East, almost 7.5 million more than in 1892. As for Russia, it was able to achieve an increase of only 3.8 million crates of kerosene during that year.

The American challenge was soon followed by a strong response from Russia. The country's rapid construction of the Trans-Siberian Railroad, with its Chinese Eastern Railway segment, and the railroad's commissioning created favorable new conditions for a rapid increase in deliveries of Russian petroleum products. Whereas in 1897, Russian entrepreneurs exported 4.1 million barrels of kerosene to the markets of the Far East (for comparison, only 2.2 million barrels were sent to Europe), in 1901 they exported 6.2 million barrels, and in 1904 the volume of export deliveries reached 7.3 million barrels. That is, over seven years Russian Far East exports of kerosene had reached impressive figures and had grown by a factor of 1.8.

From the viewpoint of the administration of the US, the beginning of Trans-Siberian Railroad operation significantly strengthened the Russian presence in the Far East and struck a serious blow against the administration's policy of "open doors" and "equal opportunities." Such considerations played into the US's support for Japan in its war with Russia. A weakened and distracted Russia would eliminate one of the US's main obstacles to the realization of its geopolitical ambitions, including that of increasing American kerosene exports. US President Theodore Roosevelt conveyed this position clearly in his letter of January 18, 1903 to Secretary of State John Hay: "I want the Russians to know that I do not intend to give in. With every year I am more and more certain that the country will support me in the most extreme measures in this matter."

A tight knot of complex contradictions between the great powers in the Far East caused the breakout of the Russo-Japanese War in 1904.

The major work of the Soviet historian Boris Romanov, *Sketches of the Diplomatic History of the Russo-Japanese War* [*Ocherki diplomaticheskoy istorii russko-yaponskoy voyny*], offers a detailed analysis of the reasons for the formation of the anti-Russian bloc and describes the tactics directed against Russia on the diplomatic and military fronts (in the chapter "The Anglo-Japanese-American Block (1901–1902)" and the section "The Anglo-American Agreement"). The book also touches on the complex foreign trade factors that contributed to the outbreak of the war.

Among these factors was the American Standard Oil Company's actions leading up to the conflict. Early in the spring of 1904, Rockefeller's company struck a serious blow against Russian kerosene export deliveries to Europe markets. The newspaper *Neftyanoye delo* reported: "To understand the fierceness of this struggle, it is sufficient to remember that the price of bulk retail kerosene in the main import ports of England fell from 5¾ pence per gallon in March 1904 to 2½ pence (that is, 43 kopecks per *pood* [36 pounds]), in June of this same year.... In March, the average quoted price for our boiler kerosene in Baku was 29.3 kopecks per *pood* [36 pounds]. Consequently, in Batumi it would cost 50.3 kopecks per *pood* [36 pounds], assuming constant expenses of 21 kopecks between Baku and Batumi (railroad freight: 19 kopecks, port charges: 1 kopeck, pumping and storage in Batumi, leakage and interest on freight: 1 kopeck). Comparison of these figures clearly illustrates the complete inability of our kerosene to compete with American kerosene."

Nikolay Iznar, a well-known oil industrialist, noted in an article in the same newspaper: "At various times the necessity of keeping the market in its hands forced the Standard Oil Co. to lower prices drastically on export kerosene in New York. This reduction was sometimes so significant that, for example, in August 1904 a gallon of export kerosene was quoted at 4.8 cents, while at the same place a gallon of crude oil cost 5 cents, that is, 0.20 cents more than the refined product."

Furthermore, in April 1904, the American financial company Kuhn, Loeb & Co., which was under the control of the Rockefeller group, opened a subscription for an initial set of Japanese bonds in the amount $25 million. A second offering of Japanese bonds was soon issued, this time for $60 million, followed by a third and a fourth. They were all successfully purchased in equal portions in the US and Great Britain.

Nevertheless, despite such anti-Russian actions carried out by the US, in 1904 Russia was able to export 13.5 million barrels of kerosene, which accounted for 30.7% of total world exports. Meanwhile, the US accounted for 55.9%, the Netherlands 8.4%, Romania 2.7%, and Galicia 2.3%.

Russian kerosene exports in 1904 broke down as follows: Europe received 6.2 million barrels and Eastern markets received 7.3 million barrels, with China alone receiving 880,845 barrels of kerosene, or 57.6% of American deliveries.

However, these impressive gains would not last long as the tragic events of August 1905 plunged the Russian oil industry into a deep crisis. As a result, Russia lost the European and Far East markets, and the volume of its exports of petroleum products was set back by several decades, putting an end to the high figures that had earlier impressed contemporaries.

The Tragedy of August 1905

The development of the Russian oil industry in the late 19th and early 20th centuries was clearly on an upward track; the industry exhibited rapid rates of growth in oil production and refining, becoming essentially a world leader. Volumes of Russian petroleum products exports to the world market grew steadily, despite crises in several countries in Europe, Asia, and the Far East.

As noted above, the world market for petroleum products in the late 19th and early 20th centuries was characterized by increased competition between the leading Russian oil companies and the American transnational corporation Standard Oil Company. At the same time, there was a clear tendency toward substantial consolidation of Russia's competitive position on the petroleum products market, both in Europe and elsewhere in the world. For instance, whereas Russian kerosene supplied to Great Britain in 1897 amounted to only 14.2% of American kerosene exports to that country, by 1903 it had already reached 42.4%.

The Russian industry's great potential was clearly shown by statistical indicators, especially from 1900–1904, compared to the performance of the American oil industry. The commissioning of powerful high-flowing wells by American oil industrialists in Texas in 1902 altered the rankings somewhat, but the potential of the Russian industry remained fairly high, and a return to a leading position on the "oil Olympus" was thought to be entirely possible.

Table 5. Russian and US Oil Production, 1898–1904
(in millions of tons)

	Russian Oil Production	US Oil Production
1898	8.77	8.47
1899	9.5	8.7
1900	10.85	9.74
1901	12.09	10.63
1902	11.48	13.59
1903	10.77	15.31
1904	12.03	17.91

Source: Dyakonova, I. A. *Oil and Coal in the Power Industry of Tsarist Russia in International Comparisons [Neft i ugol v energetike tsarskoy Rossii v mezhdunarodnykh sopostavleniyakh].* Moscow, 1999, p. 166.

However, the events of only a few tragic days in August 1905, at the Absheron Peninsula fields, completely dashed any hopes for Russia's restoration as leader of the world oil industry. To fully understand these events, it should be noted that an important aspect of Russia's oil industry development was its highly multinational working class. In 1904, of the 147 oil production companies on the Absheron Peninsula, eight produced about 50% of all the oil. The peninsula's major fields and refineries employed 50% of the entire work force in 1903, and by 1907 that figure was 55.2%. At the same time, the Russia-wide figure was 54%. The proportions of workers of various nationalities in 1903 were as follows: Azerbaijanis 41.2%, Armenians 20.5%, Russians 20.3%, Dagestanis 12.5%, and others 6.5%.

At the same time, it should be noted that a social component also began to manifest itself more and more distinctly in the operations of Russian oil companies during those years. On December 30, 1904, at Sabunchu, on the Absheron Peninsula, in a building housing the executive board of the Electric Power [*Elektricheskaya sila*] Joint-Stock Company, negotiations were concluded between authorized labor collectives and oil industrialists, resulting in the signing of the first collective-bargaining agreement in the history of the Russian oil industry.

This event ended a major oil field strike that had lasted more than two weeks and had involved over 40,000 workers from various occupations. The first collective-bargaining agreement, which the trade-unionists began to call the "residual oil constitution," was a major achievement for the working class in the battle to improve working and living conditions. Under the terms of the agreement, the work day in the field was reduced to nine hours; regular night work, overtime and detachment work was abolished; days of three eight-hour shifts were introduced for drillers, bailers, stokers, and oilers; and a day off finally appeared in the work week. In case of illness, workers had to be paid half their wages for three months and treatment had to be provided at the business owner's expense. The collective-bargaining agreement also reflected various demands of the workers, such as polite treatment by the administration, abolition of unauthorized searches, provision of quality drinking water, and common access to bathhouses.

The 1904 collective-bargaining agreement was a major victory for Russian oil workers. It seemed to everyone that this progress in the social sector had considerably lessened the level of tension in the working class environment, and nothing portended the complications that would soon arise in the oil fields. However, the events of the first Russian revolution of August 1905 burst forth on the Absheron Peninsula, writing the most tragic pages in the history of the domestic oil industry. The devastation that occurred over several August days on the Absheron Peninsula, when oil workers set industrial sites on fire in acts of deliberate sabotage, plunged the Russian oil industry into a deep, long-term crisis.

What was the main cause of the tragedy of August 22–25, 1905? Unfortunately, even a hundred years later, we still do not have an exhaustive answer to this question. In their study, "On the Question of the Causes and Nature of the Tragic Events of August 1905 at the Absheron Peninsula Oil Fields," which appeared in the anthology, *The Eve of the Petroleum Era* [*Predvestiye ery nefti*], the Russian historians Sergey Khizhnyakov and Valery Osinov made one of the first attempts at an unbiased scientific analysis of the events.

In the absence of a definitive explanation, let us try to at least reconstruct a logical sequence of events from the available facts. At the Absheron Peninsula fields alone, there were over 5,000 Persian citizens (20%), and they formed the bulk of the unskilled laborers: bailers, who pulled the oil out of the ground and poured it into tanks; blotters, who gathered oil from the ground and water surface with rags; and carters, who hauled oil day and night from the fields to the Black City outside Baku. A step higher in the working hierarchy were the drillers, brakers, and carriers. And to these we should add a large number of Persians who, while not on permanent staff at the oil companies, were employed in all types of temporary jobs (collecting ditch oil, cleaning oil pits, etc.) for up to 8–15 days a month. By some estimates, this unskilled labor force comprised another several thousand workers.

Written sources from that distant time offer further information about the situation at the fields. In an article titled "Explanatory Note of Elected Representatives of Baku Workers" from *Neftyanoye delo* no. 20–21 for 1905, we find very remarkable eyewitness testimony of the tragic August events: "For the workers, this carnage was completely unexpected. In the first days, especially, it seemed so absurdly wild; we simply didn't believe that all this was not a dream, but real life. It's true, though, that since the December strike, leaflets were being distributed to workers containing warnings to Armenians, supposedly from Muslims, to leave the Muslims alone, otherwise they, the Muslims, would beat up all the Armenians."

The article also contains a key fact that sheds light on the August tragedy: "They gradually attracted Persian laborers as well, among whom *softa-mullahs*[54] appeared, preaching a Muslim union, and that only a Muslim will improve the life of a Muslim, and that every infidel deserves death. This preaching, given the oppression under which the Muslim workers lived, had an unquestionable effect.... The most heartrending role fell to the Persian laborers. They were literally driven to pillage. They were driven to arson. They wept, but they went and burned." Thus, the *Neftyanoye delo* fairly clearly identified the oilfield arsonists, and the people who inspired those excesses—the *softa-mullahs*.

The *Neftyanoye delo* of October 11, 1905 contained a report from the Statistical Office of the Congress of Oil Industrialists in Baku on the impact of the arsonists' actions: "We have established that the ruffians systematically engaged in ruining wells by throwing various objects down the shafts.... The 1,429 burned production derricks had a daily June output of 920,924 *poods* [110,592 barrels] or 58.1% of the total daily output.... The cost of the burned derricks based on the above evaluation has been put at 12,066,000 rubles, in addition to which workshops valued at 1,757,500 rubles were burned and destroyed, as well as boiler rooms worth 1,141,400 rubles, housing worth 2,719,600 rubles, 5,896,861 *poods* [708,142 barrels] of oil reserves worth an average of 23 kopecks per *pood*, or 1,356,300 rubles, storage facilities worth 1,582,000 rubles, materials stores worth 2,510,300 rubles, pipelines worth 1,987,400 rubles, and miscellaneous property worth 557,100 rubles. The total is 25,478,300 rubles. Thus, without counting the costs of downhole work necessary to restore wells to a normal condition and to restore their proper equipment, the oil industry currently needs capital of at least 40 million rubles (12,430,000 to restore production wells, 9,525,000 to restore wells being drilled and deepened, and some 19 million rubles for miscellaneous property)."

The *Neftyanoye delo* also presented the following data: "By our approximate calculation, total oil production in 1905 was expressed as 410 million *poods* [49.2 million barrels], 216 million less than in 1904. The consequences of last year's events are not limited, however, to this colossal shortfall.... But that's not all. The devastation of the oil industry has had incalculable adverse repercussions in all branches of Russian industry."

Emanuel Nobel (1859-1932) (son of Ludvig Nobel) with senior employees of the
Partnership's Baku plant (1904). E. Nobel led the Partnership for 30 years.

An oil distillery in the Black City, Baku.

The traditional draft cart for transporting oil in wooden or metal drums (Baku) was gradually replaced by new forms of transport: tankers, tanker cars and oil pipelines.

Barges of the Artemyev brothers for transporting kerosene along the Volga River.

Oil tank cars in Uleshi, Saratov.

The first oil pipeline in Russia (Balakhany-Black City) was designed by 25-year-old Vladimir Shukhov for the Nobel Brothers Petroleum Production Partnership and extended 10 km (1878).

The journal *Transactions of the Imperial Russian Technical Society.* Articles about oil (1889).

Dmitry Mendeleyev (1834-1907), ideologist and pioneer of processes for highly refining oil, was the first to propose transporting oil in the holds of special vessels.

Первый наливной пароходъ въ мірѣ „Зороастръ".

The first metal tank steamer (tanker) the *Zoroastr* was built according to a special design in Sweden by the Nobel Brothers Petroleum Production Partnership and made regular trips beginning in 1878 in the Caspian Sea. By 1913, the Nobel brothers owned 89 ships and transported more than 70 million *poods* [8.4 million barrels] of tanker freight, primarily oil and crude oil, annually on their ships from Astrakhan along the Volga River.

Share of the V. I. Ragozin & Co. Oil
Production Partnership.

Viktor Ragozin (1833-1901).
The first to develop and organize in 1875 the
industrial processing of petroleum residues
and heavy oil.

The Konstantinovka Refinery of the V. I. Ragozin & Co. Partnership (Yaroslavl Province).
Here and at other factories, the V. I. Ragozin & Co. Partnership industrially produced oil
lubricants (oleonaphthas) that earned it the gold medal at the 1878 Paris World's Fair. In
1880, the entire French Navy shifted to Russian oleonaphthas supplies.

George Kerry, new territorial map of the Russian Empire (London, 1807).

W. Simpson: *Oil Well Drilling* and *Oil Fountain*,
from a cycle of paintings of Baku (1886).

Oil fields of the Nobel Brothers Petroleum Production Partnership in Romany, Baku.

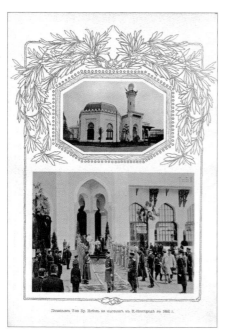

Russian Emperor Nicholas II's visit to the pavilion of the Nobel Brothers Petroleum Production Partnership at the National Industrial Art exhibit in Nizhny Novogorod in the summer of 1896.

Emperor Nicholas II (1868-1918), the last of the Romanov imperial dynasty, abdicated the throne during the February Revolution of 1917 (which began at a Nobel factory in St. Petersburg) and was shot in July 1918, in Yekaterinburg along with the other members of his family.

Vladimir Shukhov (1853-1939), a leading Russian engineer, architect, inventor and scholar who actively cooperated with the Nobel Brothers Petroleum Production Partnership.

He was the designer and chief engineer of Russia's first oil pipeline (Balakhany-Black City, 10 km long, 1878) and the first person in the world to design cylindrical storage tanks for pipeline infrastructure.

He designed the first pipeline for pre-heated crude oil, as well as the Baku-Batumi pipeline (883 km, 1907) and the Grozny-Tuapse pipeline (649 km, 1928). He developed a new burner for burning crude oil, the famous "Nobel burner." He developed and created the first thermal cracking plant, introduced a new method for airlifting oil and invented a new water-tube steam boiler.

Model of V. Shukhov's continuous oil distillery. He obtained the rights for the distillery in 1891.

Gift frame by K. Faberge; given to V. G. Shukhov (1895).

Postcards of oil fountains near Baku (early 20th century).

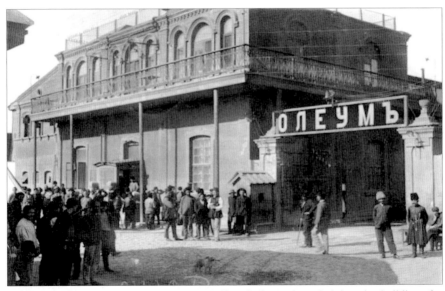

Harbinger of coming revolutionary events. Strikers in front of an administrative building of the Oleum firm, 1905. "Koba" Dzhugashvili (Stalin) was active in Baku during these years.

We can add one more illustrative example to the above. Production in fields operated by the industry leader, Nobel Brothers Petroleum Production Partnership, was reduced by a third, from 8.5 million barrels in 1904 to 5.5 million barrels in 1905, and kerosene production also declined by a third, from 4 million barrels in 1904 to 2.5 million barrels in 1905, while the company's export deliveries declined 29%, from 1.6 million barrels to 1.2 million barrels.

Overall, we should emphasize that the tragic events of August 1905 set Russia back nearly a decade in terms of production level. Russian petroleum products exports fell 57%, from 14.3 million barrels in 1904 to 6.2 million barrels in 1905.

A few years later, in 1908, Russian petroleum products exports were only 18.6% of American exports. The former head of the Caucasian Excise Tax Administration, Ludwig Perschke, cited the following figures, which speak volumes: "The loss of Far East markets was especially painful for the Baku industry, since the huge populations of India, China, and Japan offer a field for the widest development of kerosene trade…. There have been no deliveries to China since 1906…. Russia's share of India's total kerosene supply has fallen from 78% to 2%."[55]

As for the pride of the United States, the Standard Oil Company, it regained its dominant positions on the European and Eastern kerosene markets and opened up the enormous Chinese market for its petroleum products. Meanwhile, Great Britain, on the eve of the merger of Shell Transport and Trading Company with Royal Dutch, also gained a guaranteed sector for petroleum products sales in Asia and the Far East. But its principal gain was the opportunities it created by snapping up the ruined fields on the Absheron Peninsula literally for a song, paving the way for a massive expansion of British capital into the weakened Russian oil industry.

The First Labor Union of Russian Oil Workers

The creation of the first labor union in the Russian oil industry was preceded by a significant event. On March 4, 1906, the Russian government released "Temporary Rules on Professional Associations," which gave workers the legal right to legitimize their labor unions.

On September 29, 1906, the first workers' assembly was held in Balakhany, and special steps were worked out to establish a labor union. Intensive organization proceeded through the month of October, and on November 7, 1906 the authorities approved the charter of the Oil Industry Workers Union. At the end of the month, the union held a general meeting at which a 12-member governing board was elected. The board was located in Balakhany, and the union had divisions in Bibiheybet, Surakhany, and in the Black City outside Baku.

The Oil Industry Workers Union did not limit itself to production problems, but attended to the most varied issues. Library reading rooms at oil fields in Balakhany, Sabunchu, Ramana, Bibiheybet, and Keshle became a focus of the labor union's activities. These libraries became true centers of economic, political, and cultural education for the working class. The union paid a great deal of attention to issues of oil worker health preservation as well, as the oil industry was among Russia's leaders in the number of accidents involving workers. According to factory inspectorate data, from 1907 to 1909, over 5,600 accidents occurred in the oil industry in the Baku oil district alone, which amounted to 11.2 injuries per 100 workers. In the second half of 1908, under pressure from the Oil Industry Workers Union, the Council of the Congress of Baku Petroleum Industrialists organized a Physician's Bureau for Certification of Maimed Workers. Under the terms of the agreement reached between the Council of the Congress and the Council of Oil Industry Workers, two of the four doctors making up the Bureau were to be elected by the workers themselves. The union's representative, in the person of its secretary, was obligated to participate in all meetings of the Bureau.

In addition to work-related injuries, epidemics were also a constant threat to workers' lives and health. When a cholera outbreak threatened the Absheron Peninsula in the summer of 1907, the union was very active in preventing imminent disaster. On August 26, 1907, the union's board decided to convene a meeting of field and factory commissions to discuss ways of combating cholera, and adopted specific steps to fight the epidemic. In addition, important issues relating to the organization of physician care for certification of maimed workers and improvement of medical service to drilling crew and ancillary field workers were submitted for consideration.

The Oil Industry Workers Union's energetic activity produced tangible results from the start, reflected primarily by the growth of its ranks. Even in its early days, in late 1907 and the first half of 1908, the union counted over 9,000 members.

The first months of the union's operation saw an emerging need for it to create its own print publication. On August 12, 1907, it released the first issue of the *Gudok* ["Whistle"], the voice of the Oil Industry Workers Union. This publication regularly explored the most important practical issues of the labor union movement, reported in detail on the position of the multinational oil industry working class, and fought for its rights.

Then, beginning on September 6, 1908, the weekly newspaper *Bakinsky rabochy* ["Baku Worker"], became the new print voice of the Oil Industry Workers Union. Addressing its readers, the paper wrote: "Comrade readers! After a long interval, we have gained another opportunity to interact closely with you through the printed word. We were forced to keep silent at the key point of our struggle with the oil industrialists, when the printed word, discussion of pressing issues, and the exchange of opinions were especially needed.... We don't need to disseminate much about our program, about the paths we will take and to which we will call the Baku working class. We are old acquaintances of the Baku workers and know each other well.... Comrade workers! The *Bakinsky rabochy* will be your newspaper, as was the *Gudok* before us, so the more interest you take in us and the more actively you participate in it, the more fully it will reflect your needs and desires.... Do not forget this, and try to help your newspaper do what good it can for you."

The oilfield and refinery workers answered the call. The paper established a firm relationship with the broad masses of workers, and became their favorite publication, in whose pages they found answers to the burning issues of their lives.

It should be noted that beginning in 1906, another labor union was operating on the Absheron Peninsula, alongside the Oil Industry Workers Union. This was the Mechanical Production Workers Union, for specialists involved in the servicing of oil fields and refineries. For some time, despite the fact that they addressed essentially the same issues, these two labor unions were often unable to coordinate their activities properly. Not until several years had passed were they able to overcome their differences and address the question of forming a single labor union—the Union of Oil Workers and Allied Trades. Formed in February 1912, the Union did much to help raise the level of activities to protect the vital interests of oil workers.

Oil on the Agenda of the State Duma

The history of Russian parliamentarianism provides the best argument against any idea that Russia has no democratic traditions. The Russian Federation, just like other nations, came to parliamentarianism by a long route, using the method of trial and error. Here we must mention the predecessors of domestic parliamentarianism: land, urban, and university self-government in the Russian Empire; class self-government in the centralized Muscovite state; and finally, the *veche* (public assembly) in many cities of Kievan Rus.

Russia's first representative parliamentary institution (in the modern sense of the term) was founded by Emperor Nicholas II's Manifesto establishing the State Duma and the Law Creating the State Duma, both promulgated August 6, 1905. Under pressure from the liberal wing of the government, represented mainly by his Prime Minister Sergey Witte, in an atmosphere of massive revolutionary demonstrations, Nicholas II decided to cool down the political situation in Russia by showing his subjects that he intended to consider the public need for a representative branch of government. This is explicitly stated in his Manifesto: "The time has now come, following their good beginnings, to call elected people from all Russian lands to permanent and active participation in the drafting of laws by including, to this end, a special legal-consultative establishment among high government institutions, which is authorized to carry out the preliminary development and discussion of draft legislation and to review the list of state revenues and outlays." As the Manifesto makes clear, the new body was initially conceived with only a consultative role.

The following Manifesto of October 17, 1905, "On the Improvement of State Procedures," substantially expanded the Duma's authority. The Russian emperor's sovereignty, i.e., the autocratic nature of his power, was retained. The procedure for elections to the first Duma was defined in an election law promulgated in December 1905, which instituted four curias, or citizen classifications, for the purposes of election: landowners, urban residents, peasants, and workers. We should note that the elections themselves were still not universal (they excluded women, people under 25 years of age, soldiers, and a variety of ethnic minorities), nor were they equal (one member of the landowners' curia represented 2,000 voters; one member of the urban curia represented 4,000; one member of the peasant curia represented 30,000; and one member of the workers' curia represented 90,000) or direct (election was a two-stage process, and for workers and peasants, it was a three- and four-stage process).

Having accorded legislative powers to the State Duma, the tsarist government did everything possible to limit them. In the Manifesto of February 20, 1906, it transformed the Russian Empire's supreme legal-consultative establishment, the State Council (which had existed since 1810), into a second legislative chamber with veto power over decisions of the State Duma. On April 23, 1906, Nicholas II approved a code of Basic State Laws, which the Duma could amend only at the initiative of the tsar himself. In particular, these laws specified a whole series of severe restrictions on the activities of the future Russian parliament. The tsar retained full power to govern the country through a ministry answerable only to him, to manage foreign policy, and to control the army and navy; during recesses between sessions, he could promulgate laws that were then merely formally ratified by the State Duma (Art. 87 of the Basic Laws).

The first State Duma lasted from April to July 1906 and convened only one session. Of 499 deputies elected to the first Duma, the most numerous bloc was members of the Constitutional Democratic Party, numbering 179 deputies. The Octobrists were represented by 16 deputies, and the Social Democrats, by 18. The so-called ethnic minorities had 63 representatives, and another 105 representatives were unaffiliated. Representatives of Russia's agrarian labor party, or, as they were called at the time, the "Trudoviks," comprised an impressive bloc of 97 deputies, and retained this quota through practically all of the Dumas. Sergey Muromtsev (1850–1910), a professor at the College of Roman Law at St. Petersburg University, was elected chairman of the first Duma.

From the very outset, the first Duma demonstrated that it did not intend to accommodate caprice or authoritarianism on the part of the tsarist government. In response to the emperor's throne speech of May 5, 1906, the State Duma adopted a message demanding amnesty for political prisoners; real exercise of political freedoms; universal suffrage; elimination of land set aside for the treasury, appanage, and monasterial property; and so forth.

In turn, the emperor's disparaging attitude toward the Duma became apparent when the first bill he sent to the deputies for consideration involved the question of allocating 40,000 rubles to build a palm conservatory and a laundry facility at Yuryev University (now Tartu University).

During its brief life, the first State Duma discussed a large number of issues: repeal of the death penalty and amnesty for political prisoners; freedoms of the press, of unions, and of assembly; civil equality; the Black Hundreds pogrom in Bialystok and others; labor unions; assistance to the unemployed and starving; and naturally, one of the main issues, the agrarian question. In all, it considered 391 requests from the Russian government and approved 261. The government rejected all parliamentary proposals expressed as wishes for partial political amnesty, creation of a "government answerable to the State Duma," expansion of suffrage and other freedoms, increased peasant land ownership, etc. In turn, the Duma passed a resolution of complete lack of confidence in the government and demanded its resignation, whereupon the Duma was dissolved by Nicholas II, going down in history as the "Duma of Public Anger."

The second Duma was convened in February 1907. As chairman, it elected the noted land movement figure and Deputy for Moscow Province, attorney Fëdor Golovin (1867–1937), one of the founders of the Constitutional Democratic Party. In all, this Duma operated for 102 days during only one session. Most of its meetings were devoted to problems of procedure. This became a unique way of fighting the government during the discussion of various bills, which the government believed the Duma had no right to raise or discuss. The government, answerable only to the tsar, did not wish to consider the deputies' opinions, and the deputies, regarding themselves as the people's elected representatives, did not wish to submit to this state of affairs, striving to achieve their goals by one means or another. Ultimately, this confrontation became one of the main causes of the second Duma's dissolution on June 3, 1907.

As a result of the introduction of a new election law in Russia, a third State Duma was formed, the only one of the four that survived its full five-year term under law, from November 1907 to June 1912. It held five sessions. As chairman, the Duma elected Nikolay Khomyakov

(1850–1925), a leader of the October 17 Alliance. In March 1910, he was replaced by Aleksandr Guchkov (1862–1936), a noted politician and leader of the October 17 Party, and a year later, the Duma elected Mikhail Rodzyanko (1859–1924), a major political figure and one of the leaders of the October 17 Party.

The fourth Duma, the last in the history of autocratic Russia, arose during a period of increasing crisis for the country and the whole world: the eve of the First World War. Five sessions were held between November 1912 and October 1917. The fourth Duma differed little in makeup from the third, except that a considerable number of clergy were added to the ranks of deputies. The chairman of the fourth Duma for its entire term was Mikhail Rodzyanko. It should be noted that the Fourth State Duma played a leading role in instituting the Provisional Govern-ment after the collapse of the autocracy. Beginning in March 1917, it operated through private meetings, but on October 6, 1917, the Provisional Government of the Russian Republic ordered the Duma dissolved in connection with preparations for elections to the Con-stitutional Convention.

In all four State Dumas, the ranks of the deputies were dominated (in various proportions, of course) by members of the landed gentry, trading and industrial bourgeoisie, urban intelligentsia, and peasantry. They brought to the institution their ideas of ways for Russia to develop and their skills in public debate. It was especially illustrative that the intelligentsia used skills acquired in university lecture halls and court-rooms, while the peasants brought many democratic traditions of community self-government. In their work, the deputies made wide use of a system of inquiries. In response to any emergency, after collecting a certain number of signatures, the deputies could submit an inter-pellation, that is, a demand that the government account for its actions, to which one or another minister had to respond. Thus, the birth of Russian parliamentarianism provided valuable experience combating authoritarian propensities in the activities of rulers. The practice of discussing various bills in the Duma is still of unequivocal interest for modern parliamentarians. For example, the third Duma had some 30 deputy committees. The more important committees, such as the budget committee, had several dozen members. The Duma's own legislative initiative was limited by the requirement that each proposal have at least 30 sponsors. Based on one such initiative, the Duma developed and adopted one of the most progressive factory and plant laws in Europe.

In the opinion of a number of Russian historians, on the whole, the work of the State Duma was an important factor in the political development of early 20th-century Russia, substantially affecting many sectors of public life, including the development of the oil industry. This is where the first attempt was made to begin truly meaningful, systematic efforts to introduce civil law principles into the use of mineral resources, and to correct contradictions in the framework of the rigid administrative regime governing the exploitation of oil fields and the need to ensure freedom for private enterprise.

As an example, we can cite the inquiry of October 19, 1909 submitted by a group of 42 members of the October 17 Alliance bloc in the State Duma, "On the Illegal Cession of Oil-Bearing Parcels in Baku Province," which spoke of a flagrant violation of law on the part of the Russian Ministry of Trade and Industry in allocating oil-bearing lands on the Absheron Peninsula to two highly placed tsarist dignitaries, hunt director [*Jägermeister*] Vasily I. Mamantov and hunt director Pavel P. Golenishchev-Kutuzov-Tolstoy. Discussion of this inquiry in the State Duma erupted in a loud scandal, and exposed a shocking forgery with the assignment of oil-bearing lands to "dead souls"[56]—the Caucasian Partnership, which had ceased to exist in 1900, and two long-dead entrepreneurs, Bastamov and Shkhiyants. This parliamentary session was widely covered in the Russian and foreign press, and evoked a strong public response, which ultimately caused the minister of industry and trade, privy councilor Vladimir Timiryazev, to resign in disgrace.

In early 1913, Russia saw a substantial rise in petroleum products prices, and began to experience a shortage of kerosene, lubricants, and residual oil, which created serious problems for the normal operation of the national economy. In March 1913, the State Duma sent the government an inquiry, "On the Activities of Syndicates in the Oil Industry," where it raised the following question fairly clearly: "Is the Minister of Trade and Industry aware that the activities of major oil companies are giving obvious and clear indications of the existence of an illegal oil-industry syndicate? If so, what steps has he taken to investigate these illegal activities and to curtail further existence of the syndicate?" The discussion of this parliamentary inquiry within the government led to the development and implementation of a series of concrete steps to develop the national oil industry and correct the situation in the country's oil market, and led to a certain mitigation of the petroleum fuel shortage. But the First World War, which began in August 1914, prevented the full implementation of these plans.

We should note that the history of parliamentary activity in tsarist Russia is extraordinarily relevant and necessary today. It teaches the public representatives of our time to be combative, to be able to defend the public interest under strong pressure from the executive branch, to engage in sharp parliamentary debate, to find creative ways for the body of deputies to work together, to maintain a high degree of professionalism, and to be proactive lawmakers.

Regaining Lost Ground

After the events of August 1905, the Russian government and oil industrialists undertook emergency measures to restore the damaged oil fields on the Absheron Peninsula and exerted great efforts to rehabilitate oilfield and processing equipment, but the level of damage done prevented a quick recovery of what had been lost. Russia produced 53.8 million barrels (8.09 million tons) in 1906, 62.3 million barrels (9.36 million tons) in 1907, and 63.4 million barrels (9.53 million tons) in 1908.

During 1906 alone, three conferences were held, in February, June, and December, by the main representative organization of the industry's entrepreneurs, the Baku Congress of Oil Industrialists. The resolutions of the Congress contained specific proposals to the government for leading the Russian oil industry out of its severe crisis and restoring Russia's position as a stable, competitive supplier to the European and world petroleum product markets.

It seemed that joint government and industry efforts would soon show positive results. The government adopted a decision to grant loans worth 20 million rubles to the oil industrialists, although in fact only 13 million rubles in loans was actually disbursed. In 1906, the government held regular auctions for new oil-bearing areas on the Absheron Peninsula. Under the provisional rules in place at the time, auctions favored higher percentage payments to the treasury of produced oil; that is, whoever offered a greater share would win the desired oil-bearing parcel. At auction, the major companies that won the bids offered the treasury 57–70% of the oil produced as rent.

However, to the surprise of the oil industrialists, the Senate rejected the auction results. As justification for their decision, the senators stated that "the existing terms do not guarantee market prices for crude oil." The Senate resolution also contained this language: "The major firms do not fear large percentage payments, so long as they can secure for themselves the treasury's remaining reserves of oil lands, in order to make themselves masters of the oil market."

After voiding the results of the 1906 auction, the Russian State Duma managed, after fierce debate, to establish only "the urgent need to promulgate a new oil law." And consequently, one Russian newspaper wrote: "Beginning in 1906, the ministers of industry and trade, accepting the portfolio, zealously emphasized in their declarations that the oil law was first and foremost; what remained was only to discuss it." Understanding the urgent need to restore the industry, the Russian government proposed an auction in 1909 under new rules, but the State Duma rejected that proposal as well.

Thus, new oil-bearing lands were not leased, and for nearly the entire first decade of the 20th century, oil production on the Absheron Peninsula proceeded only in the four areas previously developed. Not until 1907 did very limited development of fields begin in new areas, particularly Surakhany.

The industry felt a pressing need to develop new oil-bearing areas, and at this point the Kuban, the home of Russia's first oil gusher, unexpectedly emerged to the forefront. After many years in oblivion, the clock struck once again for the oil-bearing foothill strip in Maykop District in the eastern Kuban Region. On August 30, 1909, near the village of Shirvanskaya, a well on a parcel belonging to the Baku and Black Sea Partnership produced a powerful gusher with a daily flow of 36,025 barrels from a depth of 253 feet. Within a week, the gusher produced as much as 240,175 barrels of crude.

For many entrepreneurs, this was a bolt from the blue. Mining engineer Yevgeny Yushkin, an eyewitness to the events, wrote: "August 30, 1909 will be remembered in the Kuban Region as the day a major oil industry was developed.... The honor of establishing the reputation of the field belongs to the Baku and Black Sea Partnership, which was organized by three people (Russian engineers) and appeared after all others, in December 1908. The company looked at the business correctly, ran its enterprise in an efficient industrial manner, and didn't begin drilling little holes, but wells. And it made the best of its goods, advertising the riches of the Kuban Region's oil-bearing ground."

The news of the unprecedented Kuban gusher near Shirvanskaya appeared in every Russian newspaper. The report was immediately picked up by foreign print media as well, which set the stage for the so-called "Maykop Oil Boom."

In October 1909, two British entrepreneurs visited the Kuban on an inspection mission, and upon returning to London established a series of companies with British capital. By 1910, some 50 joint-stock companies aimed at developing the Kuban oil fields had been formed in Great Britain, including the Australia-Maykop Company (with authorized capital of £275,000), the Austria-Maykop Company (£275,000), the Maykop Valley (£400,000), the Maykop Spies Company (£200,000), the Maykop-Absheron Petroleum Company (£450,000), the Maykop Parcels Company (£600,000), and others.

However, in addition to serious entrepreneurs, all types of swindlers also decided to play "oil roulette." Newly formed companies such as the Taman–Black Sea Oil Company (1911), the Anglo-Taman Oil Financing Syndicate (1912), the Central Caucasus Oil Industry Company (1913), the East Caucasus Oil Industry Company (1913), the Caucasus (Black Sea) Oil Company (1913), and the Caucasus Oil Syndicate (1914, with a capital of only £100), were created merely for speculative purposes.

Impatient Russian seekers of "black gold" didn't lag far behind the foreign entrepreneurs, either. That same year, the office of mining engineer

Yevgeny Yushkin received 38,000 letters, resulting in the issuance of 2,865 permission certificates for oil exploration, nearly three times as many as in the two previous years.

In his article "The Maykop Oil Fever," engineer Korzukhin noted that the period from 1909 to 1910 was a time of exceptional interest in Kuban crude, which evoked such enthusiasm that prospecting for it covered the entire region with a dense forest of claim markers.

Striving to reduce the high temperature of the "oil fever" in early 1910, a group of entrepreneurs and engineers started a special publication in Yekaterinodar, the *Kuban Oil Industry Annual* [*Yezhegodnik Kubanskoy neftyanoy promyshlennosti*], in which they published articles by geologists, mining engineers, and other specialists on issues relating to oil development in the region.

In July 1910, the Russian war department convened an extensive conference on matters related to oil prospects in the Kuban Region. As a result, a new list of known oil-bearing lands in the Kuban Region that were to be leased at auction was published in September 1910.

From 1910 to 1916, the accomplished Russian oil scientist, mining engineer Ivan Gubkin (1871–1939), worked productively in the Kuban Region. During this time, he published numerous works of relevance to prospecting in the region, including: "Report on Exploratory Work in the Neftyano-Shirvanskaya Oil-Bearing Area" (1910), "The Maykop Oil-Bearing District" (1912), "On the Question of the Geologic Structure of the Central Part of the Neftyano-Shirvanskaya Oil Field" (1913), "Report on Geologic Studies of the Anapa-Temryuk District" (1912), "Report on Geologic Studies on the Taman Peninsula" (1913), "Survey of Geologic Formations on the Taman Peninsula" (1913), "On the Need to Plug Drillholes in Kudako, Kuban Region" (1914), and "Geologic Study of the Kuban Oil-Bearing District" (1915). Additionally, his discovery of a unique oil pool, shaped like a sleeve, doubtless occupies a place of honor in the history of world geologic science.

In January 1910, work began to create a representative entrepreneurial organization in the region and soon after the Committee of the Union of Kuban Oil Industrialists was formed. Then, in October 1911, the First Congress of Kuban Oil Industrialists convened in Yekaterinodar, where it elected a board and approved a program for its subsequent activities.

The Maykop oil boom soon brought solid results. Whereas 4,368 feet of hole were drilled and 68,737 barrels of oil were produced in the Kuban in 1909, 28,077 feet were drilled and 156,691 barrels were produced in 1910, and these figures grew rapidly: in 1912, 84,910 feet were drilled and 941,158 barrels were produced.

All this required new refining enterprises. In 1909, entrepreneur Selitrennikova funded the construction of a refinery near the Cossack village of Shirvanskaya, with a capacity of 5.1 tons of crude per day. Three strands of pipeline (2, 2½, and 3 inches in diameter) were subsequently laid from the refinery to carry petroleum products to a loading station on the Maykop-Yekaterinodar highway. In 1911, a refinery with the mellifluous name, "First Kuban Refinery of the Black Sea Oil Fields" was built near the Shirvan fields. On August 31, 1911, the P. O. Ter-Gukasov & Co. refinery was put into operation in Yekaterinodar, near a railroad bridge on the Novorossiysk line. Crude oil was refined on a six-still bank, and its capacity was 2,950 barrels/day. Its main product consisted of several grades of clarified kerosene. In addition, the refinery also made gasoline on a rectification unit consisting of a 1,413-cubic-foot still and a "cap" column. Finished petroleum products were loaded via a loading gantry on the refinery grounds into tank cars supplied by the Vladikavkaz Railroad.

In addition to refineries, the Shirvanskaya–Yekaterinodar oil pipeline (69 miles) and the Khadyzhenskaya–Tuapse oil pipeline (79 miles) were built in the Kuban Region in 1911.

The year 1912 was a time of maximum production in the Kuban: 74,417 feet of hole were drilled and 1.1 million barrels of oil were produced. In January 1913, the Second Congress of Kuban Oil Industrialists convened in Yekaterinodar to discuss the prior year's results and announce its optimistic forecasts for the future.

As for the Russian oil industry as a whole, 70.7 million barrels (10.16 million tons) of crude oil were produced in 1912. However, Russia continued to lag very far behind the US in this indicator.

Table 6. Russian and US Oil Production, 1906–1912
(in millions of tons)

	Russian Oil Production	US Oil Production
1906	8.09	19.3
1907	9.36	25.42
1908	9.53	27.4
1909	10.1	28.02
1910	10.77	32.15
1911	10.13	33.69
1912	10.28	34.14

Source: Dyakonova, I. A. *Oil and Coal in the Power Industry of Tsarist Russia in International Comparisons* [*Neft i ugol v energetike tsarskoy Rossii v mezhdunarodnykh sopostavleniyakh*]. Moscow, 1999, p. 166.

A major turning point for the Russian oil industry was the unexpected departure of the Paris banking house of the Rothschild family from the Russian market in 1912. Looking at the performance of the Rothschild oil companies during the first decade of the new century, no one would have predicted that they would lose their hard-won market share to anyone. The fixed assets of the Caspian and Black Sea Oil Industrial and Trading Company at the time totaled 10 million rubles, and it held oil fields on the Absheron Peninsula at Balakhany, Sabunchu, Ramana and Bibiheybet, and also in Grozny and on Cheleken Island. Its well count reached 285, and it operated 45 steam engines and 19 electric motors. The company produced more than 3.9 million barrels of crude per year, and employed 1,269 workers. Meanwhile, the Mazut Company's fixed assets were 6 million rubles. It comprised numerous wholesale offices throughout the country, its own tanker and tug fleet, a huge number of railroad tank cars, a repair yard at Dyadkovo, Yaroslavl Province, and other service enterprises. The company's net profit in 1903 was 531,300 rubles, and it paid a dividend of 6% per share.

To a certain extent, the Rothschilds' decision to leave Russia was influenced by the bloody events of August 1905 on the Absheron Peninsula, and also by the passing of one of the company's key figures, Alphonse Rothschild. Thus, the Paris banking house of the Rothschild family entered into complex years-long negotiations with Royal Dutch Shell, culminating in February 1912 with the signing of an agreement in which the Paris banking house of the Rothschild family ceded all of its Russian enterprises to the English-Dutch concern headed by the noted entrepreneur Henri Deterding (1866–1939).

In 1912, recognizing the power of this transnational corporation, the Russian government supported the formation of a new corporation of Russian industrialists in order to hold down prices on crude oil and petroleum products. This organization was a mighty holding company whose portfolio included large blocks of stock in merged Russian enterprises. Its partners included major joint-stock companies—A. I. Mantashev & Co. Oil Industrial and Trading Company, the G. M. Lianozov Sons Oil Industrial Company, the Caspian Partnership, the Neft Petroleum Products Production, Transportation, Storage and Trading Partnership, and the Moscow-Caucasus Oil Industrial and Trading Company—but the vast majority of participants were medium-sized and even small businesses. The new oil conglomerate, formed under the aegis of Russian banks, was registered in London as a British company, the Russian General Oil Corporation. The company's board included a member of the parliament of the United Kingdom and a British representative of the London division of the Russian-Asian Bank. The Russian entrepreneurs needed this "English shell" to simplify the attraction of new capital to Russia, but multiple attempts to place the corporation's stock on leading European exchanges were not successful.

The Years of the "Great Battle of Nations"

In June 1912, the State Duma finally approved the long-awaited "Law on Leasing of Treasury Lands." The first auctions under the new law were scheduled for mid-1913. In practical terms, the Law proved extremely unsuccessful: the auctions were supposed to determine who would agree to supply the treasury a mandatory minimum of crude oil at the lowest price. The auction results were unexpected: a price of "minus 47 kopecks per *pood* [36 pounds]" was offered—that is, the oil industrialist was prepared to pay the treasury 47 kopecks for delivery of each 36 pounds of crude oil. The Russian papers wrote: "So here's what these syndicate owners are doing: not only will they not take a thing from the treasury for oil delivered, but what's more, they will pay for it.... They must be hiding something here." Naturally, what was being hidden was the simple business calculation of covering all costs of sales on the free market of the oil that would be produced over and above the mandatory minimum. However, the Senate rejected the auction results, repeating the paradoxical situation of seven years earlier.

So it is not surprising that, in part due to the unhelpful position of Russian legislatures, the domestic oil industry continued to lag behind the US in the world market competition. Whereas Russian companies produced 67.6 million barrels (10.17 million tons) of crude in 1913, their American counterparts produced 3.7 times as much—37.96 million tons.

The steady decline in Russian oil production that began in 1909 owing to the depletion of Absheron Peninsula old fields was partially compensated by the placement of new Grozny fields into industrial production. Grozny's share of the crude, which had been 4.4% in 1902, rose to 13.5% by 1913.

In 1913, the Russian industry leader, the Nobel Brothers Petroleum Production Partnership, produced 7.9 million barrels of crude, and refined 6.9 million barrels at its refineries to make 2.4 million barrels of kerosene alone. Oil production was carried on at 479 wells, and 177 steam engines and 131 electric motors operated in the oil fields. The total number of employees was 2,541. To transport the crude oil and petroleum products, the company had at its disposal 43 inland ships, 14 schooners, 209 barges, and 1,400 railroad tank cars.

Unfortunately, the year 1913 brought a major disappointment to the Kuban oil industry. Despite 79,765 feet of hole having been drilled in the Maykop District, only 576,782 barrels of crude were produced. This 47.5% drop in oil production was a very unpleasant surprise for the Board of the Union of Kuban Oil Industrialists, the entrepreneurs in the region, as well as the British stockholders of the numerous Maykop oil companies. In the following year, 1914, the Maykop fields produced only 475,169 barrels of crude from 242 wells.

In his 1915 article, "Status of the Maykop Oil Industry and Outlook for the Future," mining engineer Yevgeny Yushkin thoroughly analyzed the state of affairs in the Kuban. Despite the pessimistic assessments that prevailed among entrepreneurs, the author concluded that they should "not sit idly," but continue "research in further directions from known to unknown" and fully "use the experience of prior years." Symbolically, as if in confirmation of these words, a powerful oil gusher some 98 feet high was struck on March 10, 1915 at the village of Absheron. The gusher produced about 360,265 barrels of crude in 50 days, and total production for the year was 886,489 barrels.

Meanwhile, Royal Dutch Shell was especially active in Russia, striving to expand its participation in the development of the Grozny, Maykop, and Emba fields and attract additional investment in these regions. During its first two years, it ran its Russian branch entirely from London, but beginning in 1914, most of the functions of regional management were gradually shifted to one of the concern's major enterprises, the Mazut Company. It was this company, at the direction of top management at Royal Dutch Shell, that carried out the essential reorganization of the English-Dutch giant's entire group of Russian enterprises during the next several years.

However, any gains made by Royal Dutch Shell and other Russian oil industrialists were put on hold by the outbreak of war. On August 1, 1914, at 7 p.m. in St. Petersburg, the German ambassador to Russia, Count Friedrich von Purtales, handed Russian Foreign Minister Sergey D. Sazonov a declaration of war. The two countries entered the First World War, the "battle of nations," from which no nation was destined to emerge victorious.

Russia was not ready for war, and this became obvious within months of the opening of hostilities. The Russian military industry, which required serious modernization, could not cope with the volumes of military equipment, materiel, munitions and supplies required of it.

The acuteness of the problem of supplying and transporting petroleum products became apparent fairly quickly, partly due to the changing structure of the demand. Despite the cessation of petroleum products exports, fuel shortages and price increases began to be felt to a much greater degree. In addition, the Russian Empire's entry into the war closed off access to the Turkish straits; that is, the export of oil through the essential port of Batumi was completely halted. This meant a total loss of traditional Russian petroleum products markets in Western Europe and the Middle East, which still accounted for a fairly large share of Russia's total oil exports.

The elimination of petroleum products exports produced, in turn, another structural crisis in the industry. Since the oil industry's foreign trade was oriented toward petroleum products, a cessation of their exports inevitably led to a considerable increase in the residual oil component at domestic refineries. Whereas kerosene accounted for 25.1% of the total volume of Russian petroleum products in 1913, that figure was only 17.6% in 1915; comparatively, residual oil increased from 61.8% in 1913 to 77.0% in 1915, a rise of 15%.

The events of the First World War inevitably had a negative effect on the status of the Maykop oil district in the Kuban, which up until that point had shown signs of revival. The impossibility of selling oil through the Black Sea ports irreversibly undermined future prospects for increasing petroleum products volumes in the region.

Table 7. Russian and US Oil Production, 1913–1917
(in millions of tons)

	Russian Oil Production	US Oil Production
1913	10.179	37.96
1914	10.26	40.72
1915	10.326	43.02
1916	10.076	46.09
1917	9.656	51.29

Source: Dyakonova, I. A. *Oil and Coal in the Power Industry of Tsarist Russia in International Comparisons [Neft i ugol v energetike tsarskoy Rossii v mezhdunarodnykh sopostavleniyakh].* Moscow, 1999, p. 166.

Meanwhile, the forced structural changes in the oil industry and the general state of emergency during the war required the government to establish control over the regularity of petroleum products shipments. In late 1914, the first government fuel agency was formed, the Special Central Committee for Oil Supply, a unit of the Ministry of Trade and Industry. In March 1915, in support of this modest agency, an Inter-departmental Committee for Fuel Distribution was formed under the Ministry of Railroads.

Ultimately, the Law of August 17, 1915 undertook a new attempt at government regulation of the petroleum products market: a Special Council on Fuel [*OSOTOP*] was created under the Ministry of Trade and Industry. Council members were representatives of the State Council and State Duma, leading ministries (inland waters, finances, etc.), and social organizations (all-Russian unions, elective district councils [*zemstvos*], and cities). The council was headed by a representative of the Ministry of Trade and Industry, and everyday matters were supervised by the Provisional Office, headed by a colleague of the minister of trade and industry, the fuel commissioner-in-chief. His petroleum section was the Main Crude Oil and Petroleum Products Supply and Sales Administration [*Glavneft*]. Locally, issues of fuel supply were the responsibility of authorized representatives of the chairman of the council, and a special position, the Caucasus Fuel Commissioner, was created. *OSOTOP* even published its own newspaper, *Izvestiya Osobogo Soveshchaniya po toplivu* ["News of the Special Council on Fuel"].

OSOTOP's main objective was to assist in providing fuel to railroads and enterprises working for the army. In practice, this assistance amounted to organizing shipments and ensuring the export of fuel via rail and ship. It is notable that *OSOTOP* did not limit companies' trading operations: as before, companies set prices and were free to choose buyers. However, this did not last long, as petroleum fuel demand increased considerably as a result of the cessation of deliveries of English coal to Russia and difficulties with the export of Donetsk coal, together with the development of military procurement. This created a trend toward higher prices and toward the selection of customers from the standpoint of their ability to pay, placing railroads, the least reliable payers, in an especially difficult position.

For this reason, in January 1916 the Russian government took a major step on the path to state regulation of the oil trade by establishing mandatory price controls on shipments of petroleum products to all customers. The imposition of fixed prices was soon followed by a law on compulsory shipments, which further restricted the freedom of oil trade.

The government made feverish attempts to find an adequate administrative structure. On May 4, 1916, the minister of trade and industry approved "Rules for the Distribution of Crude and Residual Oil among Consumers," which established five categories of customers. To implement the rules, a central agency, the Central Oil Industry Administration [*Tsentroneft*], was created under the railroad administration in the fall of 1916.

On September 3, 1916, a system of permitted petroleum products shipments was established. Under this system, *OSOTOP* set priorities for providing tank cars to various categories of customers. The practice of requisitioning petroleum products had come about even earlier: i.e., in the absence of contracts for the delivery of petroleum products to important customers, *OSOTOP* could issue mandatory work orders. Late that same year, it approved a project proposed by the Mining Department to create three treasury oil fields on the Absheron Peninsula, with an expected annual production of up to 6 million barrels. Alas, there was insufficient time to implement the project. Military setbacks and economic difficulties stirred up the unstable domestic political situation in Russia. Numerous political parties of the most diverse types demanded immediate implementation of a series of major reforms, but the Russian government, headed by Nicholas II, could not retreat from its chosen suicidal path, and the serious political and socioeconomic crisis grew and deepened with every passing day, ultimately overflowing into the February 1917 revolution and the overthrow of autocracy in Russia.

Under the Fragments of the "Oil Olympus"

On March 2, 1917, in a train car at Pskov railroad station, Russian Emperor Nicholas II signed a Manifesto abdicating the throne, thereby ending the more than 300-year history of Russian government by the

Romanov dynasty.

The accession of the Provisional Government during the revolution was met with hope by many industrialists, who realized that the country needed radical transformations.

The events that occurred in the country in February 1917 were reflected both on the Absheron Peninsula and in other oil-producing regions of the country. As early as March 3 and 4, a general strike was called at all major Russian oil fields and refineries, followed by an endless series of various mass activities among the workers, including rallies, parades, and demonstrations. Everywhere, an atmosphere of faith and hope for decisive and favorable changes in Russian society prevailed.

Speaking at a meeting of industrialists, traders, and financiers with members of the Provisional Government in the Alexander Hall of the Petrograd Duma on March 8, 1917, Chairman Emanuel Nobel of the St. Petersburg Society of Plant and Factory Owners declared, "I am speaking on behalf of the whole Russian oil industry. Believing firmly in the powerful forces of the new Great Russia, we set ourselves the immediate objective of providing our armed forces with the petroleum products needed for the army and navy on land, on and under the seas, and in the air in a timely fashion."

On March 10, 1917, the Provisional Government abolished all restrictions on the oil industry that had existed in the Russian Empire. At the same time, however, the revolution laid the groundwork for a new round of tighter state control over business operations. The new rulers were essentially in a no-win situation: on the one hand, economic reforms and liberalization were being demanded; on the other, the war had to be continued, which required control over strategically important facilities.

The Provisional Government saw a way out of the emerging economic crisis through the further centralization of economic administration. In particular, it formed the Main Economic Committee, which concentrated an extensive network of supply agencies in the hands of the state. However, despite these steps, the Provisional Government could not handle the fuel and food crisis. Soon, hopes for a Russian renaissance and the restoration of its position in the world began to plummet. Industrialists and entrepreneurs became convinced of the complete inability of Aleksandr Kerensky's Provisional Government to offer Russian society a realistic plan of action.

Economic chaos in transportation and industry became an awful reality of those days. In this context, oil production volumes on the Absheron Peninsula fell to 48.4 million barrels in 1917 versus 57.2 million barrels in 1916.

It should be noted that in 1917, reduced production at the four old Baku areas, which had yielded 83.3% of all production in 1913, was inevitable. The scale of drilling had declined 20.2% in 1914, 8.0%

in 1915, and 9.0% in 1916. At the time, wells took an average of two years to drill. The average flow from a new well did not increase—it decreased—and old wells were being retired faster than new wells were being drilled. Drilling volumes fell in Grozny as well, but during the war years, previously developed high-flowing wells with gushing oil were brought online.

The direct and most acute cause of the reduction in drilling volumes was the shortage of steel, especially casing pipe. Oilmen began feeling the steel shortage as early as 1914, and acknowledged it very clearly in 1915.

The situation continued to deteriorate, and a tragic turning point in the supply of pipe and other steel products occurred in early 1917, when even the smallest orders ceased to be filled; the shortage of steel for the oil industry reached 40–50%. Nearly all steel went to complete the drilling of old wells; only 77 new wells were started in Baku in all of 1917, compared with 319 in 1913. The main cause of the lack of steel was that its production had declined sharply. As the managing director of the Prodmet syndicate reported to the war and naval ministry on March 21, 1917: "Just under 50% of blast furnaces are inactive, and those that are still operating are at half-capacity. Most rolling mills have been shut down, and the smelting of pig iron is systematically declining, having fallen from 16.5 million *poods* [2 million barrels] in October 1916 to 9.5 million *poods* [1.1 million barrels] in February 1917. The main cause of the catastrophe is transportation and fuel."

Yet another force that struck a serious blow against the industry was the destructive actions of social organizations of field workers. One of the first acts of the Provisional Government was to promulgate the "Statute on Worker Committees at Industrial Enterprises," referring to committees that soon began making decisions regarding issues such as general management and personnel. The incompetence and capriciousness of these spontaneous bodies soon had negative results. *Neftyanoye delo* reported during this period that: "In the Baku oil district, we observe an ever-increasing number of field and factory administrative personnel removed by workers. For example, through May 14, workers had removed the managers of the Zubalov company and Bibiheybet Oil Company, as well as Field Director Shibayev. In addition, the field director of the Caspian Partnership, the enterprise manager of the Nobel Brothers, and the field director of the Participators' Partnership [*Souchastniki*] left under pressure from workers. In nearly every company, a great many engineers and heads of divisions and field parcels have been removed."

The unauthorized seizures of oil fields and expulsions of owners and administrators from the fields, as well as the establishment of worker self-government, were generally ineffectual. They only served to exacerbate negative trends in the industry and led to a complete crash of the Russian oil business. Domestic oil industrialists pleaded with the authorities more than once for them to put an end to the seizure of fields by workers. The Provisional Government's minister of labor, Mikhail Skobelev, urged Russian workers to end the violence against white-collar workers and attempts at unauthorized seizure of enterprises. Naturally, the minister's speech had no effect, and the oilfield workers put forth an increasing number of new demands.

After the overthrow of the Provisional Government on October 25 (November 7), 1917 and the accession to power of the Bolsheviks led by Vladimir Lenin (Ulyanov) , a new epoch in the history of the Russian oil industry began—the "communist experiment," which lasted over seven decades.

Chapter TWO

Oil in the Land of the Soviets

On the Wave of Soviet Nationalization

The October Revolution and the ensuing political and military battles ushered in a series of drastic changes for all aspects of Russian cultural, political, and economic life.

On October 25, 1917, the Second All-Russian Congress of Soviets opened at 10:45 p.m. at the Smolny Palace in Petrograd. Delegates came to this congress from 400 soviets [councils] of workers' and soldiers' deputies from all over Russia, and also from isolated peasants' soviets. Of the 649 delegates that were registered at the beginning of the Congress, 390 were Bolsheviks, 160 were Left Social Revolutionaries and 99 were Right Social Revolutionaries. The agenda of the Congress included the following key items: the organization of power, war and peace, and the Constituent Assembly. While the delegates were working, they received a report that the members of the Provisional Government had been arrested at 2:10 a.m. in the Winter Palace by resolution of the Military Revolutionary Committee. After that, Anatoly Lunacharsky (1875–1933) read an appeal on behalf of the Bolshevik faction from the Military Revolutionary Committee of the Petrograd Soviet of Workers' and Soldiers' Deputies "To the Citizens of Russia," which stated: "The Provisional Government has been overthrown. State power has passed into the hands of the Petrograd Soviet of Workers' and Soldiers' Deputies of the Military Revolutionary Committee, which stands at the head of the Petrograd proletariat and garrison." The approval of this document by the delegates of the All-Russian Congress of Soviets thus legalized the Bolshevik overthrow of the Provisional Government, the liquidation of the former Russian Republic, and the establishment of a dictatorship of the proletariat.

On October 26, 1917, at the following plenary session of the Congress, the Bolshevik leader Vladimir Lenin (Ulyanov) (1870–1924) gave speeches about peace and land. After his speeches, the delegates approved the "Decree on Peace," which proposed that all countries and peoples "immediately begin negotiations for a just democratic peace," a peace without annexations or reparations, and conclude an armistice until the negotiations were finished.

A second act, the "Decree on Land," abolished landed estates in Russia, and did so "immediately, without any compensation." Land, mineral resources, forests, and waters were declared the property of the entire people. Landed estates, as well as monastery, church, and appanage lands, with all livestock, implements, and buildings, passed without compensation into the hands of local land committees and soviets of peasant deputies. A component of the decree was the peasant mandate on land, which had already been written by the Socialist Revolutionaries before the October Revolution on the basis of 242 local peasant mandates. These mandates equalized the use of land, which was divided based on labor or usage. The "Decree on Land" called for peasants to receive 412.5 million acres of land from Soviet rule at no cost, and to be excused from repaying 3 billion rubles of debt to banks and landowners, and also from paying an annual land rent of 700 million rubles in gold.

The Congress of Soviets made a series of other decisions as well, including abolishing capital punishment at the war front; releasing imprisoned soldiers and officers arrested for revolutionary activity; and arresting the chairman of the Provisional Government, Aleksandr Kerensky (1881–1970).

The Second Congress of Soviets approved the Council of People's Commissars (CPC), headed by Vladimir Lenin, as the highest executive and administrative body of state power. The Congress of Soviets resolution, in particular, said: "A temporary government of workers and peasants shall be formed, which will be called the Council of People's Commissars, to administer the country until the Constituent Assembly is convened."

At the time it was created, the CPC included 13 commissions that managed separate branches of state life: internal (domestic) affairs, agriculture, labor, military and naval affairs, railroads, trade and industry, foreign affairs, foodstuffs, public education, finance, justice, post and telegraph, and ethnic affairs. The chairmen of these committees—people's commissars appointed by the Congress—became members of the first Soviet government.

The Congress also elected an All-Russian Central Executive Committee [*VTsIK*], headed by Yakov Sverdlov (1885–1919), and comprising 101 members (62 Bolsheviks, 29 Left Socialist Revolutionaries, six Social Democrat Internationalists, and four representatives of other parties).

On December 5, 1917, the CPC adopted a decree on the Supreme Council for the National Economy [*VSNKh*], which specified that, "The task of the *VSNKh* is to organize the national economy and finances. With this goal, the *VSNKh* shall develop general standards and plans for regulating the country's economic life, and for coordinating and unifying the activity of central and local regulatory institutions (conferences on fuel, metal, transportation, the central foodstuffs committee, etc.)." The *VSNKh* included representatives of all people's commissariats, and also the All-Russian Council of Workers' Control. All of the most important bills on national economic questions were introduced to the Council of People's Commissars only after they had been approved in the *VSNKh*.

For the next three months following the October Revolution of 1917, general democratic and republican moods continued to persist in Russian society. The clearest expression of these sentiments was the idea of convening a Constituent Assembly to determine Russia's future system of government. Before the decisions of the Constituent Assembly, all executive bodies that came into being and functioned on the territory of the former Russian Empire were unavoidably qualified as temporary, with the exception of the governments of Finland and the Kingdom of Poland, which had become part of the Empire with special rights.

Although the convening of the Russian Constituent Assembly contradicted the fundamental interests of the Bolsheviks, they were nevertheless compelled by prevailing mood of the public to confirm November 12 (25), 1917 as the date of Assembly elections.

Despite struggling with the harsh conditions of war, the country held elections for delegates to the Constituent Assembly. Of 90 million eligible voters in 79 districts, around 45 million persons voted in 54 districts. To the enormous disappointment of the Bolsheviks, they received less than a quarter of the seats in the Constituent Assembly. A total of 715 deputies were elected, of which 370 were Right Socialist-Revolutionaries, 175 were Bolsheviks, 40 were Left Socialist-Revolutionaries, 17 were Constitutional Democrats, 15 were Mensheviks, and 86 were deputies of various national organizations and movements. A decree of the Council of People's Commissars of December 20, 1917 (January 2, 1918) set a new date for convening the Russian Constituent Assembly: January 5 (18), 1918.

However, the Bolsheviks were not prepared to assume the minority role in the new Russian government, no matter what the majority of voters wanted. On December 12 (25), 1917, the Central Committee of the Russian Socialist Democratic Labor Party (of Bolsheviks) adopted the theses of Vladimir Lenin: "The Constituent Assembly, convened on the basis of the rolls of parties that existed before the proletarian-peasant revolution, clashes with the will and interests of the workers, and the interests of the revolution stand higher than the formal rights of the Constituent Assembly. The only chance for a painless resolution of the crisis... is an unequivocal declaration of the Constituent Assembly to recognize Soviet power, the Soviet revolution, and its policies in the question of peace, land, and workers' control.... Unless these conditions are met, the crisis connected with the Constituent Assembly can only be resolved by way of revolution, no matter what slogans and institutions counterrevolution might use to cover itself." Explaining this decision at a rally, the prominent Bolshevik functionary Yakov Sverdlov (1885–1919) declared: "For us there is no doubt that the highest power is that of the working people personified by its Soviets, and that there can be no higher power in Russia."

The Bolshevik leadership's policy caused a vigorous protest throughout Russian society, and the democratic community decided to hold a mass demonstration in Petrograd on the opening day of the Russian Constituent Assembly in support of freedom and democracy in the country.

The Bolsheviks decided to take harsh measures in response. On January 5 (18), 1918, the newspaper *Pravda* ["Truth"] published a resolution signed by Moisey Uritsky (1873–1918), a member of the Presidium of the All-Russian Extraordinary Commission for Combating Counterrevolution and Sabotage, prohibiting any rallies or demonstrations in regions adjacent to the Tauride Palace. The resolution went on to state that any such demonstrations would be suppressed by military force.

Despite the threats, the demonstration in support of the Constituent Assembly did take place in Petrograd. According to several estimates, the lead column numbered around 60,000 persons. It was composed of blue-collar and white-collar workers, the intelligentsia, and students. They moved toward the Tauride Palace and were fired upon by machine guns and rifles of Bolshevik regiments of Latvian and Lithuanian Red Army soldiers. According to official data published on January 6 (19), 1918 in the newspaper *Izvestiya VTsIK* ["News of the All-Russian Central Executive Committee"], 21 persons were killed and several hundred were wounded. The dead included prominent members of the Socialist-Revolutionary Party. Even the proletarian writer Maxim Gorky was unable to hold back his indignation about the events: "The People's Commissars fired upon the workers of Petrograd without warning and ambushed them, firing through openings in fences in a cowardly way, like real murderers."[1]

On January 5 (18), 1918, at 4 p.m., the first and only meeting of the Russian Constituent Assembly opened in Petrograd; it was attended by 410 of the 715 deputies who had been elected. At the very beginning of the meeting, the Bolshevik representative Yakov Sverdlov unceremoniously interrupted the speech of Semën Shvetsov, the oldest deputy of the convention, and proposed himself as chairman of the meeting of the Constituent Assembly. In the voting, Viktor Chernov (1872–1952), one of the leaders of the Socialist-Revolutionary Party, was elected as chairman by a majority of votes, while Socialist-Revolutionary Party member Mikhail Vishnyak was elected secretary of the meeting. Fierce debates erupted concerning acceptance of the agenda, on which the Bolsheviks were trying to place items that were most acceptable to them.

In his speech, the well-known political and public figure Irakly Tsereteli (1881–1959) made the following declaration: "The Social Democratic bloc calls on the entire working class of Russia to reject the unrealizable and disastrous attempts to thrust the dictatorship of a minority on the entire revolutionary democracy, to stand up in defense of the sovereignty of the Russian Constituent Assembly, and to demand that all agencies of power that arose because of the Civil War recognize the supreme power of the Constituent Assembly." In voting, this proposal of the Socialist Revolutionaries received a majority of 237 votes.

After a short break in the meeting, it was decided, on the basis of an extraordinary petition of the Social Democrat Matvey Skobelev (1885–1938), to elect a nonpartisan committee to investigate the circumstances of the shooting that occurred during the worker demonstrations on the opening day of the Constituent Assembly and to establish who was responsible for these shootings. After this, the Bolshevik Fëdor Raskolnikov (Ilin) (1892–1939) read a statement from his faction: "A large majority of Russia's workers demanded that the Constituent Assembly recognize the achievements of the great revolution: the Soviet decrees on land, peace, workers' control, and above all to recognize the power of the soviets of workers', soldiers', and peasants' deputies. The All-Russian Central Executive Committee proposed to the Constituent Assembly that it recognize this will as binding on it. A majority of the Constituent Assembly rejected this proposal... we declare that we are leaving this Constituent Assembly to allow Soviet power to make the final decision about its position vis-à-vis the counterrevolutionary part of the Constituent Assembly." After finishing his statement, the Bolshevik functionary, along with the members of his faction, left the hall of the Tauride Palace. The discussion continued, but around 3 a.m. on January 6 (19), the Left Socialist-Revolutionary bloc also decided to leave the meeting. Their leader Vladimir Karelin (1891–1938) announced: "The Constituent Assembly has entered on the path of struggle with Soviet power to turn everything to the advantage of the class of exploiters while the two camps struggle. We are leaving this assembly."

Toward 4 a.m. on January 6 (19), 1918, with 215 deputies remaining in the hall, the anarchist sailor Anatoly Zheleznyakov (1895–1919) made his infamous appeal to Viktor Chernov, chairman of the Constituent Assembly: "I have been instructed to let you know that everyone present should leave the meeting hall, because the guard is tired." After this ultimatum, the Constituent Assembly quickly accepted the part of the law on land that was read, as well as a peace resolution, an appeal to allies, and a resolution proclaiming the creation of the Russian Democratic Federal Republic. A recess was announced, and the meeting was adjourned at 4:40 a.m. on January 6 (19). The members of the Constituent Assembly who gathered at 5 p.m. later that same day found all doors of the Tauride Palace tightly locked. That night, the All-Russian Central Executive Committee, which was under the control of the Bolsheviks, adopted a decree dissolving the Constituent Assembly.

Subsequently, CPC Chairman Vladimir Lenin, in a discussion with his closest comrade-in-arms, Leon Trotsky (1879–1940), characterized the position of the Bolshevik leadership rather precisely: "The dissolution of the Constituent Assembly by Soviet power is a complete and open liquidation of formal democracy in the name of the revolutionary dictatorship."

On January 18 (31), 1918, the Third All-Russian Congress of Soviets of Workers', Soldiers', and Peasants' Deputies in Petrograd adopted a resolution, "On the Federal Institutions of the Russian Republic," giving the country a new state name: the Russian Socialist Federative Soviet Republic. The resolution said that the state was "founded on the basis of a voluntary union of the peoples of Russia, as a Federation of the Soviet Republics of these peoples." Moreover, the congress approved the dissolution of the Constituent Assembly and adopted a resolution updating the language of all Soviet laws by removing references to their nature as provisional, "pending the convening of a Constituent Assembly."

Nevertheless, according to the logic of the political struggle, the flag of the democratic national Constituent Assembly was convenient to use against Soviet power, and this was in fact done at the very first opportunity. A catalyst for the explosion of "democratic counterrevolution" of 1918 and the beginning of the Russian Civil War that lasted many years was provided by the mutiny of the Czechoslovak Volunteer Corps on May 26, 1918.

Having taken power into their own hands, the Bolsheviks began, from the very start, to place economic policy under state control. As early as April 1917, Lenin had delineated the party's position in relation to highly developed industries: "... our proposal must be immediately practical: these mature syndicates must be made the property of the state. If the Soviets want to take power, then it is only for such purposes. There is no reason for them to take anything more."[2]

Lenin reaffirmed this platform position on the eve of the October Revolution of 1917. In his pamphlet, *The Impending Catastrophe and How to Combat It* [*Grozyashchaya katastrofa i kak s ney borotsya*], which was published in September 1917, he wrote: "Nationalization of the oil industry is possible immediately, and is obligatory for the revolutionary democratic state, especially when it is suffering a great crisis, when it is necessary at all costs to spare the people's labor and increase the production of fuel."[3]

The Bolsheviks considered the establishment of workers' control at enterprises to be an important step along the path of "socialization" of Russia's industry, and the law on workers' control was adopted on November 14, 1917. Lev Kritsman, a well-known party activist of those years, wrote: "The idea of workers' control is first to learn from your class enemy how to run all parts of the enterprise, the technical, administrative, and commercial, to check all his actions and, consequently, to observe all his habits."

The idea of creating "peoples' oil fields" soon followed and was discussed at the CPC meeting of January 27, 1918. It was during that same meeting of the Soviet government that the question of nationalizing the Russian oil industry was first considered. The CPC decision instructed the *VSNKh* to develop, without delay, a plan for nationalizing the industry. The *VSNKh* responded by creating a special committee on the nationalization of the Russian oil industry, which immediately began working on ideas.

On February 15, 1918, the CPC considered a draft decree on nationalization, which was accepted as a basis, and a committee was created to definitively resolve this issue. On February 21, the draft was sent to the People's Commissariat for Finance for an opinion, and on March 1, the CPC created a new committee, made up of representatives of the *VSNKh* and of the people's commissariats of labor and finance, to complete a draft on methods of carrying out the nationalization of the oil industry.

Given the dire economic and political circumstances in the country, the Bolshevik tactic proved successful; by the spring of 1918, real preconditions had arisen for establishing Soviet power in many regions of the country. Practical production questions appeared on the agenda for resolution, with regard to which the government undertook a series of steps to organize oil industry management.

A *VSNKh* resolution dated March 2, 1918 appointed a chief commissar for the oil industry, who was given broad authority, in particular, the right to sequester individual enterprises. The reliable party functionary and former bookkeeper Isidor Gukovsky was confirmed in this post. One of his first actions was to prepare a government resolution, dated March 25, 1918, establishing price controls on petroleum products.

However, the small staff of the chief commissar of the oil industry and the lack of a clear definition of his authority in relations with other departments and people's commissariats proved to be insurmountable obstacles to carrying out such a large-scale operation as nationalization of the oil industry.

Therefore, two-and-a-half months later, on May 17, 1918, the CPC of the RSFSR issued a decree abolishing the post of chief commissar of the oil industry and establishing, in its place, a special body: the Main Petroleum Committee [*GNK*], which had broad authority and was called upon to control and regulate "the entire private oil industry and trade in petroleum products." The Main Petroleum Committee was composed of the Bolsheviks N. Solovyёv (chairman), G. Pylayev, I. Gukovsky, A. Shibinsky, K. Makhrovsky, Sahak Ter-Gabrielyan, and the well-known geologist Ivan Gubkin, who was later appointed the Committee's deputy chairman.

The Main Petroleum Committee was authorized to administer the oil business on an all-Russian scale, and was charged with developing and implementing measures related to the organization of the state oil economy. The decree emphasized that: "The Main Petroleum Committee shall be the sole body managing all questions connected with production, refining, distribution, and consumption of crude oil and petroleum products. The Main Petroleum Committee shall control and regulate the entire oil industry and trade in petroleum products; develop and practically implement measures related to the transition of the private oil industry to state ownership, and manage the state petroleum economy."

The establishment of a special organizational body to administer the oil industry and the government's efforts to gain control over trade in petroleum products were decisive steps on the road to the planned government takeover of the oil industry.

A decree dated June 20, 1918 nationalized the Russian oil industry and began a new chapter in the industry's history.

The basic tenets of the decree were laid out as follows:

"1. The following are declared to be state property: oil producing, refining, and trading enterprises, ancillary drilling and transportation equipment (cisterns, oil pipelines, oil storage facilities, docks, pier structures, etc.), with all real and personal property, wherever located and however composed.

"2. Minor enterprises of the type named in paragraph 1 shall be exempt from this decree. The justifications and procedure for a designated exemption shall be defined by special rules to be elaborated by the Main Petroleum Committee.

"3. Trade in oil and its products is declared a state monopoly.

"4. Administration of nationalized enterprises as a whole, as well as determination of the procedure for carrying out nationalization, is assigned to the Main Petroleum Committee [*Glavkomneft*] under the Fuel Department of the Supreme Council for the National Economy.

"5. The procedure for forming local bodies to administer nationalized enterprises and the scope of their authority shall be defined by special instructions of the Main Petroleum Committee, upon approval by the Presidium of the Supreme Council for the National Economy.

"6. Pending full assumption of control over enterprises being nationalized by the Main Petroleum Committee, the former boards of the named enterprises must continue their operation to the full extent, taking all measures to protect the national property and assure that operations continue without interruption.

"7. The former board of each enterprise shall compile a report for the whole year of 1917 and for the first half of 1918, as well as a balance sheet for the enterprise as of June 20, which the new board will use to verify and take actual control of the enterprise.

"8. The Main Petroleum Committee shall have the right, without awaiting the presentation of balance sheets and before full transfer of the nationalized enterprises to administration by the agencies of Soviet power, to send its commissars to all boards of oil enterprises, and also to all centers of oil production, refining, transportation, and trade. The

Main Petroleum Committee may, moreover, assign its authority to its commissars.

"9. All rights and obligations of the soviets of congresses of oil workers are transferred to the corresponding local agencies for administration of the nationalized oil industry.

"10. All white-collar workers of enterprises and institutions being transferred to the control of the Main Petroleum Committee are directed to remain in their jobs, without interrupting their assigned functions.

"11. Until the Main Petroleum Committee issues the instructions, directives, and rules envisioned in the decree, local councils of the national economy (or other local agencies of Soviet power where these local councils do not exist) shall have the right to issue them for their region.

"12. This decree shall enter into force immediately upon publication."

It should be noted that implementation of this decree in practice led to the rather hasty and ill-considered merger of private oil industry assets within the territory of Soviet Russia into a unified whole on the basis of existing major monopolies. As a result, the administrative structure turned out to be extremely irregular and chaotic. Moreover, the newly introduced equalizing tariff in the industry created little incentive for blue-collar and white-collar workers to work efficiently.

At the time of nationalization, there were 787 petroleum products storage facilities in Russia with a total capacity of 4.06 million tons. Storage facilities in various provinces contained 6.4 million barrels (0.96 million tons) of crude oil and petroleum products. Pëtr Imber, the authorized representative of *Glavkomneft*, sent a telegram to Moscow on June 20, 1918 that said: "In Tsaritsyn, private warehouses now contain no less than 12 million *poods* [1.4 million barrels] of various petroleum products, not to mention those in Rybinsk and Saratov." The inland fleet consisted of 222 iron and 432 wooden vessels, capable of carrying 2.26 million tons. The railroad tanker fleet numbered more than 10,000 cars.

The all-Russian congress of white-collar and blue-collar workers of the Nobel Brothers Petroleum Production Partnership, held in June 1918 in Saratov, initially made a desperate attempt to hold off the hasty collectivization of the industry, and made a special appeal to the *VSNKh*. However, after receiving news of the publication of the decree nationalizing the oil industry, the delegates to the congress adopted a resolution stating that "for the benefit of the business and the state, the former Nobel Brothers Petroleum Production Partnership, as experienced people, temporarily offer their services for preliminary development of instructions to implement nationalization and further management of the business."

It should be noted that the Bolshevik leadership did have a sense of pragmatism, which is evident in the following order issued by the Main Petroleum Committee: "The entire local administration of the former oil companies shall continue to perform its duties and bear full responsibility to the Main Petroleum Committee for safeguarding all the property of these companies and for correct management of the business, submitting to the control of the local agencies of the Main Petroleum Committee.... White-collar workers in positions of responsibility at these companies can be dismissed only with the prior permission of the Main Petroleum Committee."

Meanwhile, the *VSNKh* decided that, starting July 1, 1918, price controls would be imposed on kerosene, and effective November 15 of the same year, controls would be imposed on all other petroleum products. Soon the country was showing the first outlines of an impending "fuel famine."

On the whole, the nationalization of foreign and private property was the result of a general tendency of the system of state socialist administration that was taking shape in Soviet Russia. It was not by chance that this nationalization, a phenomenon whose economic and political consequences were far from uniform, was initiated by Lenin and his comrades-in-arms. They felt that the activity of private capital did not promote the development of the country's economy and did not serve the interests of the broad masses. Therefore, they considered nationalization a measure intended to protect and strengthen Soviet power.

However, nationalization of the oil industry could not help but create serious problems for the fledgling Soviet state, especially in the realm of foreign policy, which was already on shaky ground. For example, on July 8, 1918, a Swedish envoy chaired a meeting of the ambassadors of the neutral governments of the Netherlands, Spain, Norway, Denmark, and Switzerland to discuss the problem of Russian oil industry nationalization and the property claims that arose as a result of it. The meeting issued a coordinated protest to the People's Commissariat for Foreign Affairs [*NKID*] and the CPC in connection with the adoption of the nationalization decree, which had caused "great losses" to the foreign owners of the oil industry. The declaration pointed out that "the governments represented at the meeting reserve the right to make subsequent demands for restitution of the loss."

In the "Fuel Famine" Wave

The beginning of the post-revolutionary period in Soviet Russia was characterized by extremely negative events in industry, transportation, and agriculture. After three-and-a-half years of war and the first months of the revolution, the country's economy was in ruins. The Bolsheviks lost control of the richest regions: Ukraine, the Baltic republics, the Volga region, and Western Siberia. Furthermore, the economic ties between cities and villages had long ago been severed, while strikes and lockouts of business owners finished the destruction of the economy that the war had started. Meanwhile, the process of nationalization in various industries was at times disorderly, and often assumed the form of repressive measures against business owners who attempted to resist workers' self-government. Even those enterprises that were nationalized could not be counted on to produce the necessary economic results. According to the data of the industrial census of August 31, 1918, Soviet Russia had a total of 9,750 nationalized industrial enterprises, of which 3,690, or 37.8%, were not operating.

Under these conditions, the Bolshevik government began to carry out harsh political and socioeconomic measures of an ambiguous character, which were given the name "war communism." The basic motivations for this policy were both the extremely difficult economic situation in the country and the dogmatic Marxist outlook of the Bolsheviks. Ignoring the immaturity of the objective preconditions for a socialist revolution in Russia, a significant part of the Bolshevik leadership after the October Revolution insisted on immediate implementation of socialist transformations in all spheres of society, including, first and foremost, the economy. They stubbornly refused any compromises whatsoever with the world or Russian bourgeoisie, and insisted on the rapid expropriation of all forms of private property, curtailment of commodity-money relations, abolition of money, and introduction of the principles of equalizing distribution and socialist procedures literally "starting today." Starting from the premise that every revolution is violence, they made wide use of revolutionary coercion. A popular Soviet poster of 1918 proclaimed: "We will use an iron hand to drive humanity to happiness!"

To a significant extent, the policy of war communism was also predicated on the hopes of Russian communists to accelerate world revolution. The Bolshevik leaders considered the October Revolution to be the beginning of the world revolution, which they were expecting to happen any day. This led them to the firm conviction that compromises with bourgeois counterrevolution were unacceptable, that the country had to be turned into a single fighting camp, and that all aspects of national life had to be militarized.

War communism was based on emergency measures to provide the cities and army with foodstuffs, to curtail commodity-money relations, to nationalize all industry, including small business, to manage food apportionment, and the provision of rationed foodstuffs and industrial products to the population, to establish a universal duty to work, and the maximum centralization of the administration of the national economy and the country as a whole. A class-equalizing principle of distribution was established and starting in June 1918, a ration card supply system was introduced.

A characteristic feature of war communism was extreme centralization of national economic administration. At first, the administrative system was built on the principles of collectivism and self-government, but as time passed the unsoundness of these principles became obvious. The factory and plant committees of workers had neither the competence nor the experience to administer production efficiently.

The Bolshevik leaders understood that they had previously exaggerated the degree of revolutionary consciousness of the working class, which was not ready to administer enterprises. Therefore, a fundamental decision was made to establish a rigid vertical line of state control over all economic life that emanated from the *VSNKh* and its main committees and centers, with each being a type of state monopoly in its corresponding branch of production. By the summer of 1918, local (province, district) regional economic councils had been created in all provinces that had submitted to the Soviet government and were subordinated to the *VSNKh*.

Overall, the economic system that had taken shape did not stimulate productive labor, and productivity steadily fell. Per-worker productivity in 1920 was less than a third of the prewar level. In the fall of 1919, the pay of a highly qualified worker exceeded that of an unskilled laborer by only 9%. Material incentives for labor disappeared, and along with them any desire to work. At many enterprises, absenteeism accounted for up to 50% of working days. Forced labor soon became a necessary measure in the absence of economic stimuli, and because of the catastrophic shortage of workers. Unfortunately, the Bolsheviks' hopes regarding the proletariat's class consciousness also proved unfounded.

Another basic feature of the policy of war communism was the complete curtailment of commodity-money relations. This was most apparent in the introduction of nonequivalent natural trading between cities and villages, especially as it pertained to grain. Under conditions of runaway inflation, peasants did not want to sell grain for depreciated money. In February and March of 1918, the consuming regions of the country received only 12.3% of the expected quantity of grain. In Russia's industrial centers, the ration card norm for grain was reduced to 50–100 grams per day. To make matters worse, Russia had lost several of its largest grain-producing regions under the terms of the Treaty of Brest-Litovsk, which only served to aggravate the food crisis further. After acceptance of the "Decree on the Grain Monopoly" (May 13, 1918), trade was actually prohibited and food detachments were formed to confiscate foodstuffs from the peasantry. Such food detachments operated according to the principle formulated by Aleksandr Tsyurupa, people's commissar of foodstuffs: "If it is impossible to take grain from the village bourgeoisie by usual means, then it must be taken by force." To assist in these efforts, Poverty Committees composed of non-landed peasants and assorted hooligans from nearby towns were created on the basis of the

Central Committee decrees of June 11, 1918. Such measures forced the peasantry to take up arms. In the words of the prominent economist Nikolay Kondratyev, "The village, which had been inundated with soldiers returning after the uncontrolled demobilization of the army, met the armed forces with armed resistance and a whole series of uprisings."[4] However, neither the foodstuff dictatorship nor the Poverty Committees were able to resolve the food problem. Attempts to prohibit city-village market relations and the forceful confiscation of grain from peasants only led to a widespread black market in grain at high prices. The city population was receiving no more than 40% of the grain it consumed from ration cards; the other 60% was received through illegal trade. Commodity-money relations were also further curtailed by the Bolsheviks' complete prohibition in the fall of 1918 of wholesale and private trade in most of Russia's provinces. After nationalizing the merchant marine (January 23, 1918) and foreign trade (April 22, 1918), the government started general nationalization of all enterprises having capital of more than 500,000 rubles in June of 1918.

The centralized administration system dictated a command style of leadership, and one of the features of war communism policy was the system of extraordinary agencies, whose tasks included subordination of the entire economy to the needs of the front. On November 30, 1918, the *VTsIK* resolved to create a new extraordinary agency of the Soviet state: the Council of Workers' and Peasants' Defense of the RSFSR. Its task was to mobilize all forces to wage the Civil War successfully. Resolutions of the Council of Defense were binding on all departments. It comprised representatives of the *VTsIK*, the Revolutionary War Council, the People's Commissariat for Railroads, the Extraordinary Committee to Supply the Red Army, the People's Commissariat for Foodstuffs, the All-Russian Council of Trade Unions, the *VSNKh*, and the Main Committee on Labor. The Council of Defense was directed by the chairman of the CPC, and as a rule, it met twice a week and decisions were made by majority vote. When necessary, the Council of Defense created numerous committees, including one on fuel, and sent authorized extraordinary representatives with broad powers into localities, including the right to dismiss all officials and prosecute them before revolutionary tribunals.

The oil industry also suffered shortages following the October Revolution. For a long time, the terrible events of the Civil War had interrupted deliveries to Central Russia of coal from the Donets Basin and the Kuznetsk Basin, as well as of oil from the North Caucasus and Transcaucasus. As recently as November 24, 1917, Chechen bandits had burned down new Grozny fields. In December 1917, the journal *Neftyanoye delo* published a report by the chairman of the Tersk Military Industrial Committee, who reported to Petrograd: "The oil fields of the new Grozny region, which were producing 5–6 million *poods* [600,000–720,000 barrels] of oil per month, have been destroyed and completely burned. It is impossible to restore the fields under existing circumstances." The Grozny fields burned for almost 17 months, and according to some estimates this fire consumed oil worth almost a quarter of the annual prewar budget of the Russian Empire.

By the end of 1918, the situation was dire: Soviet Russia needed 2.6 million barrels to meet the plans of 1919, but only had around 10,000 barrels of fuel oil on hand. As for alternate energy sources, all the Soviet government really had left at its disposal at this time was the Moscow coal basin, which was capable of producing only a small quantity of low-quality brown coal.

The Red Army's failures in the early spring of 1919 in the Volga region and in the east produced an even greater strain on the fuel supply. On April 26, 1919, Lenin sent the following directive to the Revolutionary War Councils in the Volga region: "In view of the critical situation with fuel oil, it is prohibited, under penalty of the strictest accountability, for anyone to use or issue fuel without permission of the Main Committee on Fuel. Those guilty of unauthorized seizure or distribution of fuel shall be immediately prosecuted by a revolutionary court."[5]

Several days later, on April 29, 1919, he sent a new telegram: "The threat of [White Army leader Aleksandr] Kolchak to the Volga necessitates prompt measures to remove petroleum products from the threatened area, and timely transportation of petroleum products destined for wharves in the upper Volga through the threatened area. To carry out the indicated tasks successfully, it is ordered that: 1) The Main Petroleum Committee immediately send its representatives to the Volga wharves to load the petroleum products into pilotage barges of vessels carrying petroleum products; 2) The Main Water Committee provide the necessary loading vessels and tugboats per agreement with the Main Petroleum Committee; 3) All military and civilian powers cooperate fully with the representatives of the Main Petroleum Committee and in no way interfere with their directives on vessel loading or movement. Those in violation of this provision shall be subject to prosecution before military revolutionary tribunals under martial law."

Table 8. Breakdown of the Soviet Russian Fuel Budget

	Coal	Petroleum	Wood	Peat, Oil, Shale
1918	14%	12%	71%	3%
1919	3.5%	5%	88%	3.5%
1920	36%	10.5%	50%	3.5%

Source: *Civil War and Military Intervention in the USSR* [*Grazhdanskaya voyna i voyennaya interventsiya v SSSR*]. Moscow, 1987, p. 598.

Removal of the oil was under the constant daily control of the Soviet government, and the stream of telegrams signed by Lenin was continuous. Another telegram, this one from June 25, 1919, provides further evidence of the dire fuel situation: "The Council of Workers' and Peasants' Defense orders that the most energetic measures be taken immediately to move all petroleum product reserves from Tsaritsyn to Saratov, in accordance with the directive of the Main Petroleum Committee. The measures taken and also every shipment sent should be reported by telegraph to the Supreme Council for the National Economy and Main Petroleum Committee; in the telegraph office, go to the head of the line without waiting, and use a direct line to send this report. No consumption of petroleum products shall be allowed without permission of the Main Petroleum Committee. Those guilty of disobedience will be prosecuted."

It was also during this time that the oil industry was incorporated into another of war communism's primary tenets—the militarization of labor. Initially, the policy covered blue-collar and white-collar workers in defense industries, but by the end of 1919, all industries and railroad transportation had been put on a war footing. On June 27, 1919, fuel industry workers accepted the resolution "On Counting of All Blue-Collar and White-Collar Workers in the Main Forestry Committee, the Main Coal Committee, the Main Petroleum Committee, the Main Peat Committee, and the Main Fuel Committee as Military Personnel, Leaving Them at Their Workplaces," which said, in particular: "All blue-collar and white-collar workers of the Main Petroleum Committee, irrespective of their age, are considered called up for active military service, effective the day this resolution is promulgated."

To monitor the fulfillment of the universal labor duty, a special committee was created, the All-Russian Extraordinary Commission [*Cheka*], headed by Feliks Dzerzhinsky (1877–1926). The system of military and communist measures included abolition of payment for urban and interurban rail transportation, for fuel, fodder, foodstuffs, mass consumer products, medical services, housing, etc. Furthermore, on November 14, 1919, the CPC of the RSFSR accepted the "Provision on Workers' Disciplinary Comrade Courts." It provided such punishments as sending malicious violators of discipline to hard-labor public works, and in the case of "stubborn unwillingness to submit to comrades' discipline," to subject them "as a non-labor element, to dismissal from enterprises and transfer them to a concentration camp."

On November 1, 1919, only 204,000 barrels of oil remained in Soviet Russia. The country was in the grips of a "fuel famine," which could have easily resulted in the Bolsheviks falling from power. However, understanding the importance of the energy problem as a whole, the Bolshevik leadership undertook extreme measures to solve the crisis in supplying the economy with fuel. In November of 1919, in a circulating letter from the Central Committee of the Russian Communist Party (of Bolsheviks) [RCP(b)] to party organizations titled "On the Struggle with the Fuel Crisis," Lenin emphasized: "The fuel question has come to stand at the center of all other questions. The fuel crisis must be overcome at any cost; otherwise, it will not be possible to solve either the food problem, or the military problem, or the general economic problem."[6]

Another of Lenin's telegrams, sent in February 1920 to the party functionaries Ivars Smilga (1892–1937) and Sergo Orjonikidze (1886–1937) regarding the Kuban and Grozny fields, read: "We desperately need oil. Consider a proclamation to the population saying that we will slaughter everyone if they burn and destroy oil or the oil fields, but on the other hand we will grant life to everyone if they turn over Maykop and especially Grozny intact."

By the spring of 1920, the Bolshevik leadership considered the Civil War to be coming to a close and began looking ahead to developing the postwar Soviet state. At this time, the Ninth Congress of the RCP(b) discussed the transition to a militarized economic system, the essence of which "must consist of bringing the army as close as possible to the production process, since the living human force of certain economic regions is simultaneously the living human force of certain military units."

Meanwhile, on June 15, 1920, the Council of Workers' and Peasants' Defense of the RSFSR resolved that the oil industry be separated into a separate strike force for supply. All state agencies had to satisfy the requirements of the Main Petroleum Committee for materials, equipment, etc.

In November 1920, the CPC of the RSFSR issued a decree extending nationalization in Soviet Russia to all "enterprises having more than 10 workers, or more than five workers using a mechanical engine," of which there turned out to be around 37,000. Of these, 30,000 had not appeared earlier in the basic lists of the *VSNKh*.

At the end of December 1920, the Eighth All-Russian Congress of Soviets adopted a plan from the State Commission for Electrification of Russia [*GOELRO*], which, among other things, established priorities for developing the branches of the fuel energy complex. For instance, production of shale, Moscow coal, and peat needed to grow at the fastest rates, and oil at lower rates. The *GOELRO* plan was accepted at the peak of the policy of war communism, when an attempt was being made to administer everything possible from the center. Accordingly, the types of fuel were evaluated according to this basic criterion: Do they or don't they contribute to centralization? Shale and peat, which had to be burned in small electric power plants (state power plants, of course), did contribute to centralizing administration. But, as Soviet leader Gleb Krzhizhanovsky (1872–1959) pointed out at the Congress, petroleum fuel, which could both be burned in oil burners and used in internal combustion engines, "contributed only to decentralization," in other words, a producer that used such fuel was technologically independent of state power, in contrast to a consumer using only electricity.

However, the harsh realities of the time and the wave of popular uprisings that broke out in the country soon forced the Bolsheviks to reexamine the foundations of war communism, and thus the Tenth Party Congress (1921) declared war communism methods of management, which were based on coercion, to be obsolete. In the spring of 1921, the Bolshevik leadership announced the transition to the New Economic Policy (NEP), which was aimed first and foremost at the economic rebirth of the country. Helping the Bolsheviks in this regard was the fact that by this time all of the primary oil-producing regions of the former Russian Empire had fallen under the influence, if not outright control, of the Bolshevik government.

Caucasian Oil Gets a Red Bow

In 1915, oil production in the Russian Empire totaled 68.7 million barrels, of which 54.5 million barrels (79.3%) came from the oil fields of the Absheron Peninsula. The economic and geopolitical importance of the oil-producing Caspian region was not lost on the government of Soviet Russia, and the years following the October Revolution were marked by the ongoing struggle of the Soviet leaders to take control of this vital region.

After the end of the First World War, it became clear that development of the world economy in the 20th century would be determined largely by national access to and uninterrupted delivery of crude oil and petroleum products. Here, Caspian oil would play a critical role. The Soviet leadership's position on this was articulated most clearly by Joseph Stalin (Iosif Dzhugashvili) (1879–1953), people's commissar for ethnic affairs: "The Caucasus is very important to the Revolution not simply because it is a source of raw materials, fuel, and foodstuffs, but because of its position between Europe and Asia, in particular between Russia and Turkey, and the presence of critical economic and strategic roads (Batumi-Baku, Batumi-Tabriz, Batumi–Tabriz–Erzurum).... Who will ultimately gain a foothold in the Caucasus, who will use the oil and critical roads leading deep into Asia, the Revolution or the Entente? That is the question."[7]

After seizing power in Petrograd in October 1917, the Bolshevik leaders were initially confident that their hold over the oil industry of the Absheron Peninsula was unshakable. This conviction was based on the fact that on October 31 (November 13), 1917, the Baku Soviet of Workers', Soldiers', and Sailors' Deputies declared itself "the local authorized Revolutionary legislative body," acknowledging the power of the Petrograd Council of People's Commissars over it.

The Bolshevik leaders came to believe the entire Caucasus region would soon follow the Baku example and, as a result, on December 3 (16), 1917, the Petrograd Council of People's Commissars appointed Stepan Shaumian (1878–1918) as its extraordinary commissar for Caucasian affairs. In his "Address to All Soviets and All Workers of the Caucasus," published in the first issue of the *Kavkazsky vestnik Soveta narodnykh komissarov* ["Caucasian Herald of the Council of People's Commissars"] of January 31, 1918, published in Azerbaijani, Armenian, and Russian, he emphasized: "Strive to make your uprising universal, so that Muslim peasants carry out an organized seizure of the *beys'* land everywhere, and create peasant committees that are to take this land."

In turn, adoption of the "Declaration of Rights of the Peoples of Russia" by the Council of People's Commissars on November 2 (15), 1917, and of the subsequent "Address to the Working Muslims of Russia and the East," gave a new impetus to the practical implementation of the idea of federalizing the country along geographic and ethnic lines.

However, as Professor Aleksandr Vasilenko, doctor of political science, emphasized in his study, "Caspian Oil in the Geopolitical Strategy of the Leaders of Soviet Russia (1917–1922)" in the anthology *Soviet Union's Oil [Neft strany Sovetov]*, the progress of political processes in the Transcaucasus in a relatively short time after October 1917 raised a number of substantial obstacles to the realization of Soviet Russian strategic interests in the region. Throughout the peripheral provinces of the former Russian Empire, a variety of ethnic states began to appear: the Transcaucasian Commissariat (November 1917), and then the Transcaucasian Democratic Federative Republic (April 1918), as well as the Mountain Republic (November 1917) and the North Caucasus Mountaineers Republic (May 1918), etc.

The creation on January 18 (31), 1918, of the Russian Socialist Federative Soviet Republic was "founded on the basis of a voluntary union of the peoples of Russia as a Federation of the Soviet Republics of those peoples." The term "voluntary union" was understood by the Bolshevik leadership only in terms of class. However, just as the interpretation of the principle of ethnic self-determination was to be "the means of fighting for socialism and must be subordinate to the principles of socialism," the leaders of Soviet Russia were "for autonomy, but for such autonomy where all power would be in the hands of the workers and peasants, where the bourgeois of all ethnic groups would be removed both from power and from participation in elections to government bodies."[8]

On March 15, 1918, the Fourth Extraordinary All-Russian Congress of Soviets ratified the Treaty of Brest-Litovsk between Russia and the Quadruple Alliance (Germany, Austria-Hungary, Bulgaria, and Turkey). Under Article 4 of the treaty, several Transcaucasian territories, including Batumi, Ardahan, and Kars, passed to Turkey. For the leaders of

Soviet Russia, Article 14 of a Supplemental Agreement to the Treaty of Brest-Litovsk was extremely important; it recognized Baku District as unconditional Russian territory, and required the delivery of a portion of the crude oil and petroleum products produced on the peninsula to Germany.

In his memoirs, the noted Georgian revolutionary Noe Zhordania (1869–1953) later wrote: "After the Constituent Assembly dispersed, we remained alone and had to think about ourselves. In practice, this meant secession from Russia and creating our life as we saw fit. This conclusion flowed from the following well-known facts: the Bolshevik revolution in Russia, whose authority we did not recognize; and the Treaty of Brest-Litovsk, which deprived us of part of our territory."

On February 10 (23), 1918, the first meeting of the Transcaucasian *Sejm*, the region's legislature, was held in Tiflis. The *Sejm* included deputies elected to the All-Russian Constituent Assembly from the Transcaucasian region. The *Sejm* was opened by Nikoloz Chkheidze (1864–1929), a noted politician and deputy to the third and fourth State Dumas and former chairman of the executive committee of the Petrograd Soviet of Workers' and Soldiers' Deputies. At the second session, Chkheidze was elected chairman of the *Sejm*. The Azerbaijani delegation consisted of 44 deputies representing the parties Musavat ("Equality"), Hummet ("Energy"), and Ittihad ("Union"), as well as a Muslim socialist bloc. The delegation was led by the noted politician Mammed Amin Rasulzade (1884–1955).

The region's value was no doubt obvious to the *Sejm*, especially in light of the fact that, despite the burden of wartime and post-October unrest, the oil fields of the Absheron Peninsula produced 48.7 million barrels of crude in 1917, amounting to 77.8% of all Russian production.

Naturally, the *Sejm's* discussion of Caspian oil did not escape the attention of the leaders of Soviet Russia. Based on directives from Moscow, the Bolsheviks switched tactics from direct boycott of the *Sejm* to organizing mass rallies and other activities in Tiflis, in an effort to impede and undermine its work.

On March 15, 1918, learning of a possible compromise between the *Sejm* blocs, the Baku Soviet decided to take preemptive offensive measures. The Soviet's meeting resolution stated: "The Baku Soviet considers it its revolutionary duty to come to the aid of the fraternal working class and peasantry of the entire Transcaucasus and join with them to overthrow this counterrevolutionary criminal rule of the *Sejm*." This position was immediately supported by the Soviet government. A telegram from Lenin to Stepan Shaumian in Baku read, "In ecstasy over your firm and decisive policy. Strive to combine it with most careful diplomacy, grounded, naturally, by the present difficult situation, and we will win."[9]

In late March 1918, armed conflicts broke out in Baku between the soldiers of the "wild division"—armed units of the *Dashnaktsutiun* ("Armenian Revolutionary Federation")—and detachments of the Military Revolutionary Committee of the Baku Soviet. On March 30, 1918, the Baku Committee of Revolutionary Struggle was formed in Baku as a Bolshevik organization. It was led by Stepan Shaumian, and proclaimed itself the city's supreme military-political body. All oil workers were assembled in the Baku Soviet building, where the committee announced the imposition of a tax of 50 million rubles to organize armed units of the Red Army in Baku.

The centralization of power and skillful coordination of actions between military units ended with the destruction of the opposition forces and consolidation of Soviet rule in the city. By decision of the executive committee of the Baku Soviet in early April 1918, a military mobilization was declared in the city, enabling a considerable increase in the manpower of the armed units.

Around the same time, however, on April 22, 1918, the Transcaucasian *Sejm* proclaimed the creation of the independent Transcaucasian Democratic Federative Republic (TDFR), consisting of Baku, Tiflis, Kutaisi, and Yelizavetpol Provinces and the Batumi Region. The republic soon formed a government headed by Akaki Chkhenkeli, a noted politician, deputy to the Fourth State Duma, and former member of the All-Russian Central Executive Committee. The government also included five representatives of Baku: Fatali Khan Isgender oglu Khoyski (minister of justice), Khudadat bey Aghabey oglu Malik-Aslanov (minister of railroads), Nasib bey Usubbeyov (minister of education), Mammad Hasan Jafargulu oglu Hajinski (minister of trade and industry), and Ibrahim bey Heydarov (minister of state inspection).

Commenting on the formation of the Transcaucasian Democratic Federative Republic, Stalin wrote: "The *Sejm's* declaration of the independence of the Transcaucasus (April 22), intended to give a free hand to the Tiflis 'government,' has actually thrown it into a trap of international predators.... One thing is clear: the independence of the Tiflis Mensheviks and their government from the Russian revolution will inevitably end in their enslavement to Turkish-German 'civilized predators.' "

One key point on the agenda of the meeting of the TDFR government was the question of establishing control over the Absheron Peninsula and its oil fields. At the suggestion of the Bolshevik faction, in order to counteract any actions by the TDFR government on this issue, a meeting of the Baku Soviet of Workers', Soldiers', and Sailors' Deputies on April 25, 1918 resulted in the formation of a Board (Council) of People's Commissars headed by Stepan Shaumian. The new governing body immediately declared that it did not recognize the jurisdiction of the Transcaucasian Democratic Federative Republic over the territory of Baku Province.

At the same meeting, Shaumian was also appointed people's commissar for foreign affairs, while Baku trade union leader Ivan Fioletov was named people's commissar for economic affairs. Later, the special position of people's commissar for petroleum was added, to which Sahak M. Ter-Gabrielyan (1886–1937) was appointed while retaining his position as chairman of the Extraordinary Commission for Combating Counterrevolution and Sabotage.

On May 1, 1918, the Baku Council of People's Commissars issued a special declaration stressing that it would "implement, taking local conditions into account, all decrees and directives of the worker-peasant government of Russia, i.e., the Supreme Council of People's Commissars." The Baku Council stated the main objective for the oil industry as follows: "Russia's fate depends on the amount of oil sent from Baku. Without fuel, without our residual oil, without our lubricants, the factories of Moscow and Novovoznesensk, of St. Petersburg and the Volga, cannot run, villages cannot be supplied with chintz, nails, or farm implements... nor can the revolutionary Red Army be redeployed in time or with proper speed to defend the republic."

On May 15, 1918, the leaders of Soviet Russia, striving to provide diplomatic support to the Baku Bolsheviks, sent a note to the governments of Germany and Turkey, stressing that "Baku has declared numerous *Sejm* members usurpers. Lankaran, Alyat, Derbent, Petrovsk, Hajigabul, Kurdamir and the whole eastern Transcaucasus in general as far as Yelizavetpol [Ganja] have expressed themselves similarly."

At the same time, the first month of the Transcaucasus Democratic Federative Republic was marked by substantial differences in the positions of ethnic political parties. The sharp contradictions among members of the seven main blocs in the Transcaucasus *Sejm*—the Armenian Revolutionary Federation, the Social Revolutionaries, the Muslim socialist bloc, the Social Democrats (Mensheviks), the Russian Muslim Party, Musavat, the Socialist-Federalists, and the National Democrats— did not allow even for a brief period the survival of the new national entity. The governing bodies of the federative republic proved incapable of offering the population a real program to solve the crisis, while the Bolsheviks, not allowing even the slightest slip by the TDFR government to go unreported, made their own contributions to destabilizing the situation.

Thus, on May 26, 1918, at the initiative of the Georgian representatives and "in view of the fact that radical differences have appeared on the issue of war and peace," the Transcaucasus *Sejm* decided to disband, bringing the brief existence of the Transcaucasus Democratic Federative Republic to an end.

In its place, three independent states immediately arose: The Georgian Declaration of Independence of May 26, 1918 proclaimed the formation of the Georgian Democratic Republic, in which Noe Zhordania (1869–1953), the noted Social Democrat and deputy to the first State Duma, took command of the Georgian National Council, while the noted politician Nikoloz Chkheidze (1864–1926) was elected chairman of the Constituent Assembly.

The Azerbaijani Democratic Republic was formed on May 27, 1918. The Republic's government was headed by Fatali Khan Khoyski (1875–1920), a deputy to the second State Duma and former minister of justice in the TDFR government. Mammed Amin Rasulzade (1884–1955), chairman of the central committee of Musavat, became head of the Provisional National Council.

On May 28, 1918, the Armenian National Council proclaimed the formation of the Democratic Republic of Armenia, and approved Hovhannes Kachaznuni as head of its government.

The appearance of three independent ethnic states in the Transcaucasus provoked serious concern in Soviet Russia. Stalin stressed: "The so-called independence of the so-called independent Georgia and Armenia… is only a deceptive semblance, covering the full dependence of these, if I may say, states on this or that group of imperialists."

The proclamation of an independent Azerbaijani Democratic Republic immediately provoked a corresponding reaction from the Baku Bolsheviks. On May 29, 1918, they held a meeting of the Baku Soviet of Workers', Soldiers', and Sailors' Deputies and a congress of peasant deputies of Baku District, where all those who had voted for the formation of the Azerbaijani Democratic Republic were declared "enemies of the people." The resolution emphasized that: "As an inalienable part of the great Russian Soviet Federative Republic, we tie our fate intimately to the fate of revolutionary Russia."

Meanwhile, well-founded concern for the fate of Caspian oil prompted the leaders of Soviet Russia to take immediate steps to nationalize the oil industry on the Absheron Peninsula. First, on May 17, 1918, the presidium of the Supreme Council for the National Economy [*VSNKh*] directed the fuel section to wire a directive to all regional economic councils and local councils prohibiting the requisitioning of oil reserves in Baku Province without knowledge of the Fuel Department and its authorized organizations. Then, on May 22, 1918, the RSFSR Council of People's Commissars allocated 100 million rubles to the *VSNKh* Fuel Department for payment of wages to oilfield workers and for removal of oil from Baku. And, finally, on May 23, 1918, Lenin sent a telegram to Baku that read: "The Council of People's Commissars has resolved that a large lot of grain is to be sent by water from Tsaritsyn to Baku for disposition by the Baku Soviet of Deputies."[10]

Thus, the groundwork was in place for decisive action. On May 28, 1918, Baku received a telegram from Stalin, which read: "The Council of People's Commissars has approved nationalization of oil industry. Detailed instructions sent with [People's Commissar for Petroleum] Ter-Gabrielyan, who departed May 26. Petroleum Commissariat abolished, all responsibilities assigned to Main Petroleum Committee." Based on this telegram, the Baku Council of People's Commissars adopted a decree on June 2, 1918 nationalizing the oil industry. In all, over 400 enterprises were nationalized. The same decree also abolished the Congress of Baku Oil Industrialists, which had operated since 1844 as the authoritative representative organization of Russian entrepreneurs.

The nationalization of the industry continued to be followed closely by Moscow, and on June 5, 1918, Lenin again ordered the chairman of the Baku Council of People's Commissars Stepan Shaumian to "make petroleum your top priority."[11]

After the nationalization of the oil industry was complete, the Bolshevik leadership turned its attention to ensuring the reliable delivery of Baku crude to Soviet Russia. As the Caspian trading fleet was privately owned, the Baku Council of People's Commissars nationalized it on June 5, 1918. Implementation of this decision, however, ran into wholesale resistance by small and medium shipowners, which was immediately reported to the leaders of Soviet Russia.

In response, Stalin told the Baku Council of People's Commissars of the need to take the most radical actions: "On the question of nationalization of the Caspian fleet, you can act decisively.... You can be confident that the Council of People's Commissars will support you.... Do not take all this as my personal opinion, but as the recommendation of Lenin, with whom I spoke directly by phone yesterday on all the issues raised."[12]

This was followed by a telegram from Lenin, sent on June 18, 1918, in which he ordered the Baku Council to: "Take all steps to expedite shipment of petroleum products to Volga. Report daily to Main Petroleum Committee on status of oil industry."

For the Baku Council of People's Commissars, the whole of June 1920 was a period of considerable structural reorganization of the oil industry. The result was the creation of 19 major business associations, 17 of which covered the oil production fields, while the other two covered refineries and pipeline systems. Each of the associations was headed by a five-member board: two worker-elected representatives, one representative of the engineering and technical staff, and two representatives of the Baku Council of People's Commissars.

On July 9, 1918, Stepan Shaumian sent a telegram to Stalin in Tsaritsyn, updating him on the situation: "From May through June 1, New Style, we shipped 16,609,332 *poods* [1,994,581 barrels] of petroleum products, and in June, from June 1 through July 1, New Style, we shipped 26,449,405 *poods* [3,176,256 barrels]. We reduced only the shipment of gasoline: in May we shipped 16,652 *poods* [2,000 barrels], but in June we shipped 12,216 *poods* [1,467 barrels], because of a lack of shipping vessels."[13] In all, 4.7 million tons of crude oil and petroleum products were shipped to Soviet Russia during the spring and two summer months of 1918.

At the same time, an alignment of forces in the region was steadily unfolding against the Bolsheviks and the threat of losing of strategic positions loomed ever greater. Under these conditions, the Bolshevik leadership decided that Soviet Russian armed units had to be deployed to the Transcaucasus. On August 31, 1918, Stalin wrote Lenin: "Dear Comrade Lenin, A struggle is underway for the south and the Caspian. To hold this whole region (and we can hold it!), we must have several light minelayers and about two submarines. I beg you to break down all barriers and facilitate this, to move the cause forward for immediate receipt of what is needed. Baku, Turkestan, the North Caucasus will (certainly!) be ours if these requirements are promptly met."[14]

However, emergency transportation of the required warships could not be arranged from the Baltic to the Caspian via inland waterways. Instead, the Soviet Russian leadership decided to send an armed strike force down the Volga by ship. In a telegram sent to Saratov and Tsaritsyn, Lenin wrote: "The Lenin Regiment is advancing on Baku. Take urgent steps to expedite advance. Strict accountability for any delay."

By then, some military units of Soviet Russia had seen action, such as the detachment under the command of former warrant officer Grigory Petrov (1892–1918), who had received a mandate from a commissar of the RSFSR Council of People's Commissars in the Baku industrial region. From June 23, the Moscow armored car detachment also engaged actively in combat. However, their actions could no longer halt the rapid evolution of events in the region.

It was at this time that, faced with a joint Turkish-Azerbaijani offensive, sharp disputes regarding the organization of the city's defense erupted between the Baku Soviet of Workers', Soldiers', and Sailors' Deputies and the Council of People's Commissars, leading the Soviet of Deputies to adopt, by a majority vote on July 25, a decision to invite an English detachment to Baku. In response, Council of People's Commissars Chairman Shaumian, acting on behalf of the Bolshevik faction, declared: "We disavow the criminal policy that you are initiating, and resign from the positions of people's commissars." On August 1, 1918, in place of the Bolshevik Council of People's Commissars, who had all resigned, the Baku Soviet of Workers', Soldiers', and Sailors' Deputies decided to form a new executive body, which it named the Central Caspian Dictatorship. Its objective was to organize the city's defense in order to prevent Turkish troops from entering Baku. However, despite stubborn resistance, Turkish-Azerbaijani troops entered the city on September 15, 1918, overthrowing the Central Caspian Dictatorship and the Baku Soviet of Workers', Soldiers', and Sailors' Deputies. Shortly thereafter, the governing bodies of the Azerbaijani Democratic Republic settled in Baku.

On October 7, 1918, the government of the Azerbaijani Democratic Republic annulled the Baku Council of People's Commissars decree of June 2, 1918 nationalizing the oil enterprises on the Absheron Peninsula and returned the oil fields and refineries to their previous owners. The further development of events at the close of the First World War led to Germany's defeat, and under the terms of the Armistice of Moudros between Turkey and the Entente (October 30, 1918), Turkish troops were withdrawn from the Absheron Peninsula.

On November 13, 1918, negotiations were held between British and French delegations, which affirmed the agreement of December 23, 1917 on "division into spheres of influence" in Russia. On that basis, on November 17, 1918, the British 39th Infantry Brigade landed in Baku, commanded by Major General W. M. Thompson, soon named Governor General of the city. On December 6, 1918, Captain Webster, representing the British command, arrived in Batumi, and in a conversation with Georgian government representative D. A. Topuridze, stressed that his aim was to learn about the status of the Baku–Batumi pipeline.

On December 7, 1918, the parliament of the Azerbaijani Democratic Republic, initially consisting of 97 members, began its work. As chairman, the parliament elected Alimardan Alakbar oglu Topchubashov (1862–1934), former editor of the newspaper *Kaspiy* ["Caspian"] and deputy to the first State Duma (1906). (It should be noted that Azerbaijan became the first Muslim country to introduce a republican form of government.) On June 27, 1918, the Turkish (Azerbaijani) language[15] was declared the national language of the Azerbaijani Democratic Republic. By government decision, essential steps were taken to establish a system of national primary and secondary education and to restore the people's ancient cultural heritage. On September 9, 1918, the Azerbaijani Democratic Republic adopted a flag in the form of a tricolor consisting of light blue, red, and green bands with a white crescent and an eight-pointed star. In accordance with the decision of the Paris Peace Conference, British troops left the Absheron Peninsula in late August 1919, thereby voiding the Bolsheviks' claim of a "foreign intervention" in Azerbaijan.

The loss of Baku crude in the summer of 1918 was a serious blow to the Soviet Russian economy, and proved unacceptable to the Bolshevik leadership. Likewise, the creation and continued confident existence of three independent states in the Transcaucasus, and their support by the Entente, convinced the political leaders of the RSFSR that the achievement of their geopolitical goals would require a change in tactics and the use of new methods, forms, and means to regain their lost positions.

At this time, Bolshevik policy continued to be dominated by ideas of the rapid coming of world revolution and the creation of a unified proletarian state throughout Eurasia. One Bolshevik leader, Leon Trotsky, spoke very frequently of this: "Revolutionary war is an indisputable condition for our policy."[16] The noted Bolshevik theoretician Nikolay Bukharin made a similar remark in his *Economics of the Transition Period* [*Ekonomika perekhodnogo perioda*]: "The dictatorship of the proletariat cannot win if the proletariats of the various countries are isolated from one another. So the struggle inevitably involves coupling, linking, welding, and uniting all the new proletarian republics.... For the proletariat, this economic and political unity is a matter of life and death."

However, the Soviet leadership also had to take into account the links created among the independent Transcaucasian Republics by several international treaties. For example, on May 28, 1918, the Georgian Democratic Republic and Germany signed a treaty at Poti. On June 4, 1918, Turkey and the Azerbaijani Democratic Republic signed a treaty of peace and friendship. On November 23, 1919, with the mediation of the Georgian government in Tiflis, the governments of the Azerbaijani and Armenian Republics signed an agreement under which the parties committed to halting all armed conflicts underway between them and resolving disputes, including the border issue, by peaceful means. Even Soviet Russia had played a part in strengthening the cause of the independent Transcaucasian Republics: On August 27, 1918, the RSFSR and Germany signed a supplemental treaty, and in Article 13 of that treaty, Soviet Russia consented to Germany's recognition of Georgia as an independent state.

The situation that emerged produced a so-called double standard in the RSFSR's foreign policy. On the one hand, official diplomatic correspondence regarding the Transcaucasian Republics consistently avowed a striving to develop mutually beneficial relations and peaceful coexistence. On the other hand, with the ongoing strategic aim of realizing a proletarian revolution, a broad range of measures were undertaken to foment armed rebellion and overthrow the republic governments of Azerbaijan, Armenia, and Georgia. In this context, the Soviet Russian government regarded diplomatic activities in the Caucasus as a necessary step that could serve to mask preparations for more decisive action.

The Caucasian Territorial Committee of the Russian Communist Party (of Bolsheviks), or RCP(b), headed by Grigol "Sergo" Orjonikidze, became the coordinator of such subversive activities in the region. In November 1918, the Transcaucasian organizations of the RCP(b) held their first conference near the village of Digomi outside Tiflis and set their course for overthrowing the national governments.

The RCP(b) created a whole series of institutions to supervise and coordinate actions in the Transcaucasus. In Moscow, it formed a Central Bureau of Communist Organizations of the Peoples of the East, attached to the RCP(b) Central Committee, with separate Azerbaijani, Armenian, and Georgian sections within it. A second important agency was the Section for Transcaucasian Muslim Affairs, established on January 16, 1919 under the RSFSR People's Commissariat for Ethnic Affairs. An important role in implementing decisions was accorded to the Commissariat for Muslim Affairs, headed by Nariman Narimanov (1870–1925), and operated out of Astrakhan.

On May 2, 1919, a meeting of the Baku city Party Conference formulated the slogan "Independent Soviet Azerbaijan" as the main political objective for the future. As historians have noted, "In view of the errors committed in 1918 on the ethnic issue, and in order to wrest the banner of struggle for national independence from the hands of the Azerbaijani bourgeoisie and landowners, communist organizations carrying out Lenin's instructions have adopted the slogan, 'Independent Soviet Azerbaijan.'"[17] The slogan of national independence was reinforced by another essential tactical change—the creation of a Communist Party of Azerbaijan. Initially discussed in May 1919 by the Party's Caucasian Territorial Committee, the idea of an "independent" Communist Party of Azerbaijan and its future course of actions was thoroughly discussed at meetings in July, September, and December in Moscow of the Politburo and Organizing Bureau of the RCP(b) Central Committee.

At the same time, the Bolshevik leadership took a hard-line position on official recognition of the Azerbaijani Democratic Republic and establishment of diplomatic relations. In a telegram dated February 12, 1920, addressed to People's Commissar for Foreign Affairs Georgy Chicherin (1872–1936), Stalin stressed that "we consider the unconditional and categorical recognition of the independence of Azerbaijan unacceptable."

On January 3, 1920, the Politburo of the RCP(b) Central Committee adopted a resolution, one item of which read: "The struggle with local chauvinism and the creation of favorable conditions for promoting socialist revolution among ethnic groups under the aegis of tsarism makes it necessary for communist organizations in the 'independent' states that formed within the former Russian Empire to operate as independent communist parties. This method of organization is especially important in the East."[18]

On February 11–12, 1920, a Congress of communist organizations was held at the Workers' Club in Baku, where the Azerbaijani Communist Party (of Bolsheviks) was formed. Mirza Davud Baghir Huseynov was elected chairman of the presidium of the Central Committee and the Congress identified the preparation of armed rebellion to overthrow the government as the top priority for Party organizations.

The situation in the region soon escalated and on March 22, 1920, civil unrest and armed demonstrations initiated by local communist organizations broke out in densely populated Armenian areas in the Ganja and Kazakh Districts and in the Karabakh hills. This forced the government of the Azerbaijani Democratic Republic to send its few armed units to these areas, leaving its Dagestani border effectively undefended, so that by mid-April, units of the Caucasian Front's 11th Army had marched right up to the northern borders of Azerbaijan.

The 11th Army was headed by former Staff Captain Mikhail Levandovsky (1890–1937), and Sergey M. Kirov (1886–1934) and Konstantin Mekhonoshin (1889–1938) were members of the Revolutionary War Council. The Caucasian Front was commanded by former Second Lieutenant Mikhail Tukhachevsky (1893–1937), and the old Bolshevik Sergo Orjonikidze (1886–1937) was a member of the Revolutionary War Council.

Before the military operation, Lenin told the Revolutionary War Council and commanders of the 11th Army: "I ask you once again to act cautiously and always show the maximum good will toward the Muslims…. In every way, demonstrate… sympathy for Muslims, their autonomy, and their independence in the most serious manner."[19]

On April 15, 1920, the head of state of the Azerbaijani Democratic Republic, Fatali Khan Khoyski, sent an urgent telegram to People's Commissar for Foreign Affairs Georgy Chicherin: "We are observing a concentration of considerable military forces of the Russian Soviet government within the borders of Dagestan in Derbent District along the border of the Azerbaijani Republic. The Azerbaijani government, which has not been informed of the Soviet government's intentions, urgently requests an explanation of the reasons and purposes of the concentration of troops in these districts." However, no response from Moscow to Baku was forthcoming.

On April 27, 1920, units of the Caucasian Front's 11th Army crossed the border of the Azerbaijani Democratic Republic and entered Baku without opposition the next day. In his memoirs, the noted Soviet statesman Anastas Mikoyan (1895–1978) described the situation: "The Revolutionary War Council of the Army appointed me its representative, and I was to be dispatched along with the vanguard of trains commanded by Yefremov. This detachment had been charged with coming to the aid of the Baku proletariat, in order to prevent the bourgeois government from destroying the oil fields…. The lead armored train arrived at the Baku terminal at daybreak on April 28, where Soviet rule won peacefully, without bloodshed due to the overwhelming numerical advantage of the revolutionary forces."

With the entry of Soviet troops into Baku, the Azerbaijani Democratic Republic ceased to exist. A statement by the Provisional Revolutionary Committee dated April 28, 1920 read: "All authority in the country has passed into the hands of the working classes. A bright new era of socialism is opening up for the workers and peasants of Azerbaijan." The following day, April 29, 1920, Lenin noted that: "The position of Soviet Russia will change for the better; we know that our industry lacks fuel, and we have now received news that the Baku proletariat has taken power into its own hands.... This means that we now have an economic base on which to revitalize all our industry.... Thus, our transportation and industry will receive substantial assistance from the Baku oil fields."[20]

On May 5, 1920, Baku received a telegram from Lenin, stating: "The Council of People's Commissars welcomes the liberation of the working masses of the independent Azerbaijani Republic and expresses its firm confidence that, under the leadership of its own Soviet Government, the independent Republic of Azerbaijan, together with the RSFSR, will defend its freedom and independence from the sworn enemy of the repressed peoples of the East, from the imperialists."[21]

From its very inception, Soviet Azerbaijan began organizing massive shipments of crude oil by sea to Astrakhan. From April 30 to May 2, 1920 alone—that is, literally immediately after establishment of the new government on the Absheron Peninsula—it sent 12 steamers to the RSFSR carrying 156,115 barrels of crude. By late May of the same year, the quantity of crude supplied had increased to 1.8 million barrels, and by June it stood at 2.5 million barrels of crude oil and petroleum products. But even so, these delivery rates did not satisfy the RSFSR leadership. On August 4, 1920, the Council of Labor and Defense adopted yet another resolution on steps to increase petroleum products exports from Baku.

The newly proclaimed Azerbaijani Soviet Socialist Republic, formed on the model of the RSFSR, did not remain "independent" for long. On September 30, 1920, the RSFSR and Azerbaijani SSR signed a military and political alliance treaty that unified the military organizations and military commands of the two republics, as well as their regional economic councils, supply and transportation agencies, and people's commissariats of finance, mail, and telegraphy. On the same day, a foreign trade agreement was also signed. In addition, the RSFSR and Azerbaijani SSR signed agreements to conduct a unified economic policy and consolidate their food supply policies.

Speaking in December 1920 at the Eighth All-Russian Congress of Soviets, Lenin emphasized with satisfaction: "Now, with the tremendous enthusiasm being exhibited by workers in the Azerbaijani Republic, with the friendly relations that we have established, and with the skillful leaders sent by the Regional Economic Council, the oil business is going well, and we are beginning to stand on our own feet."

Once a regime controlled completely by the RSFSR had been established in Azerbaijan, there arose the question of delivering Baku crude to the European market via the port of Batumi on the Black Sea. In the opinion of RSFSR political leaders, the existence of republic governments in Armenia and Georgia was the main impediment to delivery of crude to the European and world markets, and so it was decided to apply the same successful scheme used in Azerbaijan to oust the national governments of these countries.

In June 1920, the Armenian Communist Party (of Bolsheviks) was formed, and in September 1920, the Caucasian Bureau of the RCP(b) Central Committee approved the membership of the Armenian CP(b) Central Committee. At the same time, Soviet Russian political leadership charged the People's Commissariat for Foreign Affairs with the task of making full use of diplomatic methods to create a legal basis for the operation of national communist parties.

In late May 1920, negotiations began in Moscow between the government delegations of Soviet Russia and the Republic of Armenia. The Soviet Russian delegation included People's Commissar for Foreign Affairs Georgy Chicherin and his deputy Lev M. Karakhan; the Armenian delegation was led by the Armenian politician Levon Shant. As it turned out, the agreement signed August 10, 1920 in Yerevan between the RSFSR and the Republic of Armenia was unable to prevent active hostilities by Turkish troops, and in September 1920, Turkish troops switched to the offensive. By the 20th of that month they occupied Sarikamish and Kaghzvan. On October 30, they took Kars, and on November 6 they took Alexandropol.

Amid these hostilities, the government of the Republic of Armenia resigned on November 4, 1920. On the same day, a new government headed by Simon Vratsyan was formed. In its declaration, the new government was forced to acknowledge the country's untenable position, but was unable to identify a solution.

Then in mid-November 1920, the Armenian Revolutionary War Committee was formed in Baku, headed by Sargis Kasyan. Later that month, the Armenian Revolutionary War Committee relocated to the town of Kazakh, near the border, where the Armenian regiment, formed from rebels who had retreated to Soviet Azerbaijan after the rebellion of May 1920 was put down, was also located.

On the morning of November 29, 1920, members of the Armenian Revolutionary War Committee (ARWC) crossed the border along with the Armenian rebel regiment. The border troops of the republican army offered no resistance, and the ARWC's declaration proclaiming Armenia a Soviet Socialist Republic was adopted in Ijevan the same day. The next day, again encountering no resistance, ARWC forces occupied Dilijan. The Armenian Revolutionary War Committee sent a telegram from there to Lenin asking for aid, after which units of the 11th Army of the Caucasian Front, previously stationed in Azerbaijan, crossed the border and commenced hostilities.

On December 2, 1920, Lenin sent a telegram to the Chairman of the ARWC, Sargis Kasyan, saying: "I greet you as the representative of a

Soviet Armenia of labor liberated from the yoke of imperialism. I have every confidence that you will make every effort to establish fraternal solidarity among the workers of Armenia, Turkey, and Azerbaijan."

Also on December 2, RSFSR Ambassador Plenipotentiary Boris Legran and ARWC Chairman Sargis Kasyan signed an RSFSR–Armenian SSR Friendship Agreement. Under this agreement, Armenia was allocated a cash loan in the amount of 3 billion rubles and was obligated to deliver 144,000 barrels of crude oil and petroleum products. The hurried signing of the Alexandropol Treaty between the governments of the Republic of Armenia and Turkey on the same day could no longer alter the state of affairs. On December 4, Red Army troops entered Yerevan, and the former Armenian government was finally deposed.

Once Soviet rule had been established in Armenia, the last obstacle to complete Soviet control of the Transcaucasus was the existence of the Georgian Democratic Republic. In conducting its policy regarding Georgia, the Soviet leadership was forced to reckon with the fact that the leading European powers of England, France, and Italy had recognized the independence of the Georgian Democratic Republic on January 20, 1920. Thus, energetic efforts along diplomatic lines came to the forefront. On May 7, 1920, Deputy People's Commissar for Foreign Affairs Lev M. Karakhan and Georgian Constituent Assembly member Grigol Uratadze signed a treaty in Moscow, under which the RSFSR recognized Georgia's sovereignty and full independence. Under the terms of the treaty, the government of Georgia assumed the obligation of assisting in the withdrawal from Georgia of the armed forces of Great Britain, stationed in Batumi.

In addition, a secret codicil to the treaty specified that the Communist Party would be legalized in Georgia and given freedom to operate, and that participants in rebellions and demonstrations organized by the Bolsheviks would be released from prison. Having been given complete freedom of action, the Georgian Communist Party (of Bolsheviks) was formed that same month.

In June 1920, a Soviet mission was sent to Tiflis, headed by noted Party leader Sergey M. Kirov, and rapidly grew to some 400 members. The enormous size of the mission raised doubts in Georgia about its diplomatic purpose. Shortly thereafter, in September 1920, Kirov was replaced as authorized representative of the RSFSR to the Georgian Democratic Republic by experienced diplomat Aron L. Sheynman.

After meeting with Kirov in Baku regarding the future of the Georgian Democratic Republic, Stalin was pointedly blunt in a September 30, 1920 conversation with a correspondent for the newspaper *Pravda* ["Truth"]: "The catastrophic economic and food situation in Georgia is a fact admitted even by the bosses of today's Georgia. Georgia is entangled in the tentacles of the Entente and therefore deprived both of Baku oil and Kuban bread. This Georgia, which has been transformed into a major base for the imperialist operations of England and France and has therefore entered into hostile relations with Soviet Russia, is now living the last days of its life."

On November 14, 1920, RSFSR Ambassador Plenipotentiary Aron Sheynman, Azerbaijan SSR People's Commissar Mirza Davud Baghir Huseynov, and Georgian Democratic Republic Deputy Minister of Foreign Affairs K. Sabakhtarishvili signed a trade and transit agreement in Tiflis, under which the RSFSR and the Azerbaijan SSR were to deliver 120,000 barrels of crude to Georgia monthly, and Georgia agreed to the free-transit export of coal, timber, and other materials of equivalent value to the petroleum products received. A special secret codicil to the agreement stipulated the terms and conditions of operation of the oil tank farm at Batumi: "Georgia shall lease to Russia and Azerbaijan [the following facilities] for storage of petroleum products in the oil city at Batumi Station: tanks numbering no more than four stations, with a total capacity of 6 million *poods* [720,000 barrels], including 4.5 million *poods* [540,000 barrels] suitable for the storage of kerosene, 500,000 *poods* [60,000 barrels] suitable for the storage of crude oil and residual oil, and 1 million *poods* [120,000 barrels] suitable for the storage of lubricants and gasoline, rail spurs, loading facilities, appropriate pumping stations with necessary associated residential premises, pipelines to pumping stations and to a pier and loading facilities on the pier, with all listed storage facilities and devices in serviceable [condition] and suitable for immediate operation.... Russia and Azerbaijan shall pay Georgia for providing said tanks with the listed facilities and including a fee for the provision of tank cars for loading at 60 kopecks per *pood* [36 pounds] of tankage per month and at 60 kopecks per *pood* per month for storage of petroleum products over and above rated periods in the tanks of Kobuleti and Batumi Kerosene Pipeline Stations."[22]

On November 23, 1920, Stalin returned to Moscow from the Transcaucasus and presented a report on the situation to the Politburo. Afterward, in a resolution drafted by Lenin, the Politburo stated: "The most conciliatory policy possible shall be adopted with respect to Georgia, Armenia, Turkey, and Persia, aimed most of all at avoiding war."[23]

The "most conciliatory policy possible" with respect to Georgia became apparent on December 15, 1920, when a session of the Caucasian Bureau of the RCP(b), after hearing Orjonikidze's report on the situation in Georgia, passed a resolution on the need to foment armed rebellion in the republic. Earlier, on December 9, 1920, the RSFSR government notified its ambassador to Georgia, Aron Sheynman, that he was to suspend the export of crude oil to Georgia in view of the latest actions of the Georgian government, which were not compatible with the friendly treaty relations established between the RSFSR and the Georgian Republic. Official Georgian assurances that no unfriendly actions had actually occurred were disregarded.

On January 2, 1921, Kirov and Orjonikidze sent another letter to Moscow justifying "immediate military assistance to the workers of Georgia in their struggle to establish Soviet rule." The commander of the 11th Army, former Staff Captain Anatoly Gekker (1888–1938), presented a detailed plan for organizing combat operations of Red Army units on Georgian territory.

On January 20, 1921, Russian People's Commissar for Foreign Affairs Georgy Chicherin reported to Lenin that "Georgia has become insolent again" and it had to be "Sovietized" by military force. On January 26, 1921, a plenary session of the RCP(b) Central Committee discussed the Georgian question, and adopted the following decision at Lenin's recommendation: "1) The People's Commissar for Foreign Affairs is directed to delay the break with Georgia, systematically collecting precise material on its violation of the treaty and more insistently demanding the passage of munitions into Armenia; 2) The Caucasian Front is to be asked about how prepared our available armed forces are in case of immediate or imminent war with Georgia, and a committee comprised of Comrades Trotsky, Chicherin and Stalin is directed to formulate the question, specifying Georgia's extreme insolence; 3) A directive is to be issued to the Republic's Revolutionary War Committee and the Caucasus Front to prepare for war with Georgia if this becomes necessary."[24]

The ensuing events followed the familiar scenario. First, on February 7, 1921, a revolutionary war committee was formed in the Lori neutral zone, headed by Ivan Lazyan. Armed demonstrations began on February 11, and soon Borchalo district was in rebel hands, whereupon the rebel leaders sent a message to Moscow requesting military assistance.

On February 14 and 15, 1921, Lenin sent successive telegrams to the 11th Army Revolutionary War Council, giving specific recommendations for the conduct of operations in Georgia. On February 16, 1921, a Georgian Revolutionary Committee was formed in the settlement of Shulaveri [now Shaumyani], consisting of Philipe Makharadze (chairman), Mamia Ora-khelashvili, Aleksi Gegechkori, Shalva Eliava, Amayak Nazaretyan, and others. The Georgian Socialist Soviet Republic was proclaimed there on February 18, 1921, followed by a request to the RSFSR government for armed assistance to save the "insurgent Georgian proletariat."

This request was immediately honored; units of the Caucasian Front's 11th Army crossed the Georgian frontier and engaged Georgian border forces. The Georgian head of state, Noe Zhordania, attempted to contact Moscow by telegraph, but the leaders of the RSFSR People's Commissariat for Foreign Affairs refused to correspond. At the same time, the RSFSR ambassador plenipotentiary to Georgia, Aron Sheynman, officially announced—on the first day the Red Army initiated hostilities—that Soviet Russia was uninvolved in the attack on Georgian border troops in Borchalo District.

The Soviet Russian government finally issued an official reply on February 18, 1921 via the Georgian Democratic Republic's envoy to Poland, while a note from RSFSR People's Commissar Georgy Chicherin to the Georgian government contained accusations of repressions against the population of the Lori neutral zone, which had provoked an uprising against Georgian occupation troops.

Multiple desperate radio appeals by Georgian head of state Noe Zhordania on February 20, 21, and 22, 1921 to the leaders of Soviet Russia demanding they halt the invasion of RSFSR armed forces into the territory of independent Georgia went unanswered.

The stubborn resistance of the armed forces of the Georgian Democratic Republic forced the government of Soviet Russia to utilize additional armed forces of its own. The Red Army offensive developed simultaneously in three directions: along the Georgian Military Road from Vladikavkaz; from Mamison Pass toward Kutaisi; and along the Black Sea coast from Sochi. Thus, the troop operation involved units of the 11th, 2nd, and 8th Armies coordinating with units of the 1st Cavalry Army under the command of Semën Budënny. Finally, on February 25, 1921, units of the Red Army entered Tiflis, and on March 18, Soviet rule was established in Batumi. The Georgian Democratic Republic had at last ceased to exist.

Following the fall of the Georgian Democratic Republic, one of the priorities of Soviet Russia's representatives in Georgia was to ensure restoration of the transportation corridor in order to resume oil exports. By March 12, 1921, operation of the Baku–Tiflis pipeline had been restored. Lenin immediately brought this news to the delegates of the Tenth Congress of the RCP(b): "Have you read in the newspaper about the Baku–Tiflis oil pipeline opening? You will soon read about a similar oil pipeline to Batumi…. The point is to improve our economic situation, strengthen the technical equipment of our republic…. In this respect, any easing is of gigantic importance to us."

On May 21, 1921, the RSFSR and the Georgian Socialist Soviet Republic signed a treaty creating a military and political alliance and integrating the main economic structures of the two states. Soviet rule had thus been established throughout the entire Transcaucasus. Later, characterizing the national policy of the RSFSR government in the region, the noted Azerbaijani writer, politician, and public figure Mammed Amin Rasulzade (1884–1955), who had fled Soviet Russia, wrote an open letter to Stalin which he published abroad in December 1923, saying: "What is happening in Russia is practically indistinguishable from what happened here 100 years ago. Just as was the case 100 years ago, Russia is again annexing more and more new colonies. The replacement of great-power chauvinism with workers' cosmopolitanism essentially changes nothing, and will also ultimately result in the destruction of small nations. By the force of your arms, you are also suppressing national movements in the

Caucasus and Turkestan, and you say that you are doing it in the interests of the local proletariat…. Without a shadow of a doubt, you have trampled on the lawful right of the absolute majority of the local population to self-determination and independence. Thus, it is perfectly clear that the dictatorship of the proletariat proclaimed in Azerbaijan and Turkestan is essentially that same dictatorship of Moscow, and nothing more."

And indeed, even under conditions of limited sovereignty, the "independent" Soviet republics of Azerbaijan, Armenia, and Georgia would not have long to live. In November 1921, at Lenin's recommendation, the Politburo adopted a resolution: "1) That the Federation of Transcaucasian Republics be deemed in principle absolutely correct, and certainly subject to implementation…; 2) That the Central Committees of Georgia, Armenia, and Azerbaijan (through the Caucasian Bureau) be invited to raise the question of federation more broadly for discussion among the Party and worker and peasant masses, and that federation be energetically promoted and carried out through congresses of the Soviets of each republic."[25]

On March 12, 1922, a conference of representatives of the soviets of Georgia, Armenia, and Azerbaijan in Tiflis created the Federal Union of Soviet Socialist Republics of the Transcaucasus (the Transcaucasian Federation). Subsequently, in early October 1922, a Plenary Session of the RCP(b) Central Committee discussed the question of combining all the Soviet republics into a single state. On December 30, 1922, the Congress of Soviets adopted a declaration forming the Union of Socialist Soviet Republics.

Once Soviet rule had been established throughout the Transcaucasus, an unimpeded path for Baku crude was opened to the world market. Soviet control over this key region brought immediate results: while 320,000 barrels of petroleum products were exported in the period from December 1, 1921 to May 1, 1922, the export volume jumped to 814,000 barrels in the period from May 1, 1922 to October 1, 1922.

Thus, by the early 1920s in the Transcaucasus, the leaders of Soviet Russia, using Caspian oil both as a priority goal and as an effective means of military-political reorientation of Azerbaijan, Armenia, and Georgia, had basically solved the main geopolitical problem of establishing and strengthening their dominant positions in the region.

Oil Concessions in the RSFSR: Plans and Reality

By the spring of 1921, it had become clear to the Bolshevik leadership that the beginning of the world revolution would be "somewhat delayed." Accordingly, Soviet Russia was forced to consider substantial adjustments to its domestic and foreign policy. The latter became especially critical as the RSFSR found itself encircled by an "imperialist blockade."

As oil was one of Soviet Russia's key commodities, it naturally played an important role in the strategic plans of the Soviet leadership. In early February 1921, the RCP(b) Politburo focused on a review of the problems of the oil industry, primarily from the standpoint of the practical realization of the oil concession policy in the RSFSR. In a memorandum presented at the meeting, People's Commissar for Foreign Trade Leonid Krasin (1870–1926) noted the most important point up front: "Salvation is possible only through a very strong and decisive policy, which should consist of granting, to three or four major syndicates competing on the world market, as well as the governments of Italy and perhaps France and Belgium as well, attractive enough areas in respectable parts of Baku District and especially Grozny District."

A resolution of the Politburo of the RCP(b) Central Committee adopted February 5, 1921 read: "On oil concessions: a) Comrades Krasin and [Deputy Chairman of the Labor and Defense Council Aleksey] Rykov are directed to submit to the Central Committee Politburo within three days— over their own signatures and those of responsible specialists—a precise formulation of specifically how, when, and for what reasons a catastrophe looms in the operation of oil fields in Baku and Grozny, and to give their thoughts on why and to what extent granting concessions could prevent this catastrophe. The report of the specialists must be transmitted secretly to obtain the opinion of local Baku and Grozny executives and workers, a list of whom will be drawn up at an upcoming meeting of the Politburo."[26]

We should note that several days later, on February 14, 1921, the RCP(b) Central Committee Politburo continued their discussion of the status of the oil industry and steps to turn it around. As in the past, the problem of transportation was critical, so a decision was made to order 500 Canadian and 1,000 English tank cars. The situation was also dire with the tanker fleet: in 1920, the Caspian oil fleet consisted of only six motor vessels, 52 steamers, and 14 scows. Thus, oil shipments via the Caspian Sea and Volga basin were equated to "super-priority military operational" assignments and serious steps were thereby undertaken to increase the volume of seagoing and inland petroleum products shipments.

On the evening of March 8, 1921, speaking at the opening of the Tenth Party Congress, Lenin declared the importance of oil concessions: "The Central Committee, and I personally, have come to view these concessions as necessary, and we will ask you to support this view with your authority. This alliance with state-owned trusts of other leading countries is absolutely necessary for us because our economic crisis is so deep that we cannot revive the damaged business by our own efforts without equipment and technical assistance from abroad."[27]

The position of the Soviet head of state was reflected in a resolution, which read: "1. The Congress approves the policy of Soviet authorities aimed at establishing normal trading relations between the Soviet republic and other countries by the execution of trade treaties and agreements. 2. The Congress also approves the Council of People's Commissars decree of November 23, 1920 on the general economic and legal terms and conditions of concessions."[28]

Four days later, relying on the opinion of the Party's majority, Lenin sent a telegram to Krasin in London: "The Party Congress has approved the line I proposed on concessions in Grozny and Baku. Expedite negotiations on this and on any other concessions. Send frequent updates." People's Commissar for Foreign Trade Krasin was in London at that time as the RSFSR's official representative in Great Britain and had already signed the first Soviet-British trade agreement.

Nine days later, on March 28, 1921, Krasin received a directive that not only implied the complete acceptance of his February proposal on helping the Baku and Grozny oil fields find a way out of the acute crisis, but also gave him a certain freedom of action: "Basic provisions of oil concessions: 1. The concession term to be set at 25 years with the right of early buy-out after 15 years. 2. The following areas are to be offered for concession: a) the entire Bibiheybet oilfield area in the Baku District, not including offshore parts of Baku Bight; b) the entire western half of the Old Grozny oil area, approximately up to the meridian of Mamakayev Gorge; c) 80 *desyatinas* [220 acres] in the area of Solënaya Gorge in one section; d) the entirety of the Chermoyev lands in the New Grozny District. 3. Payment for concessions to be made by proportional deductions from gross productivity. The proportional deduction is to be about 3% for Bibiheybet, and about 40% for Grozny District. The annual minimum production, beginning from a specific date stated in the contract after the acceptance of the concession, is to be set at 90 million *poods* [10.8 million barrels] for Bibiheybet, and 50 million [6 million] for Grozny. 4. A condition for the concession of Bibiheybet, over and above the proportional deduction, is the delivery of necessary equipment for electrification of fields in Baku District and laying of a 10-inch oil pipeline from Petrovsk to Moscow. A condition for the concession of Grozny, over and above the proportional deduction, is the delivery of equipment for a paraffin refinery with a refining capacity of 100 million *poods* [12 million barrels] of crude oil and laying of a 10-inch oil pipeline from Grozny to Moscow. Both the oil pipelines and the refinery and the electrical stations, upon construction, shall be at the disposal of the RSFSR government. 5. Raw and ancillary materials shall be provided to the concessionaire by the RSFSR government under a special agreement applicable to foreign market prices, taking account of the difference in the cost of transportation. (We regard the above terms as illustrative, to give an immediate basis for the beginning of specific negotiations; we emphasize in particular that we will make specific concessions provided the paraffin refinery and oil pipelines are built and equipment delivery is expedited.)"[29]

The negotiations, which Krasin pursued right away, ran into a virtually insurmountable obstacle almost immediately. Henri Deterding, head of Royal Dutch Shell, as well as the leaders of several other firms including Petrol Grozny Ltd., expressed their willingness to take some of the Baku and Grozny oil fields in concession, and even to begin construction of a paraffin refinery and oil pipelines. However, they all demanded that the Soviet state not grant them just the lands defined in the "Basic Provisions," but also those that they had bought from the former emigrant owners after October 1917.

On June 30, 1921, the Council of Labor and Defense adopted a resolution creating the Concession Committee of the Supreme Council for the National Economy, headed by Pëtr Bogdanov (1882–1939), who monitored the progress of negotiations in London as well. Despite the involvement of this new committee, after eight months, People's Commissar Krasin still could not agree with a single major foreign oil company, even in principle, on the basis of the "Basic Provisions of Oil Concessions" received from Moscow.

In October 1921, however, hope seemed to appear—negotiations began with the Foundation Company, one of the biggest American construction companies, which had long cooperated with leading oil concerns, and was studying the possibility of participating in new projects after having completed a refinery in Mexico.

On October 19, 1921, Leonid Krasin reported to Moscow as follows: "Colonel Abbott, representing the Foundation Company, visited me yesterday on the Continent and informed me that his company is interested in building a paraffin refinery and Grozny–Black Sea oil pipeline, and construction on credit with payment in proportional deduction of the oil carried is possible. An indispensable preliminary condition, however, is the performance of engineering studies by the company's American engineers, otherwise financiers and politicians would not be drawn to the project. I asked him to draw up a preliminary estimate for the dispatch of several American specialists, with second-level technical staff to be provided by us. I will send you the figures when I receive them. I accord the highest importance to this matter as the first serious business contact with extremely prestigious Americans. Please review the question as a matter of urgency and wire instructions. In case of a favorable decision, I believe a trip to America is possible in the immediate future."[30]

Krasin received an answer 11 days later in the form of a specific decision by the RSFSR Council of People's Commissars: "We agree to allocate up to $100,000 to pay for studies by the Foundation Company, provided our workers and specialists participate and all study requirements are communicated. We consider it hugely important to attract American capital to construction of a paraffin refinery and oil pipeline in Grozny. Please advance this matter with maximum speed and energy."

However, information on the negotiations underway in London leaked into the local press, and subsequent negotiations suggested that the representatives of the Foundation Company had come under strong pressure from some third party. First, the American company unexpectedly abandoned its own proposal to build a paraffin refinery and oil pipeline, and then it limited its prospective activities to simply drawing up plans for those facilities. By early December 1921, the company broke off talks entirely.

On December 8, 1921, after receiving news of this from Krasin, the members of the RCP(b) Politburo discussed the turn of events and answered him the very same day, expressing their dissatisfaction in a rather harsh tone: "The Politburo is perplexed at your telegram of 12/8/21. 1) The question of oil concessions, previously formulated by you and discussed with your participation, was decided favorably by the CC. 2) At that time, you were also instructed to move the oil concession matter forward as energetically as possible. 3) We have received no specific proposals on oil concessions from you, so there can be no question of practical hindrance of the matter. 4) Now your telegram gives material for further discussion and includes no specific proposals. 5) The Politburo affirms its previous decision ordering you to move this matter practically forward as energetically as possible."[31]

Meanwhile, on December 31, 1921, the first All-Russian Congress of Oil Workers opened in Moscow, drawing a more than representative group of industry workers. Among those attending were Mikhail Lyadov, head of the Central Oil Industry Administration of the Supreme Council for the National Economy; one Shteyngauz, head of the Central Shale Fuel Administration; Aleksandr Serebrovsky, manager of Azneft; Iosif Kosior, manager of Grozneft; and prestigious oil specialists Ivan Strizhov, Ivan Gubkin, and Vasily Frolov.

The congress's resolution on the first agenda item, adopted on January 5, 1922, read: "Management of such a profitable business as the oil industry of Baku and Grozny must be a matter for the state itself; the granting of concessions to the operational fields in these districts must be recognized as unconditionally wrong."

Despite such objections, Soviet representatives continued carrying out concession negotiations in London, and also began talks in Berlin with a group of German financiers led by the head of the well-known Deutsche Bank. The RCP(b) Politburo soon gathered again (also on December 31, 1921) to review reports from the Concession Committee. Concerning one report on oil industry concessions by State Planning Committee Chairman Gleb Krzhizhanovsky and Concession Committee Chairman Pëtr Bogdanov, an intermediate resolution was adopted deferring a final decision indefinitely, as had been done in the past: "d) The question of granting a concession to oil areas is deferred, requiring a precise formulation of an opinion opposite to that of the CC commission. Concrete proposals from Comrade Krasin in connection with negotiations shall be sent to the Politburo upon receipt; e) Comrade Smilga is directed to conduct negotiations with the Deutsche Bank without the right to make any final decisions without the Politburo; f) Comrade Smilga is asked to familiarize himself in advance with the status of negotiations being carried on by Comrades Krasin and Stomonyakov and to continue them in full contact with them. All materials must be delivered to Comrade Smilga."[32]

On February 18, 1922, a session of the RCP(b) Politburo reconsidered this issue, and adopted the following resolution: "On oil concessions: a) The Supreme Council for the National Economy is directed to send Comrade Smilga a telegram reporting the dispatch of materials and departure of requested experts, stating that specific instructions will be given after Comrade Krasin's arrival in Moscow, and recommend that Comrade Smilga speak with Comrade Krasin if there is a possibility of arranging a meeting with him in Berlin, but to continue negotiations for now; b) It is recommended that the People's Commissariat for Foreign Affairs take the most energetic steps for the immediate departure of oil concession experts Ramzin, Strizhov, and Shibinsky for Berlin."

However, progress in Berlin proved to be slow, and the next RCP(b) Politburo resolution emphasized that: "a) In the matter of real implementation of concession agreements based on negotiations broadly underway in Berlin, nothing has yet been undertaken; b) The Concession Committee, jointly with Comrade Kursk, is directed to review the procedure for approval of concession agreements; c) Oil concessions with the Deutsche Bank, and Kryvyi Rih ore and agricultural concessions with Krupp, are deemed possible in principle, and it is recommend that the Concession Committee hear the reports of Comrades Stomonyakov and Krasin as soon as possible and move the matter forward on an expedited basis, before the Genoa Conference."[33]

It the opinion of the Soviet Russian leadership, it was precisely these oil concessions that would be the most "tasty" Russian proposal offered to the Entente countries at the upcoming international conference in Genoa in the spring of 1922.

The Russian Oil Question at the Genoa and Hague Conferences

In the early 1920s, Western oil entrepreneurs behaved as if they were certain that Soviet rule in Russia was just a temporary phenomenon. Even after the city of Grozny was captured by the Red Army, French financial groups founded the Société des Pétroles Essences, Naphtes joint-stock company in Paris on April 2, 1920. The company "acquired" parcels in Grozny that had previously belonged to the entrepreneur Chermoyev, as well as a controlling interest in the New Caucasian Oilfield Company. French specialists believed these parcels should yield up to 9.6 million barrels of crude per year.

In 1920, another company intending to pump oil from Grozny was founded in Antwerp: the French-Belgian Trust Franco-Belge de Pétrole joint-stock company. The company hoped to obtain up to 7.2 million barrels of crude per year in Grozny. Thus, all Grozny crude had "owners" in the West, and it was their opinion that this crude absolutely could not be sold on foreign markets by the Soviet government. The Franco-Belgians, who had also founded the Société-d'Emba Grosny company in that same year of 1920, also held stock in companies producing oil on the Emba. Moreover, the emigrant Chermoyev, together with Trust Franco-Belge de Pétrole, founded the Société pour le Transport du Naphte de Grosny in Paris in 1921 to transport Grozny crude via Novorossiysk and contracted with the "lawful owners" of the Vladikavkaz Railroad, who were residing in the West and had granted exclusive rights to build an oil pipeline along the railroad bed.

Accordingly, the West came to regard the Grozny and Emba oil fields as Franco-Belgian, and most of the fields on the Absheron Peninsula as English property, and this was the position promulgated and taken up among the West in preparation for an international conference in Genoa, which was to resolve the complex issues of the postwar economic system in Europe.

On April 10, 1922, an international conference of representatives from both the winning and losing countries of the First World War opened in the Italian port city of Genoa. This conference was intended to finally close the books on the recently concluded war and work out steps for Europe's political and economic recovery. The participants included 29 nations and five dominions of Great Britain; the US declined to participate and was represented by only a single observer. Soviet Russia also sent a delegation, which was difficult to assign clearly to any of these groups.

At a preliminary meeting in Boulogne, France on February 25, 1922, British Prime Minister David Lloyd George (1868–1945) and French Prime Minister Raymond Poincaré (1860–1934) agreed that the main issue at the conference would be the "Russian question." A special committee of experts, who worked in London from March 20 to 28, 1922, prepared a draft resolution in which Soviet Russia would be required to acknowledge all debts and financial obligations of all former Russian authorities, and to assume responsibility for all losses due to the actions of both the Soviet and preceding governments or local authorities. According to this draft, all loans concluded with Russia after August 1, 1914 were to be considered paid after payment of a certain sum yet to be determined, and all nationalized enterprises were to be returned to their foreign owners.

In its turn, the government of Soviet Russia carried out a series of important organizational and political preparations. To ensure the complete diplomatic unity of the Soviet republics, a protocol was signed in Moscow on February 22, 1922 granting the RSFSR the power to defend the rights of the Union republics (Ukraine, Belorussia, Georgia, Armenia, Azerbaijan, the Buxoro [Bukhara] and Khorezm Republics, and the Far Eastern Republic) at the Genoa Conference, and to execute and sign documents and certain international treaties and agreements developed at the conference on their behalf. A protocol was then signed in Riga on March 30, 1922 at a special conference of representatives of the RSFSR, Estonia, Latvia, and Poland dedicated to coordinating the actions of the delegates of these states at the Genoa Conference, in which the delegates of Estonia, Latvia, and Poland expressed the opinion that the Soviet Russian government had to be recognized *de jure*.

In addition, the RSFSR Council of People's Commissars decided to create a special commission to calculate the debts of the tsarist and provisional governments and compute the losses inflicted on the Russian economy during the years of the anti-Soviet imperialist intervention of 1917–1922. As it turned out, Russia's debts totaled 18.496 billion gold rubles, while the losses inflicted on the country's economy were 39 billion gold rubles.

A speech given at the first session of the Genoa conference by RSFSR People's Commissar for Foreign Affairs Georgy Chicherin (1872-1936) contained a proposal for broad economic, political, and cultural cooperation between capitalist and socialist countries, noninterference in internal affairs, recognition of the principles of nonaggression, full equality, and mutual benefit, as well as resolution of all conflicts by peaceful means, economic cooperation, and development of trade relations. The program set forth by the representatives of the Soviet state met the fundamental interests of the peoples of all countries, and was aimed at establishing world peace. The Soviet government was prepared to accept the prewar debts and preferential right of most owners to receive the property that had previously belonged to them via concession or lease, provided the Soviet state received *de jure* recognition and was granted financial aid, and its war debts and interest thereon were forgiven.

A proposal submitted by the Soviet delegation for universal arms reduction was very important. People's Commissar Chicherin declared the readiness of the Soviet state to support all attempts aimed at eliminating the threat of new wars. But the Soviet delegation's call for disarmament caused confusion among the conference delegates. French representative Jean Louis Barthou even spoke openly against the proposal, although the delegations of other powers, concerned about public opinion, refrained from making similar sharp comments.

In response, a resolution of allied delegations was announced on April 15, 1922 and contained the following requirements for Soviet Russia: "1. The allied creditor states represented in Genoa cannot accept any obligations regarding claims made by the Soviet government. 2. However, in view of Russia's severe economic state, the creditor states are inclined to reduce Russia's war debt to them in percentage terms, the amounts of which are to be determined later. The nations represented at Genoa are inclined to take under consideration not only the question of deferred payment of current interest, but also of deferred payment of some overdue or delinquent interest. 3. Nevertheless, it must be finally established that no exceptions can be made for the Soviet government regarding: a) debts and financial obligations assumed to citizens of other nationalities; b) regarding the rights of these citizens to restoration of their property rights or to compensation for the damages and losses they have suffered."

As a result, the Soviet Russian delegation found itself in an unusually difficult position. Only Soviet Russia was presented this memorandum containing a series of harsh, ultimatum-like demands. Furthermore, when Georgy Chicherin and Leonid Krasin declared the government's willingness to meet all financial obligations—but only those of tsarist Russia and those assumed before the beginning of the world war—it was evident from the ensuing speeches by representatives of the Entente countries that the issue really boiled down to a single question: How and in what form did the Bolsheviks intend to cover the losses of the former owners of the Baku and Grozny oil fields?

As the Genoa Conference continued, it became clear that British Prime Minister David Lloyd George and Foreign Minister Lord Curzon openly supported the position of Great Britain's oil companies, and John D. Rockefeller's American Standard Oil Company was secretly backing the French and Belgian delegations at the conference. It is telling that the representatives of companies interested in southern Russian oil enterprises soon openly declared the need to establish a special panel on petroleum affairs at the Genoa Conference, which would include the participation of Royal Dutch Shell, the Anglo-Persian Company, and the Standard Oil Company, among other groups.

It is no surprise that during the conference the topic of Russian oil was addressed by publications both abroad and in Soviet Russia. For example, alongside articles on the Genoa Conference and speeches by the heads of delegations, the official *VSNKh* organ, the newspaper *Izvestia* ["News"] began publishing materials that it would normally place under the rubric "Oil Concessions." On May 5: "Krasin dismissed a report in the Paris paper *Le Matin* on the Soviet government's signing of a treaty with some 'foreign oil company' for the exploitation of all Russia's fields." Then, on May 9 and May 25, coverage of an interview given by Leonid Krasin to a *Matin* correspondent: "I can absolutely assure you that we have not signed a contract with Shell. The supposition that we will give all our oil to one party is completely contrary to our principles and to our interests. Our oil riches were exploited before the war in a most foolish manner. The parcels were located extremely irregularly as small oases. The gaps between them were not exploited. Each parcel required special equipment and separate technical staff. In addition, each of the owners of these small parcels drilled at their boundaries in order to drain oil already found and being exploited from their neighbors. We intend to proceed completely differently. In Baku District, we will continue the experiment of direct exploitation of oil by the state on approximately a quarter of the territory. We will divide the rest into three or four areas, fairly large ones, to permit benefits from concentration of both equipment and technical supervision of the business. In addition, such wide areas allow drilling to be done along directional lines that match those of the petroleum deposits. But it is in our own interests to concede areas to different companies—English, American, French, Belgian. We will reward the previous owners with concessions in these areas. The Belgian viewpoint seems strange to me. The Belgians are the very ones who possess a large number of these small parcels, which have no value without renovating everything. In fact, what good is the parcel to its owner if electrical, hydraulic, and other services are not restored in the entire basin? The English completely agree with this scheme of ours, and the Russian government will also invest in the capital and materials needed for exploitation. This course is the best way to compensate former owners of small oil parcels, because they could invest in these companies."[34]

This interview with People's Commissar Krasin, in which he disclosed the coordination and commonality of the Anglo-Soviet position, merely poured oil on the fire, as can be seen in the following report dated May 9: "Negotiations are underway in Genoa on the question of oil concessions. The English financier Samueli has come to Genoa, as has Grassouin from France. In addition, Rockefeller's secretary is already in Genoa. Such a congress shows best of all that the question of Russian oil has been made a top priority. Standard Oil has filed a protest against all the exclusive concessions that Russia is considering granting to Royal Dutch Shell. Belford conferred on this matter with Secretary of State Hughes, and assured him that the US would not accept any agreements contrary to the interests of American capital in Russia. The American government has instructed its ambassadors in London and Rome to learn whether the Soviet government has conducted negotiations with Shell. If this turns out to be the case, the US will file a protest with the English government." Then on May 10: "The French government has sent several oil production experts to Genoa, who intend to force Lloyd George to convene a special conference of representatives from countries interested in Russian oil concessions. Lloyd George has assured the American ambassador that England will not sign an oil concession agreement with Russia without American participation. Foreign newspapers note that the oil issue has thrown North America off balance. The Standard Oil representatives arriving in Genoa are interested in whether Krasin is negotiating with other oil groups. The members of the Commission for Assistance in Restoring Italian-Russian Economic Relations met with Krasin yesterday, specifically on the question of oil exports. The negotiations went well." And again, on May 11, the respectable British newspaper, *The Times*, reported: "The whole conference reeks of oil," and the London *Daily Telegraph* echoed: "When Lloyd George met with Barthou, the oil question played the leading role." On May 14, the American paper *New York World* underscored the situation at the conference: "Russian oil is the big trump card in the Soviet delegation's hand."

On May 18, 1922, *Izvestia* published the following statement on Genoa by Soviet People's Commissar Leon Trotsky: "How justified are the rumors that the Russian government is supposedly negotiating with English entrepreneurs to grant them concessions to Russian oil fields? I am not specifically informed on these negotiations, but I have no doubt that our petroleum resources represent a tremendous field for the application of foreign capital, both in the area of efficient exploitation and in the area of further exploration. The conduct of the negotiations is in the hands of Krasin, the people's commissar for foreign trade. What role English entrepreneurs are playing at the moment I cannot say precisely. But I have no doubt that if Lloyd George were to finally abandon Urquhart's ultimatums and ensure the success of a military and political agreement, economic negotiations would proceed swiftly and the Soviet Federation's oil industry would occupy one of the primary positions in these negotiations."

As Soviet Russia rejected the Entente's ultimatum and the conference essentially collapsed, British Prime Minister Lloyd George offered to refer the "Russian question" for further study to a commission of experts, which was to gather a month later at a different site, in The Hague.

On May 19, 1922, commenting on the collapse of the conference, the French newspaper *L'Internationale* stressed that "the failure of the Genoa conference is due entirely to the fight between Royal Dutch and Standard Oil. The conference participants are not interested in the question of rebuilding Europe; they need only Caucasian oil." The German paper *Neue Freie Presse*, reporting along the same lines, wrote that: "It is extremely important for Great Britain to gain a monopoly over Caucasian oil, mainly because the English merchant marine is switching more and more to petroleum fuel."

The day after the conference ended, May 20, *Izvestia* wrote: "One thing is clear: the question of Russian oil was at the focus of all the behind-the-scenes intrigue at the Genoa conference. And the conference was killed primarily by the tacit interference of America, which is to say, of Rockefeller, the head of its oil trust. The second act of this oil tragicomedy will play out in The Hague. All other issues, right up to the question of our recognition of foreigners' private property, are only secondary sideshows compared to oil. That isn't the point; the discussion is about oil and only oil—the insiders know this—and oil is our main trump card.... And while Royal Dutch Shell has not yet signed a contract with us, they will. They or another trust; in the end, we don't care. But they are the supplicants, not we."

The Hague International Financial and Economic Conference that followed took place from June 15 to July 19, 1922, drawing delegations from the same nations as had attended the Genoa conference two months earlier. The Entente delegations again stubbornly tried to force the RSFSR to recognize the debts of the tsarist government, return nationalized businesses to their former foreign owners, and grant restitution of nationalized property as the sole form of realistic compensation.

Guided by the principle of equality among nations, the Soviet delegation defended the same position as it did in Genoa. The Entente representatives were told of Soviet Russia's willingness to discuss demands provided the country was granted credits for restoration of the economy destroyed by the anti-Soviet imperialist intervention of 1917–1922 and blockade, and the question of the repayment of war debts was taken off the table. Once again, the Soviet delegation presented a list of businesses that could be granted to their former foreign owners under concession or lease arrangements. As for private property, there would be no discussion of any mass restitution, although the Soviet delegation stated a willingness to discuss compensation on a case-by-case basis.

Further negotiations showed a general reluctance by participating nations to grant credit to the Soviet government. The implacability of the former foreign owners regarding restitution of oil fields and businesses ultimately forced the Hague Conference to a dead end.

At the last session, on July 19, 1922, RSFSR Deputy People's Commissar for Foreign Affairs Maksim Litvinov (1876–1951) reiterated the Soviet government's willingness, in principle, to repay its prewar debts and realistically compensate those foreigners who previously owned property in Russia and would not receive satisfaction through concessions by offering them profitable participation in joint ventures. However, in the end, the total unwillingness of the Western representatives to budge on oil restitution, and their unwillingness to continue The Hague Conference on a constructive basis, forced it to adjourn without achieving any positive results.

Soviet political leaders learned serious lessons from the experience, however, which were reflected fairly quickly in tactical changes by Soviet representatives in establishing mutually profitable economic relations with leading Western countries. Within a year after the Genoa and Hague conferences, Soviet Russia had concluded economic agreements with 14 European countries, in which the delivery of Soviet petroleum products to the European market played a far from minor role.

The First Successes of Soviet Russia's Oil Strategy

After years of civil war and several transitions to rule by different political forces, the Soviet Russian oil industry region was in a difficult position. By early 1921, only 960 production wells were operating on the Absheron Peninsula, versus 3,500 in 1913. The volume of oil refined had also fallen to 110,000–165,000 tons, down from 275,000 in 1918. The situation in the Grozny oil region and the Kuban region was no better.

These difficulties were magnified by an "oil blockade" of Soviet Russia created by the combined efforts of several Western governments and leading corporations.

In a prescient interview in the March 1922 issue of *Ekonomicheskaya zhizn* ["Economic Life"], People's Commissar Leonid Krasin noted the beginning of the collapse of the economic blockade of Soviet Russia as a result of trade treaties with Great Britain and Germany. He added that: "The same fate also befell the oil blockade, which the former oil owners tried to organize when we exported oil reserves." Speaking further about the issue of oil exports, Krasin emphasized the importance of "the creation of special export agencies, which will supervise the export of critical products abroad."

Likewise, RSFSR State Planning Committee [*Gosplan*] specialists assumed, in early 1922, that "Russia can export petroleum products and crude oil worth about 160 million gold rubles at current prices in 1925, and up to 500–600 million gold rubles by 1932.... Thus, we must export the maximum possible amount of crude oil and petroleum products, both to obtain critically necessary hard currency and to improve our fuel supply."

Still, there were plenty of skeptics on the other side, voicing their doubts at the top of their lungs. For example, in an article in the *Financial Times* of May 10, 1922, the noted English businessman Leslie Urquhart, who had worked for many years in Russia, expressed frank skepticism regarding the restoration of the Russian oil business: "1) The Russian oil fields cannot export crude oil abroad; 2) In order to restore production even to the low level of 1917, they will have to begin by drilling new wells, which has not been done for five years; 3) This operation will require outlays amounting to at least £20 million, not to mention major outlays required to bring the fields back to their former condition; 4) Even if the

1917 production level is achieved, all production will be absorbed by Russian transportation and industry. For many years, Russia will remain an oil importer, not an exporter."

However, the pessimistic forecasts of Western specialists would soon receive a convincing answer. In the early 1920s, the Soviet authorities, having achieved notable successes in the domestic and foreign policy arenas, diverged from the policy of war communism, with its militarized foundations, and began to implement the New Economic Policy (NEP). The principal characteristic feature of the NEP was the use of a series of market methods of management in a government-controlled economy. The main objective of the NEP was to revive the damaged economy and as a result, to restore it more quickly. In the same period, the administration of the oil industry was restructured through the so-called "trust reform." To manage the biggest businesses, the Soviets created trusts—Azneft, Grozneft, Embaneft—which operated on a self-sufficient basis. Furthermore, in early March 1921, a segment of the Baku–Batumi pipeline to Tiflis was restored, considerably accelerating the export of petroleum products. It delivered its first batch of kerosene on May 22, 1921.

On March 21, 1922, the RSFSR Council of People's Commissars began requiring all customers to pay for petroleum products. Using the newly formed state trusts, the Soviet government attempted to fully control the domestic and foreign markets, not allowing excessive unraveling of market relations, and eliminating competition within the industry.

On March 13, 1922, the *VTsIK* adopted a decree "On Foreign Trade," which reaffirmed that foreign trade was a state monopoly and operated only through the People's Commissariat for Foreign Trade [*NKVT*]. Under this decree, state agencies and enterprises, as well as the Russian Federation Central Alliance of Consumer Societies [*Tsentrosoyuz*], were authorized to deal directly on the foreign markets with special permission of the *NKVT*, but only if contracts and agreements were submitted in advance to the *NKVT* for approval.

This entailed substantial changes for the oil industry. A *VSNKh* resolution dated July 1, 1922 formed a new economic agency, the All-Union Oil Trading Syndicate [*Neftesindikat*], which merged the huge Azneft, Grozneft, and Embaneft trusts, and was to engage, among other things, in trading operations abroad. Valentin Trifonov (1888–1938), an Old Bolshevik and professional revolutionary, was named head of the new entity.

In syndicate trade, prices were set primarily from above in a centralized manner. The People's Commissariat for Railroads, the army and navy departments, defense plants, and the power stations of Moscow and Petrograd were entitled to firm prices.

Neftesindikat's first serious practical action was to enter into a concession agreement, which initially seemed very promising, with the American International Barnsdall Corporation. The latter was to deliver several dozen rotary drilling rigs and powerful pumps to the Baku oil fields, and then place more than 1,000 abandoned wells in service. Payment for both the equipment and the work was specified in the traditional form—the company would receive up to 20% of the oil produced.

The idea was supported by Deputy Chairman of the Labor and Defense Council Aleksey Rykov (1881–1938), People's Commissar for Foreign Trade Krasin, *VSNKh* head Pëtr Bogdanov, and Deputy People's Commissar for Foreign Affairs Lev M. Karakhan. At their recommendation, the RCP(b) Politburo adopted a resolution on September 21, 1922, "On Well Drilling Concessions in Baku." Provisions of the resolution included: "a) No objection shall be made to the execution of a concession agreement with International Barnsdall Corporation; b) On the question of arbitration (Para. 24), an attempt shall be made to alter the makeup of the arbitration tribunal in order that the chief arbitrator be selected from among six (or more) candidates nominated by the Academy of Sciences, without framing this as an ultimatum; c) The draft agreement shall be distributed to all Politburo members." Under the concession agreement, the American company was required to deliver 20 rotary drilling rigs with the necessary tooling and downhole pumps, and in exchange, it was promised 20% of all oil produced.

For a number of reasons, the high hopes on both sides for the successful fulfillment of the agreement were not realized. Ultimately, the American company was unable to meet its obligations, and after two years the RCP(b) Politburo was forced to invoke the most fitting form of denouncement in a resolution "On the Barnsdall Corporation:" "a) The Main Concession Committee is directed to place a series of notes in the foreign press, under *NKID* supervision, indicating a breach of contract on the part of the concessionaires; b) The Main Concession Committee is invited to present a report to the Labor and Defense Council on the economic performance of the Baku contract drilling concession."

In early 1923, the journal *Azerbaydzhanskoye neftyanoye khozyaystvo* ["Azerbaijan Oil Business"] published an article by the economist Bondarevsky titled "More Attention to the Oil Industry," in which he said: "Other countries have taken into account and realized the importance of the fact that their future well-being will be built on an oil foundation. We seem not to have completely grasped all this, nor have we recognized the colossal scale of the game. The true objective of state power is to create an apparatus from Russian oil that will, in the future, support an industrial life for the entire country, make us independent, and place us on a par with the powers that dictate oil policy to the world."

However, following the Genoa and Hague Conferences, the Soviet government was decidedly aware of the colossal role that the export of Soviet petroleum products abroad could play, especially in terms of providing the hard currency so badly needed to restore the economy.

And soon, by skillfully playing the oil giants Royal Dutch Shell and Standard Oil Company off against each other, RSFSR representatives were able to crack the initially monolithic front of Western countries, thereby finally burying the ultimatum-like terms of the 1922 Genoa Memorandum.

In late 1922, Royal Dutch Shell began secretly purchasing Soviet kerosene, which it then resold in the Far East. At the time, it managed to conceal these ties. The company's head, Sir Henri Deterding, was guided in this by a desire not only to obtain short-term profit, but also to stake a claim in Soviet Russia for further development to spite his main competitor, John D. Rockefeller. Then in the spring of 1923, the small English firm Sal purchased 33,000 tons of Soviet kerosene, which was immediately reported throughout the Western press. Admittedly, it was not known at the time whether Royal Dutch Shell was behind the deal. In any event, Deterding immediately took the opportunity to announce that no oil blockade of the USSR now existed, and not because of Royal Dutch Shell, but because of the actions of Sal, whose example others would certainly follow. Almost immediately, "in view of changed circumstances," Royal Dutch Shell openly purchased 1.3 million barrels of kerosene from the Soviet *Neftesindikat*. Responding to criticism, Deterding declared that he had been forced to make the deal because Sal was pursuing a separate policy anyway.

The concern in the press over Royal Dutch Shell's relations with the USSR gradually eased, and in September 1923, Deterding received authorization from the International Association of Oil Companies in Russia[35] to conduct negotiations with the Soviet government. In response, the Franco-Belgian entrepreneurs refused to support the decision, and recalled their representative from the International Association. The oil blockade's unified front thus collapsed, and Deterding could make full use of his monopoly advantage as the only major company trading with the USSR.

With the blockade lifted, the Soviet government was free to openly pursue economic relations with a vast array of partners. Over the course of a single year, from October 1, 1922 to October 1, 1923, the USSR *Neftesindikat* achieved much: it created two foreign offices, one in Berlin for Western European countries headed by Yakov Ter-Oganesov, and one in Baku for the Middle Eastern countries headed by Aleksandr Serebrovsky. *Neftesindikat* built tank farms in London to hold 28,000 tons of oil, in Hamburg for 9,900 tons, and in Reval [Tallinn] and Riga for 4,400 tons each. Using the three ports of Batumi, Novorossiysk, and Leningrad, *Neftesindikat* sold about half a million tons of various petroleum products (kerosene, gasoline, machine oil, residual oil, diesel oil, and crude oil) for 23.4 million gold rubles, a very considerable sum for the USSR.

With the enormous demand for cash assets, *Neftesindikat* found a way to obtain bank loans collateralized by goods. To this end, it signed two agreements with the State Bank [*Gosbank*]: one to transfer oil storage facilities in six western provinces to the bank for leased operation, and another to sell the bank up to 180,000 barrels of kerosene for cash. This brought *Neftesindikat* some relief, although it was not a complete solution to the financial issue for the oil industry. To further consolidate its market position, *Neftesindikat* set up production of new petroleum products. For example, at its Baku refineries, it began making petroleum lacquer drying oil, naphthalene, and lubricant grease. *Neftesindikat's* participation in the All-Union Agricultural Fair in Moscow in August 1923, where it exhibited a wide range of products, was especially important for expanding the petroleum products market.

Once *Neftesindikat's* export successes became obvious and indisputable, this aspect of its operation was codified. A *VSNKh* order dated September 12, 1923 determined that "the Syndicate is the monopoly for the sale of oil, both on the domestic and foreign markets, reporting directly to the USSR *VSNKh* as represented by the Main Administration for Fuel [*GUT*]."

With every passing year, the volume of Soviet oil exports rose exponentially. Whereas the Soviets exported 1.2 million barrels of petroleum products in 1921–22 to only five countries, by 1922–23, over 2.4 million barrels of Soviet oil was being exported to 13 countries. Thus, the battle for "a place in the sun" on the European and world markets intensified.

The success of *Neftesindikat's* operations enabled the USSR to obtain considerable hard-currency income, which the country needed badly at the time, thus cementing the importance of crude oil and petroleum products exports in the minds of the Soviet political leadership.

Aleksandr Serebrovsky's Trip to the USA

A significant contribution to restoring and accelerating the industrialization of the Soviet oil industry was made by the engineer Aleksandr Serebrovsky (1884–1938), an outstanding production organizer.

In 1911, he completed the full curriculum of the Brussels Polytechnic School and received a degree in mechanical engineering. Upon returning to Russia, he worked in various engineering jobs. In May of 1920, the RSFSR Council of People's Commissars (CPC) sent him to the Absheron Peninsula to head Azneft, one of the newly created conglomerates of nationalized enterprises.

At that time, the oil industry of Soviet Russia was in an extremely serious position: its 1920 oil production total of 4.243 million tons was significantly less than the prewar volume of 10.147 million tons produced in 1913.

Serebrovsky warmly welcomed the transition from war communism to the New Economic Policy, since the NEP's initial phase gave society certain hopes for positive change, including the accelerated recovery of the domestic oil industry. The basic principles of the NEP proposed giving limited independence, based on cost accounting, to commercial entities, which defined a type of "corridor of economic freedom."

Serebrovsky's strategy for restoring and modernizing the Russian oil business focused on the creative use of advanced foreign know-how, primarily American, on the assumption that Russia had the necessary technical and production culture to adopt American innovations in the oil industry. He was striving, through the use of the latest American technologies, to realize his strategic plans of converting Azneft into one of the most competitive oil companies in the world.

His business trip to the US in the second half of 1924, which lasted several months, played a decisive role in the realization of these plans.

The organization of his visit was one of the first successful transactions of the Soviet-American joint-stock company Amtorg (American Trading Corporation), which was created on May 27, 1924 and registered under the laws of the state of New York. This company was headed by Isay Khurgin (1887–1925), an experienced trade representative who simultaneously occupied the post of authorized representative of the USSR People's Commissariat for Foreign Trade in the US.

Aleksandr Serebrovsky first set foot on American soil on July 29, 1924. The very next day, accompanied by Amtorg employees, he visited the central office of the Standard Oil Company of New York located on Battery Square in downtown Manhattan. During the negotiations, Walter Teagle, a Standard Oil executive director, showed great interest in cooperating with one of the highest directors of the Soviet oil industry and agreed to allow Serebrovsky to visit the company's main oil fields and refineries without restrictions. Moreover, hoping to deepen and develop business relations, Teagle even expressed willingness to help the Soviet representatives purchase modern oilfield equipment. All this pointed to a sea change in the American oil giant's steadfast position over the preceding two years, and in their subsequent relations with Soviet Russia, Standard Oil decided to pursue the convincing example set by their main competitor, Sir Henri Deterding of Royal Dutch Shell.

Aleksandr Serebrovsky's main obstacle in acquiring American oilfield equipment, however, was the question of payment. At the time, Azneft did not have the necessary foreign currency resources and was totally unable to get credit from foreign banks. Nor could Standard Oil's Teagle even give guarantees to equipment suppliers; in the American framework, this was viewed as granting Azneft long-term credit. According to Teagle, the question of payments could be decided only by the elder John D. Rockefeller, the founding father of Standard Oil Company, who in those years only involved himself in the corporation's business in exceptional cases. (Incidentally, at that time the company was the largest in the world: its market capitalization on January 1, 1924 was $1.037 billion, while that of Royal Dutch Shell was only $826 million.)

The Russian oil representative decided to take a chance and wrote a letter to Rockefeller requesting a personal meeting; to everyone's surprise, Rockefeller consented. Serebrovsky described this meeting in his memoirs: "The old man almost always lived at one of his country estates. Having traveled about a hundred *versts* [66 miles] from New York, we turned into a park enclosed by a fence with beautiful gates. The house was rather simple, as were all its furnishings, comfortable and adapted to the habits of the old businessman. The old man received me in his room, where he was relaxing after work. He was trying not to seem aloof or untidy, as I was told. He showed the ability to smile and said that now was the time in his routine for relaxation, but that he knew me as a pleasant person to talk with and was certain that he would get even more relaxation from our conversation. He was very well-informed about things in Baku... and about our resources. He emphasized several times that they were willing to support Soviet industry on the condition that we be his allies.... I proposed two arrangements. First, he would give a letter of guarantee to his bank to pay our supplier invoices from future earnings on petroleum products.... Rockefeller thought for a long time, and then looked at me attentively and unexpectedly agreed. Second, he would give a letter to suppliers in which he would recommend us as buyers well known to him and recommend that we be given the same discount on invoices as Standard Oil. Rockefeller accepted this much more readily. It was around five in the afternoon, and tea was served. The old man poured tea for me, offered me cookies with jam, and then invited me to take a stroll. He walked quickly and for a long time, half an hour, and we went around the entire forest park. I was hardly able to keep up with him, and my leg ached. The two of us dined, and then he went to look at his mail, leaving me to spend the night since I did not ask to go to New York.... In the morning I was awakened before dawn. The old man was going on a stroll before breakfast and wanted to talk along the way.... After breakfast I bid him farewell and left."

Serebrovsky later found out one of the reasons why Rockefeller agreed so quickly to the Soviet proposals. It turns out that the oil magnate had noticed that one of the low-cut boots worn by the Azneft director had a small patch on it, and he told his financial director: "This man can be trusted in debt. He is not a spendthrift, does not drink wine, does not smoke, and I like him." According to Rockefeller's relatives and close associates, he was very stingy and was impressed by modest and thrifty people.

After meeting with "America's oil king," Serebrovsky spent several months visiting the oil-producing regions of the US. In Pennsylvania, he examined several refineries and studied in detail the organization of the supply of materials and equipment. Next, he visited all the main fields of the so-called "oil valley" and examined the famous sites of the "oil fever:" Oil City, Rouseville, Petroleum Center, and Titusville, and then he went on to New Jersey, Philadelphia, Chicago, Detroit, and finally to Texas and California.

At the Long Beach fields in California, Serebrovsky spent some time working at drilling, performing the difficult tasks required of the average worker, trying to learn how to drill like the best American specialists. He attentively studied the activity of oilfield equipment operators, getting into the particulars of the field service of machines and mechanisms.

Aleksandr Serebrovsky had reached Oklahoma when he received a telegram from Amtorg saying that he had to return to New York. There, after careful examination of drawings, templates, and instructions offered to him by American suppliers, he ordered the necessary oilfield equipment. It was at this point that, after studying the documentation, the Azneft director began to write a book about the oil industry, which later became a standard reference work that was used for many years by Soviet oil workers.

Afterward, Serebrovsky traveled to Tulsa, Oklahoma, where the International Petroleum Congress and national oil exhibition opened in early October 1924. There he gave a detailed talk about the status and outlook for development of the Russian oil industry. His talk enjoyed widespread media coverage, receiving commentary by the influential *New York Times* and other leading American newspapers, after which it was published in a series of English and French oil publications.

Over the course of his long return sea voyage from the US to Europe, Serebrovsky was able to finish his book *The Oil and Gas Industry in America* [*Neftyanaya i gazovaya promyshlennost v Amerike*], which summarized his stay in the US. During his brief stay in London, he had the book published in Russian.

After returning to Moscow, on January 15, 1925 Serebrovsky gave a public lecture at the Business Club, where he was already giving copies of his book out to oil industry workers as accompanying information.

On the whole, engineer Serebrovsky's trip to the US had a long-term positive influence on the development of the Azneft trust, and, consequently, on the entire Soviet oil industry.

For example, in the area of production administration, he proposed, on the basis of his analysis of American administrative practice, that work at Azneft be organized according to the model of leading US companies, which had moved to a divisional organizational structure. Such a structure involved giving company subsidiaries practically full authority to make operational administrative decisions, while the company's central office decided strategic administrative questions and controlled the activity of the company as a whole.

In trying to determine the most acceptable organization model for Russian conditions, Serebrovsky carefully analyzed, above all, the experience of the Standard Oil Company. He explained: "I will not speak about the nationwide unification of this company. This is too large a machine for us; let us take individual Standards, for example its California organization. What do we see there? First, the Standard Oil Company of California is a completely independent enterprise (and not just for the purpose of anti-trust law); it is connected with the center by the most tenuous of financial ties, which are imperceptible, but very strong. And in California itself, you will find fields that are completely independent and a completely independent refinery company. There is an independent pumping company, and there appears to be a completely separate supply company (National Oil Supply), but all these taken together make up California Standard. Their operations run much better than ours, because the very lowest-level companies do all the work, and the center only administers."[36]

Aleksandr Serebrovsky strived to realize this approach in the administration of Azneft by working to relieve the administrative center from getting involved in the minutiae of the trust's daily operations and transferring part of the administration and part of the responsibility to separate regions and enterprises. He felt that providing greater independence to the regions and enterprises and putting them on full cost accounting allowed them greater freedom to develop and the ability to further technical and organizational improvements at their respective locations. As later events showed, the divisional structure that Serebrovsky proposed based on his analysis of American oil companies was perfectly suited to Azneft, since it took into account the large size of the trust, the geographic dispersion of its offices and enterprises, its orientation toward a wide assortment of petroleum products intended for completely diverse groups of customers, etc. However, implementation of his proposal turned out to be incomplete in many respects, as it did not take into account his recommendations regarding the introduction of market principles into the organization of petroleum products trade and the development of the oil economy as a whole.

Serebrovsky also made substantial contributions in the realm of oil production. The samples of oil production equipment that he purchased greatly helped promote the use of electric downhole pumps and put rotary drilling technology into practice. Russian oil workers called these methods of drilling and production "American." As director of the trust, Serebrovsky started to put these methods into practice at Azneft as early as 1923, although it was not until 1925 that they started to have a perceptible economic effect. Serebrovsky's contributions to production were critical to the development of the Russian oil industry: without electric downhole pumps rotary drilling was impossible.

Serebrovsky later wrote: "The first thousand downhole pumps received were from America and were the beginning of the transition to the systematic replacement of sand-line reels and bailers with modern economical machines. A great many obstacles stood in the way of this replacement: inertia, the habit of using the old methods, the shortage of qualified workers, the difficulties of operation at sandy sites, etc., but all this was overcome." By October 1928, 2,554 (78.8%) of the 3,238 wells were already using downhole pumps, while the number of wells that employed bailing, an old production method that had been most common earlier, had sharply decreased from 86.5% in 1923 to 13.5%.

Overall, from 1924 to 1928, changes in drilling technology increased hole-making speed by more than tenfold, and the use of downhole pumps reduced the cost of oil production by approximately 50%. Over four years, the total savings from using the American methods for drilling, production, and electrification amounted to more than 200 million rubles (a significant figure compared to total oil industry capital investments during this period of 743.4 million rubles).

During his trip abroad, Serebrovsky placed special emphasis on refining. The technological backwardness of the Russian refining sector as compared to the rest of the world became acutely apparent in the 1920s, when significant innovations began to appear in the industry, for example, in the cracking process. There is no doubt that American companies were leaders in this field, and that these companies, which had more than 2,500 patents in this area by the beginning of the 1920s, had been leading the development of refining processes since 1860. Their experience convincingly demonstrated the promise of the cracking process, which made it possible to increase the output of light fractions and improve the quality of gasoline.

During Serebrovsky's visit to the US, he conducted negotiations with the management of the Sinclair Oil Corporation for the purchase of $25 million worth of American refining equipment. And although the deal fell through, Serebrovsky's presentation nonetheless prompted the Soviet government to purchase cracking units overseas and to enlist the help of foreign companies and specialists to get the acquired equipment working properly. Subsequently, the use of American technologies and equipment made it possible to produce a series of products that were new at the time (cracked gasoline, etc.). Moreover, modernization of the industry made it possible to produce special grades of lubricants (bright stock) from specific grades of Baku petroleum. The expansion in the production of high-quality petroleum products also made the goal of industrializing the national economy a much more realistic endeavor. Before that, no serious discussion had been possible on developing the industry for the domestic manufacture of tractors, automobiles, ships, etc. Moreover, the modernization of the refining sector played a key role in meeting the government's fuel needs, as the improvement in fuel quality opened the way for the wholesale construction of modern military hardware.

Serebrovsky also paid special attention during his American business trip to acquiring the equipment necessary to create a modern domestic infrastructure for the production of drilling and refining machinery. The development of such an infrastructure allowed not only a subsequent reduction in the Soviet oil industry's dependence on massive deliveries of imported equipment, but also accelerated the industry's development by saving significant financial resources. As Serebrovsky noted: "Indeed, if we acquired all the equipment we needed overseas, we would not have enough foreign currency. If we ordered it at factories in the center of the Soviet Union, the equipment would be very expensive and would not arrive by our deadlines. Therefore, we first put our Baku machine–production plants on a firm basis by equipping them with machine tools ordered from America. We built two basic plants: one for making drills and drilling equipment, and the other for making only downhole pumps. The plants were built according to an American design and operated according to American methods."[37] At his initiative, in 1925 the *VSNKh* created a standing committee on the oil industry to study the organization of production and to purchase machines and equipment overseas.

Thus, starting in the mid-1920s, the Russian oil industry succeeded, with the broad participation of foreign capital, in realizing a policy of replacing imports and instead supplying the industry with well-drilling and operating equipment that was domestically produced according to American models.

As for marketing and sales, again taking American experience into account, Aleksandr Serebrovsky spoke out against the situation that had developed in the domestic industry, where all produced petroleum products came under the complete control of *Neftesindikat*, which sold them on the domestic and foreign markets. "The basis of business is production, and production must be the master of trade. *Neftesindikat's* position will only be correct if it becomes merely an office for selling the trusts' marketable output, and if the People's Commissariat for Finance and the authorities do not consider it to be a separate enterprise."[38] He considered overcoming the divorce of trade and production, which contradicted all world practice, to be the most important precondition for introducing true cost accounting and for checking the trust's performance empirically.

Incidentally, similar proposals were made by other oil specialists, including Ivan Strizhov and Mikhail Barinov. However, the Soviet political leadership disregarded their recommendations, and during the NEP years oil enterprises never actually switched to true cost accounting.

Here, the decision regarding the organizational form of trade in petroleum products was made primarily on the basis not of economic considerations, but of ideological and political ones caused by an internal Party struggle and a striving not to allow the restoration of capitalism.

As for the specific effects of Aleksandr Serebrovsky's trip on the development of export oil trading, it laid the foundation for large-scale cooperation with American companies concerning deliveries of Russian oil on the foreign market. The first major Soviet export contracts with American oil companies were signed in 1924 and 1925, which had great significance for strengthening both Soviet and American positions in world trade in petroleum products. By early 1928, the oil industry had become the USSR's largest export industry, and by the late 1920s, income from international trade in petroleum products was able to compensate somewhat for the sharp decline in grain export revenue.

Understanding the pressing need to master advanced technology, Aleksandr Serebrovsky made arrangements with the management of a number of American oil companies to schedule trips abroad for Soviet engineers and workers to study American technology in the oil industry.

The first group of oil workers sent to America for periods ranging from six months to two years consisted of 20 workers and 15 engineers. They were well-received in America, since the companies manufacturing the equipment and striving to deliver it to the USSR in greater and greater volumes were interested in training the personnel that might be handling their machines. With the help of these companies, Soviet specialists were sent around to factories, drilling sites, and fields to learn production practices. According to Serebrovsky's plan, the specialists were sent to various American companies to study specific technical processes: pumping, gas recovery, cracking, etc.

Social questions did not escape his close attention and during his trip, the "Red director" Serebrovsky paid special attention to the living arrangements and daily life of American oil workers. In particular, he paid attention to the buildings in which American oil workers lived. These cottages had a well designed, convenient layout and an attractive exterior. Also important was the fact that these buildings were simple to build.

Striving to solve the extremely acute housing problem at the Baku fields, Aleksandr Serebrovsky ordered a whole small town of these cottages from American manufacturers. This measure not only succeeded at improving the housing conditions of oil workers, but also served to adorn the suburbs and several residential neighborhoods of Baku with very original buildings of constructivist-style architecture, thus transforming the city and giving it a unique flavor.

Along with the structural parts and equipment for the cottages that had been ordered, other objects also arrived in Baku that were strange for those times: mobile clinics, gas kitchen stoves, washing machines, vacuum cleaners, and even soccer balls. It is interesting that upon returning from America, Serebrovsky took the initiative to organize soccer teams at the fields and arrange the first soccer match in Baku. The Azneft team, which was later called Neftchi, became one of the most popular teams in the country. Thus, an unexpected outcome of Serebrovsky's trip to America was the development of soccer on the Absheron Peninsula.

From today's perspective it is easy to see that the impressive results of Aleksandr Serebrovsky's trip to the US in 1924 laid a very productive foundation for successful and mutually beneficial Russian-American cooperation in the area of oil.

In the context of the ongoing energy dialog between Russia and the US, the experience of the 1920s cannot, of course, provide ready answers to the numerous questions now facing the management of Russian and American oil companies. Nevertheless, it provides modern managers rich factual material for analysis in making administrative decisions for the development of mutually beneficial cooperative efforts with foreign companies and attraction of foreign capital into the business as a whole.

Developing Success in the Export Direction

On May 9, 1924, the Labor and Defense Council approved a new version of the *Neftesindikat* Charter, confirming a commitment at the highest level to strengthen and develop the export direction of the Soviet oil industry.

During the 1920s, all the new Western companies began trading oil with the USSR. As of the 1923–24 fiscal year, *Neftesindikat* had business contacts with 28 trading companies in 20 countries. Crude oil and petroleum products exports continued to grow steadily, reaching 5.2 million barrels in fiscal 1923–24. By fiscal 1921–22, Soviet crude oil exports were double their 1913 levels, and by fiscal 1923–24 they were over 100 times the prewar levels. Likewise, 1.2 million barrels of petroleum products were exported in fiscal 1921–22, a total of 2.4 million barrels was shipped abroad in 1922–23, followed by the export of 5.5 million barrels of petroleum products from Baku and Grozny in fiscal 1923–24.

With Soviet oil exports almost doubling each year, the national oil industry became more and more oriented towards exports. While the share of overall Soviet oil production exported amounted to 6.1% in fiscal 1922–23, this figure increased to 11.8% in 1923–24. Moreover, crude oil and petroleum products accounted for 23.6% of total industrial exports and 7.2% of all USSR exports by value.

At the end of this two-year period, *Neftesindikat* Chairman Georgy Lomov (Oppokov) (1888–1938) stated: "In the current 1924–25 [fiscal year], our oil exports will be worth approximately 56–60 million rubles, accounting for about three-quarters of all the country's industrial exports in terms of value."[39]

As Doctor of History Yury Zhukov noted in his report "The Oil Factor in the Policy of the Soviet Ruling Elite (1921–1929)" in the collection *Soviet Union's Oil* [*Neft strany Sovetov*], the USSR political leadership constantly focused on the issue of increasing oil exports and was faced with a difficult question: What Soviet petroleum products should be offered to the Western market to maximize profit? Specialists from the State Planning Committee and *Neftesindikat* believed gasoline exports would be the most preferable option. In less than a decade, for example, from 1911 to 1920, the gasoline share of US petroleum product output grew from 13% to 30%, while kerosene's share fell from 34% to 12%. Demand for gasoline was also growing rapidly in Europe, and although overall kerosene imports by European countries fell 30% from 1913 to 1924 as people stopped using kerosene lamps as a source of lighting, there was still a market for kerosene in less developed countries; Egypt, Syria, Turkey, Persia, Bulgaria and Greece accounted for 67% of total Soviet kerosene exports in fiscal 1924–25. At the time, demand for gasoline in the USSR was extremely low, while the export profits for gasoline were very high due to Western Europe's need for large amounts of gasoline. Consequently, the export-oriented Soviet oil industry required immediate modernization, a feat that ultimately proved impossible to accomplish in a timely manner.

Following a lengthy government debate, a decision nevertheless was made to proceed with exports of residual oil, which was in great demand on the global market. The State Planning Committee noted in 1922 that residual oil was becoming more popular in the global refining industry, and that residual oil had accounted for 48% of all petroleum products produced in the US in 1919. In early 1922, a ton of residual oil was worth 6–10 times more than a ton of coal on the world market.

Exports of residual oil, which began *de facto* in fiscal 1923–24, increased by an order of magnitude in the following 1924–25 fiscal year and exceeded the prewar level by several times. Thus, a clear shift can be noted in the trajectory of petroleum products exports: whereas Russian oil exports consisted more of kerosene and oil prior to World War I, this trend had clearly transitioned to residual oil and gasoline by 1924–25. For example, in 1913, kerosene and oil accounted for 77% of total Russian oil exports, but only 23.5% in 1924–25.

In fiscal 1924–25, oil and petroleum products exports from the USSR once again almost doubled compared to the previous year, to 9.8 million barrels. During Alexander Serebrovsky's time in the US in the second half of 1924, the Standard Oil Company purchased Soviet petroleum products for the first time. The British-Dutch company Royal Dutch Shell also purchased Soviet petroleum products for resale in the Middle and

Far Eastern markets. *Neftesindikat* did not have its own sales network in these markets and was unable to cooperate with firms independent of Standard Oil or Royal Dutch Shell since such companies did not exist. These transnational oil giants organized the wholesale and retail sale of petroleum products in Middle and Far Eastern countries and prevented anyone else from entering this market.

Consequently, 44% of all Soviet kerosene was sold via Standard Oil and Royal Dutch Shell in 1924–25, while 33% was sold via these companies in 1926–27. These corporations managed all Soviet exports to India and Egypt, while a regional branch of *Neftesindikat* was able to sell kerosene to Turkey independently, from its own storage facilities, since an agreement on specific standards for the import of Soviet petroleum products was in effect in this area.

Neftesindikat was able to use a different marketing strategy in Western European markets that generated more profits than in the markets of colonial countries. It did so by selling small consignments of petroleum products to medium and small-sized European companies that were operating independently of the global giants and were extremely interested in such supplies. As a result, foreign partners emerged who were interested in developing business contacts without fear or favor. In addition, state-run organizations of several Western European nations such as Italy, Spain, Portugal, France and Germany started purchasing Soviet petroleum products. Italy and France were the main buyers of Soviet residual oil in the mid-1920s; Italy purchased residual oil for its navy and to sell on the free market, while France bought the product solely for its navy. *Neftesindikat* thus managed to set up a rather extensive sales network in Western Europe for Soviet petroleum products.

In the mid-1920s, *Neftesindikat* employed Soviet capital to create several specialized sales companies to sell petroleum products abroad, which operated in accordance with local laws. On August 23, 1924, representatives of *Neftesindikat* registered a company called Russian Oil Products, Ltd. (ROP) in London with charter capital of £100,000, with an address at London, Moorgate, E.C.2. By the next year (1925), entire trains of railroad cars were being used to ship ROP brand petroleum products, principally gasoline and kerosene, throughout the country. The company had as many as 100 of its own tankers with capacities ranging from 500 to 1,000 gallons. A truck fleet purchased from Messrs. Leyland Motors Ltd. was also quite impressive. Trucks and gasoline tankers of automobile brands well-known at the time—such as Albion, Vulcan and Morris—were unable to cope with the shipments. During its first years of operation, ROP placed orders for the construction of sea terminals in Avonmouth and Grangemouth, as well as storage facilities throughout the United Kingdom. The company's popularity was growing rapidly in the country.

During the same year, the German-Russian Oil Company (*Deutsche-Russische Naphta Kompanie*) was set up in Germany. In addition, another Soviet oil trader called Derop was operating on the territory of the Weimar Republic. Subsequently, companies such as the French Petroleum Products Company and Petrolea in Italy were created, in addition to similar firms in Scandinavian and Baltic countries.

On February 10, 1925, the USSR Supreme Council for the National Economy issued a decree, signed by its chairman, Feliks Dzerzhinsky, increasing the number of *Neftesindikat* employees abroad by three employees in France, six in Turkey, two in Sweden and Norway and two in Austria and Czechoslovakia. In addition, *Neftesindikat* opened new branches in Greece (six employees) and Finland (four employees).

Neftesindikat set up a joint company in Spain with Argus Bank of Barcelona, which had the exclusive rights to sell Soviet petroleum products in Spain, Portugal, and their colonies.

Trade with Persia also increased, and the export company Persazneft was created in July 1924. Persazneft was founded by the Russian-Persian joint venture Sharkom (which owned 34% of the company's capital), Azneft (51%) and the USSR Trade Delegation in Persia (15%). Kerosene exports from Baku to Persia were already much higher in fiscal 1924–25 than the levels of 1913, and Persia soon became the USSR's main trading partner in the East, accounting for roughly half of all Soviet foreign trade with Eastern and Asian countries.

In 1925, Soviet petroleum products enjoyed a roughly 8% share of the European market, and it seemed there would be a steady trend towards further growth. Starting in spring 1925, however, trade relations between the Soviet Union and transnational oil companies began to deteriorate significantly. Purchases of Soviet petroleum products by global oil monopolies, particularly of the most expensive commodities like gasoline, began to decline rapidly, while the role of independent companies and state-controlled Western European entities continued to grow. Soviet gasoline quickly reached a 10% share of the British petrol market, and it was sold without the involvement of the oil giants, which viewed Soviet gasoline as a threat to their monopolies and began actively using unfair methods of competition.

An extensive campaign was launched against Soviet petroleum products on the British market in late 1925 and early 1926 under the auspices of the British Association of Creditors of the Russian Empire, although the actual initiator of the campaign was the Royal Dutch Shell group. Articles on "predatory Bolshevik nationalization" and "oil stolen by the Soviets" reappeared in British newspapers. The Standard Oil Company, also wanting to prevent Soviet petroleum products from entering Western European markets, supported the anti-Soviet rhetoric of the British business leaders.

As a result of this campaign, exports of Soviet residual oil to Great Britain fell from 162,800 tons in fiscal 1924–25 to 50,800 tons in 1925–26. In 1926–27, *Neftesindikat* did not export a single ton of residual oil to Great Britain. Total residual oil exports from the USSR fell by approximately 10% in fiscal 1925–26. In the same fiscal year, however, Soviet petroleum products exports grew 7.8% in volume and 14.1% in value due to an increase in global prices.

However, the joint and coordinated efforts of Soviet diplomats and trade representatives in various European countries soon managed to calm the outburst of anti-Soviet rhetoric and the USSR's position in world markets began to improve markedly. In December 1926, *Neftesindikat* signed a concession agreement with the Standard Oil Company of New York for the construction of a modern refinery on the Black Sea coast. Under the concession agreement, the Rockefeller-led company built a refinery in Batumi to produce kerosene and export it to Asian markets in India, Indochina, Indonesia, and other Asian and Far Eastern countries. The refinery opened on August 1, 1927 and produced 179,000 tons of kerosene during the first eleven months of operation, or 13,000 tons more than its designed annual production capacity.

Exports of petroleum products from the USSR surpassed 2.2 million tons in fiscal 1926–27, up by more than 25% from the previous year. Total residual oil exports increased by 45% immediately. The USSR exported 14.3% of its residual oil and crude in 1926–27, while the share of gasoline exported was much higher, at 87.8%. Gasoline exports continued to grow consistently, and Soviet gasoline accounted for 6.8% of European imports in 1925, 8.3% in 1926, and 11.5% in 1927.

As of October 1, 1926, the capacity of oil storage reservoirs in European countries set up with the participation of the USSR was 33,000 tons. Meanwhile, the USSR share of global petroleum products exports amounted to 4.5% in 1926–27.

Hailing the active marketing of ROP, the British journal *The Petroleum Times* noted in October 1926 that "the entrance of the Soviet Oil Syndicate [*Neftesindikat*], which controlled up to 40% of the known crude oil reserves at the time, into the market is a positive factor and is bound to have a significant targeted impact on the state of the British fuel business." The journal added, "The English public believes in healthy competition." It is no coincidence that standard gasoline prices fell by 3.5 pence per gallon in the country as soon as ROP was registered, which proved advantageous to hundreds of companies and millions of Britons. Moreover, *The Petroleum Times* noted that ROP automobile gasoline was of higher quality than other types, and it was also sold for a penny less than similar gas from other sources. Multiplying these savings by the 880,000 tons of petroleum products imported into the British Isles by *Neftesindikat* made the benefits of such imports even more apparent.

By fall 1926, British consumers had already saved £800,000 using this gasoline.

In 1927, Soviet gasoline accounted for 10% of total gasoline imports to England, 18% to France, 15% to Germany, 30% to Spain, and 17% to Italy. Almost all the gasoline produced in the USSR was exported. Demand within the country was still very low in 1927 as the Soviet automobile industry was just starting to develop.

Not surprisingly, the battle between global oil monopolies and *Neftesindikat* entities took another turn for the worse in 1927, with Great Britain once again serving as the main battleground.

In the first half of 1927, the United Kingdom had imported 50 million gallons of petroleum products from the USSR, including 19.667 million gallons via ROP. Of the latter amount, automotive fuel accounted for 14.189 million gallons, kerosene for 3.414 million gallons, and gas oil for 2.062 million gallons. The remaining petroleum products were imported via British oil traders, including Lubricating and Fuel Oils Ltd., Harris & Dixon Ltd., Newcastle Benzol Company, Messrs. Cory Bros. & Co. Ltd., and others.

On May 11, 1927, England's Westminster Bank provided the Soviet Union with a large loan that was to be used, among other things, to finance operations needed to develop the Soviet oil industry. The next day, however, London police seized the building of the Soviet company ARCOS (All-Russian Cooperative Society Ltd.), an event that received wide international publicity. This company had been operating legally in the UK since June 1920 as a representative of cooperative organizations conducting business inside and outside Russia.

The ARCOS affair had very serious repercussions for relations between the USSR and Great Britain, and even led to the temporary severance of diplomatic relations between the two countries. Analyzing the causes of this international conflict, French researcher Francis Delaisi concluded that the "police invasion" of the ARCOS business premises was "inspired by big oil interests."

Meanwhile, across the globe, *Neftesindikat* had just wrapped up lengthy negotiations with Standard Oil of New York in June 1927. The US company had agreed to purchase a quarter of all petroleum products exported by *Neftesindikat*. This move did not go unnoticed by Royal Dutch Shell, the second key player on the global oil market, and on July 19, 1927, Sir Henri Deterding wrote: "Standard Oil of New York is transferring its sales organization in British India to the Soviet government in order to sell stolen oil there." He continued: "Since this affects our direct interests, we shall retaliate and the retaliation will be fierce." Deterding made it clear that his corporation would fight any attempt by the Standard Oil Company to sell Soviet oil in India.

When Royal Dutch Shell reduced its kerosene prices in India on

September 23, 1927, the Standard Oil Company, which was buying cheap Soviet kerosene, did the same. A kerosene price war broke out and quickly spread from India to other regions. Kerosene prices declined by more than 30% by the end of 1927 and the two oil monopolies incurred total losses of roughly $17 million.

In an effort to end the price war, the three leading oil corporations—the Standard Oil Company, Royal Dutch Shell and Anglo-Persian Oil Company—signed the "Red Line Agreement" under which an international oil cartel was created. The price war between the oil giants came to an end.

At the same time, the so-called "Sakhalin oil concession" occupied a special place in the Soviet leadership's oil strategy, vividly demonstrating the priority political interests held over purely economic interests in the economic policy of the USSR in the 1920s.

The story of the Sakhalin oil concession began back in 1921, when the Far Eastern Republic, an ally of Soviet Russia, began holding talks with the American company Sinclair on the development of oil-bearing land in North Sakhalin.[40] With regard to the draft concession, the Bolshevik government thought: "A clash of interests between Japan and America in the Far East would be extremely beneficial politically."

After the Far Eastern Republic joined Soviet Russia, the agreement with the Americans was endorsed in Moscow on January 26, 1923. Sinclair, however, was unable to begin developing the field as Japanese troops still remained in North Sakhalin. Moreover, the Japanese were extracting Sakhalin oil without permission from the Soviet government and without paying for it; in 1924 they extracted 13,300 tons of oil at the rich Okha fields. During negotiations later that year, Japan agreed to withdraw its troops from North Sakhalin but demanded concessions for the development of Sakhalin oil in exchange.

The USSR and Japan signed a convention establishing diplomatic relations in Beijing on January 20, 1925. Among other issues, the agreement offered Japanese entrepreneurs oil and coal concessions in North Sakhalin. An agreement was signed on December 14, 1925, providing oil concessions to a specially created Japanese company that became known as the North Sakhalin Oil Joint-Stock Company in 1927. The company's stockholders included some of Japan's largest companies: Mitsui, Mitsubishi, Sumitomo as well as Okura Kochyo, Nihon Sekyo and Kuhara.

The concessions for the use of the open fields were granted for 45 years, while concessions for prospecting new fields were granted for 11 years. The Japanese concessioners were required to pay annual rent amounting to 4% of production. In addition, royalties of 5% of the initial 33,000 tons produced were paid to the treasury. This share increased by a quarter percent for every additional 11,000 tons produced. Once production reached 253,000 tons, the Soviet government was paid a flat royalty of 15%. Royalties were negotiated separately for flowing oil (from 15% to 45% depending on the volume produced) and for gas production (from 10% to 35% depending on gas content). The Japanese also paid a land tax amounting to 3.84% of total production. The payment obligations in the agreement were consistent with standard international practice in those years.

The first chief executive of the Japanese concession company was Admiral Nakasato, who represented the interests of the Japanese Navy, the main consumer of Sakhalin oil at the time. Later, throughout the 1930s, North Sakhalin Oil maintained a close relationship with the Naval Ministry, with the Japanese selecting the company's management and some of its staff from among its naval personnel.

North Sakhalin Oil produced 33,000 tons of oil in North Sakhalin in 1926, 77,000 tons in 1927, 146,000 tons in 1928 and 165,000 tons in 1929. The North Sakhalin concession accounted for approximately 13% of Japanese oil consumption in 1929, but above all the oil was of great importance to the Japanese Navy.

In late 1928, the USSR Labor and Defense Council passed a resolution on capital investments in the export industries of the economy. In drawing up the capital construction plan for the 1928–29 fiscal year, the State Planning Committee was instructed to pay special attention to the issue of financing for industrial sectors connected with exports, including oil exports. In order to increase USSR oil exports in the mid-1920s, the government decided that it was necessary not only to increase oil production, but also to provide proper conditions for its transportation (above all, to Black Sea ports), to adjust the structure of refining to the changing demand in European countries, to build oil storage facilities abroad, and to establish a viable sales network.

In this vein, the second most important domestic refinery, after Standard Oil's Batumi refinery, was built in Tuapse with considerable assistance from America's Graver Corporation to refine Grozny oil. Foster Wheeler Corporation (New York), Badger and Sons (Boston) and Winkler-Koch Corporation (Wichita, Kansas) performed the design and engineering for the new Soviet oil refineries, while General Electric handled most of the electrical equipment supplies (pumps, compressors, control devices, etc.).

Leading Soviet engineers traveled to America regularly to gain the experience necessary to operate the foreign equipment. Ivan Strizhov (1872–1953), senior director of the oil industry at the Supreme Council for the National Economy, left for America on October 1, 1927 to study the latest achievements in refining. Strizhov visited 23 refineries in 10 US states during his six-month trip. Later he remarked: "I never received a refusal for the inspection of any refinery or part of a refinery. I was welcomed with open arms. They showed me everything I wanted to see."[41] Upon returning to the USSR, Strizhov published a book titled *American Refineries* [*Amerikanskiye nefteperegonnyye zavody*], in which he gave a detailed description of all the newest refining systems of the time.

With the use of foreign technologies and efficient equipment, Soviet refineries began producing several products that were new at the time, including cracked gasoline and a special sort of lubricant called "bright stock." The share of the most valuable light petroleum products in overall oil production grew to 10.1% in 1927–1928 and then to 15.1% in 1932 because of the significant contribution of these products.

The growth in the volume of high-quality petroleum products quickly justified the capital investments in the industry. Almost one-third (31.85%) of all petroleum products produced in the USSR were exported in fiscal 1928–29, including 88% of all gasoline manufactured.

In response to increased exports, oil tanker fleet tonnage also began expanding at an accelerated rate. In a report for 1928, *Neftesindikat* remarked: "Over the last two years, the fleet has added four new ships: the *Azneft*, the *Grozneft*, the *Elbrus,* and *Neftesindikat.* Construction is nearing completion on the oil carriers *Embaneft, Soviet Oil,* and *USSR Miners Union.* Once these carriers are introduced, overall tonnage should reach 66,000 tons. In addition, Soviet shipyards are building another five ships ordered by *Neftesindikat,* having an overall tonnage of 44,000 tons."

By the late 1920s, *Neftesindikat* had branches, agencies and firms in Milan, Vienna, Prague, Constantinople, Smyrna (Izmir), Tallinn, Helsinki, and Harbin.

Russian Oil Products, Ltd. (ROP) once again became very active in Great Britain. Exports of Soviet petroleum products to Britain amounted to 95 million gallons in the first half of 1929, a 50% increase from the first six months of 1928. Lamp oil accounted for 40.7 million gallons of that amount, automotive fuel for 38.5 million gallons, and lubricants for 9 million gallons, while heating oil and gas oil accounted for the rest. In other words, almost 11% of all petroleum products delivered to British ports came from the Soviet Union. For the year 1929 as a whole, 217 million gallons of Soviet petroleum products were delivered to the British Isles, an increase of 94 million gallons over the previous year. Expecting further growth, ROP hurriedly built additional terminals and storage facilities at ports in England, Scotland, and Ireland, while industrial production of small packages of lubricants began under the ROP name in the town of Barking. The Soviet company's investment program was quite large for the time, £700,000. During that period, Soviet oil exports were geographically structured as follows: the largest importer of USSR oil and petroleum products in fiscal 1927–28 was Italy (with 545,000 tons), followed by the UK (427,000 tons), France (391,000 tons), and Germany

(379,000 tons). The same four countries were also the leading importers of Soviet petroleum products in 1929, although not in the same order.

On February 28, 1929, *The New York Times* reported: "On Thursday, Deterding and British oil firms made peace with the Soviets. An agreement has just been signed for three years that not only ends the price war between the British and the Soviets (ROP) on the British market..., but also puts an end to Deterding's political hostility towards the Soviets.... The key achievement for the Soviets is that there is no clause in the agreement regarding compensation to be paid to Deterding for the nationalized property on which he continued to make such persistent claims."

Prominent Soviet figure Grigory Sokolnikov (Brilliant) (1888–1939), who chaired *Neftesindikat* at the time, commented on the agreement: "The recently concluded oil agreement in London between companies representing all the world's largest businesses on the British market— Standard Oil, Shell, the Anglo-Persian Company, and *Neftesindikat* as represented by ROP—has an importance that goes far beyond resolving their commercial relations on the British market. This agreement is one of the most important phases in the process of strengthening the USSR's position on foreign markets; it directly concerns the main issues of the policy of the imperialist powers towards the Soviet Union.... The political importance of the agreement is that, first, it was concluded with no discounts offered to former owners of oil fields and, second, as the British press emphasized, oil policy issues in England are not resolved without the participation of organizations connected with the government."

The agreement with the Western oil corporations, however, was more of political than economic importance for the USSR. With the start of the Great Depression in late 1929, oil prices fell sharply on the global market and the Soviet Union and the Western companies were therefore unable to agree on a further price policy. Global oil production (excluding the USSR) fell 17% from 1929 to 1932, while oil output in the Soviet Union increased 56.5% in the same period. By 1932, oil production levels in the USSR exceeded refining capacity by more than 3.3 million tons.

From the start of the 1930s, the USSR understandably began to develop new, more distant oil markets. Soviet petroleum products appeared in southern China and Korea for the first time in 1931 and in Canada and New Zealand in 1932.

On the whole, the first decade of the Soviet oil industry's development following nationalization in 1918 can rightly be considered a success. The Soviet Union managed to turn the export of oil and petroleum products into a huge source of currency revenue by skillfully taking advantage of conflicts between Standard Oil Company and Royal Dutch Shell. The Soviet oil industry not only emerged from the crisis in which it found itself during years of turmoil but also managed to restore production by first achieving the prewar production level and then surpassing it. In

1928, the USSR produced 12 million tons of oil, a level consistent with the industry's output under the Russian Empire in the early 20th century when the country was recognized as the global leader.

At the same time, this period marked the end of any illusions within the oil industry of continued NEP-era freedoms. On December 5, 1929 the Central Committee of the All-Union Communist Party (of Bolsheviks) passed a resolution, "On the Reorganization of Industrial Management." The "economic independence" of Azneft, Grozneft and Embaneft soon came to an end as these entities were merged as business units into Soyuzneft, the All-Union Oil Industry Association.

John D. Rockefeller's Envoy

The oil factor was one of the key components that helped form mutually beneficial economic relations between the Soviet Union and the US in the second half of the 1920s. Ivy Lee (1877–1934), a well-known American journalist who handled public relations for John D. Rockefeller, Sr., played a key role in this process. Lee visited the USSR in 1927 and paved the way for the subsequent establishment of diplomatic relations between the US and Soviet Russia.

Relations between the two countries were rather complicated and contradictory during this period due to profound changes and social upheaval throughout the world. Like other Western nations, the US broke off diplomatic relations with Russia after the Bolsheviks came to power in 1917, a move that created serious barriers for the development of business ties which remained frozen for a long time.

US businesses, however, began visibly expressing more interest in this new economic partner in the mid-1920s. After persistent lobbying by businesses, the US government decided to allow trade with Soviet Russia in summer 1920, but only at the individual company's own peril and risk. The business community, however, remained dissatisfied with the government's inconsistent position on trade with the USSR since it was only through mutual diplomatic recognition that the two countries could develop trade via lending, set up embassies and consulates, simplify visa procedures, validate the rights of citizens and organizations in both countries, and participate in global politics on equal terms.

The US government's nonrecognition policy led to an artificial decline in trade volume between the two countries, including US exports to the USSR. This policy repeatedly created all kinds of barriers and obstacles in Soviet–US economic relations throughout the 1920s. Statistics show a rather sharp decline in US exports to the USSR in fiscal 1925–26 compared to 1924–25 (94 million rubles versus 158 million rubles).

This was primarily due to the fact that the development of Soviet trade organizations within the US depended largely on financing of purchases by banks and companies as well as a transition to short-term and long-term lending for imports. Representatives of the Soviet company Amtorg noted on several occasions that short-term loans would not increase the volume of Soviet purchases in the US. From 1925 to 1927, some licenses issued for operations on the US market had to be transferred to Germany, where long-term loans could be obtained.

Given the development of relations between the two countries in trade, concessions, science, and technology, as well as the growing number of requests from significant business circles for closer economic relations with the USSR, it became more and more difficult for the US government to justify the advisability and validity of continuing its nonrecognition policy against Soviet Russia.

The international oil business, in turn, was a kind of barometer for the political state of affairs at the time. On May 27, 1927, when the British government, in Neville Chamberlain's famous note, accused the USSR of fomenting anti-British sentiment and carrying out subversive activities in Britain and subsequently broke off diplomatic relations with the USSR, Rockefeller's corporation decided to take advantage of this favorable situation and go behind the back of its chief competitor Royal Dutch Shell.

It should be noted that Rockefeller's approach to Soviet Russia was one of duplicity and double standards. Even as a staunch opponent of communism, Rockefeller nevertheless handled "the Russian issue" with a kind of dual personality. The management of one of his core companies—Standard Oil of New Jersey, led by Walter Teagle—purchased stock in 1920 in the Baku-based Nobel Brothers Petroleum Production Partnership, which was nationalized shortly thereafter. Realizing the futility of its claims for restitution following the Genoa Conference of 1922, Standard Oil displayed extreme intolerance and hostility towards everything that had to do with Soviet Russia as well as equitable business relations with its representatives. At the same time, two other Rockefeller-owned companies—Standard Oil of New York and Vacuum Oil Company—remained in constant contact with the Soviet Amtorg and *Neftesindikat* organizations out of pure business considerations and even began purchasing large amounts of petroleum products in the USSR.

As head of the giant oil corporation, Rockefeller in no way sought to set a common denominator for the actions of his subordinates. With Standard Oil of New York signing the first concession agreement with *Neftesindikat* for the construction of a refinery in Batumi in December 1926, Rockefeller was looking to carefully explore the prospects of obtaining even more favorable terms for his business in Soviet Russia in the future.

At the same time, given the ambiguous political situation in the US, Rockefeller clearly understood that this delicate mission would require the involvement of a prominent American whose activities were well-known in Soviet Russia and who was well-versed in politics, but who also was not a full-time Standard Oil Company employee.

This person could travel to the Soviet Union as a private civilian for an exotic tourist trip, and there was nobody more ideal for this role than Ivy Lee—Rockefeller's confidant, an acclaimed journalist, and the so-called "father of public relations." A graduate of Princeton University, Lee was a successful reporter for several leading New York publications and his work was very popular at the time. He later seriously considered the problem of relations between business and society and eventually laid the foundation for public relations. His phrase "Tell the truth" became a kind of motto for future generations of public relations specialists. Lee worked briefly at Standard Oil Company in 1914 before serving as an aide to the chairman of the American Red Cross during World War I.

In the early 1920s, Lee joined the movement of proponents for the establishment of friendly relations with Soviet Russia. In 1926, he wrote a famous letter to the president of the US Chamber of Commerce in which he presented a convincing argument for the need to normalize US–Soviet political and economic relations as soon as possible.

Unsurprisingly, Lee agreed to carry out the mission presented by Standard Oil Company following a confidential and detailed meeting with Rockefeller.

Prior to leaving for the USSR, Lee met with top officials from the American-Russian Chamber of Commerce, which had become the center of the progressive business community at the time and recognized the real benefits that could result from the normalization of economic and political relations with the Soviet Union. The president of the chamber was well-known financier and Chase National Bank Vice President Reeve Schley, while the chamber's vice president was Allen Wardwell, the co-owner of a large law firm and a former member of the American Red Cross's mission to Russia. The chamber's 17 directors represented financial and insurance institutions and the largest industrial firms in the US. The Soviet representatives included members of Amtorg and the local branch of the All-Union Trade Union.

As soon as reports about his upcoming visit became public, US newspapers began publishing all kinds of sensational articles, including reports that Lee was allegedly helping the Soviets gain diplomatic recognition in the US. Lee, for his part, while not hiding his true feelings about "the government of the dictatorship of the proletariat," believed that Soviet Russia was vitally interested in economic cooperation with the West despite its calls for the "export of revolution." He therefore deemed it necessary to develop relations with Soviet Russia and even recognize it, but only in exchange for an end to its policy of double standards on the international stage.

Lee's visit to Moscow was viewed as a major event and received wide attention in the Soviet press. He was given the opportunity to meet with Aleksey Rykov, the head of the Soviet government and chairman of the USSR Council of People's Commissars.

During the long and exhaustive conversation with Rykov, the American envoy stressed that his visit was strictly of a private nature. Describing his visit with Rykov, Lee later wrote: "My sole purpose, I stated, was to regard the situation 'objectively' (a word the Russians love), and that I wanted primarily to see people rather than things.... Above all I wanted to see responsible representatives of the Government or the Communist Party who would be in a position to give me candidly their own personal interpretation of the philosophy underlying their regime, and their point of view as to their own situation and its relationship with the rest of the world."

Lee asked Rykov a very pointed question during the conversation about whether there actually was a peculiar division of labor in the USSR, where the government limited itself to economic issues and signed treaties with capitalists, while the Communist International was battling these capitalists through its own organizations, and the Party Central Committee Politburo played the role of a conductor in this process. He did not, however, receive a clear answer to this question.

Lee also discussed the activities of Soviet trade unions with Mikhail Tomsky (Yefremov) (1880–1936), a Politburo member and chairman of the All-Union Central Council of Trade Unions. Tomsky told Lee that civil war, economic chaos and famine had prompted the trade unions to actively cooperate in setting up production and restoring the country's economy and that such goals could only be fulfilled though close cooperation with the Soviet authorities. Therefore, he said, the gradual governmentalization of the trade unions was inevitable because of the need to restore the labor force and ensure people's survival. Lee also noted that Soviet trade unions were overloaded by the multitude of targets they had to meet in addition to the predominance of Party dictates, which prevented them from fully performing their primary function—protecting the socioeconomic rights and interests of the workers. He took two impressions away from this conversation: a concession is a special privilege offered to foreign capitalists by the Soviet government, and since concession companies are managed by capitalists, the working class employs all possible means to defend their rights, including "revolutionary violence."

During a meeting with prominent Party journalist Karl Radek (Sobelson) (1885–1939), Lee expressed particular interest in communist propaganda, specifically, how it was organized, who directed it and whether the "united forces" of the government, Communist Party, and Communist International stood behind it.

Towards the end of his visit, Lee met with Deputy People's Commissar for Foreign Affairs Maxim Litvinov (Vallakh) (1876-1951), with whom he had a productive mutual exchange of views on specific areas of Soviet–US cooperation that could be improved. Lee stressed that the American people and government had a friendly attitude towards the Russian nation and its citizens, but the Soviet government had no credibility in the West because of its strong opposition to private property rights and its refusal to pay past debts.

Based on certain indications, Lee thought he would have the opportunity to meet personally with Stalin, who was by that time the Central Committee Secretary General, but the meeting never took place.

The American journalist recorded his impressions of his visit to the Soviet Union in two books titled *USSR: A World Enigma* and *Present-Day Russia*. The first book was released in the US in 1927 not long after his ten-day visit to Moscow, while the second appeared the following year with significant additions.

In his books, Lee did not predict the rapid downfall of the politicians he met, but did detect some contradictory beliefs and a lack of unity in the Soviet leadership. He distinguished the radical Bolshevik internationalists—the advocates of the dictatorship of the proletariat—from the nationalist-minded Bolsheviks, whom he considered to be pragmatists. Lee tried to evaluate the personalities of two radical Party leaders, Leon Trotsky and Nikolay Bukharin, based on their statements in the press, which he quoted in his book. He considered Bukharin the most dangerous radical for the world community, citing his inflammatory Communist International speeches. Lee was well aware that such slogans as "Down with imperialism!," "Proletarians of all countries, unite!," and "Factories to the workers!" did not pose a real threat to the US or the Western world. There was nothing behind these slogans except a desire to influence mass consciousness in the direction the Bolsheviks wanted. Lee maintained that the strongest antidote against this was a high standard of living.

Lee unexpectedly discovered a key thought in Leon Trotsky's writing, of which he took note: if clear signs of the economic downfall of capitalism were not seen in the West in the next few decades, the USSR would not be able to surpass it in terms of labor productivity and product quality. It was pointless to chase an express with a freight train, and the Bolsheviks would have to admit that their Marxist theory-based socialistic experiment had proven to be a fatal mistake. Lee had no doubts that capitalism would win out despite the shortcomings of Western civilization, and the Soviet system would have to adapt to capitalist society by initially borrowing its accomplishments and then ultimately joining it.

As for establishing diplomatic relations with the US, Lee said the USSR needed to meet several preliminary conditions. It had to earn the respect of the global community by fulfilling all of its international obligations, even to the capitalists, and exile all organizations calling for revolution in other countries. In this regard, he emphasized the deconstructive role of the Communist International. "The Russian people as a people are all right. The great enemy of mankind is the Communist International. The supreme problem is how to drive a wedge between the Communist International and the Russian people so that the Russian people themselves will come to feel that they want none of the International or its works." In addition, as an advocate of liberal values, he called for introducing "real freedom of thought, action and belief" in the USSR and creating a judicial system based on the principles of true justice and law.

Even though for obvious reasons he concealed the actual role he was playing in fulfilling Rockefeller's instructions during his trip to Moscow, Lee represented his ideas as his own personal thoughts and even arranged for his book to be printed privately. In the US, he was nevertheless accused of conducting the policy of the Red Commissars in the country and of having being "bought" by the Soviets.

Soviet authorities were not particularly thrilled with the book, either. While Deputy People's Commissar for Foreign Trade Lev Khinchuk called the book "timely and important as an expression of the position of the business community," he also found the ideas put forward in the book unacceptable for Soviet society. The popular Soviet newspaper *Za industrializatsiyu* ["For Industrialization"] wrote that "Ivy Lee expects the communist spirit to 'disintegrate' from the development of trade."

Nevertheless, it can be said with a certain degree of confidence that Lee's visit produced positive results, as he might have presented another decisive argument for the Soviet leadership to finally chart its course towards the possible expansion of multilateral cooperation with the United States.

On September 1, 1927, the Politburo founded the Permanent Commission for Technical and Scientific Relations with America. The commission included Aleksandr Serebrovsky, the head of Azneft who had visited the US three years earlier and met personally with Rockefeller.

That same year, the American-Russian Chamber of Commerce opened a permanent representative office in Moscow. The chamber's subsequent activities were crucial in coordinating the efforts of the most forward-looking and clear-headed members of the US business community towards normalizing political and economic relations with the USSR, as well as expanding trade and economic ties between US banks and companies and Soviet economic organizations. The fact that members of the American-Russian Chamber of Commerce were the ones concluding the largest financial and trade contracts with the USSR economic agencies in 1927 and 1928 illustrates the importance of the chamber's role.

Brochure: *The Situation of the Oil Industry in the Baku Region.*

Vladimir Lenin (Ulyanov) (1870-1924). Despite his belief that nationalization was premature, on June 20, 1918, he signed the "Decree on the Nationalization of the Oil Industry."

Grigory Orjonikidze (Sergo) (1886-1937), Joseph Stalin (Dzhugashvili) (1878-1953) and Anastas Mikoyan (1895-1925) (1925).

In 1918, the CPC approved the "Decree on Establishing the Moscow Mining Academy." The first director of the academy was I. M. Gubkin. In 1930 he founded and directed the Moscow Institute of Oil, created on the basis of the oil department of the Moscow Mining Academy. The building is now the I. M. Gubkin Russian State University of Oil and Gas.

The oldest educational institute in pre-revolutionary Russia for training oil industry workers. It was founded in 1887 as a city vocational school. After the establishment of Soviet power, it became the basis for the Baku Polytechnical Institute. After 1928 it was named the Azerbaijan Polytechnical Institute; in 1930 it was renamed the Azerbaijan Institute of Oil, and from 1959 until 1991 it was known as the Azibekov Azerbaijan Institute of Oil and Chemistry (Baku).

Drilling at the Ilyich Bay oil field (Baku, 1925). The first offshore oil well was drilled from an artificial island and drew oil from a depth of 461 m. Oil workers reported in 1929: "We have erected more than 200 oil rigs on the sea floor in the past five years, outpacing the rate of the Americans: This is our proletarian pace." By that time, the oil field had already yielded 2.5 million tons of oil.

Narrow-gauge oil railway in Surakhany, Baku (1932).

Share of Standard Oil Company.

John D. Rockefeller (1839-1937): The world's largest oil magnate. In 1870 he founded the Ohio Corporation, which after its incorporation, became Standard Oil - the largest international corporation. ExxonMobil, a vestige of Standard Oil, remains the largest corporation in the world.

Henry Deterding (1866-1939): A Dutch oil magnate and founder of Royal Dutch Petroleum. He headed Royal Dutch/Shell beginning in 1907 to compete with Standard Oil. The transport tankers he saw on the Caspian Sea and Volga River gave him an idea for a way to compete for the world market.

In 1904, Rockefeller's Standard Oil controlled 91% of all oil refineries and 95% of all sales in the United States, necessitating the adoption in 1890 of a special antimonopoly law, the Sherman Act. The United States Justice Department filed a lawsuit against the corporation, which in 1911 was split up into 34 companies.

The major U.S. oil companies Chevron, Exxon (Esso), ConocoPhillips, Amoco and Mobil are all successors of Standard Oil's empire.

Kola Superdeep Borehole No. 3. It remains
the deepest well in the world (12,262 m).
The discovery of concentrations of methane
at great depths confirms the possibility that
oil may originate in the Earth's mantle.

Vladimir Shukhov remained in Russia after
the 1917 revolution. The Baku-Tuapse oil
pipeline, a cracking plant, an oil reservoir
and more than 500 bridges were built on the
basis of his designs. Almost all major
projects of the first Five Year Plan were
associated with Shukhov's name.

A collection of oil and products distilled from
oil. Baku deposits, latter half of the 19th
century. Mining museum in St. Petersburg.

A contemporary collection of oil and gas
condensate from various deposits throughout
the country.

A model of the "Grandma Well," Well 20,
which in 1929 produced the first oil in Perm.

Posters from the 1940s. These were not only means for propaganda and agitation, but a distinctive portrait of the era. They offer a clear sense of the pulse of the time. Even the number indicated on the postage stamp is taken from a speech given by Stalin in 1946.

Wartime poster.

Refueling of a military fighter plane.

Baku, to the frontline.

ZIS-5V fuel tanker truck (1941-1945).

Urals, to the frontline.

Refueling of an Il-2 plane by a ZIS-6 airfield fuel tanker. Soviet forces used more than 16 million tons of various grades of fuel during World War II.

Issue 58 of the Komsomolets Tatary (May 14, 1971), dedicated to the first billion tons of oil produced by the Tatar Republic. Another billion tons would be produced just 10 years later.

A group of oil workers in front of Well 3 of the Romashkino oil field (1981). During testing of this well in 1948, a thick formation was discovered in the Volga-Urals oil and gas province that proved to be one of the largest in the world. The region subsequently started to be called the "Second Baku."

Even after the US State Department and Department of Commerce lifted some restrictions on lending for Soviet purchases in the second half of 1927 and trade volume increased, the nonrecognition policy nevertheless continued to have a negative effect on the development of economic relations between the two countries.

By 1927–1928, further growth in US–Soviet economic ties and pressure exerted by business groups on the US administration to create an environment in which such ties could expand finally prompted the US government to lift a number of restrictions on trade and economic relations with the USSR.

One of the biggest changes in this new policy was renewed lending for US exports to the USSR. In October 1928, Amtorg signed a contract with General Electric for a five-year loan worth up to $26 million, to be used to buy electrical equipment in the US and export it to the USSR. The agreement with General Electric led to more active talks with other large companies such as Ford Motor Company and General Motors. On May 31, 1929, talks with Ford culminated in the signing of a large contract for shipment of automobiles and spare parts to the USSR in addition to providing technical assistance in building the Gorky Auto Works.

US exports to the Soviet Union were on the rise in 1927 and 1928, and the USSR became the biggest importer of several types of US engineering products. In 1928 the USSR imported 10.1% of all tractors exported by the US, 4.6% of all metal-working machinery, 7.1% of all mining equipment, 6.9% of all petroleum equipment, 8.9% of all excavators, and 1.6% of all electrical equipment. In 1929, these percentages all increased, roughly doubling for tractors, metal-working machinery, and electrical equipment.

In 1928 and 1929, Graver Corporation provided Winkler-Koch cracking units to the Batumi refinery on the basis of a long-term loan. Graver Corporation later also supplied cracking units to refineries in Tuapse (1930) and Yaroslavl (1932). Other US companies that supplied equipment to the Soviet refining industry from 1928 to 1930 included Foster-Wheeler Corporation (New York) and Badger and Sons (Boston).

Relations between the two countries were bolstered by concession agreements and special contracts on technical assistance signed by Soviet organizations and US companies. As of October 1, 1928, there were nine US concessions active in the USSR and six contracts under which US companies were providing technical assistance, including in the oil industry. By the late 1920s, Soviet-American economic relations were at a level either equal to or higher than the USSR's relations with Great Britain or Germany with respect to key areas of economic cooperation.

It should be noted that Ivy Lee made two more visits to the USSR and lived to see the establishment of diplomatic relations between the US and USSR in 1933. During the last years of his life, his biggest concern was that Soviet Russia, after pushing for accelerated industrialization and collectivization, not become totally isolated from the global community. "The Russians turned from the ideas of the internationalists to their domestic affairs and realized that they would soon become economically independent and could manage without the United States," he told his friends. Lee gave his own government just one piece of advice—develop relations with Soviet Russia in such a way that once it saw the achievements of other countries, it would gradually and voluntarily renounce socialism and communism. This is how he suggested solving the "the world enigma of the USSR." It is now clear that Lee's prophecy came true; it just took more than 55 years to happen.

Engineer Kapelyushnikov's Turbodrill

The aggressive implementation of a government program to retool the oil industry was producing visible results by the mid-1920s. The American method of rotary drilling had replaced the rod-tool drilling method in drilling equipment, and by fiscal 1928–1929, rotary drilling had become the undisputed technique of choice in the domestic oil industry (used for 86.7% of drilling in Baku and 73.2% in Grozny). The new technology resulted in a more than tenfold increase in drilling speed and a reduction in drilling costs. Less casing pipe was consumed during well casing using the American method than the old rod-tool method since the well structure was simplified, the initial diameter was reduced, and fewer pipe strings were used. The volume of steel pipes used at production fields was cut by 65–75%, and the cost of drilling decreased from 111 rubles per foot in fiscal 1923–24 to 53 rubles per foot in fiscal 1927–28. Aleksandr Serebrovsky, head of Azneft, said his company realized more than 100–120 million rubles over those four years solely as a result of the improved drilling method.

At the same time Soviet oil fields were starting to employ the new US method, testing began on a new well drilling method which was to open a new era in the development of the oil industry and was the brainchild of the talented Russian engineer Matvey Kapelyushnikov (1896–1959). Kapelyushnikov graduated from the mechanical department of Tomsk Technological Institute in 1914 and then worked as a design engineer for a company in Baku. In May 1920, he was appointed chief engineer at one of Azneft's largest production companies. After analyzing the drilling business and correctly concluding that rotary drilling was replacing the archaic rod-tool drilling at fields on the Absheron Peninsula, Kapelyushnikov very perceptively uncovered a serious flaw in the American method. In rotary drilling, the engine rotor that spins the drill string holding the drill bit is located on the surface, so if the drill pipe string is very long, all that weight has to be rotated just to spin the small drill bit which is drilling rock at great depths. Only a small part of the energy used for rotation is used productively, while the rest is wasted. Pipes gyrate, their outer walls rub against the rock walls of the borehole, and the inner walls are worn away by the sand that is always present in clay drilling mud. As a result, the drill pipes wear down quickly, break, become warped, and require frequent replacement.

Kapelyushnikov began to ponder ways to rectify this flaw. A detailed study of scientific and technical literature pointed him in the right direction and he realized the only solution was to construct a reliable, high-performance downhole drilling motor.

Technical solutions for building downhole drilling motors and similar drilling technology appeared at the end of the 19th century and resulted in a hydraulic downhole motor (Brandt, 1875), a turbine downhole motor (Westinghouse, 1883), a rotating downhole hydraulic motor (Russian engineer Kuzma Simchenko, 1895), a downhole hydraulic motor (Valitsky, 1895), and a turbine ram for quick-blow drilling (Prushkovsky, early 20th century). The inventors designed these drilling devices so that the motor controlling the drill was not located on the surface but attached directly to the drill bit to rotate it. Design flaws prevented these motors from being put into actual use, but still, all downhole motors had one thing in common—the drill bit was rotated directly without intermediary gear mechanisms.

Kapelyushnikov's hard work finally produced the long-sought-after result: the first efficient downhole motor—the geared turbodrill. Kapelyushnikov submitted a patent application for the invention in Moscow on September 26, 1922.

The first test design of Kapelyushnikov's turbodrill weighed about one ton. The turbodrill's cylindrical shell held a motor with a single-stage turbine, which was put into motion by the flow of drilling mud pumped in via the drill pipe. The turbine was connected to the drill bit via a gearbox which reduced the drill bit rotation speed.

The turbodrill prototype was tested for the first time in summer 1923 in water off a pier belonging to the former Baku Oil Company. It was then tested at a well at the Surakhany oil field. Several feet were drilled during this test, which was conducted in the presence of Party official Kirov and all the Politburo members of the Party's Baku committee. In 1924, at the Surakhany oil fields, the world's first well was drilled using Kapelyushnikov's turbodrill, with a depth of about 2,000 feet.

Tests of the downhole motor designed by Kapelyushnikov confirmed the motor's operating capability. The benefits of such a turbodrill, namely that only the drill bit rotates during drilling, were immediately apparent to petroleum engineers. The heavy pipe string did not rotate and only ran along the inside of the well as it became deeper. It turned out that it was much easier to drill with the turbodrill at great depths since the pipe did not cause any friction with the well wall. The accident rate with pipes also declined considerably compared to the old rotary drilling method. With the support of Kirov, huge orders were placed with the Maltsev mechanical plant for production of the new turbodrills.

The Soviet government gave Kapelyushnikov two major awards for his invention: the Order of the Red Banner of Labor and the Order of Lenin. The government of the Republic of Azerbaijan granted him the title of Hero of Labor of the Azerbaijani Socialist Soviet Republic.

Further testing revealed, however, that the distinct advantages of Kapelyushnikov's turbodrill as compared to rotary drilling were somewhat blunted by the fact that the turbodrill could only operate for a few hours at a time and the average operating speed of turbine drilling lagged behind that of rotary drilling under identical conditions. The weakest components of the first turbodrill design were the turbine and the gearbox. The turbine could only operate for a few hours, while the moving parts of the gearbox wore down quickly as a result of high pressure and the flow of drilling mud entering the crankcase, requiring frequent replacements.

The news of Kapelyushnikov's patent was published in the Soviet press on August 31, 1925. The patent was officially granted for 15 years effective September 15, 1924. Curiously enough, Kapelyushnikov had applied for and received a patent in Great Britain back in October 1923.

The invention of a turbodrill in the USSR soon attracted the attention of the US engineering community. In 1928, the US journal *Petroleum* asked Kapelyushnikov for a description of his invention and invited him to present a report on the turbodrill at the World's Fair of Petroleum Equipment in Tulsa, Oklahoma in 1929. In addition, Standard Oil of New York and Texaco Inc. asked Amtorg officials to demonstrate well drilling using the turbodrill at US oil fields. The Soviet government decided to grant the request and sent a drilling crew to the US led by Kapelyushnikov with two gear-based turbodrills.

Kapelyushnikov presented reports in the US on the operating principles of his turbodrill and then demonstrated drilling with the downhole motors the crew had brought from the USSR at a well owned by Texas Oil in Earlsboro, Oklahoma.

In an interview with a leading Soviet newspaper, Kapelyushnikov commented on the early stages of his trip: "We agreed to drill consecutively, first with the rotary drill and then with our turbodrill. The experiments showed that under identical conditions, i.e., a depth of about 700 meters [2,300 feet], with 16.5 liters [4.4 gallons] of drilling mud being pumped per second, the turbodrill drilled 60% faster than the rotary method—which amazed everybody. Energy consumption by the turbodrill was about a third of the amount used in rotary drilling. As we wrote to Moscow, this success resulted from the powerful pumps and rolling cutter bits. We also discovered several more flaws in the design of the turbodrill. We determined that the drilling mud needs to be cleaned of sand, which sometimes comprises up to 50% of the mud. The presence of sand led to severe wear on the blades in the single-stage turbine. At the same time, the idea arose to build a multistage turbine like the one successfully designed by engineer Lyubimov."

The Soviet drilling crew conducted more demonstrations with the turbodrill in the US over the next two years and on the whole withstood a tough test by experienced and demanding US drilling specialists.

Emphasizing the crew's success, Kapelyushnikov described the results of the turbodrill testing: "The appearance of our turbodrill in summer 1929 made a big impression on American drilling equipment manufacturing engineers as well as drill operators. Petroleum engineering groups in America are currently very interested in the problem of deep drilling at 10,000 feet since it is extremely difficult to drill at such depths using the rotary method. Following the testing of the turbodrill, US petroleum publications have recently been printing more and more statements saying that the delivery of drilling power to the bottomhole is the only solution to the problem of deep drilling."

The two years Kapelyushnikov's crew spent working at US oil fields likewise made an enormous impression on the international business and engineering community. Several foreign companies—and not just US firms—began contacting Soviet trade representatives, and Kapelyushnikov directly as well, with proposals to purchase or license the new invention. The Soviet government, however, decided instead to make further improvements to the turbodrill on its own and retained the exclusive rights for its use. Little justification for this decision could be found, though, since the Soviet Union did not produce rolling cutting bits or powerful pumps at the time and did not employ methods to clean drilling mud satisfactorily. Under such conditions, the introduction of turbodrilling, which would be pursued vigorously over the next nine years by Party leadership as well as Sergey Kirov personally, failed to produce the desired result. Turbodrilling accounted for only 1.1% of drilling throughout the country in 1927, and by 1932 this share had only increased to 3.9%.

The turbodrill was used for the first time in the New District at the Grozny oil fields in 1928. Grozneft noted in its industrial and financial plan that "18,478.6 meters [60,625 feet] were drilled in the New Grozny District in the 1927–28 operating year using the rotary method, of which turbodrilling accounted for 483.7 meters [1,587 feet]."

The turbodrilling system introduced by Kapelyushnikov provided a clear direction for how to resolve complex engineering challenges that would be faced in building a commercial version of the turbodrill, which occurred in 1934 when a creative group of Soviet engineers led by Pëtr

Shumilov developed a multistage gearless turbodrill. By 1940, this group had built a new multistage turbine equipped with a reinforced single-stage gearbox that provided the required drilling speed directly on the shaft and could be adapted to drill every kind of rock seen in the field. This not only changed the negative attitude that drilling experts had displayed towards downhole motors but also led to the adoption of turbodrilling in almost 80% of USSR drilling operations.

The 1929 Ukhta Expedition

The USSR's transition to a policy of accelerated industrialization in the late 1920s forced Party leadership to devote more attention to the exploration and development of hydrocarbon resources in new areas, including the Timan-Pechora region.

By that time, the Komi (Zyryan) Autonomous Region had been in existence on this territory for eight years, and questions had begun to arise about the region's economic foundation, including its industrialization, and about the development of the Komi territory's natural wealth, both its forests and its subsurface resources, but above all Ukhta petroleum. Fundamental changes needed to be made to the economy of the primarily agricultural region, which was not in a position to resolve such issues on its own, owing to a lack of roads and a proper work force. Party leadership thus came up with the idea of using prison labor to carry out economic operations under the supervision of special agencies. They were called correctional labor camps, and their mission was to develop natural resources in the remote areas of the European part of the North.

On June 27, 1929, the Politburo passed a secret resolution, "On the Use of Prison Labor," which was officially put into effect by a resolution of the USSR CPC on July 11. The Joint State Political Directorate [*OGPU*], a state security organization, was put in charge of its implementation. After receiving approval from the Politburo, the *OGPU* began implementing the project. On June 28, the *OGPU* set up the Northern Special Purpose Camp [*SEVLON*], which was given instructions to develop natural resources near Ukhta and Pechora, explore for crude in Ukhta-Izhma District, cut down forests in the Arkhangelsk Region, and build a railroad from Pinyug to Ust-Sysolsk (179 miles) and a highway from Ust-Sysolsk to Ukhta (205 miles).

Prior to this, *OGPU* officials met in Moscow in spring 1929 to determine what measures needed to be taken to implement the important mission of exploring for oil fields in the region. As part of preparations for the meeting, the *OGPU* consulted with two respected geologists: Professor Aleksandr Chernov, a well-known researcher of the Pechora territory, and former Deputy Director of the Geologic Committee Nikolay

Tikhonovich, who was also a prisoner at Butyrka Prison. He later recalled: "I was invited to a meeting by eight people I did not know. They asked me point-blank how to get to Ukhta, what kinds of things to take, what kinds of equipment, how many provisions, etc. I wrote down the route for them and what kind of supplies to take. I wrote that everything needs to be brought there, right down to the last nail. I showed them two routes: the old route and the sea route by which heavy cargo could be transported.... We organized an expedition of 195 people."

What emerged from the Moscow meeting was a route for the expedition, a plan for transporting complex drilling equipment and instruments to the taiga and roadless region, and a group of qualified workers that had been selected for the mission from among the prisoners. In May 1929, the *OGPU* central office sent two senior officials, Sergey Sidorov and Eduard Skaya, to the Solovetsky prison camp to resolve some practical issues. Meanwhile, necessary equipment was being prepared for shipment to the Pechora territory. All-Union Communist Party (of Bolsheviks) [AUCP(b)] members Dmitry Rusanov, a fifth-year student in the geologic department of the Mining Academy, and Ivan Kosolapkin, a drilling expert from the Grozny fields, were invited to take part in this work. By July 1929, the expedition staff had been assembled at the Solovetsky camps and provided with the necessary equipment.

The National Archives in the Komi Republic provide details about the trip and the first months of the *OGPU* expedition. These documents include copies of dispatches to the director of the department for the northern camps from *OGPU* expedition head Sergey Sidorov (in August–September 1929), a report on the travels of the Ukhta Expedition, and a report on the condition of the Chibyu fields. Among other things, the reports say, "The expedition began loading onto the *USEVLON* ship *Gleb Boky* on the pier of the city of Kem at 7 a.m. on July 5, 1929 and finished at 11 p.m. the same day. The ship could not accommodate all the cargo, which resulted in more than two rail cars worth of flour as well as some food and household goods being left behind in Kem. A group of 139 prisoners was then loaded onto the ship, which left the Kem pier at 2 a.m. on July 6."

On August 21, 1929, the *OGPU* expedition arrived at its destination at the mouth of Chibyu Creek, where the Chibyu production field of the former Neft Partnership had previously been located, and where the production field of the Arkhangelsk Regional Economic Council had been located in 1920–21. All the buildings at the former field had been boarded up and sealed by the Izhemsk Local Economic Council. A cursory inspection revealed a steam engine, two boring and drilling machines, a kerosene refinery taken from the field of the engineer Gansberg, and other equipment. Expedition member Aleksandr Kulevsky recalled the trip in his memoirs: "We arrived in Chibyu during the day and my heart sank at the sight of the wild and bleak picture we saw. A black, ridiculously oversized single tower and two miserable huts surrounded by nothing but taiga and swamps."

The crew, already exhausted from the difficult trip, faced an enormous amount of work. Fifteen barges had to be unloaded immediately and the remaining structures needed major repairs. Meanwhile, barracks, a sauna, a bakery and several other facilities had to be built in order to somehow accommodate the crew.

Bad weather and the approaching fall drove the prisoners to complete work as quickly as possible. On the second day after arriving, they were split up into different work areas and a 12-hour workday was established. They began repairing the surviving facilities, installing equipment, and logging.

A second group of 50 prisoners, including 20 specialists, arrived via the same route along the Izhma River in October 1929. Two of these specialists were the well-known geologist Nikolay Tikhonovich, who later took over the camp's geologic service, and Ilya Ginsburg, a specialist in geology and mineralogy who was to handle the extraction of radioactive water from the Ukhta field. Mining engineers also arrived, including Pëtr Antonov, Konstantin Erdely, Zinovy Khurgin, Andrey Voloshanovsky, and Ivan Kosolapkin, the drilling expert from Grozny.

Also arriving with this group were *OGPU* officials who would later go on to become the core of the Ukhta-Pechora camp: Yakov Moroz, G. Ivanov, V. Gauk, and others.

The final structural touch was put on the expedition in late October and early November 1929 when, on November 2, *Chekist* Yakov Moroz (Iosema) (1898–1938) was appointed head of the expedition with special authority.

The expedition members went to work with a minimal amount of equipment and a small work force. During the initial stage, the geologists were asked to determine the actual probability of extracting commercial crude. Their attention was first drawn to the presence of oil shows and the likelihood of its commercial extraction. They determined that the well drilled by the Neft Association in 1917 had produced a slight oil flow after being repaired. This, combined with oil flows at other wells, enabled the expedition to produce the first five tons of oil in the region over a four-month period in 1929.

Geologist Nikolay Tikhonovich (1872–1952) determined the best area to drill new exploratory Well 5, and the well was sunk and construction began in late November 1929. However, the winter of 1929–1930 was especially harsh, creating serious difficulties for the expedition, and the transition from preliminary excavation to drilling was not made until April 4, 1930, and it was not until October 25, at a depth of 1,270-1,275 feet, that light crude began to flow out at a rate of more than 4 tons per hour. The Chibyu industrial field of Devonian oil had been opened and the first major success of the *OGPU's* Ukhta Expedition had been recorded.

In April 1930, the Pechora Group was formed as a part of the Ukhta Expedition to perform further geologic work. It was comprised of Nikolay Zhigalovsky, the head of the group; Konstantin Voynovsky-Kriger, the head of operations; Semën Zhemchuzhin, the topographer; Andrey Dukhovsky, the collector; and seven workers. On April 8, the group set off on horseback and on foot for a month-long trip to the village of Medvezhskaya, where a farmer named Loginov had discovered oil shows near the Little Kozhva River.

Once the ice began to melt in Pechora in late May, the group was able to travel to the prospective area, which was 50 miles from the mouth of the river. The low levels of surface oil shows they found there were not sufficient to confirm the presence of a large oil field. The Pechora Group nevertheless decided to focus on the Ydzhid-Kyrt region, where a coal deposit was discovered.

In addition to performing a large amount of construction work, the prisoners were also hurriedly building oil derricks. Whereas only two derricks were built in 1929, ten were erected in 1930. A total of 4,167 feet of hole were drilled in 1930, compared to only 768 feet in 1929. Significant progress was also seen in 1930 in the extraction and processing of Devonian crude. Some 97 tons were extracted that year, with 49 tons refined and 12 tons of kerosene produced. The expedition also discovered large coal reserves while recovering radium from Ukhta field formation water. A road was built connecting the Ukhta oil-bearing area with other parts of the country, and a real opportunity emerged to create an industrial base for the Komi Autonomous Region.

The size of the expedition increased significantly in late 1930, reaching 824 people by the end of the year. Of this number, 445 individuals were working outside the main Chibyu base, while the rest were working at internal facilities.

The main outcome of the *OGPU's* Ukhta Expedition in 1929–30 was the creation of a solid foundation to subsequently increase production of crude reserves, coal and other subsurface resources discovered by the expedition. Camp leadership highly praised the significant results the expedition had achieved. Lazar Kogan (1889–1939), head of the Main Administration of Prison Camps [*GULAG*], expressed gratitude to the head of the Ukhta exhibition, Yakov Moroz, and the entire management group for the "exceptional energy and perseverance they displayed in performing difficult assignments of special national importance." The archives do not indicate how the *OGPU* rewarded the prisoners whose heavy labor made it possible to achieve these results.

Soviet political leadership viewed Kogan's report on the success in the Timan-Pechora region as confirmation of their strategy. A special commission led by Valery Mezhlauk (1893–1938), the deputy chairman of the *VSNKh*, was set up as part of the Labor and Defense Council in 1931. This commission held several meetings in April 1931 that were attended by representatives of the *OGPU*, Soyuzneft, the Main Geologic Exploration Administration, the People's Commissariat for Water Transportation, the Northern Territory, and the Komi Autonomous Region. In a resolution dated April 18, 1931, "On Ukhta Petroleum," the commission decided "to allocate five percussion drilling units; approve a program for the drilling of 17,185 meters [56,381 feet] of exploratory wells in various parts of Ukhta, Verkhne-Izhma, and Pechora in 1931–32; send a gravimetric group from the Main Geologic Exploration Administration to work in the Ukhta-Pechora region in summer 1931; and allocate an additional 2.56 million rubles for 1931 from the reserve of the USSR CPC in addition to the 1.2 million rubles previously allocated."

On April 21, 1931, the *VSNKh* passed a resolution, "On the Development of a Fuel Base in the Northern Territory," which proposed that the Ukhta Expedition considerably expand its exploration operations for crude. The People's Commissariat for Water Transportation was instructed to provide support for expedition cargo shipments and to reinforce the Pechora river fleet, while the People's Commissariat for Railroads was instructed to cover the prepared section of the Ust–Vym–Ukhta road with gravel during the summer season of 1931. The decree also called for the construction of three to four exploratory mines near Vorkuta and the Adzva (a tributary of the Usa River) and for the production of at least 7,700 tons of coal.

In summer 1931, the *OGPU's* Ukhta Expedition was transformed into the Ukhta-Pechora Correctional Labor Camp, and *OGPU* Senior Major Yakov Moroz was appointed its director. Five territorial camp divisions were created: Chibyu, Vodnin, Verkhne-Izhma, Pechora, and Usa (the center was the village of Ust-Usa, which would shift later to Vorkuta). Each camp division was comprised of several sites "filled" to varying extent—from several hundred to several thousand prisoners—and had its own director, office building, registration and distribution department, accounting department, commandant's office, mess hall, food and clothing storerooms, medical unit with dispensary, hospital (about 20 beds), cultural and education center, mandatory isolation cell for punishment, and camp investigative unit.

The central management structure of the Ukhta-Pechora camp also began to expand at the same time. The prisoner personnel center turned into the registration and distribution department and other divisions were also set up, including a civilian personnel department, a special department, an encoding bureau, a general accounting office, a medical department, a cultural and educational department, a central isolation cell for punishment, an *OGPU* operations department, a central hospital at Vetlosyan, a separate paramilitary security service unit, a camp prosecutor's office, and a camp court.

On November 16, 1932, the USSR Labor and Defense Council passed a resolution, "On the Organization of the Ukhta-Pechora Trust," charging the trust with "exploring and developing subsurface resources of commercial value in the Pechora Basin and all auxiliary work related to it; building railroads and dirt roads; constructing housing and cultural institutions; and building repair plants to support existing and future mines, oil fields and river shipbuilding.... The *OGPU* is charged with the trust's management." *OGPU* officials immediately approved the Charter of the State Ukhta-Pechora Trust, with detailed regulations for its extensive production activities.

The first preparatory stage of the Timan-Pechora region's industrial development had been completed. The village of Chibyu had been built in the area where the Chibyu Creek meets the Ukhta River and was surrounded by a large number of camp sites that previously had provided labor for the construction of industrial and housing facilities. In a relatively short time, the prisoners had built a power station, a machinery and repair plant, and a refinery, which at the time consisted of an atmospheric tube installation and bitumen production equipment. In addition, minable radium deposits were also discovered near the Chut River during the search for crude. A field was set up to extract the radioactive water and a concentrate plant was built to recover radium via a complex chemical process.

The First Permian Oil

During this period of accelerated industrialization, systematic geologic exploration for crude oil was carried out for the first time in several promising regions of the country in response to instructions from Soviet Party leadership.

In early May 1929, the *VSNKh* Presidium declared it necessary "to perform an extensive search for new oil fields" and "to draw up a plan for the broad survey of the Urals to search for oil and gas fields." The Uralneft state trust of the Ural oil industry was set up not long after this declaration. News from Perm about the discovery of the first oil field in the Urals had a major impact on the decisions passed by *VSNKh* officials.

The trailblazer of the Perm oil rush was mining engineer Pavel Preobrazhensky (1874–1944), a former Omsk government minister under [White Army leader] Admiral Kolchak, who fell into the hands of the Bolshevik tribunal and only just managed to avoid being shot as the result of a personal appeal made by writer Maxim Gorky to Lenin. Preobrazhensky's death sentence was commuted to exile in Perm, where he began working as a geology professor at Perm University. Shortly thereafter, the Geologic Committee's Ural Division asked him to research the archives of the former owners of Perm mining and salt plants, a group that included the businessmen Stroganov, Lazarev, and Ryazantsev, among others. In the archives, he found reference to a local pharmacist who, at the request of a technician from one of Nikolay Ryazantsev's plants in Solikamsk, analyzed samples of yellow salt with bright red streaks in 1910 and discovered a considerable amount of potassium in them. Professor Preobrazhensky also studied samples of rock taken during the drilling of several brine wells and discovered samples of pink salt while examining the salt collection at the Berezniki Soda Plant, where several boreholes had been drilled. Reports from 1916 indicated that samples from the Lyudmilinskaya brine well had included sylvinite (KCl + NaCl). In addition, a 1918 analysis of brine from a Solikamsk plant revealed slightly elevated potassium content in several samples from the salt mines at Solikamsk and Usolye. Preobrazhensky also noticed that the Perm salt had a slight light-blue and yellow tint and a bitter taste. All of these factors gave him reason to conclude that this region had prospects for potassium. Based on an analysis of the materials he had collected, as well as the research of well-known scientist Nikolay Kurnakov (1860–1941), Preobrazhensky presented a report to the Geologic Committee's Ural Division on the Solikamsk region's prospects for potassium salts and proposed a plan for exploration drilling.

Soviet agriculture was in dire need of vast amounts of potash fertilizers at the time and had been relying on imports from Germany, and so the Geologic Committee as well as the *VSNKh* paid close attention to Professor Preobrazhensky's report and were very hopeful about reported prospects. That same year, Preobrazhensky was promoted to the position of senior geologist in the nonmetallic minerals exploration department of the Geologic Committee's Leningrad Division.

On the basis of his preliminary work in the Kama River Valley and with the Geologic Committee's permission, Preobrazhensky began planning and preparing an expedition. Even in those difficult times, sufficient funds were found to organize a geologic expedition to prospect for potassium in the Solikamsk region. The professor decided to conduct exploratory drilling near the former salt mines and began prospecting in spring 1925. He managed to acquire a Calyx drilling rig, brought in a mobile steam power plant from Leningrad, and transported the required drilling equipment and tools from the Caucasus and Urals. One of his major challenges was determining where to drill the first well. After analyzing all the geologic data, Preobrazhensky selected an area just outside the city of Solikamsk, on the shore of the Usolki Creek, which fed into the Kama River. Drilling of the first well began in early September 1925. On the night of October 5, the well hit a thick mass of potassium salt (secondary sylvinite with KCl content of 17.9%) at a depth of 301–

303 feet. Well 2, which was located about a mile to the west, revealed a potassium deposit more than 360 feet thick. Thereafter, large potassium deposits were discovered in all the wells drilled in 1926, eventually culminating in the opening of the famed Verkhnekamsk potassium salt field. Preobrazhensky later said that drilling produced "stunning results." The 19 wells drilled in Solikamsk and Berezniki all revealed thick layers of carnallite and sylvinite.

In an effort to delineate the boundaries of the new field more clearly, Preobrazhensky decided to drill the 20th well in an area near Verkhnechusovskiye Gorodki [Upper Chusovaya River Settlements], where table salt had been produced since the time of the Stroganovs. On October 18, 1928, the crew of drilling expert Prokopy Pozdnyakov began drilling a well on the shore of the Rassoshka River. Core drilling was used for much of the work, with retrieval of rock cores to the surface. At a depth of 509 feet, rocks were drilled that could have contained potassium salt, but no signs of the salt could be found in the well. Preobrazhensky nevertheless insisted work be continued, and on March 30, 1929, a column of cracked rocks was brought to the surface from a depth of 1,076–1,086 feet containing traces of petroleum and escaping gas. On April 16, oil-covered rock was raised from a depth of 1,198–1,217 feet, which was described in a drilling journal as "an exuberant film of oil with gas bubbles." The heavy oil of the Kama Valley had made its first appearance.

The geologist Slyusarev delivered the first bottle of oil to the Ural Regional Economic Council in Sverdlovsk on April 26, 1929. The regional newspaper *Uralsky rabochy* ["Ural Worker"] reported the news the next day in an article titled "Oil Found in Urals." On April 28, the seventh Ural Congress of Soviets opened in Sverdlovsk. As the Party had issued a directive at the Congress "to decisively strengthen the prominence of the Urals and make it one of the most important industrial regions of the USSR" over the next five years, the first batch of oil was seen as a kind of gift to the regional leadership. The Perm delegate's address was followed by the ceremonial presentation of a bottle of oil and oil-bearing rock samples to the Congress, as well as optimistic assurances that a "second Baku" would soon emerge in the region. The local newspaper *Zvezda* ["Star"] triumphantly published an article on April 30 stating: "Oil Discovered in Perm Region."

Drilling work near Verkhnechusovskiye Gorodki intensified following the discovery of oil. At a depth of 1,312 feet, the oil-saturated limestone turned watery, a sign that the lower boundary of the petroleum deposit had been reached. Drilling operations were stopped on May 1, 1929 out of fears that an oil gusher could be produced and there would not be sufficient earthen dikes or containers to collect the oil.

On May 4, 1929, *Zvezda* wrote: "Another pearl has been added to the countless riches of the Urals—Permian oil. The size of the reserves and what kind of revolution it will create throughout the entire Urals economy will be seen in the near future. The bedding of the oil reservoir is located in the heart of a solid industrial triangle between Perm, Chusovaya and Lysva and is also in close proximity to the industrial mining railroad."

Moscow soon received word of the oil prospects in the Kama Valley, and the *VSNKh* Presidium passed a special resolution, "On Oil Exploration in the Urals," on May 7, 1929. The minutes of that meeting state: "It is hereby noted that, when the Geologic Committee was drilling an exploratory well for potassium salt on the Chusovaya River at a distance of 10 *versts* [6.6 miles] from the Komarikha railroad station, porous limestone containing oil and gas was found at a depth of 350 to 400 meters [1,148 to 1,312 feet].... The discovery of oil in the Central Urals near a number of metallurgical plants is enormously important. A widespread search for new oil fields in the Urals must be launched."[42]

The government's decision to accelerate the development of the Perm field was proven correct on May 12, 1929, when Preobrazhensky, the head of the geologic expedition, sent a telegram to Sverdlovsk stating that hand bailing of oil from the well had determined it could indeed be used commercially.

On May 14, 1929, the Presidium of the Verkhnechusovskiye Gorodki District Executive Committee passed a special resolution stating: "The discovery of oil in the Urals near our district is of great state importance. All industries in the Urals will undergo a radical change, and the discovery of oil is of significant economic importance for our district as well." Two days later, on May 16, *Zvezda* published another article under the huge headline "Such Oil Has Never Been Seen Before in the USSR." The article, datelined Verkhnechusovskiye Gorodki (May 15), read: "Comrade Ukhtin, head of the technical division of the USSR Geologic Committee, told our correspondent that the Urals oil is different from the Grozny and Baku oil in terms of color and smell. The Urals oil is of higher quality than the Grozny oil and it burns very well. Urals oil will apparently not be suitable for motors without first being refined, but it is so viscous that asphalt can be manufactured from it. Such oil has yet to be seen in either Baku or Grozny."

Academician Ivan Gubkin praised the reports from Perm and said: "We could be dealing with oil reserves whose significance for industry is difficult to imagine. One thing is for certain—we have oil on the slopes of the Ural Mountains. Moreover, according to preliminary data, it is available in quantities that are of commercial significance." The opinion of this respected oil scholar played a decisive role in the passage of *VSNKh* Decree 731 of May 18, 1929, on the creation of an organization within the Main Mining and Fuel Administration [*Glavgortop*], to be named the Uralneft Special Bureau, which was to manage all work related to exploration for oil and gas fields in the Urals.

News of the discovery of Perm crude spread quickly throughout the country. A telegram sent in May 1929 by the North Caucasus territorial committee of miners to the Urals regional committee stated: "The newly discovered oil region is of paramount importance to the Soviet Union, and as we wish to develop the region quickly, we will assume a leadership role in this area along with Grozneft. We are sending equipment and 49 skilled workers. Please telegraph what is needed most urgently. We will provide all possible assistance."

A government commission led by Iosif Kosior (1893–1937), deputy chairman of the *VSNKh* Presidium, arrived in Perm on May 21, 1929. The next day, the delegation traveled to Verkhnechusovskiye Gorodki along with Professor Preobrazhensky aboard the steamship *MOPR*. A rally was held on the pier as soon as the ship had docked. The tone of the speakers and the mood of the many people who had gathered to meet the ship were best reflected by a giant banner that read "We Shall Wake the Sleeping Resources!" It did not take much time for the commission members to inspect the drill site and listen to Preobrazhensky's convincing report. The results were obvious—there was every indication to confirm the presence of "big" oil in the Kama Valley. The first test of Well 20 was conducted after the government commission had left in early June, and the flow rate was 44 tons per day. *Pravda*, the Party's central newspaper, reported the well was producing oil on June 11, 1929.

The visit of Kosior's commission and the successful test of the well resulted in the implementation of new organizational measures. On June 12, 1929, the *VSNKh* issued Decree 827, which informed Party leaders of the statute the *VSNKh* Presidium had approved on June 6 concerning the Uralneft bureau within *Glavgortop*. On the same day, the council issued Decree 830, appointing Roman Buchatsky director of the Uralneft bureau, with Ya. Pelevin and P. Yermolayev as his deputies. On August 15, the Upper Chusovaya oil well was put into commercial production and assigned number 101. Approximately 8,800 tons of oil was produced from this first well over its 11 years of operation (until October 1940).

Before long, an even higher government agency was studying the issue of the Perm oil. On September 6, 1929, the Labor and Defense Council passed a resolution instructing "the USSR *VSNKh* and the USSR State Planning Committee to support 1929-30 target figures for a Uralneft rate of development that would enable at least 50 wells to be drilled with the assured use of the most advanced drilling methods and of methods most suitable for the soil." On September 30, the *VSNKh* passed a terse resolution, "On the Plan for Uralneft Operations in 1929–1930," which read: "In accordance with the Labor and Defense Council's resolution of September 6, 1929, the drilling program presented by Uralneft is approved."

Given the importance of the work and the large amount of drilling that needed to be completed, the *VSNKh* passed a decision creating the

Uralneft Trust on October 27. The Sterlitamak office of exploratory drilling led by Konstantin Kholdyrev and Kirill Prits was soon set up within the organization. Veteran oil expert Dmitry Shashin managed the drilling operations, while the respected geologists Aleksey Blokhin and Varvara Nosal were in charge of the geologic service. In a report on operating activities for fiscal 1929–30 signed by Roman Buchatsky, the Uralneft Trust indicated that it employed 650 blue- and white-collar workers as of December 1929. By the winter of 1929–1930, a total of 29 wells had been started near Verkhnechusovskiye Gorodki, plus two more near Kizel-Gubakha and one each at Cherdyn, Usolye, Shumkovo, and Ust-Kishert.

On June 1, 1930, *Uralsky rabochy* published an article titled "36 Derricks at Uralneft Fields," in which it stated: "Well 1 was put into operation on May 24 with a daily production rate of 55 tons. Drilling continued at Wells 2, 3, 4, 6, 8, 11, and 14 on May 21–25. Over this period, 132.3 meters [434 feet] of hole were drilled (935.7 meters [3,070 feet] were drilled in early May). The foundation and steam boilers are being modified at Well 12, the boiler room and frame are being built at Well 13, the foundation is being laid under the steam engine at Well 15, the foundation is being fortified at Wells 18 and 25, the boiler room and bridge deck over the river are being assembled at Well 25, and circular saws are being installed at Well 27. Wells 101 and 1 have produced 364 tons over 25 days. At present, Uralneft has 36 wells that are being operated, drilled or are in the process of being built."

The ambitious program for the development of the Chusovaya oil region required the creation of a special construction organization. On January 27, 1930, the All-Union Oil and Gas Industry Association issued Decree 18, in which it proposed that the Neftestroy Trust "urgently set up a separate office in Perm called *Uralneftegazstroy* ['Ural Oil and Gas Industry Construction and Erection Trust']." A. Gollender, a former deputy head of *Azneftestroy*, was appointed director of the new company.

Senior Soviet Party leadership attached particular importance to Perm oil at the time owing to the realization of rather ambitious plans in the Urals region as part of the USSR's industrialization. On February 19, 1930, the *VSNKh* confirmed as much when it issued Decree 868 "On the Renaming of Uralneft's Verkhnechusovskiye Gorodki Oil Fields as the Comrade Stalin Oil Fields," a reflection of how the oil industry's role was perceived in the industrialization process. As part of plans to fortify the infrastructure and logistics of the exploration being carried out in the Urals, in May 1930 Azerbaijan sent 104 rail cars to the region carrying equipment and instruments (including 17 drilling rigs and a power station).

Even though record milestones had been prescribed for the oil industry, the bar was set even higher by a Central Committee report presented by Stalin at the 16th Congress of the All-Union Communist Party on June 26, 1930. In that report, Stalin noted: "Under the Five-Year Plan, the oil industry was to produce 977 million rubles worth of products by 1932–33. But, in 1929–30, it is already producing 809 million rubles in products, that is, 83% of the amount projected in the Five-Year Plan for 1932–33. That means we are fulfilling the Five-Year Plan for the oil industry in some two-and-a-half years."[43]

Expressing his support for the Party line at the Congress, Valerian Kuybyshev (1888–1935), the chairman of the *VSNKh* Presidium, stated: "No mission is more important for the geologic agencies than to firmly establish our ore reserves and fuel resources which can be used to further develop metallurgy." A resolution passed by the 16th Congress on July 12 states: "The country's industrialization can no longer be based solely on one southern metallurgical foundation. A vital condition for the country's rapid industrialization is the creation of a second core coal and metallurgical center for the USSR in the East using the coal and ore fields of the Urals and Siberia."

Following a Party forum in Perm in July 1930, a conference was held at the Uralneft office that included academicians Ivan Gubkin and Aleksandr Arkhangelsky, as well as Ural Regional Executive Committee Deputy Director V. Andronnikov, Uralneft Director K. Rumyantsev, and other prominent workers. The conference resulted in the creation of a broad program to perform a geological survey of the oil-bearing capacity of the Kama Valley.

The arrival of 725 skilled specialists from Azneft and Grozneft in the Ural region in October 1930 provided a new impetus for further oilfield exploration and development. In December 1930, a larger trust called Vostokneft was established on the core of the Uralneft trust to search for petroleum in the Kama Valley, Bashkortostan, Syzran, the Trans-Baikal region, and other eastern regions of the country.

The first All-Union Congress of Geologists and Petroleum Experts was held in Moscow in January 1931. The Congress discussed in detail the geologic structure of the western range of the Urals Mountains and the oil fields and drew up a new, broader plan for exploration near Verkhnechusovskiye Gorodki. The plan was approved by Soyuzneft executive committee resolutions of January 25 and February 5, which set forth plans for exploration and production wells around Verkhnechusovskiye Gorodki.

At the October 27, 1931 meeting of the oil branch of the *VSNKh* Main Administration for Fuel, Vostokneft presented a program for the following year that noted a need to complete exploration in "the following Urals regions—Verkhnechusovskiye Gorodki, Krasnousolye, and Yurezan."

Implementation of such a large-scale program, however, ran into serious obstacles owing to a lack of financing and a low level of logistics support. Ural Region officials were becoming more and more pessimistic because no new free-flowing wells were being discovered and they had been unable to report new "victories of labor" to Moscow on a regular basis. This also caused concern among local Party officials. On June 4, 1932, the secretary of the Verkhnechusovskiye Gorodki District Committee sent a memo to Ivan Kabakov, the first secretary of the Ural regional committee of the All-Union Communist Party, describing the current situation at the Verkhnechusovskiye Gorodki oil field in detail: "From the time that oil was discovered in 1929 until today, more than 50 wells have been drilled, amounting to 24,771.06 linear meters [81,270 linear feet]. Of that number, five wells were found to contain commercial quantities of oil, with flow rates of up to 1,100 tons per month, and most of the drilled wells showed signs of oil-bearing capacity.... I believe, Comrade Kabakov, that after spending tens of millions of rubles on exploration and not yet obtaining a conclusive result concerning Ural oil, it would be highly premature to leave Verkhnechusovskiye Gorodki since exploration is far from finished and considerably fewer funds are needed now than the previous millions. As much as individual employees of the company have tried to prove otherwise, the fact remains that Wells 1, 1a, and 48 have been producing oil for three years—oil that is extremely rich in terms of its chemical properties and of commercial significance."[44]

The geologic exploration carried out over the following two years did not produce any major results, but the Kama Valley oil business was aided by a lucky break. On June 16, 1934, while drilling an artesian well at the construction site of the Krasnokamsk Pulp and Paper Plant, drilling specialist Ivan Pichugin encountered water with a strong hydrogen sulfide odor and a thick oily layer at a depth of 525 feet. M. Eliashberg, the former head of the paper plant, recalled: "A well was being drilled near the building to provide the acid workshop with cold artesian water. I was extremely concerned that water had yet to surface despite the considerable depth of the well. Finally, when the well was at a depth of 180 meters [591 feet], drilling specialist Ivan Mikhaylovich Pichugin joyfully shouted 'water!' Water had indeed surfaced, but it smelled strongly of hydrogen sulfide. We could not even think of using it for production. The drill specialist and I dejectedly poured the water into a bottle and a film formed on the surface at that moment.... It became clear: this was oil! This occurred on June 16, 1934."[45]

The People's Commissariat for Heavy Industry noted in a report: "By early 1935, the Sverdlovsk region and the western slope of the Urals had been enriched with another oil field, at Krasnokamsk. By late February 1935, after six months of exploration, a field was discovered with 8.5 square miles of oil-bearing deposits and indisputable total oil reserves of 66–88 million tons. Field research over the next three to four months should determine the best method for organizing the industrial production of Krasnokamsk oil."[46]

Several more new discoveries later took place on Perm lands, along with many remarkable events that are now considered milestones in the storied annals of the Russian oil industry.

In the Squeeze of the Early Five-Year Plans

In December 1927, at the 15th Congress of the AUCP(b), Soviet political leadership decided to transition the country to "five-year plans" of economic development. The First Five-Year Plan (1928–1932) called on group "A" enterprises (i.e., heavy industry) to accelerate development, and the strategic goal of the country became industrialization. In the USSR the reforms of the NEP were successively rolled back, and the Soviet leadership transitioned to total control over the economy, continuing to accelerate the formation of an administrative command system dominated by directive and noneconomic methods.

In his work, "Particularities of the Development of the Oil Industry in the USSR during the Years of the First Five-Year Plans (1928–1940)," in the anthology *Soviet Union's Oil* [*Neft strany Sovetov*], Professor Aleksandr Igolkin, Doctor of Historical Sciences, emphasized that the deep contradiction present in the Soviet Union, associated with the complex foreign and domestic processes of the 1930s in which dictatorial and bureaucratic aspects of the command-administrative system predominated, could not help but leave its mark on the development of the Soviet oil industry.

Fiscal 1929–30 saw some advancement in the USSR's oil industry as compared to 1928–29, but the rate of development could not keep pace with the demands of the time. For example, in 1929–30, domestic consumption of light petroleum products reached the level planned for the last year of the Five-Year Plan. This called for a radical reexamination of the Five-Year Plan for the oil industry.

In a resolution of the AUCP(b) Central Committee dated November 15, 1930, Soviet leaders outlined the future development of the oil industry: "Based on the size of the national economy's demand for petroleum products and the prospects for development of exports, the CC proposes: 1. The *VSNKh* shall raise the production of oil in 1933 to 49–50 million tons, with no less than 44–45 million tons coming from old and new fields of the Transcaucasus and North Caucasus.... The *VSNKh* must devote special attention to exploration and prospecting for oil in the eastern part of the USSR (the Urals, Emba, Sakhalin, the Volga region, etc.)."

At the end of 1930, Gleb Krzhizhanovsky (1872-1959), the head of the State Planning Committee [*Gosplan*], who was developing a "constructive" Party approach and emphasizing the special significance of the Soviet oil industry on the world market, announced at a meeting of his agency: "The *VSNKh* is not carrying the banner of power generation the way it should. A change of direction, a decisive break with the past, is needed in 1931. Such a position must be defended from this perspective: we need to be extremely thrifty both with money and with our proposals, etc., with the exception of this front.... In this one area, special conditions need to be created for a break with the past.... The socialist shark is supposed to swallow the entire world, but without fuel or energy nothing will be accomplished."[47]

According to Party instructions, the *Neftesindikat* organization was reformed, and in January 1930 all oil production organizations in the country were included in the All-Union Association Soyuzneft.

The Baku–Batumi trunk oil pipeline went into operation in late April 1930, carrying Caspian oil. Less than two years later, the country successfully realized, using its domestic potential, a large-scale pipeline project providing large-scale deliveries of Soviet oil onto the world market. However, as Azneft Director Mikhail Barinov had stated earlier in his letter addressed to *Glavgortop*, the new pipeline had one other important purpose: "The intended purpose of moving oil from Baku to Batumi is to bring Baku oil close to the export port of Batumi, where this oil will be refined into petroleum products, whose quantity and quality will be determined mainly by the requirements of the foreign market." As of the end of 1931, the operational trunk oil pipeline extended over 1,980 miles.

The accelerated development of USSR industry, including the oil industry, was in full swing. Colossal resources (money, materiel, and manpower) went to achieving set goals. During the years of the First Five-Year Plan, the sum invested in the oil business—more than 1.5 billion rubles—was significant for the time.

On April 1, 1931, the directors of the Azneft Association sent a triumphant report to the AUCP(b) Central Committee stating that they had fulfilled the First Five-Year Plan in 2.5 years "by technical renovation of the industry, increased labor productivity, development of new fields, increased drilling, and heroic labor on the part of the oil workers." Production figures confirmed this: Whereas 1928 oil production on the Absheron Peninsula was 8.38 million tons, in 1931 it was 12.3 million tons. This gave top Soviet leaders an exaggerated idea of the ability of Soviet industry to reach any heights and overcome all obstacles, without having the necessary resources or reserves to do so. Indeed, the achievements and successes hid a great deal that did not reflect the true state of affairs.

In assessing the rates of Soviet industrialization and its achievements, the American historian Professor Hiroaki Kuromiya of Indiana

University noted the following in his work *Stalin's Industrial Revolution: Politics and Workers, 1928–1932*: "Soviet industrialization gave birth to superhuman efforts that were heroic, romantic, and enthusiastic."

In 1931, the Grozny oil industry's share of the USSR's total production reached 36.1% of its crude oil and 73.0% of its gasoline (the leading product). For its high achievements, the Presidium of the Central Executive Committee of the USSR awarded the Order of Lenin to Grozneft.

In response to rapidly growing demand for petroleum products on the foreign and domestic markets, central Soviet agencies repeatedly amended Five-Year Plan production goals almost every year. Such plan reviews adversely affected the operations of petroleum enterprises, especially given the severe limits on capital construction and the insufficient availability of materials and equipment in the oil industry. Achievement of success and avoidance of the negative consequences of such chaos required a series of emergency measures by economic, Party, and social organizations.

One of a series of organizational restructurings of the administrative system of the national economy created the USSR People's Commissariat for Heavy Industry on July 6, 1932. It was headed by Sergo Orjonikidze, and its structure included the Main Administration of the Oil Industry.

The next plan established by the new agency started with a production volume of 46 million tons of oil for 1932–1933 instead of the 24 million tons that had been adopted earlier. In accordance with the adjusted development program for 1932–1933, oil production in the USSR had to be substantially increased.

But practically speaking, it was impossible to achieve a further sharp increase in oil production volumes on the Absheron Peninsula and in the North Caucasus. Many fields showed a natural decline in oil production volumes, and this applied in particular to the Surakhany petroleum area, which had been producing two-fifths (38.6%) of Azneft's total production.

At the start of the 1930s, it should be noted that the Soviet oil industry was operating in the midst of a general world economic crisis and an oil crisis in particular. World oil production in the first half of 1931 had fallen by 8.6%. During the same period, oil production in the USSR increased by a quarter (24.2%) over the corresponding period in 1930. Thus, at the start of 1931, the USSR was the world's third largest oil producer, behind only the US and Venezuela.

At the height of the world economic crisis, the physical volume of the USSR's petroleum products exports steadily began to grow, but at the same time, its earnings from oil exports began to decline. Whereas crude oil and petroleum products exports were 4.25 million tons in 1929, earning the nation 138 million rubles, these figures were 5.19 million tons and

157 million rubles, respectively, in 1930, and 5.7 million tons and 116 million rubles in 1931.

The increase in the volume of Soviet oil exports over the years of the Great Depression caused great concern on the part of the leading oil companies of the West, which had combined into a world oil cartel. In May 1932, an oil conference opened in New York, with Soviet participation, whose basic question had to do with the export of Soviet oil. English and American oil companies proposed that the USSR refrain from acting independently on world markets and deliver 5.5 million tons of oil to them every year for 10 years at a fixed price. The proposal by the Western partners to eliminate Soviet oil sales organizations overseas was rejected by the Soviet Union. Moreover, the Soviets immediately responded with excessive counterdemands. Joseph Stalin, general secretary of the AUCP(b) Central Committee, wrote about this to the prominent Party functionary Lazar Kaganovich, a member of the AUCP(b) Central Committee Politburo: "The oil group is economically stronger than we are. It can always interfere with our oil exports; it can drive down prices and cause us great losses, even if we assume that we will have more and more worthless oil for export. But the point is that we will not have more worthless oil, and our fund of export oil will decrease because of the colossal and constantly growing demand for petroleum products by ships and railroads, the freight and automobile industry, and the tractor and aviation industry.... [Commissar of Foreign Trade] Rozengolts's directive does not take into account the strength and relative importance of oil workers in the matter of interventions. It does not take into account the fact that it is beneficial to us to more or less politically neutralize the Anglo-American oil group if we really want to protect the peace for at least the next two to three years."

Intense negotiations continued in New York for several weeks, but given the unreasonable nature of the proposals and the impossibility of reaching a mutually acceptable decision with the Western partners, the Soviet representatives never achieved the necessary agreement.

Table 9. USSR Oil Production by Year, in millions of tons

Year	Oil Production
1927	11.33
1928	12.82
1929	15.08
1930	20.34
1931	24.68
1932	23.6

Source: *Economy of the USSR [Narodnoye khozyaystvo SSSR]*. Moscow, 1959, pp. 204–208.

Despite the raging world economic crisis, the Soviet government targeted a sharp increase in the volume of oil exports as it prepared the goals of the Second Five-Year Plan. For example, in December 1931, *Gosplan* planned for USSR oil exports to climb to 11.5 million tons by 1937; among export products, first place was to be occupied by gasoline and naphtha with 4.68 million tons; then residual oil with 2.48 million tons; kerosene with 1.3 million tons; gas oil with 1.1 million tons; and lubricants with 579,000 tons. According to this version of the plan, crude oil was to account for less than 6% of oil exports, or 661,000 tons.

At first, everything went according to plan, and 6.7 million tons of Soviet crude oil and petroleum products were delivered in 1932, earning 107 million rubles. However, USSR oil export volumes significantly declined at the beginning of the Second Five-Year Plan, and in 1933 only 5.39 million tons of crude oil and petroleum products were delivered to foreign countries, bringing in only 76 million rubles. This was largely due to the fact that the growth in oil production in the industry had sharply slowed, while the domestic demand for petroleum products had continued to grow. Gasoline had become necessary for transportation using automobiles, the numbers of which had increased dramatically. For example, automobile production in the USSR grew from 671 units in 1927–1928 to more than 2,000 units in 1932. The situation with tractor production was similar: in comparison with 1926–1927, the consumption of fuel by tractors in the Soviet Union increased by a factor of 18.7 during the Five-Year Plan. And more and more petroleum products were being demanded by the Soviet armed forces—the army, air force, and navy.

The new Five-Year Plan, begun in 1933, placed special emphasis in the oil industry on accelerating the development and exploitation of new oil fields.

In the middle of the 1930s, several developments were introduced in Grozny that did not have any precedent in drilling practice in the USSR or elsewhere in the world. In 1932, metal derricks began to be used in the Grozny region. In 1934, the first experiments were carried out with directional drilling, and work began using apparatus for rotary drilling with the help of casing pipes. In 1935, scientist A. N. Shangin studied the mechanism of borehole deviation. An attempt at turbodrilling was made at that time by lowering a turbodrill on a cable. The height of drilling derricks increased from 112 to 135 feet, which made it possible to work with 82-foot drill stands.

The intensive search for new fields in the Bashkir Autonomous Soviet Socialist Republic (ASSR) continued. On May 16, 1932, a well near the village of Ishimbayevo on the territory of the Bashkir ASSR became a gusher that brought around 55 tons of oil to the surface within four hours. After the discovery of this field, the academician Ivan Gubkin wrote: "There could be hundreds of millions of tons of petroleum reserves in Bashkiria. And what if Ural petroleum is not limited to Bashkiria? If the Verkhnechusovskiye Gorodki fields compelled prospecting along the Urals, then the Ishimbayevo field will compel prospecting work to be performed broadly along the entire western approaches to the Urals and the entire Volga region."

Ishimbayevo District soon had 10 geologic and six geophysical groups working within it. At the suggestion of geologists K. Chepikov, N. Gerasimov, and Ye. Tukhvinskaya, a detailed study of the geologic structure of the western regions of Bashkiria was begun. In the fall of 1934, craelius core drilling was begun there, and in 1935 strong oil shows were detected in Kungurian and Artinskian deposits.

A significant contribution to the development of the industry during the Second Five-Year Plan was also made by the engineering and technical community. In August 1933, Baku hosted the First Congress of the All-Union Scientific Engineering and Technical Society of Oil Workers [*VNITON*], and the 202 delegates that participated represented production enterprises, scientific organizations, and the governing bodies of the Soviet oil industry. The first man elected chairman of *VNITON* was academician Ivan Gubkin, a scientific authority whose popularity among oil industry workers did much to involve many major oil specialists actively in the work. The same *VNITON* Congress defined the basic directions of its activity, involving broad social assistance to the industry in solving scientific problems on the one hand and, on the other, discussing engineering production questions and developing solutions to them, increasing qualifications, and publishing reference works. During the early Five-Year Plans, the Society conducted a series of important conferences, meetings, debates, competitions, and other measures to promote stable development of the Soviet oil industry, and actively pursued publishing and professional development through courses, lectures, and speeches intended to raise the production qualifications of oil specialists.

Besides exploring for petroleum in the Volga region, specialists turned their attention to other territories of the country whose geology had not yet been investigated. On December 5, 1934, Moscow hosted the first conference of geologists devoted to the oil prospects of Western Siberia. The conference was chaired by academician Gubkin, and featured a detailed talk by engineering geologist Viktor Vasilyev about oil shows on the Bolshoy Yugan and Belaya Rivers. The decision of the specialists was unanimous: large-scale work to explore for petroleum had to begin immediately in this region.

However, despite the progress of the USSR oil industry, there were substantial shortcomings in its development. Principal among these were a low rate of making headway and slow mechanical drilling speed, an insufficient use of roller cutter and multiblade drill bits, complexity of oil-bearing deposits (petroleum lying in strata up to 6,500 feet deep that were oriented perpendicular to the Earth's surface), and a high accident rate (due principally to drill pipe defect rates of up to 45%).

Although crude oil production grew by 20%, kerosene production by 38%, and gasoline and naphtha production by 7% from 1933 to 1935, the rates of gasoline and naphtha production were rather low, and did not correspond to the level of development of aviation and the fleet of motor vehicles and tractors. To address these needs, the USSR resumed mutually beneficial economic relations with the US in the oil industry, and on June 4, 1935, an agreement was concluded between the American company ALCO and the Amtorg Soviet-American Joint-Stock Company to supply the Soviet Union with a refinery capable of processing 12,000 barrels of Sterlitamak oil per day and refining it into high-octane gasoline, motor fuel, boiler fuel, residual asphalt, and gas.

The obvious shortcomings in the development of the oil industry in those years were noted by *Pravda*, the central Soviet newspaper. The lead editorial of this Party publication for October 14, 1936 stated: "Are not 2,000 accidents in nine months the result of incompetent placement of personnel and the lack of personal responsibility, technical leadership, and elementary order at the enterprises?!"

Nevertheless, progress was visible in 1936: the oil industry produced around 32 million tons of oil and gas, drilled more than 6.8 million feet of hole, and started more than 1,600 new wells. In 1936, both oil production trusts in the Volga-Urals region, Bashneft and Embaneft, produced around 1.7 million tons of crude (compared with 750,000 tons in 1935).

In 1936, work began on two new Central Asian fields, Khaydag and Uchkizyl, which produced around 330,000 tons of oil in that year. In Turkmenistan, Nebit-Dag produced around 385,000 tons of oil and preparations were being made to open up two new fields.

The first to fulfill the plan for all years was the Sakhalinneft Trust, where preparations were being made to develop the new Ekhabi field. Meanwhile, commercial oil was being produced at Chongelek field in the Crimea, while the new oil areas of Shongar and Kizyl-Tene in the western Absheron Peninsula and Pirgasat in the Amet District yielded commercial oil in the Azerbaijan Soviet Socialist Republic.

In 1936, oil production began in Dagestan. Regions such as Achi-Su, Izberbash, and Kayakent were to produce more than 1.1 million tons of oil in 1937. New sites also appeared at the Mayneft Association in the Kuban region: the "Asphalt Mountain," Kuisskoye, and Kura-Tsetse fields. Such a rapid rate of development of a large number of fields was primarily related to accelerated rates of exploration and an increase in drilling speed.

In the mid 1930s, the 440-mile Caspian-Orsk oil pipeline was placed in service, carrying Emba oil to the Orsk Refinery. In 1936, the 118-mile Makhachkala-Grozny oil pipeline was placed in service.

On December 20, 1936, the state committee formally accepted the commissioning of all the equipment at the Ishimbayevo Refinery, which had an annual capacity of 550,000 tons of oil. At the end of that same year the Ufa Cracking Refinery, which had a design capacity of 1.1 million tons of crude, was prepared for start-up. The refinery was expected to refine 80% of Bashkir oil. In January 1937, the first gasoline production system was put into operation at this refinery, and the first gasoline was produced.

On the whole, however, the USSR oil industry did not fulfill plan figures. Fulfillment was 68.2% for drilling; 63.6% for drilling speed; 88.3% for oil production; 84.15% for gas production; and 92.6% for refining. Thus, within the system of the USSR People's Commissariat for Heavy Industry, which ended 1936 with a "triumphant report about fulfillment of the Five-Year Plan in four years," the oil industry ended up on the list of industries that had fallen behind.

People's Commissar for Heavy Industry Sergo Orjonikidze issued an order on September 5, 1936, noting that the oil industry had fallen seriously behind, asking for decisive steps to overcome deficiencies, and defining basic production goals for 1937. The People's Commissariat planned to develop 14 new fields in 1937 and continue development in the eastern part of the country. The order of the people's commissar spoke of a struggle to increase the quality of all work in the oil industry.

In 1937, Baku hosted the All-Union Conference of Oil Workers, which examined questions of improving equipment and technology of well drilling, oil production, transportation and storage, and also the introduction of new forms of labor organization.

By way of background, it should be noted that in that period the USSR oil industry had lost its export orientation, and crude oil and petroleum products export volumes had begun to decline rather quickly. By 1935, the proportion of exported gasoline production had decreased from 91.5% in 1929 to 21.4%, and kerosene exports decreased from 34% in 1929 to 8.5%.

This trend persisted into the Third Five-Year Plan. For example, although Soviet petroleum products and crude oil exports amounted to 2,127,000 tons in 1937, such exports dropped to 1,531,000 tons in 1938, and to only 791,000 tons in 1939.

Another factor that had a substantial negative effect on the oil industry of the 1930s was the implementation of mass political repression in the USSR. This dealt a substantial blow to the industry's engineers and technicians, along with the most varied strata of the general population.

At the beginning of the First Five-Year Plan, the *OGPU* held the so-called "Shakhty Trial," a show trial that affected many engineers not only in the coal industry, but also in other industries of the USSR. On March 2, 1928, Genrikh Yagoda (1891–1938), deputy chairman of the *OGPU*, reported to Joseph Stalin that "this counterrevolutionary organization directs sabotage not only in our coal industry, but also in other branches of our economy."

The Shakhty Trial gave rise to subsequent trials in other industrial sectors. Speaking at the November Plenum of the AUCP(b) Central Committee, Party functionary Lazar Kaganovich said that after the Shakhty Trial, cases of "wrecking" were undertaken at a series of industrial enterprises, including Azneft, Grozneft, and *Neftesindikat*, which were set aside into separate legal proceedings. Soon, the *OGPU* made arrests, and after a short investigation, cases concerning a "counterrevolutionary, wrecking, and spying organization in the oil industry of the USSR" were sent to the "most humane proletarian court." As a result of the first trials, many prominent engineering and technical specialists were convicted and sentenced to various terms of imprisonment, including: Professor Ivan Strizhov, oil industry director of the *VSNKh*; Nikolay Tikhonovich, deputy director of the Geologic Committee; Nikolay Lednëv, senior geologist of the Geologic Committee; Pëtr Polevoy, an authoritative petroleum geologist; Doctor of Mineral Geology Ilya Ginzburg; Aleksey Anosov, regional geologist of Grozneft; Grigory Surabekov, deputy director of the Azneft refineries; Vladimir Delov, an experienced drilling engineer of Azneft, and many others. The choice of where their "proletarian punishment" sentence was to be served was quickly determined, and was strongly influenced by the aforementioned resolution of the *VSNKh* Presidium, "On the Development of a Fuel Base in the Northern Territory" of April 20, 1931. Exploration and development of the northern hydrocarbon fields required, first and foremost, qualified specialists, such as geologists and mining engineers, mechanical engineers, and production engineers; in fact, the very people forming the basic contingent convicted in the "oil" trials. Several years later, the oil industry was hit again by a new and even more severe wave of repression. Many leading industry workers were arrested, convicted, and shot, including: Aleksandr Serebrovsky, who had led Azneft at its most difficult restorative period; Mikhail Barinov, head of Glavneft; Sergey Ganshin, director of the Soyuzneft Association; Noy London, deputy head of Glavneft; Semën Slutsky, head of Azneftekombinat, and many others.

Mass repression among engineering and technical workers inflicted serious damage on the USSR oil industry as a whole, and was the tragic result of deep contradictions in social, economic, and political processes that were occurring under the very difficult conditions of the authoritarian and despotic regime of Joseph Stalin and his closest associates.

Despite the losses suffered by the oil industry during this period, it was still expected to fulfill the Five-Year Plan. One of the basic goals of domestic refining in the Third Five-Year Plan (1938–1942) was to accelerate the production of gasoline. "The country demands more and better gasoline" was the basic slogan of Soviet refinery workers in 1938. Moreover, the Third Five-Year Plan assigned the oil industry the following goals: 1) accelerated mechanization of all processes of exploratory drilling; 2) sharp expansion of the role of motor vehicle transportation in geologic exploration; 3) increased volume of shallow mechanical drilling and craelius core drilling; and 4) use of the American practice of reusing oil wells. To address this goal, Amtorg signed a contract in 1938 with the American company Universal Oil Products to construct a new aviation fuel refinery in the Bashkir ASSR.

On October 12, 1939, the USSR CPC issued a resolution dividing the People's Commissariat for the Fuel Industry into two parts: oil and coal. AUCP(b) Politburo member Lazar Kaganovich was appointed People's Commissar for the USSR Oil Industry, and he spent nine months in the post. On July 3, 1940, the Presidium of the Supreme Soviet of the Soviet Union issued an edict appointing engineer Ivan Sedin (1906–1972) in place of Kaganovich.

In the period from the beginning of 1938 through the end of 1940, the number of tank farms in the USSR increased from 1,520 to 1,686. The largest among them were located in Makhachkala, Astrakhan, Saratov, Gorky, and Yaroslavl. The basic type of tank was the standard riveted airtight tank operating at a positive pressure of 0.79 inches of water column. Experimental vertical welded metal tanks of small capacity (under 175,000 cubic feet) were constructed at the same time.

Table 10. USSR Oil Production by Year, in millions of tons

Year	Oil Production
1933	23.5
1934	26.8
1935	28.9
1936	30.2
1937	31.4
1938	31.3
1939	33.4
1940	34.3

Source: *Economy of the USSR [Narodnoye khozyaystvo SSSR]*. Moscow, 1959, p. 205.

The end of the 1930s saw the finalization and approval of the tank farm as a clearly defined idea: a sales enterprise that would receive, store, and dispense various grades of petroleum products, and do so on a profitable basis. Thus, new organizational branches of the industry—oil transportation, storage, and supply—were formed.

In 1938, a new subdivision was created within the Soyuzneft All-

Union Association: Glavneftesbyt ["Main Crude Oil and Petroleum Products Sales and Transportation Administration"]. It was assumed that organizing three independent main administrations—Glavneftedobycha ["Main Oil Production Administration"], Glavneftepererabotka ["Main Refining Administration"], and Glavneftesbyt—for oil production, refining, and sales, respectively, would provide their administrations with the necessary conditions for real operational management.

Glavneftedobycha faced a gradual transition from flowing well operation to mechanized production, taking into account that given 88.3% fulfillment of the oil production plan, flowing wells supplied only 27.4%. As of January 1, 1938, 35% of wells in the USSR were idle. One reason for idle wells was that well operation was assessed on the basis of figures calculated for a group or field, without regard for the peculiarities of each individual well.

Along with stimulating oil fields in old regions, the leadership of the industry did not abandon its intention to organize geologic prospecting and exploratory work in Siberia. On September 10, 1939, Vasily Senyukov, head of Glavgeologiya ["Main Geologic Exploration Administration"], sent the people's commissar for the fuel industry a special memorandum "On Organizing a Large Geophysical Expedition to Western Siberia in 1939–1940," that emphasized: "In compliance with your instructions to accelerate oil prospecting in Siberia, it is proposed that preparations be made in 1940 to locate a series of deep wells within the Western Siberian Plain. To single out regions and points for deep exploratory drilling, it is proposed that a large geophysical expedition be organized in the winter of 1939–1940 within the system of the Main Geologic Exploration Administration of the People's Commissariat for Fuel.... It is proposed that the expedition be composed of nine pendulum crews (770 points), three gravimeter crews (1,300 points), one seismic crew, two electrical prospecting crews, 10 magnetic crews, two variometric crews, and four geodetic crews.... The expedition should have 32 crews with a staff of 300." The Glavgeologiya leadership's proposal was accepted, and on November 22, 1939 the USSR people's commissar for the oil industry signed an order "On Expanding Oil Prospecting in Siberia." The expedition was given the basic goal of carrying out geologic studies over an area of 190,000 square miles and preparing regions for deep rotary drilling for oil by the fall of 1940. The experienced geologist A. Shayderov was named leader of the expedition. However, this very complex mission was not adequately supplied with financial, human, or equipment resources, and the preparatory period dragged on for months, pushing out the deadlines for beginning work by almost a year.

According to 1940 data from the newspaper *Neftyanoye khozyaystvo* ["The Oil Industry"], the results of the first years of the Third Five-Year Plan were as follows: "Over the last two to three years, the oil industry's progress has slowed somewhat, and current rates of development, production, and refining are completely inadequate; in any event they do not correspond to the rich reserves present in oil production and refining. This slowing in the development of the oil industry has created a gap between the production of and demand for these products in the USSR economy. The rates of production adopted by the people's commissar for the oil industry in the first quarter of 1940 are clearly insufficient, so much so that oil workers must not only fulfill, but exceed the plan for 1940."

A significant reason for the industry slowdown was that, over the past three years, prospecting drilling decreased to a level that threatened further operational drilling. For example, whereas 437,000 feet of prospecting drilling was done and 153 wells were completed in 1936, the 1937 figures were, respectively, 207,677 feet and 50 wells; in 1938, they were 157,480 feet and 40 wells; and in 1939, they had fallen to 134,186 feet and 21 wells. A direct consequence of this was a sharp drop in oil production. In 1939, production from new wells significantly decreased in comparison with 1936, and did not make up for the decline in old wells. In 1940, 34.3 million tons of oil were produced, but the sale of all petroleum products in the USSR amounted to 27.6 million tons. The Plan non-fulfillment was thus 5.6 million tons of crude.

By 1940, Soviet oil exports had fallen 88.2% in comparison with 1932, to 522,000 tons of petroleum products and 269,000 tons of crude oil. Over the same years, kerosene exports fell by 93.5%, and gasoline exports by 94.2%.

In 1940, the Malgobek–Grozny oil pipeline (9.8 inches in diameter, 62 miles long) and Gora–Gorskaya oil pipeline (7.9 inches in diameter, 35 miles long) were built. In total, 355 miles of trunk oil and petroleum products pipelines were built and placed in service during the Third Five-Year Plan (1938–1941). The main goal of the economic and design studies carried out at that time to justify the choice of a pipeline network route was to improve the supply of crude oil and petroleum products to the eastern regions of the country.

By 1941, craelius core drilling had prepared more than 100 promising structures and prospecting drilling had discovered 14 oil fields, and so intensified and accelerated prospecting for new oil areas and increased drilling volume were set as the basic goal for the year. In terms of geologic petroleum reserves, the USSR was first in the world (5.2 billion tons), but in terms of production, the USSR lagged quite substantially behind the US (201.6 million tons in 1940).

In 1941, a large-scale program of economic construction and further enhancement of the country's defensive capability was proposed in connection with the war in Europe, which had been going on for more than a year.

One of the pre-war characteristics of the USSR's oil industry was its territorial arrangement. By the beginning of 1941, oil production and refining were concentrated in the southern regions of the USSR, on the Absheron Peninsula and in the North Caucasus, while the areas of the "Second Baku"—the Volga-Urals region—were producing around 2.2 million tons, which represented only 6% of total Soviet production.

The geographic distribution of the oil production and refining industry that emerged, with an inordinate concentration of production and large reserves of raw hydrocarbons in the south of the country, coupled with an underdeveloped pipeline and transportation infrastructure, created great difficulties in the delivery of oil from production points to regions where it was consumed, and proved to be one of the key factors behind the extraordinary complications faced by the Soviet Union in the organization of oil supply and production.

The Harsh Years of the Great Patriotic War

Early on the morning of June 22, 1941, German armed forces crossed the national border of the USSR without a declaration of war, and thus began World War II for the Russian people.[48]

What followed was the fiercest and bloodiest war the country has ever experienced. It forced its way into every home, every family, and into the heart of every person. It lasted 1,418 days, from June 22, 1941 through May 9, 1945. More than 27 million citizens of the Soviet Union gave up their lives for their country.

Adolf Hitler's inhuman plans for conquest to achieve world domination were determined to a great extent by energy resources, and the oil factor had a substantial influence on the nature and course of the war. To a certain extent, the limited nature of fuel and energy reserves predetermined the strategy and tactics of Nazi Germany's actions in theaters of military operations. As one European country after another fell to the Nazi regime, the *Führer*'s first order of business was to examine the conquered countries' oil reserves.

In preparing for war, the Nazi leaders had bet on producing synthetic gasoline. In the 1930s, Adolf Hitler issued several orders to expedite the construction of refineries to produce synthetic gasoline from coal. On the eve of military actions in Europe, Germany organized mass production of "synthetic" gasoline on the basis of the Fischer-Tropsch hydrogenation process, using hard coal and brown coal as raw material. With government support, the companies Ruhrchemie AG and Wirtschaftsgruppe Kraftindustrie built a wide network of hydrogenation plants, and from 1934 through 1938 the production of liquid motor fuel increased almost eightfold, reaching 1.7 million tons of synthetic gasoline. Although the production of such fuel was expensive, the *Führer* noted: "The German fuel industry must now develop with maximum speed... and cost is no object in obtaining raw materials."[49] German production of synthetic fuel continued to develop at a very rapid pace. At the time of the attack on Poland in September 1939, Germany was operating 14 hydrogenation enterprises, and by 1941 the number had risen to 22, with a total production capacity amounting to 6.7 million tons of synthetic fuel.

By June 1941, Nazi Germany controlled 93 refineries with a total capacity of 29.2 million tons in the annexed and occupied territories (Austria, France, the Netherlands, Belgium, Poland, Czechoslovakia, Denmark, and Norway). *Wehrmacht* forces seized more than 8.8 million tons of petroleum products as they occupied Europe. In 1941, Germany itself produced 1.72 million tons of oil. Romania, a German ally, possessed a significant oil area in the Ploiesti region, and before the attack on the USSR, the Romanian regime of Marshal Antonescu was supplying 58% of oil delivered to the Reich.

It should be noted that in the initial period of World War II, limited volumes of Soviet oil (only around 725,000 tons) were delivered to Germany only after August 1939, when Germany and the USSR signed a nonaggression pact, and they continued until June 22, 1941, i.e., for less than two years. Therefore, they could not have had any significant influence on the course of military operations.

Oil played a significant role in Hitler's decision to attack the Soviet Union, and according to the testimony of Albert Speer, minister of armaments and war production, it was a prime motive. According to the *Führer*'s associates, he was always obsessed by the idea of seizing the oil in the Caucasus. This, he felt, would make his German Reich truly invincible.

But what determined Hitler's eastern military strategy? He understood that moving westward would unavoidably lead to a confrontation with the US, the most powerful military force in the western world, while he considered the Soviet Union to have a weak economy and military. Military intelligence reports available to German headquarters said that German troops would enter Russia "like a knife through butter." Hitler called the USSR "a giant on clay legs," which would crumble at the first blow. Operation Barbarossa was to be another exercise in blitzkrieg warfare, which had already brought success in the defeat of Poland, France, Norway, Yugoslavia, and Greece.

Hitler's "cannibalistic" economic calculation remained the same, i.e., the number of German victims from an attack on Russia would not exceed the number occupied in the production of synthetic fuel. The German command was counting on Russia being finished by winter of 1941: Moscow would be captured, and a border would be reached running from Arkhangelsk to Astrakhan. A program for occupying seized

Russian territories, the *Generalplan Ost* ["Master Plan East"] was developed at the same time as Operation Barbarossa. The resources of such territories, including petroleum, were to become property of the Reich. A special ministry, the *Reichsministerium für die besetzten Ostgebiete* ["Reich Ministry for the Occupied Eastern Territories"], was created to deal with the eastern territories. A number of regions would be colonized by Germans, while Russia itself was to be "thrown across the Urals." The local population would be a source of cheap labor. Some inhabitants would be physically eliminated, including any and all Jews, Gypsies, and the physically and mentally handicapped, wherever they might be, as well as the "commissars" and communists, Hitler's principal ideological enemies.

It should be noted that Germany's attack on June 22, 1941 took the Party political and military leadership of the Soviet Union, headed by Joseph Stalin, by surprise. The initial period of the war was especially tragic. In the first three months, during the course of bloody battles, the superior enemy forced the Red Army to retreat to the distant approaches of Moscow. Concentrated aerial bombing strikes destroyed airfields, oil storage facilities, and tank farms of the Special Western Military District. At the beginning of the war, the Red Army's Fuel Service had 247 stationary storage facilities and fuel bases with a total bulk capacity of 23 million cubic feet, and up to 2,000 rail cars for packaged products and goods. Ninety percent of all army storage facilities were distributed in military districts near the border. The People's Commissariat for Defense held 1.34 million tons of petroleum products in reserve. In the first six months, the People's Commissariat for Defense lost 176,000 tons of day-to-day fuel supplies and 330,000 tons of mobilization reserves. Only around 66,000 tons were evacuated.

Lacking fuel, most aircraft, tanks, and automobiles on the western borders of the USSR were destroyed. German tank wedges outflanked the Red Army on the territory of Belarus, inflicting crushing defeats. The lack of reliable communications between headquarters and units due to sudden strikes also played a role, as did the lack of fuel for military hardware.

Although the defeats were largely due to mistakes in Stalin's leadership, the entire blame, as was customary, was placed on the command of the Special Western Military District, headed by Army General Dmitry Pavlov (1897–1941). The accusations made against him included disintegration of the rear echelon's supply capability.

In those grave days, mass heroism on the part of privates and officers, who gave up their lives trying to do everything to protect their homeland under unbelievably difficult conditions, became a clear form of demonstrating patriotism. Soon, Red Army units were able to recover from the initial shock of Germany's unexpected attack, and near Yelnya they made their first successful counterattack.

At the beginning of the war, the loss of important economic regions of the country had a serious effect on the Soviet economy. As a result of the enemy occupation of a large piece of Soviet territory, the country lost an area that was home to 80 million people (41.4% of the entire population) before the war and produced 46% of all the country's industrial output, including 68% of its steel, 67.8% of its rolled products, 60% of its aluminum, and 62.5% of its mined coal. The damage caused to the oil industry was addressed in particular in the financial reports of the USSR People's Commissariat for the Oil Industry, which stated the expenses and losses for 1941 as 19,647,000 rubles, and those for 1942 as 55,645,000 rubles.

From the first days of hostilities, the country undertook measures to put the economy on a war footing. On June 24, 1941, the USSR CPC created the Evacuation Council. Key figures in this emergency government agency were the talented leaders Aleksey Kosygin (1904–1980) and Mikhail Pervukhin (1904–1978). Three days later, the USSR CPC and the AUCP(b) adopted a resolution, "On the Procedure for Removing and Distributing Human Work Forces and Valuable Property."

The State Committee for Defense went on to adopt resolutions "On Measures to Develop Oil Production and Refining in the Eastern Regions of the USSR and Turkmenistan" (July 30, 1941) and "On the Evacuation of Maykopneft and Grozneft to the Bashkir ASSR" (October 28, 1941).

In accordance with Soviet government decisions, around 1.5 million railroad cars carrying people and various cargo were sent into the eastern regions of the country from July through December 1941, and more than 1,360 major industrial enterprises were evacuated. By July 1941, the Odessa, Kherson, and Berdyansk cracking refineries had already been dismantled and relocated from Ukraine to the eastern regions of the country.

Massive Red Army conscription stripped the production labor force, and there was a catastrophic shortage of workers. Extreme measures were undertaken to provide personnel to defense-critical branches of production, including oil production and refining. Most workers were now teenagers and women, who were mobilized into production, industrial training schools, and trade schools. Mobilization measures were accompanied by increasingly frantic conditions at enterprises, especially where martial law or a state of siege had been imposed. In December 1941, an order was adopted holding blue-collar and white-collar workers of defense enterprises responsible for leaving work without authorization or arriving for work late. Everyone employed at such enterprises was considered to be mobilized on the labor front, and violators were considered "labor deserters" who could be tried under wartime laws.

Incidentally, the severe measures introduced by Soviet leaders at that time found support and understanding among the population, and it was a time of mass labor enthusiasm and heroism. For example, in August 1941, the Soviet Information Bureau reported that Soviet oil workers were steadily increasing the production of fuels and lubricants necessary for the front and rear. At industry enterprises there was a widespread patriotic movement of "200 percenters"—workers who fulfilled at least 200% of their quotas during their shifts. They gave their work all they had under the slogan: "Everything for the front! Everything for victory!"

Under the most difficult conditions of the initial wartime period in the USSR, the question of supplying sufficient volumes of fuel and lubricants became especially acute. Colonel General Vasily Nikitin, head of the USSR Armed Forces Fuel Service, estimated that in 1941 the Soviet oil industry was able to supply the People's Commissariat for Defense with only 26.6% of its war year requirements for aviation gasoline; 67.5% of its requirements for diesel fuel; and 11.1% of its requirements for aviation oil.

On July 15, 1941, the State Committee for Defense adopted a resolution, "On Increasing the Aviation Gasoline Production Plan for the Third Quarter of 1941," which confronted the USSR People's Commissariat for the Oil Industry with complex challenges to supply fuel to aviation units.

On July 30, 1941, the State Committee for Defense adopted a resolution, "On Measures to Develop Oil Production and Refining in the Eastern Regions of the USSR and Turkmenistan." This decree called for increasing the capacity of the oil fields and refineries and accelerating the construction of refineries at Ufa, Syzran, Saratov, Ishimbayevo, and elsewhere.

Answering the government's call, Soviet oil workers made colossal efforts in the first year of the war to increase oil production. At the fields of the Absheron Peninsula, 3 million feet of hole were drilled and 752 wells were put into production. In the first year of the war, the Baku region gave the country 25.9 million tons of oil and 91.8 million cubic feet of natural gas, which was the highest level of raw material production in the country's entire history of industrial oil production. The Grozny region also made its contribution to the common cause, producing 3.3 million tons. On the whole, the USSR produced 36 million tons of oil in 1941, thereby exceeding the level of the last prewar year.

In August 1941, the AUCP(b) Politburo approved a military and economic plan for defense of the country. For the fourth quarter of 1941, the USSR people's commissar for the oil industry set the amount of drilling in the regions of the "Second Baku," Kazakhstan, and Central Asia at 1.1 million feet, including 442,913 feet of exploratory drilling. For 1942, the amount of drilling planned was 5.8 million feet, including 2.1 million feet of exploratory drilling. Plans called for starting 1,550 new development wells, and accelerating the construction of a number of new refineries.

Having met fierce resistance on the central front, the German command began redeploying its reserves. Forces were insufficient, however, to mount a general attack on all fronts, as called for by Operation Barbarossa, and thus nowhere did they completely succeed in achieving their aggressive plans.

Meanwhile, combat operations revealed shortcomings in the Nazi blitzkrieg strategy, including an acute fuel problem. When traveling on Soviet roads (which were poor if they existed at all), German military vehicles consumed two to three times more fuel than planned. There was an immediate fuel shortage. Supplying attacking German troops, which had become separated from their rear support units, became substantially more difficult.

In the fall of 1941, a gigantic battle took place near Moscow. At its start, German units had reached the city limits. Yet here again, it became apparent that the German command had miscalculated, and that logistical supply of attacking troops was in jeopardy. Counting on rapid success, the Nazi military leaders had not prepared their forces to fight in fall and winter conditions. German equipment got stuck in the mud, and it literally had to be pulled out by hand. And when early frosts came, another problem became apparent: German tank and aircraft engines that ran on synthetic fuel did not easily start in the cold, and lubricant congealed. The closer the Germans came to Moscow, the fiercer was the resistance from Red Army units, who were receiving fuel and lubricant supplies without interruption from the rear echelon. In the end, the Germans retreated from Moscow.

At the beginning of 1942, Hitler's Reich had recovered somewhat from the defeat near Moscow, and the German command started to prepare a new Russian offensive. The operation, which was given the code name *Fall Blau* [Case Blue], had been developed with Hitler's direct involvement, and assumed a clearly pronounced nature as an "oil crusade." Hitler's Directive 41 of April 5, 1942 planned to strike a blow in the southern direction and seize the Caucasus and the Absheron Peninsula from the USSR, thereby winning a dominant strategic position and cutting Soviet lines of communication with allies in the anti-Hitler coalition. To accomplish this, Army Group A was formed, which was supposed to reach Baku and then, in coordination with friendly Turkey, to continue to the Middle East, into oil-rich Iran, Iraq, etc. A supportive strike was made by Army Group B, which was supposed to overcome the Volga line in the region of Stalingrad and cut off routes connecting the oil regions of the Caucasus with the center of the country.

The diary of General Franz Halder, chief of staff of the Army High Command [OKH], who wrote down Hitler's speech, contains the following words: "The time has come to look ahead. It has become possible to capture the Donets Basin and the Caucasus oil region. Operations in the Caucasus will require large forces, but any price should be paid for oil.

All the more so, seizing the Caucasus will allow the occupation of Iran and the straddling of the passes on the Iran-Iraq border."

The summer and fall of 1942 brought a succession of failures for the Red Army. Grozny became a front city. On August 10, 1942, the Nazis occupied Maykop; on August 22, Krasnodar; and on August 25, Mozdok as well.

In connection with the threat of attack by Nazi troops, on September 13, 1942 the State Committee for Defense adopted Resolution 2298, "On Dismantling the Grozny Refineries," which soon had a very strong effect on fuel deliveries to the army. Fierce battles broke out when Nazi troops began to mount an active attack from the region of Mozdok, on the approach to Grozny. On October 10, 1942, the city literally burst into flames from the bombs that had been dropped on it. Buildings and structures were destroyed, oil tanks burned, and around 100 wells were knocked out of service. Nevertheless, the enemy failed to seize this most important oilfield region or to knock it completely out of service. In 1942, Grozny provided the country with 1.5 million tons of oil.

In response to the German advance, martial law was declared in the Transcaucasus in the fall of 1942, and the situation in Baku soon became critical. Only 1.8 million tons of oil were shipped before navigation was halted, instead of the planned 6.6 million tons. A number of oil-producing enterprises that did continue to operate had to release produced oil into mountain depressions for storage. Special wells were designated, into which hundreds of thousands of tons of oil that had undergone gas-gasoline processing were pumped. The shortage of containers led to work stoppages. In the fall of 1942, oil was actually being produced by only a single trust: Neftechala.

It should be emphasized that from the first days of the war, there were widespread efforts throughout the country to help the army and navy. For example, workers in the rear gave the Defense Fund 17 billion rubles in cash contributions, 289 pounds of gold, 29 pounds of platinum, 20,985 pounds of silver, jewelry worth 1.7 billion rubles, government debt bonds worth more than 4.5 billion rubles, and half a billion rubles were transferred through contributions in savings banks. These resources were used to build 2,500 warplanes, several thousand tanks, eight submarines, 16 military cutters, thousands of artillery pieces, mortars, and various infantry arms.

A significant contribution was also made by oil industry workers who, every month, contributed one or two days of pay to the Defense Fund.

Another widespread patriotic initiative in the industry was the collection of money from individuals to build "named" tanks, airplanes, and even ships. For example, the money of the Soviet oil industry was used to build airplanes for the units "Bashkir Oilman," "Kuybyshev Oilman," "Syzran Driller," "Okhta Oilman," the fighter "Bashkir Geophysicist," the tank columns "Stavropol Oilman," "Ukhta Oilman," "Kazakhstan Oilman," and so on.

The difficult situation of the Caucasus oil regions intensified the role of eastern regions in oil production and refining. On September 22, 1942, the State Committee for Defense adopted a decree "On Measures to Expedite in Every Way Increased Oil Production at Kazakhstannefte-kombinat, Permneftekombinat, and at the Buguruslanneft, Syzranneft, Ishimbayneft, Tuymazaneft, Turkmenneft, Kalininneft, and Voroshilov-neft trusts." In essence, this was an elaborate program to create a mighty oil production and refining region in the Volga-Urals region. It planned, by the end of 1942, to increase average daily production in eastern regions by a factor of 1.5 over August of the same year. Before the end of 1942, the amount of development drilling was set at 684,711 feet; exploratory drilling, at 306,430 feet. By that deadline, plans called for putting 482 wells into production and an additional 580 wells in the first quarter of 1943.

To realize these plans, major organizations with experienced geologists and drillers, as well as equipment for exploratory work, were relocated from the old oil regions to the Bashkir and Tatar ASSR, and to Samara, Orenburg, and Perm Provinces. From just the Krasnodar and Grozny regions, 17,486 persons traveled east and into Central Asia; of these, 1,351 were engineers and technicians.

Highly qualified production organizers were appointed to head the new oil enterprises: E. Tagiyev was appointed director of Permneftekombinat, S. Kuvykin was appointed director of Bashneftekombinat, A. Vasilyev was appointed head of Kuybyshevneft, and Ts. Astvatsaturov was appointed head of Saratovneft.

On September 22, 1942, the State Committee for Defense adopted the important Resolution 2326, "On Expediting in Every Way Increased Production of Aviation Gasoline, Automobile Gasoline, Toluene, Oil, and Lubricants at the Refineries of the Center, East, and Central Asia," which planned urgent measures to substantially increase the production of fuels and lubricants.

The Fuel Component of Lend-Lease

Contemporary historical literature and domestic Russian press publications on the role played by crude oil and petroleum products in supporting military actions during World War II speak mostly in general terms. Numerous memoirs recount in detail the tank breakthroughs, sea battles, air raids, and heroic deeds at the fronts. However, most of these fail to mention the fact that, without fuel, the crews of tanks, airplanes, and naval vessels could not have carried out their assigned combat missions.

For the rear echelon, the need for fuels and lubricants was one of the most acute problems.

The oil factor had a substantial effect on the nature and progress of World War II. To a certain degree, the limited availability of fuel and energy resources, including oil, predetermined the strategy and tactics of Nazi Germany in the theaters of war. The German high command bet on a blitzkrieg strategy for operational use of large mechanized formations and the application of massive air power to support its infantry. In turn, this meant the preliminary stockpiling of adequate reserves of armaments, fuels, and lubricants during a preparatory period, followed by a sudden attack on the enemy. This explains the existence of definite intervals between Nazi Germany's occupation of Poland, the seizure of much of France, and the attack on the Soviet Union. However, having occupied much of Europe, and in attempting to force the populations of occupied countries to work for the German military economy, Nazi leaders encountered the need to provide mineral raw materials and fuel, which was very difficult to do given their total international isolation. Anticipating a fuel shortage, Nazi leaders set an objective of mass synthetic motor fuel production. However, this could not solve all the fuel problems of the Third Reich, because while Germany proper produced 1.4 million tons of oil in 1940, imports amounted to 2.5 million tons, including 1.7 million tons from Romania.

It is thus quite logical that the 20th century war of motors was largely won by the anti-Hitler coalition of powers thanks to their ample supply of both munitions and hydrocarbon fuels. American and British armed forces together expended several times more fuel during the Second World War than Nazi Germany and its satellites.

It can confidently be said that the availability of fuel to the Red Army and Navy during the Great Patriotic War was a major factor in the Soviet people's victory in their struggle with their Nazi German occupiers. Colonel General Vasily Nikitin, head of the USSR Armed Forces Fuel Service, estimated that the Soviet Armed Forces used 18 million tons of various fuels in strategic, frontal, and army operations during World War II.

Despite the heroic labor of the Soviet oil workers, the extreme conditions of the war caused a drop in the country's oil production from 34 million tons in 1940 to 21.3 million tons in 1945, i.e., a 37.7% reduction, and correspondingly exacerbated the already difficult situation in the refining sector, which found itself incapable of fully meeting growing Air Force demands for high-octane aviation gasoline. For instance, the USSR produced 1.4 million tons of aviation fuel in 1941, but only 1 million tons in 1942. The collection *The Economy of the USSR in the Great Patriotic War of 1941–1945* [*Narodnoye khozyaystvo SSSR v Velikoy Otechestvennoy voyne 1941–1945 gg.*] presents data on the production of aviation gasoline, which amounted to 6.1 million tons during the war. At the same time, Red Army planes consumed 4.9 million tons of aviation gasoline during the war years, and naval aviation units consumed over 5.5 million tons.

It should be stressed that, from 1941 to 1945, the USSR still had fairly large consumers of aviation gasoline. These included the aviation industry, which produced 137,000 planes during the war and additionally had its own fleet of planes. Civil aviation and airborne units of the Main Administration of the Northern Sea Route [Glavsevmorputi] likewise consumed considerable volumes of aviation fuel. Even the People's Commissariat for Internal Affairs [NKVD] had its own airborne squadrons. According to the most approximate calculations, the aforementioned organizations, taken together, consumed considerably more aviation gasoline during the four war years than the 615,000 tons indirectly allocated to them by Soviet statistics.

Thus, it is reasonable to conclude that the USSR received significant volumes of aviation fuel from third-party countries from 1941 to 1945, which made up the fuel shortage.

A study by the Russian historian Alexander Matveychuk, Candidate of History, entitled "The Oil Component of Lend-Lease," published in the collection *Soviet Union's Oil* [*Neft strany Sovetov*], is the first thorough examination of the place and role of petroleum products deliveries to the USSR under the Lend-Lease program during World War II.

Subsequent study of this issue has confirmed the special importance of aviation gasoline deliveries from the USSR's allies in the anti-Hitler coalition under the Lend-Lease program. According to official data, the US delivered a total of 2,159,336 tons of petroleum products to the USSR under Lend-Lease and commercial contracts, and the volume of high-octane aviation gasoline was 1,320,113 tons, including 615,561 tons with an octane rating above 99.

An important feature of aviation gasoline deliveries under Lend-Lease was that the US delivered aviation gasoline with an octane rating of 99 or higher to the USSR at a time when the technical level of the domestic refining industry permitted only the production of low-octane aviation gasoline. Thus, in the prewar year of 1940, the vast majority of the 973,800 tons of aviation gasoline produced was fuel with octane ratings of 70 to 74, used by antiquated domestic airplanes. Understandably, this situation did not change during the war, and the pressing demand for B-78 aviation gasoline required by the new Yak-1, Il-2, MiG-3, La-5, and other warplanes could not be met by Russian refineries. And so, American high-octane gasoline was used in large quantities as an octane-boosting additive to make quality aviation fuel both under factory conditions and directly at Red Army and Navy combat units. According to available data, 53% of the total volume of high-octane gasoline was made at military storage facilities from April 1943 to May 1945.

Equally important for the supply of quality fuel to Soviet aviators were Allied deliveries of special octane-boosting additives (e.g., tetraethyl lead solutions) for the preparation of high-octane aviation gasoline for the Soviet Armed Forces and for boosting automotive gasoline octane ratings. In all, 919,798 tons of these additives were received, including 807,217 tons from the US and 112,581 tons from the British refinery at Abadan, Iran.

Thus, the investigation of this question leads to the conclusion that deliveries of high-octane gasoline and octane-boosting additives from the US were indisputably important for supporting airborne combat operations by the Soviet Armed Forces, as well as effective production operations at domestic aircraft plants and other aviation organizations.

America's other contributions should not be overlooked. From April 1943–May 1945, US deliveries also included: 294,415 tons of automotive gasoline, 18,595 tons of kerosene, 316,650 tons of residual oil, 123,100 tons of lubricants, 6,359 tons of paraffin, 5,278 tons of chemical additives, and 1,100 tons of other products.

It should be stressed that the fuel component of Lend-Lease, in addition to petroleum products, also included US deliveries to the USSR of equipment for four complete refineries, as well as drilling rigs and other oilfield equipment, casing pipe and flow tubing, portable knock-down pipelines, monitoring and measuring devices, tankers, railroad tank cars, fueling trucks, and much more.

Officially, Lend-Lease deliveries to the USSR were suspended May 12, 1945, and from that date until the Red Army's crossing of the Manchurian border in the Far East, cargo delivery was done under a "special October 17 program" and a so-called "Molotov-Mikoyan list" supplemental to that. These agreements set maximum volumes of military and civilian materials that would be allocated by the US and Great Britain to the Soviet Union.

The Pipeline Agreement, signed October 15, 1945, continued the Lend-Lease protocols and was very important to the devastated Soviet economy. This treaty, worth $222 million, also had a substantial effect on the postwar development of the Soviet oil and gas industry.

On the whole, American, British, and Canadian deliveries of petroleum products, refining and oilfield equipment, pipe, and other materials as part of the overall Lend-Lease program substantially affected the supply of fuel to Soviet armed forces, and helped modernize the Soviet oil production and refining industries and develop the nation's pipeline system.

In the conclusion of his book *Lend-Lease: Weapon for Victory*, published in 1944, American General Edward R. Stettinius, Jr., head of the Office of Lend-Lease Administration, wrote: "Cooperation through Lend-Lease as it is today was destined, of course, to end one day, but we know that the principles of mutual aid and mutual benefit that form the basis of the Lend-Lease Act must continue to operate. Now as never before, freedom-loving peoples are united in their aims and actions. In this unity, we can find strength to establish peace in a world where everyone will be guaranteed freedom and equal opportunity."

Lend-Lease was a unique phenomenon in the recent history of relations among the USSR, US, Great Britain, and Canada. Under the very difficult conditions of the Second World War, the Allies managed to reach a mutual understanding and successfully used an effective mechanism of international economic relations to achieve total victory for the anti-Hitler coalition over Nazi Germany.

The Contribution of Soviet Oilmen and Scientists to the Victory

The acute shortage of petroleum products during the war in the Soviet rear explains the USSR's elaborate campaign to conserve liquid fuel. It included a transition to gas and solid fuel, acceleration of synthetic liquid fuel production, and maximized use of additives—benzene, synol, and other liquid products of thermal processing. Previously, gas fuel had been obtained from oil production waste only as a byproduct of crude oil production. During the war, fields producing solely natural gas in the area of Buguruslan and Saratov came online. The gas was used primarily to fuel industrial enterprises and power plants. A number of long gas pipelines (Yelshanka–Saratov, Voyvot–Ukhta, etc.) were built during the war to supply gas fuel to industrial enterprises.

Soviet petroleum scientists, who participated in the development of oil and gas fields and in the introduction of advanced technologies and new oilfield equipment, also made a major contribution to the overall victory over the enemy. On June 3, 1942, a special commission was formed to mobilize the resources of the Volga and Kama River Valleys. Its oil section was headed by academician Sergey Nametkin, and the People's Commissariat for the Oil Industry was actively represented by First Deputy People's Commissar Nikolay Baybakov. The geologists of the Moscow Petroleum Institute, along with their colleagues from the All-Union Scientific Research Geologic Exploration Institute, the Institute of Petroleum, and other institutions of the Academy of Sciences, performed extensive geologic studies of oil prospects in the Volga-Urals region. Their research on oil and gas percolation in a porous medium was of tremendous importance for the selection of oilfield development methods. The following well-known petroleum geologists took active part in the analysis of materials from geologic exploratory expeditions in the Volga-Urals region: Academicians D. Nalivkin, N. Shatsky, and S. Mironov; Corresponding Members of the Academy of Sciences S. Fëdorov, M. Mirchink, K. Chepikov, and

V. Nalivkin; and geologists A. Chernov, V. Fëdorov, K. Timirgazin, A. Trofimuk, A. Blokhin, A. Bogdanov, and M. Barentsov.

The Volga-Urals region, nicknamed the "Second Baku," became a proving ground for testing and introducing new methods of oil production and refining. For example, during the war, turbodrilling was successfully introduced in Bashkiria and in the Samara and Perm regions. The method increased drilling speeds and lengthened equipment life. In the Bashkir ASSR, top crews achieved rates of 2,625 feet per rig per month, versus the usual 787 feet. Large modular drilling derricks also began to be used at this time, accelerating the drilling of oil fields in the Volga-Urals region. In 1943 and 1944, workers at the Dossor and Maqat fields in the Emba District began actively waterflooding oil formations to enhance oil production. At Ishimbayevo, hole bottoms were treated with hydrochloric acid and "shots" were detonated to stimulate oil production.

The productive collaboration of scientists and engineers soon resulted in milestone events. On December 31, 1942, the Krasnokamsk office of turbodrilling at Molotovneftekombinat ["Molotov Petroleum Integrated Works"] was the first in the world to begin turbodrilling an experimental directional well. Eventually, 208 slant wells were drilled in this manner at the Krasnokamsk oil field.

On July 25, 1943, Shugurovo Well 1 (Verey-Namurian field) in the Tatar ASSR yielded a commercial inflow of oil, which gave a powerful new impetus to further development of the promising oil area. In September 1943, exploratory Well 5 at Kinzebulatovo field in Bashkiria was the first oil gusher.

In March 1944, the USSR CPC adopted a resolution, "On the Development of Exploration and Preparation for Construction of an Oil Field at Shugurovo Field, Tatar ASSR." In turn, People's Commissar Ivan Sedin immediately followed up this important government decision by signing an order by the same title.

Triumphant reports from the Volga oilmen soon followed. On June 9, 1944, at Yablonevoy Gorge in the Kuybyshev Region, the first flowing Devonian Well 41 yielded 234 tons of oil per day. On September 26, 1944, at Tuymaza, on the slopes of the Narashtau Range, a crew led by foreman A. T. Tripolsky drilled Well 100, which became a gusher flowing at more than 220 tons of Devonian oil per day.

Oil workers who developed the Timan-Pechora oil and gas province made their own substantial contribution to the achievement of victory over the enemy. Thus, oil production in Ukhta District increased considerably during the war and the gas industry was born. From 1941 to 1945, 635,400 tons of crude and 53 billion cubic feet of natural gas were produced, and the first gas field went into production in the Verkhne-Izhma District near the village of Krutoy, 56 miles from Ukhta. In 1942, more than 7.8 billion cubic feet of natural gas was refined to soot, which was badly needed by defense plants for rubber production, as it was used as a filler to reinforce rubber mixes. Geologists played their part as well in developing the resources of this region. In October 1943, they discovered the Voyvozh gas field, and in June 1945, they found the Nibel gas field (the country's biggest, with a daily flow of 21 million cubic feet of gas).

At the war's end, the country's leadership was able to assess the status and prospects for the geologic study of the new regions more realistically, as is shown by the joint order of February 17, 1944 by the People's Commissariat for the Oil Industry, the USSR CPC Committee for Geologic Affairs, and Glavsevmorputi, "On Performing Work to Generalize Geologic Materials Regarding the Oil Content of Western and Eastern Siberia, the Far Eastern Territory, and the Arctic Part of the USSR," which set the main objective of exploring oil prospects and determining the direction of further geologic exploration for oil based on available geologic information. The All-Union Scientific Research Petroleum Institute of the People's Commissariat for the Oil Industry was placed in charge of this effort. Professor Nikolay Kudryavtsev was appointed scientific director in charge, and academician Vladimir Obruchev was named editor-in-chief.

The course of the war turned decisively after the Soviet victory in the Battle of Kursk. Reconstruction work began immediately in territories liberated from the enemy. To start with, the first oilfield reconstruction crews began work in the Kuban region. A 1943 State Defense Committee [GKO] resolution, "On Measures for the Partial Restoration of the Grozny Oil Industry," played a major role in reviving the oil industry. In February 1945, drilling of the first well at Tashkala field began in the Grozny fields, and by June 1945, a well with a good flow rate had been found. Over the whole of 1945 and 1946, 17 highly productive flowing wells were drilled in the Grozny fields.

The war caused a qualitative shift in the Soviet oil industry, allowing it to break through in the postwar years. The introduction of new drilling methods—such as slant turbodrilling to penetrate the hard rock typical of the fields in the "Second Baku"—was expedited. The "Second Baku" trusts and conglomerates increased oil production by half during the war, and the region's share of total output rose to 14.6% by 1945. Overall, the USSR oil industry began gradually increasing oil production. In 1943, the country produced 19.82 million tons; in 1944, it produced 20.13 million tons, including 13.1 million tons of crude on the Absheron Peninsula.

During the course of the war, the USSR discovered 34 oil and gas fields, 21 of them in the eastern parts of the country, thereby laying the foundations between the Volga and Urals for the creation of a powerful new fuel infrastructure.

In summarizing the activities of the Soviet oil industry during the harsh years of the Great Patriotic War, it can be said that the industry withstood this severe test honorably, and managed to deliver adequate fuel and lubricant resources to the USSR Armed Forces, thereby making a solid contribution to victory in the war. And all this despite numerous difficulties, despite the costs of the irrational and inefficient command-administrative economic system, and despite the incredibly difficult working and living conditions faced by the oil workers.

The Postwar Years

In the last year of the war, Soviet oil industry production was 77.8% of the 1940 level, greater than that of industry as a whole. A USSR CPC resolution dated March 25, 1945, "On the State Plan for Recovery and Development of the Economy in 1945," called for a 9% increase in oil production that year. However, actual production performance for the year rose 6.5%, to 21.42 million tons of crude, which was still 37.5% less than in 1940.

Compared to the last prewar year, operational drilling in the USSR was down 62.4%; exploratory drilling had shrunk least of all compared to 1940, but even here, the drop was 25.6%. The decline in oilfield equipment output was particularly large: 1945 production was only 9% of the 1940 level, which is completely understandable, as machinery factories had been converted to make war materiel, and reconversion took time. All the same, the country did make a quarter more downhole pumps in 1945 than in 1940.

The country continued to experience a shortage of petroleum products. The USSR's entry into the war with Japan and the waging of broad-scale hostilities against the Kwantung army required delivery of a large volume of fuels and lubricants.

During 1945, the Soviet government undertook a series of steps intended to increase oil production. On May 8, 1945, the State Defense Committee [GKO] adopted Resolution 8458 on the production of items for the oil industry by factories of the People's Commissariat for Heavy Machine-Building. Accordingly, the Stalin Plant in Kramatorsk was ordered to make swivels, crown blocks, and tackle blocks; the Stalin Plant in Elektrostal was ordered to make reduction gears, rotors, and reversible transmissions; the Kuybyshev Plant in Irkutsk was ordered to make high-speed winches; and the January Uprising Plant in Odessa was ordered to make sucker-rod pumps.

On October 26, 1945, the USSR Council of People's Commissars required the People's Commissariat for Heavy Machine-Building [Narkomtyazhprom] to manufacture eight sets of drilling rigs at the Ural Machinery Plant, 15 winches for drilling to 9,800 feet at the Kuybyshev Plant in Irkutsk, and 150 sucker-rod pumps at the January Uprising Plant in Odessa, and to deliver them to the People's Commissariat for the Oil Industry [Narkomnefti] by the end of 1945. Incidentally, the designers at the Ural Machinery Plant used diesel engines from T-34 tanks to power drilling rigs.

The country did not have enough oil for its economy, and so old-fashioned manual methods of production that required no capital investment or machinery and equipment came back into play. In 10 months of 1945, abandoned oil pits and wells in Baku District yielded 16,000 tons of oil using cottage-industry methods. This work in Baku District was done primarily by a few industrial cooperation enterprises that, in 1946, raised their oil production to 19,800 tons. In addition, besides "trap" crude, other Azerbaijan SSR entities outside the system of the USSR People's Commissariat for the Oil Industry produced 51,300 tons by various means. Naturally, such cottage-industry methods yielded a very small share of total production, and would soon disappear from the fields.

As of January 1, 1946, the fixed assets of the USSR oil industry were estimated at 401.9 million rubles, making it the Soviet Union's fourth biggest industry, after railroad transportation (864.2 million rubles), electric power generation (708.3 million rubles), and nonferrous metallurgy (420 million rubles).

Speaking on February 9, 1946 during the USSR Supreme Soviet election campaign at a rally for voters in Moscow's Stalin Election District, Stalin set a new objective for the industry: "We must achieve a level where our industry can annually produce up to 55 million tons of pig iron, up to 66 million tons of steel, up to 550 million tons of coal, and up to 66 million tons of crude oil. Only then can we regard our Homeland as secure against any eventuality. This may take three more Five-Year Plans, if not more."[50]

The head of the People's Commissariat for the Oil Industry at the time, Nikolay Baybakov (1911-2008), recalled his reaction to the speech: "The next day, I called [First Deputy Prime Minister] Lavrenty Pavlovich [Beria] and asked him, 'Who gave Stalin these figures? Are there any calculations, or not?' 'None of your business,' Beria shot back. 'What did the general secretary tell you? So go think and make those 66 million happen.' "

On March 18, 1946, the USSR Supreme Soviet enacted the Fourth Five-Year Plan, for 1946–1950. It called for an increase in oil production over the prewar level, to 39 million tons, only 14% more than in 1940. In reality, however, the Soviet oil workers were actually required to substantially increase oil production, because a goal 14% over the 1940 level was 82.5% over the 1945 level.

The Fourth Five-Year Plan also included targets for refining: "Develop the production of high-octane gasoline. Improve the quality of automotive gasoline, tractor kerosene, diesel fuel, and lubricants. Increase petroleum product yield from crude oil by reducing losses and extensively introducing catalytic processes and other latest methods of producing gasoline and technical oils. The Five-Year Plan requires construction of four new refineries and 16 refining installations. Three refineries are to be refurbished to provide petroleum products to agricultural and industrial regions of the South."

In early 1946, the Fourth Five-Year Plan called for constructing a refinery with a total capacity of 9.7 million tons for primary crude processing and 6.63 million tons for cracking. To meet such an ambitious plan with the limited materials and equipment available, a great deal was required from all supervisors and rank-and-file workers in the industry.

Baybakov wrote in the journal *Planovoye khozyaystvo* ["Planned Economy"] in 1946 that: "In order to achieve oil production of 39 million tons in 1950, we must increase development drilling to 2.5 million meters [8.2 million feet] and exploratory drilling to 1.5 million meters [4.9 million feet] in 1950."

In 1946, the average well depth in fields of the USSR Ministry of the Oil Industry of the Eastern Regions was 3,084 feet. Under the Five-Year Plan (the October 1946 version), this was to increase to 4,100 feet by 1950, and the number of wells in the ministry's fields was to increase by 210%.

The first year of the Fourth Five-Year Plan brought the industry some success. Oil production in 1946 rose 12% for the USSR as a whole, and 26% in eastern regions. Total headway drilled (not counting enterprises of the *NKVD* or Main Gas and Synthetic Liquid Fuel Administration [Glavgaztopprom]) rose from 2.9 million feet in 1945 to 3.8 million feet in 1946.

Although oil production on the Absheron Peninsula remained nearly unchanged, Grozny District exceeded its plan targets. In late 1945 and in 1946, Grozny oil workers discovered new oil fields at Tashkala and Suvorovskoye, and new oil fields were also discovered in older areas. The Grozny oil fields produced 1.472 million tons of crude in 1946, 45% more than in 1945, fulfilling the plan by 109.4%.

In the first year of the Fourth Five-Year Plan, restoration of production at those refineries destroyed or evacuated during the war proceeded rapidly. In 1946, Aviation Oil Refinery 3 at Grozny was completely rehabilitated. But not all refineries could be restored so quickly. For example, in the 1941 evacuation of the Odessa Cracking Refinery, all equipment (primarily a two-furnace cracking and asphalt-vacuum unit) was removed, and all facilities of the refinery's infrastructure were destroyed, including the raw-material, receiving, finished-product, and intermediate tanks.

Reconstruction of the Odessa Refinery began by 1944, though annual capital investments totaled only 70,000 rubles at the time. For 1945, the capital budget was set at 4 million rubles, but only 1.783 million rubles could actually be spent. In all, the refinery's reconstruction would cost 27.5 million rubles according to figures from the time. Delays were due to, among other factors, late arrival of main equipment for installation (it could not be manufactured) and a shortage of materials and technical resources from the USSR state fund. Even by mid-1946, only three of the 67 major pieces of equipment needed for startup had been delivered. During the first months of 1946, only 5.7% of the stated amount of cement, 7.7% of refractory brick, 5% of round timber, etc. arrived for construction.

USSR Council of Ministers Resolution 1449 of July 2, 1946 ordered the complete reconstruction of the Odessa Refinery by the fourth quarter of 1947. However, due to outside factors, this could not be done until the fourth quarter of 1949.

Meanwhile, the country continued its strict fuel economy and conservation policy. Thus, already meager fuel consumption standards were lowered 4.95% in 1949 and 4% in 1950. Given the ongoing shortage of motor fuel, the USSR started deriving fuel from nonpetroleum sources. In the fall of 1948, it commissioned a gas shale plant at Kohtla-Jarve, Estonian SSR, and it continued construction of a gas shale plant in Slantsy, Leningrad Region (commissioned in 1952). In 1946–1947, it began construction of the Angara Synthetic Products Works and the Novocherkassk Synthetic Products Plant. Somewhat later, it began construction of the Salavat Petrochemical Works. These plants were to produce liquid fuel from coal using German equipment obtained as part of reparation payments.

Although the USSR's Five-Year Plan was adopted in March 1946, the prewar practice of "correcting" plan targets was resumed just a year later. Since the industry was developing successfully in 1947, state planners began developing tougher oil production targets for 1950. At the start of 1947, the State Planning Committee proposed increasing the 1950 oil production target from the original 39 million tons to 41 million tons. A new "correction" soon followed; in the spring 1947 version of the Plan, the 1950 oil production target had been revised upward once again, to 44 million tons.

Thanks to the selfless labor of Soviet oil workers, 1947 oil production rose by a quarter (25.4%) over the prior year, to 29.93 million tons. These positive rates were achieved by increasing development drilling rates, which approached the 1940 level, and through exploratory drilling, which exceeded the prewar level by 50%. These rates allowed additional development of dozens of new fields, areas, and formations in various parts of the USSR. The year 1947 saw a further rise in production for eastern regions, whose share of national oil production nearly tripled by year's end.

Geologic surveys in the Stalingrad Region revealed the Archeda, Saush, Vetyutnev, Verkhovka, and other oil and gas structures. In

November 1948, a crew working under foreman Idris Altynbayev completed Archeda Well 4, which yielded the first inflow of oil, and on July 12, 1949, Zhirnoye Well 1 was commissioned, marking the beginning of commercial oil production in the Stalingrad Region.

New fields were also opened in other parts of the country, including the Azerbaijan SSR. In 1947, the Gurgan offshore field was discovered in the Caspian, followed in 1949 by the soon-to-be-famous Neftyanyye Kamni ["Oil Rocks"], and then in 1950, Darwin Bank.

In addition to the restoration of facilities in the production industry, the issue of transporting crude oil and petroleum products was likewise an acute problem. Nearly 90% of all crude oil from the eastern regions was transported to refineries by rail. The heavy workload of the railroads prevented additional shipments of crude oil and petroleum products, causing interruptions in oil exports and in many cases wells had to be shut in. Ongoing growth in oil production would exacerbate transportation problems even further, and for this reason, a decision was made to accelerate pipeline construction.

In 1947, the Main Crude Oil and Petroleum Products Sales and Transportation Administration [Glavneftesbyt] began the design and construction of a network of new petroleum products pipelines. Oil supplies were improved by refining Sakhalin crude on site and the continuous transportation of Sakhalin crude to the mainland via the Okha–Komsomolsk-on-Amur pipeline, as well as by refining Volga-Urals crude at the point of production and constructing new refineries in Siberia to manufacture all types of petroleum products. All this enabled the Urals, Siberia, and the Far East to be supplied with petroleum products without having them hauled from the south (Baku, Grozny, Turkmenistan).

In 1950, nearly all the equipment needed by the oil industry was made in the USSR. It was supplied by a wide array of Soviet ministries, including the Ministries of Heavy Machine-Building, Armaments, Transportation Machine-Building, Machine Tools, Electrical Industry, Automotive and Tractor Industry, Means of Communications, Construction and Road Machine-Building and Instrument-Making, Railroads, etc.

Table 11. USSR Oil Production by Year, in millions of tons

Year	Oil Production
1945	21.48
1946	23.9
1947	28.7
1948	32.2
1949	36.5
1950	41.8

Source: *Economy of the USSR* [*Narodnoye khozyaystvo SSSR*]. Moscow, 1959, p. 205.

By 1950, well drilling speeds had grown substantially thanks to the use of new technologies. The number of operational drilling rigs had grown from 322 at the start of 1946 to 1,019 in 1950, with each rig making more headway than before. Thus, by 1949, Tuymaza Petroleum [Tuymazaneft] required roughly 70 days to drill a well; about half of what it had taken only a few years earlier. By 1950, the speed of exploratory drilling for the USSR Ministry of the Oil Industry as a whole had more than doubled compared to 1935. For example, in 1949, Buzovyazy Petroleum [Buzovyneft] completed a 6,190-foot well in 16 days. Wooden derricks were a thing of the past, replaced by prefabricated metal structures. Whereas a crew of seven took an average of 10 days to install drilling equipment in 1935, by 1950 that crew could do the work in only three to three-and-a-half days.

In fact, more headway was drilled in 1950 than planned (14 million feet, as opposed to 13 million), but the ratio of development drilling to exploratory drilling was not what Minister Nikolay Baybakov had envisioned in 1946: development drilling amounted to 7,071,194 feet, while exploratory drilling was much greater than originally planned—6,979,331 feet. Furthermore, the volume of turbodrilling had risen from 7% in 1945 to 24% in 1950.

At Tuymaza field in 1946, at the suggestion of the noted petroleum geologist Georgy Maksimovich (1904–1979), edge flooding, an effective new method of stimulating oil production, was introduced for the first time in the USSR, and this process was mastered in two years. The Americans, incidentally, had begun to develop edge flooding earlier, in 1936, and had implemented it on an industrial scale in 1942. For the Soviet oilmen, however, the method was not a simple borrowing, and as the noted scientist Professor Vladimir N. Shchelkachëv (1907–2005) wrote, "quite a few fundamentally new things" were introduced. His detailed analysis of edge flooding technology showed that the engineering and organizational implementation of the idea was very original, and made possible only by Russia's fairly high scientific and technical potential.

The government did not overlook the hydrocarbon resources of the Far East, either. On August 19, 1948, the USSR Council of Ministers adopted a resolution, "On Measures to Develop Oil Production on Sakhalin Island," which guided the sharp growth in production from 838,000 tons in 1948 to 2.2 million tons in 1952.

In addition to an extensive series of engineering and technical measures, the industry carried out several steps to find the optimal administrative structure. On March 4, 1946, the People's Commissariat for the Oil Industry was split in two, into the People's Commissariat for the Oil Industry of the Eastern Regions and the People's Commissariat for the Oil Industry of the Southern and Western Regions. On December 28, 1948, however, these agencies were reunited into a single USSR Ministry of the Oil Industry. In addition, the government created a specialized Ministry of Construction of Fuel Enterprises to support oil industry construction and assembly operations.

In the first postwar Five-Year Plan, the RSFSR surpassed the Azerbaijan SSR by producing 20 million tons to the latter's 16.3 million, thus taking first place in oil production among USSR republics. This was owed primarily to the Volga-Urals region—the "Second Baku"—which had greatly accelerated its oil production.

Overall, the period of the Fourth Five-Year Plan (1946–1950) should be considered successful for the Soviet oil industry. The industry resumed operations, upgraded fields and enterprises, prepared infrastructure for further development of its pipeline network, and surpassed the prewar oil production level through accelerated development of the Volga-Urals region.

The Oil Heights of the "Second Baku"

Directives issued by the 19th AUCP(b) Congress for the USSR's Fifth Five-Year Plan (1951–1955) called for approximately a 70% increase in the country's industrial production over 1950. Party leadership devoted particular attention to the development of the oil industry: crude production was to grow at an even more impressive rate of 85%, to 86.25 million tons, by 1955.

In order to meet targets and ensure substantial growth in oil production, Soviet oil producers had to resolve several serious issues related to the exploration, development and construction of new oil fields in the Volga-Urals oil and gas province, which on a map covers a vast triangle of land between the cities of Kirov, Molotov (Perm), Chkalov (Orenburg), and Saratov, an area much bigger than the European nations of France or Germany.

Preliminary projections by the country's leading scientists and specialists on the enormous hydrocarbon resources of the province, which was justifiably called the "Second Baku" in the national press, made quite an impression on Soviet Party leadership.

Favorable economics and geography were two of the main components that played a major role in the Soviet government's strategic decision to accelerate the development of the Volga-Urals province. This was because the "Second Baku" had exceptionally favorable economic and geographic factors working in its favor, seeing as how it was located between two of the country's largest industrial bases (the central economic region and the industrial Urals region). Oilfield equipment and machinery could be brought to the region without excessive expense or cost, production areas and settlements for oil workers could be equipped quickly, and crude oil and petroleum products could be transported efficiently to primary areas of consumption. The region also had a favorable climate in which to live and work. Finally, natural geographic factors—namely, high well flow rates, the excellent consumer properties of the Devonian crude, and its enormous reserves—served as a powerful argument in favor of the rapid development of the "Second Baku."

A USSR Cabinet of Ministers Resolution of April 28, 1950, "On Measures to Accelerate the Development of Oil Production in the Tatar ASSR," played a decisive role in the early phases of addressing this important economic challenge. The resolution established the following objectives: creation of a new national oil base in this region, acceleration of oil production rates within a new organizational framework, and completion of a targeted volume of drilling and exploration, as well as the construction of production, housing, and cultural facilities. The Tatneft Association was set up as a joint entity composed of the Bavlyneft and Bugulmaneft oil production trusts, the Tatburneft drilling trust, the Tatneftpromstroy construction trust, and the Tatneftprodukt design office.

Several ministries and agencies were involved in the program to accelerate development in the new oil producing region, which had received the undivided attention of Party, Soviet, and economic agencies throughout the country's regions and republics, as well as wide segments of Soviet society. Program objectives covered several equally important areas, but the most complicated aspects were providing the oil production industry with skilled engineers and personnel, developing a proper technical policy to maintain a high rate of drilling and meet oil production targets, creating a strong logistical and production infrastructure, and setting up necessary housing and living conditions for oil workers. During the early development stages of the Volga-Urals province, personnel problems were solved mainly by sending in oil workers to Tatarstan from older oil regions such as Grozny, Krasnodar, Sakhalin, and Baku.

In an effort to step up the construction of Tatneft's field and energy resource base, the USSR Cabinet of Ministers passed a resolution in March 1951 that, among other tasks, called for the construction of Tatneft housing, as well as oil tank farms, turbodrilling bases, and several other necessary facilities. Four hundred skilled construction specialists and some 1,000 workers were sent to work at oil facilities in the Tatar ASSR on the basis of this resolution.

The discovery of the enormous Romashkino field provided a powerful incentive for the further expansion of geologic exploration in the Volga-Urals region. The top priority was to sharply increase exploratory drilling rates, continue the transition of drilling equipment from diesel power to electricity, and expand the use of turbodrilling (its volume was to grow from 24% to 70%), thus lowering the cost of drilling wells. Oilfield production also called for expanded use of methods for maintaining formation pressure and producing secondary oil.

In addition to the Ishimbay and Tuymaza fields, other large fields were discovered and successfully developed in the Bashkir ASSR during this period, including the Shkapovo, Chekmagush, Mancharovo, and Arlan fields. Two geologic exploration trusts had been set up somewhat earlier, on the basis of the Bashnefteradvedka trust, and these expanded exploratory work throughout the entire Birsk Basin. Exploratory drilling in the republic amounted to 10.5 million feet from 1951 to 1960, a fivefold increase over the previous decade. Incidentally, the Bashkir drillers were among the first in the USSR to use electric downhole drills. The successful resolution of organizational drilling problems enabled workers to develop oil fields at a faster pace.

The Soviet government maintained constant control over operations in the Volga-Urals oil and gas province. In a resolution "On the Accelerated Development of the Oil Industry in the Tatar ASSR and Bashkir ASSR," dated July 19, 1952, the USSR Cabinet of Ministers noted the high growth rates in crude output in the region and set a goal of developing oil production at an even more accelerated pace, to attain 16.5 million tons by 1955 instead of the previously planned 7.7 million tons. To achieve this goal, the Soviet government sought out the necessary logistical resources.

To implement the government's resolution, the Almetyevburneft drilling trust was set up within Tatneft, along with Almetyevneft, Tattekhsnabneft and Tatnefteprovodstroy subdivisions. The Tatneftegeofizika trust was set up that same year and performed a large amount of geophysical work. Utilizing the efforts of its enterprises, Tatneftegeofizika organized geophysical field research in addition to oilfield research.

Upon Stalin's death in March 1953, Nikita Khrushchëv (1894–1971) assumed leadership of the country following several months of behind-the-scenes political infighting. Instead of a rigid command system of management and the subordination of everything to the center, some powers gradually began to devolve to local authorities and organizations. This policy of greater independence for economic entities, in turn, led to an increased rate of growth in oil industry development.

Thus, a fundamentally new approach was taken to develop and further exploit oil fields in order to meet the goal of accelerating oil and gas industry development in the "Second Baku" over an unprecedentedly short period.

The most respected Soviet oil industry scientists and specialists were invited to work in the Volga-Urals region, and industry research centers were set up with their participation. After encountering the unique Volga-Urals province, which was not at all like the older oil producing regions, the scientists proposed fundamentally new and more efficient methods of field development that would stand the test of time and enrich the engineering and technological heritage of the country's oil industry. It was during this period that the method of formation-pressure maintenance came into use, significantly reducing the number of wells that needed to be drilled, considerably increasing total oil withdrawal, and sharply cutting production costs. The widespread use of edge waterflooding, as well as the growth of cities and worker settlements, however, made the problem of water supply a top priority. A massive search began throughout the region to find and utilize water resources as well as to manage supplies of water to industrial facilities and the public.

These groundbreaking methods and new technologies considerably accelerated the process of putting new fields into operation, increased the volume of recoverable resources, and lowered production costs. The initial gamble on the natural geologic component was thus complemented by engineering and process achievements, which resulted in more rapid and efficient development of the region.

The unique raw-materials base of the Volga-Urals Province was developed with a high level of efficiency. The production cost of a ton of Volga-Urals crude, for example, was much lower than in other regions. Whereas in the early 1960s crude cost 7.43 rubles per ton in Azerbaijan, 5.38 rubles in Krasnodar Territory, and 4.23 rubles in the Turkmen ASSR, the cost in the "Second Baku" fluctuated from region to region, between 1.33 rubles in the Tatar ASSR and 3.74 rubles in the Orenburg Region. With the cost of transporting Volga-Urals oil to the consumer much less as compared to other regions, the benefits were obvious.

The most complicated production task was arranging for the transportation of crude to refining sites. The only way to resolve the problem was to build a network of field and trunk oil pipelines, which led to the creation of the Tatar Oil Pipeline Administration in Bugulma, which was later turned into the Northwest Oil Pipeline Administration.

Table 12. USSR and Volga-Urals Oil Production by Year,
in millions of tons

Year	USSR Total Oil Production	Volga-Urals Regional Oil Production	Volga-Urals Regional Share of Total USSR Oil Production
1945	21.48	3.1	14.48%
1950	41.8	12.1	28.97%
1955	78.04	45.4	58.19%
1960	162.3	114.96	70.85%
1965	266.4	191.31	71.8%

Source: Maltsev, N. A., *et al. The Russian Oil Industry in the Postwar Years* [*Neftyanaya promyshlennost Rossii v poslevoyennyye gody*]. Moscow, 1996, p. 84.

Organizing the collection and efficient use of associated gas produced along with crude was an important and difficult part of oilfield development. Tatneft began working in this area virtually from its inception. Construction began on the 160-mile Minnibayevo–Kazan gas pipeline in 1951. The Minnibayevo Gas and Gasoline Plant was built to process associated gas, with the first phase of the plant coming on line in 1957. Oil production trusts set up specialized gas collection departments. From the beginning, gas was supplied to urban populations and to oil worker settlements.

Table 13. Total Volga-Ural, Tatar ASSR, and Bashkir ASSR Oil Production by Year, in millions of tons

Year	Total Oil Production in Volga-Urals Region	Tatar ASSR Oil Production	Bashkir ASSR Oil Production
1945	3.1	0.0077	1.4
1950	12.1	0.956	6.2
1955	45.4	14.7	16.9
1960	114.96	47.2	31.7
1965	191.31	84.3	48.4

Source: Maltsev, N. A., *et al. The Russian Oil Industry in the Postwar Years* [*Neftyanaya promyshlennost Rossii v poslevoyennyye gody*]. Moscow, 1996, p. 84.

The rapid development of oil fields, however, led to a rise in the ratio of oil produced by natural drive, from 33% in 1950 to 58% in 1958. The increase in production by natural drive, in turn, resulted in higher average well flow rates. The average flow rate in 1955 was 125% of the 1950 level. Unfortunately, the growth of natural-drive oil production was not accompanied by the development of methods and equipment to make further use of fields after formation pressure had subsided. This approach resulted in wells that could not operate after cessation of natural-drive production and which would at times be reclassified as inactive. The use of these methods also disrupted the environment. However, Soviet leaders did not consider the opinions of those scientists and specialists who were opposed to the use of such oil production methods, since the most important result for Party officials was increasing production volumes, no matter what the cost.

Regardless of concerns about these methods, it is clear that they were effective: In 1956, Tatneft produced 19.84 million tons of oil, becoming the number one oil producer in the Soviet Union.

The battle for "big" Soviet oil was just as intense in other regions of the Volga-Urals oil and gas province. Whereas oil production totaled only 552,000 tons in the Molotov (Perm) Region in 1950, 10.5 million tons of oil were extracted between 1951 and 1960 following the development of the Yarina–Kamenny Log field and several other fields. In 1957, Perm oil workers produced the one millionth ton of oil, and in 1960 the two million mark was reached in the Kama River Valley.

Another large oil field, Bakhmetyevo, was discovered in the Stalingrad Region in 1951, just north of Zhirnovsk, and put into operation in 1955. Klënovka field was opened in 1962. These three fields determined the oil output level at the Zhirnovsk Oil and Gas Production Administration for most of the next 45 years. By 1955, the region had already caught up with several older oil-producing regions in the country in terms of crude production and occupied seventh place in the USSR. Before long, the unique Korobkovo oil and gas field was discovered and turned out to be the largest in the oil and gas history of the Volgograd Region. Twelve productive oil and gas formations were uncovered in the section of this field in the depth interval from 650 to 5,750 feet. Production testing began in September 1955, and by the end of that year, the section had produced more than 1,100 tons of oil and 145 million cubic feet of associated gas. On December 29, 1955, the independent Korobkovo oil field was created.

The average annual growth in oil production in the Volga-Urals oil and gas province from 1950 to 1965 was more than four times higher than the combined output of the Azerbaijan SSR, the North Caucasus, Ukraine, Georgia, the Central Asian republics, the Komi SSR, and the Sakhalin Region. The explicit use of innovative approaches to meeting complex production challenges was instrumental in the efficient and rapid development of the "Second Baku" from its first days of operation, and as a result, oil production increased 62-fold over a 20-year period.

A powerful oil base was thus created in the Volga-Urals region, producing 78% of the country's total oil supply. The center of the USSR oil industry moved from the southern part of the country to the Volga-Urals region. Petroleum products from the regional branches of the "Second Baku" were shipped to Kazakhstan, Siberia, the Far East, and elsewhere. Transportation expenses amounted to several billion rubles each year. In an effort to lower costs, the Tuymaza–Omsk 2, Omsk–Irkutsk, Ufa–Omsk 2, and Novosibirsk–Irkutsk pipelines were planned to come online between 1956 and 1960.

More targets were set for the USSR oil industry at the 20th CPSU Congress in 1956. Directives issued by the Congress called for a significant increase in the oil industry's growth rates compared to several other heavy industries. Oil production was to grow by 91% over five years to 149 million tons in 1960, while the production of light petroleum products and lubricants was to increase by 100% and 80%, respectively. According to Party directives, proven oil reserves were to increase 65–70%, while proven natural gas reserves were to grow 85–90% compared with the figures from the first half of the decade. The "Second Baku" once again bore the brunt of meeting the targets.

In summarizing the impressive accomplishments of Soviet oil workers in the Volga-Urals region during this period, special mention should be made of the significant contributions made by the talented production organizers Aleksey Shmaryov (1913–1993) and Valentin Shashin (1916–1977), who were directors at Tatneft, as well as Bashneft association Director Stepan Kuvykin (1903–1974).

Thanks to the Volga-Urals oil and gas province, oil production plans that seemed inflated or unrealistic to some scientists were not only fulfilled but exceeded. The production target of 66 million tons, announced by Joseph Stalin in 1946 for the three postwar five-year periods, was met and exceeded within ten years. By 1960, when this figure was originally supposed to have been reached, oil production had exceeded Stalin's plan target by almost 150% and amounted to 163 million tons.

The accelerated creation of a reliable energy system, transportation routes, and machine-building industry coincided with the development of oil production and refining in the Volga-Urals region. The oil industry was essentially the foundation for creating a complex industrial infrastructure in regions that had previously been predominantly agrarian. An engineering and scientific elite took shape at this time, and skilled personnel were trained for professions that had previously been under-manned.

Over the next twenty years, the Soviet Union steadily increased its share of global oil production (from 5.5% in 1945 to 16% in 1965), remaining firmly in second place throughout the world (behind the US), and was Europe's top oil producer by a large margin. Particular mention should be made of the fact that oil production grew at a much faster pace during this period than did the economy as a whole. In addition, the USSR fuel balance had undergone significant changes: oil and gas accounted for 42.4% in 1962, as compared to 23.5% in 1955.

The Great Western Siberian Oil Saga

Serious changes in USSR Party leadership took place in fall 1964. On October 14, the Plenum of the CPSU Central Committee accused leader Nikita Khrushchëv of "a breach of collegiality and collectivity in leadership, a disregard for the views of comrades, the revival of a 'cult' atmosphere, and the destabilization of the country's overall situation as a result of ill-conceived reforms and the frequent replacement of personnel" and relieved him of all Party and government positions "due to advanced age and deteriorating health." Leonid Brezhnev (1906–1982) was elected general secretary of the CPSU Central Committee, while Aleksey Kosygin (1904–1980) was appointed chairman of the USSR Cabinet of Ministers.

The decision to dismiss Khrushchëv was met with almost unanimous approval throughout Soviet society, and by some with great joy. He was no doubt a highly controversial political figure, but as Mark Frankland, a prominent American Sovietologist, accurately noted: "Khrushchëv could say with a clear conscience that he left affairs in the government in better shape than they were when he took over."[51]

From the start, the new Soviet leadership demonstrated a determination to implement a new policy that sought to ensure the sustainable development of the country's economy on the basis of scientific and technological progress, together with the universal and complete use of the energy and enthusiasm of labor collectives.

As part of the 1965 economic reform led by Cabinet of Ministers Chairman Kosygin, oil industry management underwent significant changes. Under the reform, management was to focus on the sector principle and create an environment in which a region's development pace could be regulated depending on the economic efficiency of developing fields in that region. The Ministry of the Oil Industry (Minister Valentin Shashin) and the Ministry of the Gas Industry (Minister Aleksey Kortunov) were established on October 2, 1965, and put in charge of creating industry regulations and systems to boost oil industry output as well as to manage and improve planning. In addition to manufacturing companies, all scientific research and design organizations working on solutions for oil industry problems were incorporated into the Ministry of the Oil Industry.

Under directives from the 23rd CPSU Congress in 1966, oil production was to increase to 380–390 million tons by 1970. In order to meet this target, roughly 230 million feet of hole were to be drilled, to an average drilling depth of 8,200 feet. There were also plans to increase the volume of primary refining and the production of light petroleum products by 40–50% and to increase lubricant output by 40%.

The prospects for such a significant increase in oil production volumes in the USSR were linked above all to Western Siberia. Geoscientists estimated that this region, which contained an enormous oil province covering more than 775,000 square miles, at that time had probable reserves comparable with the Volga-Urals oil province.

There was a solid foundation for these projections, as several remarkable discoveries had been made in the Ob River Valley by this time. On September 25, 1959, the first oil flow of Western Siberia was generated by a drilling crew under foreman Semën N. Urusov. The flow rate was not particularly high, but the most important thing was that Western Siberian oil had finally become a reality. On October 4, the newspaper *Tyumenskaya pravda* ["Tyumen Truth"] reported the event as follows: "On September 25, an oil-bearing formation was discovered at a depth of 1,405 meters [4,610 feet] at the Mulymya structure near the village of Shaim with a daily flow rate of more than one ton of light oil, according to preliminary data.... Considering that the village of Shaim is located 174 miles from the village of Maly Atlym, where oil was also discovered, huge prospects can be expected for the first oil-bearing region in Siberia. The Tyumen Region will become the new Soviet Baku in the near future!"

The news of the first oil flow in Western Siberia led to the promulgation of an important government resolution. On March 20, 1960, the USSR Cabinet of Ministers passed Resolution 241, "On Urgent Measures to Boost Construction in the Area of the Western Siberian Oil and Gas Complex," which outlined guidelines for the large-scale industrial development of the Western Siberian region.

Meanwhile, work was still underway at the Mulymya structure. The next well drilled there, Well 7, produced more impressive results on April 25, 1960, with a daily flow rate of 13 tons of oil. Semën Urusov's crew began drilling yet another new well, which three months later would go down in history.

Scientists, geologists and industry officials had been impatiently waiting for commercial Siberian oil. Finally, on June 21, 1960, Mikhail Shalavin, the leader of the Shaim oil and gas expedition, sent a radiogram to Yury Ervye, director of the Tyumen Territorial Geologic Administration, with the following message: "Well R-6 flowed through the 5-inch casing string without flow tubing through a 4-inch valve into an earthen pit. The earthen pit has a capacity of 350–400 cubic meters [12,360–14,125 cubic feet]. After the well bottom was perforated and oil replaced the service water, the well flowed periodically at 385–550 tons per day. It is impossible to give an exact flow rate because the well had to be shut down twice for technical reasons. The earthen pit is almost full of oil now. I will report the pressure later."[52]

Along with Mikhail Shalavin and Semën Urusov, this joyous event was also shared by chief engineer Vladimir Sobolevsky, transportation engineer Aleksandr Krivonogov, and drillers V. Shidlovsky, L. Raspopov, V. Teterevnikov, N. Peshkov, among others. Per tradition, the oil workers washed their hands in the oil and smeared it on each other's faces. Well 6 became famous throughout the country, and not just because it represented the opening of the Shaim field but because it was the pioneering well of all Western Siberian oil.

Two days after the well began to flow, academician Andrey Trofimuk (1911–1999), director of the Geology and Geophysics Institute of the Siberian Branch of the USSR Academy of Sciences, said: "This is the first big oil in Siberia with commercial potential.... Until now, there have been skeptics among geologists who did not believe in the prospects for our regions. Now everyone will move from disputes to action.... Perhaps, most importantly, the significance lies in the fact that Shaim oil is of high quality and has low sulfur, which indicates its superiority to oil from the Volga-Urals region."[53]

Yury Ervye (1909–1991), director of the Tyumen Geologic Administration, recalled the important details of this significant event: "Well 6 was the third well sunk as part of the search for oil in the Shaim area. Its location was established by seismic data that showed a line of deposit and the possible accumulation of fossil fuels, the so-called reservoirs of the downthrown part between the Mulymya and Tri Ozera structures. Like the previous two wells, this well was drilled by the crew of experienced foreman Semën N. Urusov. Drilling to a depth of 1,523 meters [4,997 feet] was completed in 18 days. A 12-meter [39-foot] thick layer of oil sandstone was discovered at a depth of 1,488 meters [4,882 feet]. Perforation began on June 17 and signs of oil were seen after the first shot. The well began to flow on June 18. According to preliminary calculations, Well 6 has a daily flow rate of 385 tons by natural drive."[54]

During the next year (1961), several impressive events occurred in the history of the region's oil industry. On March 21, a powerful oil gusher was obtained from exploratory Well 1, with a daily flow rate of 440 tons. The well had been drilled near the village of Megion by the crew of drilling foreman Grigory Norkin from the Nizhnevartovsk section of the Surgut geologic exploration expedition and given the name Megion. On October 15, light crude began to flow at a daily rate of more than 110 tons from Well 28, which had been drilled by Semën Urusov's crew and was located in the Mortymya area northeast of Shaim field. On the same day, Well 62, which had been drilled by Yevgeny Voytsekhovich's crew in the Ust-Balyk area, started to produce oil at a rate of over 220 tons per day. By the end of 1961, five oil fields and 12 gas fields had been added to the map of the Tyumen Region.

On May 19, 1962, the USSR Cabinet of Ministers passed a resolution, "On Measures to Boost Geologic Exploration for Oil and Gas in the Regions of Western Siberia." The resolution set an objective of preparing the main formations of the Ust-Balyk, Megion, and Shaim fields for development.

Speaking at the second session of the Supreme Soviet of the USSR on December 12, 1962, Boris Shcherbina (1919–1990), a deputy from Tyumen Region, stressed: "Thirteen gas fields and four oil fields have opened on the region's territory. The discovery of the Tyumen oil and gas region, whose reserves exceed all known reserves in the country, is an enormous event in scientific and geologic exploration which deserves the highest praise."[55]

In addition, in 1962 the Tazov gas field was discovered in the polar region of Western Siberia, quickly followed by the discovery of the Novy Port, Gubkin, and other gas fields, thereby expanding the borders of the Western Siberian oil and gas province even further.

The recoverable reserves of what one might call a typical oil field opened in Western Siberia in 1961 and 1962 exceeded 330 million tons. Based on the classifications used in Soviet years, a field with recoverable reserves of more than 330 million tons was classified as "unique."

The Western Siberian fields considerably exceeded existing raw material bases (Volga-Urals region, Absheron Peninsula, North Caucasus, etc.) in terms of quality and quantity of reserves. The most notable features were the extremely high flow rates of exploratory wells and, even more important, of the production wells. During this time, wells with flow rates of roughly 110 tons per day were more the norm for Siberian oil workers than an exception. In addition, these unique oil reserves were contained at fully accessible depths ranging from 5,900 to 8,200 feet. It is important to note that all Ob Valley oil exhibited excellent chemical composition and operational performance and was relatively light, with an acceptable level of viscosity and low sulfur and paraffin content.

There was, however, one problem. This abundance of "black gold" was located in extremely harsh geographic and climatic conditions with no infrastructure whatsoever. Up to 70% of the basin territory (and frequently the most interesting areas) was covered with virtually impassable swamps. Geologists could only work there during the winter when most (but not all) of the swamps had frozen and could withstand the weight of heavy machinery. In addition to strong squally northern winds, drillers and geophysicists had to work in temperatures of −22°F (occasionally dropping to −58°F). All this work was performed under wild, uninhabitable conditions without any form of utilities, infrastructure, or communications.

Still, the discovery of the large oil and gas fields in the Mesozoic strata, as well as the promising oil and gas potential of the Western Siberian plain, particularly in the northern parts of Tyumen Region, allowed the Soviet government to raise the issue of creating a new oil-and-gas base for the country in this region that would be comparable to the Volga-Urals Oil and Gas Province. And so on December 4, 1963, the USSR Cabinet of Ministers passed a resolution, "On the Organization of Preparatory Work for the Industrial Development of Known Oil and Gas Fields and the Further Development of Geologic Exploration in Tyumen Region."

The leaders of the country's ministries understood that pursuing the Western Siberian fields would require a major increase in investment in the oil industry initially and then in the gas industry; however, it was obvious that such an investment in Western Siberian oil and gas would be highly efficient and provide immediate returns. Officials also considered the possibility of increasing investment in Western Siberia with export revenue.

The government decided to focus its efforts on the largest and most unique oil and gas fields, at least for the first few decades, which would make it possible to significantly reduce capital investment in the industry and ensure a quick return on investment. In developing the largest fields, the government hoped to ensure a major increase in fuel production while keeping expenses "per 1,000 cubic meters [35,315 cubic feet] of gas and per ton of oil... no higher than the national average."

The fact that the unique Tyumen fields were located in relative proximity to a zone of centralized fuel consumption (primarily the Urals) would also result in significant savings. This factor would lower transportation costs to a certain degree (the fuel route from the northern areas was 620 miles shorter than from Central Asia), but the most important factor was that large industrial bases could be quickly supplied with crude hydrocarbons that were cheaper than other types of fuel. There would follow a reduction in industrial production cost and a positive effect throughout the national economy. Finally, a proposal was made for the widespread use of labor performed on a rotation basis to lower the capital intensity of developing the Western Siberian oil and gas province. The issue of building future cities would be considered later, i.e., once oil and gas production in Western Siberia could provide the required financial revenue. However, the Tyumen Regional Committee was insisting on rapid social infrastructure development in the east-west Ob River Valley and in the north, forcing oil and gas officials to try to defuse this issue. Minister of the Gas Industry Aleksey Kortunov (1907–1973), in particular, defended the use of labor performed on a rotation basis. He maintained that this method would avoid major expenses on facilities for workers' families and allow rotation workers to be mobilized to meet maximum production targets. He also believed it was much easier to set up and provide supplies to small rotation camps than it was to build large cities in the taiga and beyond the Arctic Circle.

Proponents of the rapid development of Western Siberia within the Soviet government also drew attention to strategic, or rather political, considerations. Becoming a large exporter of raw hydrocarbons would not only bring the country significant hard-currency income, but also provide it with additional levers of economic influence throughout the world. Many Soviet economists realized that the era of cheap Middle Eastern oil and uncontrolled economic management by transnational oil companies was coming to an end and that the onset of a global energy crisis was becoming a reality.

Tyumenneftegaz Production Association was set up in January 1964 and put in charge of developing the hydrocarbon resources of Western Siberia. The first director of the new association was Aron Slepyan, who had previously worked at Bashneft. Vitaly Timonin, a specialist from Tatneft, was appointed chief engineer.

The association was given its first specific short-term targets for oil production: 110,000 tons in 1964 and 220,000 tons in 1965. By 1970, oil production was to rise to 11 million tons.

Tyumenneftegaz was soon transformed into the Main Tyumen Oil and Gas Production Administration [Glavtyumenneftegaz] and put under the control of Viktor Muravlenko (1912–1977), a well-known oil specialist and former director of the Middle Volga Regional Economic Council's oil administration.

The development of the largest oil and gas fields in Western Siberia was considerably constrained by the harsh climate (colder than −40°F), the absence of any social or transportation infrastructure, and the remoteness of the oil and gas fields from industrial areas. Therefore, employing traditional methods of development, planning, and use to the Western Siberian oil and gas fields risked extremely high financial and material expenses, which in turn could cast doubt on the feasibility and economic viability of widespread extraction of raw hydrocarbons. It was clear that other solutions were needed, together with unconventional new approaches to the development and exploitation of complex oil and gas fields, in order to resolve these challenging problems.

A decision was made to set up the Main Scientific Research and Design Institute for the Oil and Gas Industry [Giprotyumenneftegaz] in Tyumen to provide design and engineering support. An industrial institute was also created in Tyumen to prepare engineering personnel. On January 8, 1964, RSFSR Minister of Higher and Secondary Special Education V. Stoletov signed a decree "On the Organization of an Industrial Institute in Tyumen."

A government delegation led by Nikolay Baybakov (1911–2008), chairman of the State Committee for the Oil Production Industry under the USSR State Planning Committee, traveled to Tyumen Region in early January 1964. Not long after his visit, on January 30, the Regional Economic Council of the Middle Urals Economic District set up three new oilfield administrations within Tyumenneftegaz: Surgutneft, Igrimgaz and the Shaim consolidated field.

Each year, additional skilled oil specialists came to work in the Western Siberian oil industry from the Bashkir ASSR, the Tatar ASSR, and the Kuybyshev Region. In 1965, utilizing the experience of these specialists, Glavtyumenneftegaz drew up a program that focused primarily on the industrialization of well construction, the introduction of modular platforms, the creation of all-terrain vehicles for the transportation of drilling rigs, solutions to the problem of building and installing drilling rigs in flooded zones and swamps, the simplification and unification of installation diagrams, and improved forms of labor organization.

On March 23, 1964, the drilling of Well R-91 resulted in the discovery of the South Balyk oil field. The development and exploitation of the Megion, Ust-Balyk, Shaim, Tri Ozera, and West Surgut fields began in March 1964. In addition, eight oil fields and two gas fields were opened in the region in 1964. All told, a total of 27 oil fields were discovered in the region from 1961–1964.

An important date in the history of the development of Western Siberia was April 3, 1965, when drilling at Well R-240 led to the discovery of the Mamontovo oil field. The well had a daily oil flow rate of 7,063 cubic feet. On May 29, Well R-1 produced 10,595 cubic feet, at a depth of 6,965–6,988 feet. Within 24 days, on June 22, following the reperforation of the entire pay zone, the well produced a powerful flow of pure oil at a daily rate of 35,315 cubic feet, which officially opened the enormous Samotlor oil field. The final touch was put on this milestone year when a crew from the Ust-Balyk drilling office, led by foreman M. I. Sergeyev, set a new Soviet record. The crew drilled Well 523-bis in 64.5 hours, reaching a commercial drilling rate of 46,145 feet per rig per month, surpassing a previous record by 3,373 feet.

Oil industry officials were obviously thrilled with the discovery of new fields and oil gushers, but a problem soon arose: what to do with the oil produced? The commercial volumes of oil produced at the Shaim field were initially transported by water. On May 23, 1964, Tanker 652 (*Captain Konstantin Tretyakov*) became the first tanker to load Shaim oil at the Sukhoy Bor oil terminal on the Konda River, and regional media reported extensively on the tanker's journey along Siberian rivers to Omsk. On June 4, the tanker arrived safely at the terminal of the Omsk Refinery and started unloading.

However, with a navigational season of only 120–140 days on the Ob and Irtysh Rivers, the river transportation system could not handle the delivery of oil produced at the Shaim consolidated field.

The inability to deliver large volumes of Western Siberian oil to the country's refineries was the biggest problem in the development of this region. For this reason, the development of the Western Siberian fields marked the start of the creation and rapid construction of a trunk pipeline network. Soviet leadership understood that oil production in Western Siberia could not be increased quickly without developing a corresponding transport infrastructure. With the center of oil production shifting to Western Siberia, geographic limitations made it more difficult to locate oil production and refining facilities—which were concentrated in the European part of the country, southern Siberia, and Central Asia—in conformance with a policy that called for large refineries to be constructed in areas of high consumption. Therefore, the government, in addition to setting targets for increased oil production, decided to build pipelines as the most economical and technically sound method of transporting oil.

The Moscow-based Main Pipeline Design Institute [Giprotrubopro-vod] found a practical solution to this problem in early 1964. Field expeditions led by directors Valery Demosfenov and Khaydar Manerov managed to design a pipeline route that was significantly shorter than that envisioned in the project specifications. Surveying parties led by Anatoly Kretov and Aleksandr Pankin cleared a path through dense forests and impassable taiga swamps, crossing many rivers and water obstacles.

The Moscow experts were soon joined by specialists from the Leningrad-based *Giprospetsles* institute. The two institutes jointly decided to analyze materials in the field, instead of at laboratories, and to provide builders with blueprints on the spot as they conducted research. In doing so, the designers managed to cut the surveying period by two-thirds and were able to analyze materials and give the builders blueprints for the construction of the entire pipeline within five months, the first time something like this had happened in Soviet pipeline construction.

The first welding operations on the pipeline route were assigned to a specialized department from the USSR State Gas Industry Committee [Glavgaz], which had successfully completed welding on the *Druzhba* ["Friendship"] transcontinental pipeline. Other groups from Glavtyumenneftegazstroy later joined in this work.

A large volume of construction was completed under a tight schedule, and the 264-mile Shaim–Tyumen oil pipeline was put into operation on December 21, 1965. Oil received through the pipeline was transported from Tyumen to refineries by train. The "black gold" from the Tyumen subsurface had gained reliable year-round access to the country's main industrial centers. On December 28, *Tyumenskaya pravda* reported on a ceremonial rally near the loading facility in Tyumen. "Several banners proclaimed: 'Receive Tyumen Oil, Country!' Amid applause from everyone who had gathered, Shaim oil was shipped from the loading facility at exactly 12 noon for its long journey through Sverdlovsk, Perm, Yaroslavl, Moscow, and beyond. The first shipment consisted of 2,180 tons. It will be followed by one shipment after another, which will bring the wealth of the Tyumen subsurface to the country's refineries. Have a good trip, Shaim oil!" An even bigger pipeline, stretching more than 620 miles from Ust-Balyk to Omsk was inaugurated in 1967 and provided support for the further transportation of Western Siberian oil.

The year 1965 went down in the history of the Soviet oil industry as a milestone once the one millionth ton of oil was produced in Western Siberia. Noting the achievements of the country's oil labor collectives on the eve of this event, August 28, the Presidium of the USSR Supreme Soviet established the All-Union Day of Oil and Gas Industry Workers, which was to be celebrated each year on the first Sunday of September.

USSR Council of Ministers Chairman Kosygin visited the Western Siberian oil fields in winter 1968 and praised the work performed by the builders and oil and gas workers to develop a new oil-producing region that would soon become the country's main fuel base.

Approximately 3,000 wells were drilled and put into production in Western Siberia in 1969. Many respected specialists said, however, that such rapid drilling contradicted the plan for the efficient use of fields. A total of 248 oil and gas fields were discovered from 1966 to 1970, of which 109 were put into production. The development of the gigantic Samotlor oil field began in 1969.

With the steady increase in oil production in the region, the Tyumen Region was already producing almost 33 million tons of oil in 1970. An October 1975 report stated that the Tyumen Region had produced 550 million tons of oil since the Western Siberian fields had been put into production. Drilling totaled 3.3 million feet in 1970, and had risen to 9.2 million feet by 1975. Such remarkable results had never before been achieved in USSR oil regions. Whereas Baku oil producers had required almost 100 years to reach an annual production of 28 million tons, it took the Tyumen producers less than five years to achieve the same results.

The pace of oil production continued to rise rapidly in subsequent years. On February 2, 1975, the country's leading newspaper, *Pravda*, wrote: "Siberian oil is going to Baku. Ten years ago, such a report would have sounded like a fantasy.... Every fourth ton of Soviet oil today begins its journey on the shores of the Oka River.... It took Tatarstan 15 years to bring its annual production level to 110 million tons. Tyumen surpassed the 110 million mark only four years into the Ninth Five-Year Plan...." More than 80 oil and gas fields had been opened in the Tyumen Region by this time, with oil production amounting to 155 million tons in 1975.

In the early 1970s, more changes were made to the management of the oil industry. A General Management Plan was developed that called for a transition in production management—oil and gas would now be produced under a two-tier management system. The new document envisioned further specialization of core and maintenance production by removing maintenance functions from core production; creating conditions needed for the oil industry to transition to self-sufficiency; and using automated oil management systems to run companies, associations, and the industry. With this plan, the Ministry of the Oil Industry intended to include some independent companies and organizations as subdivisions within production associations and enlarge several existing drilling companies and future oil production units. The introduction of this general plan was aimed at optimizing the central bureaucratic structure by reducing the number of employees.

The USSR oil industry continued to develop primarily through extension in the first half of the 1970s. The considerable production volumes of Siberian oil, however, were unable to conceal several production flaws in the industry.

In order to address priority objectives, USSR Minister of the Oil

Industry Nikolay Maltsev (1928–2001) said it would be "necessary to perfect measures aimed at enhancing oil production as much as possible both at fields under development and at fields that are to be put into production. With our production volumes, raising the oil production factor by even one percent would be the equivalent of discovering and inaugurating a large oil field."

It should also be noted that the Tyumen Region Party organizations, after assuming a leading role, frequently tried to supplant Soviet and economic agencies and intervene in the decision-making process on various issues concerning the organization of oil and gas production.

Table 14. USSR Total and Western Siberian Oil Production
by year, in millions of tons

Year	USSR Total Oil Production	Western Siberian Oil Production	Western Siberian Share of Total Oil Production
1965	267.73	0.992	0.37%
1970	389	34.6	8.9%
1975	541.2	163	30.1%
1980	664.7	344.6	51.8%

Source: *USSR Petroleum [Neft SSSR]*. Moscow, 1987, pp. 106, 111, 113, 180, 181.

From the table above, it can clearly be seen that the center of Soviet oil production shifted from the Volga-Urals region to Western Siberia in the 1970s. Western Siberian oil also helped achieve another prestigious objective on the international stage—surpassing the oil production level of the US. Whereas in 1974 the Soviet Union was producing at 93.2% of the US level (for comparison, the figure was only 20% in 1955), by 1975 the USSR produced 541 million tons, which was 4.5% more than its main competitor. By 1980, Soviet oil production was 9.8% higher than US output.

As a direct participant in the development of the Western Siberian province and recalling the early stages of the Great Western Siberian Oil Saga, I can say that this was a special period comparable, perhaps, to wartime. Under harsh climatic conditions, it was the selfless labor of several thousand Soviet engineers, technical specialists, and workers, in addition to extremely high concentrations of material and financial resources, an efficient management system, and new engineering and technological solutions that enabled the domestic oil industry to achieve results that had never before been seen anywhere. It took just ten years to establish and develop an enormous domestic oil, gas, and energy complex in Western Siberia at an unprecedented pace, thus creating a reliable base for the subsequent development of the USSR's economy.

The Ups and Downs of the USSR–US Energy Dialogue

On the whole, the 1970s were a rather stable period of development for Soviet oil workers: financing, materials, and technology were provided to the industry without disruptions and in sufficiently large volumes.

Consequently, in 1976 the USSR produced 563 million tons of oil and natural gas condensate, 22 million tons more than in 1975. It put 4,798 new oil wells into production, well over a planned target of 4,453. Moreover, 1,184 wells were removed from the nonproducing well stock and 3,215 wells were switched to artificial lift. In Western Siberia, seven new fields were put into production, and a modern system was introduced to organize formation-pressure maintenance. In the Komi ASSR, the Usinsk and Vazeyskoye oil fields were put into operation in 1976, which allowed the conglomerate *Komineft* to fulfill its plan targets.

In that year, total capital investment in the industry was 4.4 billion rubles. The Nizhnevartovsk–Kuybyshev oil pipeline—with a diameter of 48 inches and a length of 1,333 miles—was put into operation. Part of the pipeline had been laid in the same corridor as the Samotlor–Kholmogory–Surgut oil pipeline, which was 139 miles long.

In the following year (1977), the USSR planned to produce 595 million tons of oil, but ensuring oil production growth of 32 million tons only required increasing development drilling by 1.6 million feet. A year earlier, however, at a meeting of industry leaders in Moscow, Oil Industry Minister Shashin gave a speech containing a key phrase that everyone basically ignored in that period of "enthusiastic reports by the winners of socialist competition and ceremonial communiqués." The minister noted that "in order to sustain the existing level of oil production, we must introduce new oil production capacity of no less than 99 million tons every year, because an ever-growing number of fields are entering the stage of declining production." At that time, industrial development of new fields in Western Siberia, with its harsh natural climatic conditions, still required significant capital investment and substantial expenditures for materials, equipment, and human resources. But these were steadily decreasing in the country, which had entered the so-called "period of stagnation."

Under these conditions, the leadership of the USSR Ministry of the Oil Industry decided to bet again on increasing the efficiency of existing production capacity, and to return to studying the advanced experience of the leading foreign oil producing countries. The country chosen here was the US, which was one of the leaders of the world oil industry, producing 508 million tons of oil in 1976.

In December 1976, on the basis of an exchange of correspondence between the cochairmen of the Joint American-Soviet Committee on Cooperation in the Field of Energy, a Working Group on Scientific and

Technical Cooperation in the Field of the Oil Industry was formed. By mutual agreement, the first meeting of this working group was held in the US, from October 26 through November 3, 1977.

The head of the American delegation and chairman of the meetings was J. Wade Watkins, who was acting deputy director of the Oil, Gas, and Shale Production Technology Division of the US Department of Energy (DOE). The American delegation included: D. Kramer, deputy director of the Division for Scientific and Technical Cooperation with the USSR and Countries of Eastern Europe of the US Department of State; J. Ball, director of a DOE research center; L. Schrader, deputy director of a DOE research center; G. Dean, director of the DOE Research Administration; R. Johansen, director of a section in the area of oil production at a DOE research center; J. Sugihara, dean of the College of Chemistry and Physics of the University of North Dakota; T. Donovan, geologist with the central office of the US Geological Survey; V. Robinson, section director at a DOE research center; A. Roberts, USGS geologist; L. Marchant, project director of a DOE research center; George Stosur, director of the DOE Sector for Enhanced Oil Production; A. Layton, engineer with the DOE Research Administration; V. Heinz, director of the physical sciences section of a DOE research center; A. Kotb, specialist in the area of fossil energy sources of the DOE International Research and Development Administration; and S. Blacklin, DOE foreign affairs officer.

The Soviet delegation was headed by Professor Gadel Vakhitov, doctor of technical sciences, director of the All-Union Scientific Research Institute for Oil and Gas; Boris Shchitov, head of the Foreign Affairs Administration of the Ministry of the Oil Industry; Doctor of Technical Sciences Leonid Zorkin, deputy director for science of the All-Union Scientific Research Institute for Nuclear Geophysics and Geochemistry; and Doctor of Mineral and Geological Sciences Vagan A. Chakhmachev, laboratory director of the Institute of Geology and Fossil Fuels Development of the USSR Academy of Sciences.

On the very first day, the Soviet and American sides agreed on the following agenda for the meetings: general information; creation of expert groups; scientific and technical discussions on subjects of mutual interest; exchange of opinions on future directions of joint scientific and technical cooperation; and the date and place of the second meeting of the Joint Soviet-American Working Group.

American scientists presented a series of extensive reports about the results of their work in the area of petroleum geochemistry, on maintaining optimal reservoir pressure and increasing oil production, on the development of new technology for use at heavy oil and tar fields, and also on new methods for determining the basic physicochemical characteristics of petroleum.

In turn, Soviet specialists presented brief reports on the future development of the USSR's oil industry, and also on the results of efforts to increase the oil production factor and other problems.

After the lively debates ended, it was unanimously decided to create two expert groups in five areas of Soviet-American oil cooperation: geochemical prospecting; basic petroleum properties; methods of maintaining pressure by injecting water and gas; new (tertiary) methods of increasing oil production; and methods of extracting hydrocarbons from heavy oil and tar sand fields.

Soviet and American specialists had a very productive day on October 26, 1977, when there were high-level scientific and technical discussions on the subjects of developing lithogeochemical methods of oil and gas field prospecting; of the problem of tar sands at the contemporary stage; and a review of individual oil production methods. And here, great interest was generated by the Soviet scientists' report on current subjects, including geochemical methods of oil and gas field prospecting (scientific research work and its prospects for development); the status and problems of using geochemical methods to determine oil content during exploratory drilling; the status, principles, and effectiveness of waterflooding in Soviet oil fields; and the use of methods to enhance oil production.

The work schedule of the Soviet-American group was so tight that some speeches prepared by Soviet specialists could not be read at meetings, so some materials were given to the American side for further study. Among such materials were "Design and Results of Using a Selective System of Waterflooding at Oil Fields" (the example given was the Aktash parcel), "State of Knowledge and Use of Methods of Oil Displacement by Steam Combined with Waterflooding," and "Use of *in situ* Petroleum Combustion Combined with Waterflooding."

During the subsequent sectional meetings, the Soviet side presented detailed working programs of potential scientific and technical cooperation, and proposed future joint symposia, exchanges of information and samples, and visits of scientists and engineers to laboratories on both sides lasting three weeks or more. During the meeting, Professor Gadel Vakhitov, leader of the Soviet delegation, officially invited the American side to send its experts on the subjects of geochemical prospecting and basic petroleum properties to an international symposium that was to take place in the Soviet Union in the spring of 1978.

The following work day became an important event in the history of Soviet-American scientific relations. Conference participants concluded that the time allocated to such meetings had to be substantially increased. The Soviet delegation again voiced its proposal that an international symposium be held in the USSR at the end of the following year, with the participation of existing expert groups, on the subject: "Formation Pressure Maintenance, Enhanced Oil Production, and Development of

Heavy Oil and Tar Fields." American scientists fully supported this proposal.

The Soviet delegation also proposed conducting joint research on the process of oil oxidation at temperatures of 212–392°F as one of the methods of stimulating oil production, with the idea that both sides would start from the minimally studied technological aspect of the problem. In turn, American scientists proposed a cycle of joint efforts to create a means for precise determination of residual oil saturation.

At the end of a productive two weeks of activity, the Joint Soviet-American Working Group approved the list and schedule of planned events for subsequent presentation to the leadership of the Joint American-Soviet Committee on Cooperation in the Field of Energy. The sides agreed that the events presented by the expert groups could be held after approval by the Joint Committee and the corresponding government institutions of the US and the USSR.

After attending meetings in the American capital, the Soviet delegates visited a series of major facilities of the US oil industry, which was undoubtedly of practical interest for them. Soviet scientists first visited the Nalco Chemical research laboratory (Sugar Land, Texas), where they had a good opportunity to familiarize themselves with the achievements of their American colleagues. Then, a visit was scheduled to the Wilmington oil field (Long Beach, California), where US Department of Energy specialists were involved in a caustic-soda injection project, and the Midway-Sunset oil field (Chanslor, California), where the US Department of Energy was involved in work to inject steam into oil reservoirs.

The Soviet delegates were very impressed by their visit to the US Department of Energy's research center in Oklahoma (Osage County), where a successful project was under way to inject micelle solutions and polymers into oil reservoirs. After that, they traveled to a Kevany oil field (Osage County, Oklahoma), where US DOE specialists were involved in an improved project of waterflooding, and then visited the field of the B&H Oil Company (Nowata County, Oklahoma), where a project was under way to inject micelle solutions and polymers.

Upon completing the extensive program of the trip, Professor Gadel Vakhitov, leader of the Soviet delegation, noted the productive nature and good organization of the visit to institutions of the US Department of Energy and oil fields, where work was being carried out successfully to introduce new methods of enhancing oil production, and where American oil workers had demonstrated their competence and high professionalism.

Members of the Joint Soviet-American Working Group also made arrangements for exchanging correspondence relating to their activity through the Foreign Affairs Administration of the USSR Ministry of the Oil Industry and the US Department of Energy.

It should be emphasized that one of the main achievements of the first meeting of the Soviet-American Working Group on Scientific and Technical Cooperation in the Field of the Oil Industry was the beginning of productive exchange of experience among Soviet and American petroleum scientists, and also the decision to carry out joint research to increase the effectiveness of waterflooding at oil fields with complex conditions.

Unfortunately, the broad program of scientific and technical cooperation that was planned between the Soviet and American petroleum scientists was never fully realized due to a sharp deterioration in political relations between the USSR and the US. The introduction of a "limited contingent of Soviet forces" into Afghanistan in December 1979 resulted in a long-term negative response by the American administration in many areas, including a substantial curtailment of scientific and technical cooperation in the oil industry.

The First International Oil and Gas Exhibition in the USSR

In the last quarter of the 20th century, Soviet society had no cause to doubt the stability of the development of the Soviet oil industry, a situation that was certainly confirmed by the Party press: "If we consider the scale of the absolute increases in society's production, the Ninth Five-Year Plan is our country's best. In the decisive year of the Five-Year Plan, our country became a mighty oil-producing power, occupying first place among the more developed industrialized countries of the world."

The USSR did, in fact, surpass the US in 1975 and assume first place in world oil production, and in its 60th anniversary year of 1977, oil production was 601.6 million tons. Despite the complexity of the geologic and physical conditions of developing oil fields in Western Siberia and other regions, oil workers exceeded plan figures set by the country's Party political leadership by placing 5,114 new wells into service, and restoring 1,595 idle wells to service.

Although the USSR's achievements in the oil and gas industry were beyond question, Soviet scientists and specialists in the area of petroleum equipment and technology required both familiarity with the latest developments in the field, and an opportunity to learn from advanced Western experience. Largely proceeding on this basis, the USSR government decided that the country would host the first International Oil and Gas Exhibition in June 1978, in Baku, the capital of the Azerbaijan SSR.

Because of the great political and economic significance attached to this exhibition, preparations began early in 1977. The site was well chosen: after all, the capital of socialist Azerbaijan, Baku, which was historically linked to the production of oil on the Absheron Peninsula, also had very rich cultural and historical traditions.

Heydar Aliyev (1923–2003), first secretary of the Central Committee of the Communist Party of Azerbaijan, emphasized in one speech: "The exhibition must play a positive role in the life of the republic. A heavy responsibility has been placed on us, both by the leaders of the country and by our multiethnic people. The exhibition must be carried out at the highest level."

To hold the exhibition, the republic's government allocated an area of more than 160,000 square feet on the grounds of the Exhibition of National Economic Achievements of the Azerbaijan SSR. The exhibition displays were to be laid out both in enclosed pavilions and in outdoor areas.

The ceremonial opening of the exhibition took place on Saturday, June 17, 1978. At the opening ceremony, the republic's Party leader, Heydar Aliyev, read the welcoming words of Leonid Brezhnev, general secretary of the CPSU Central Committee, who, along with wishing great professional success, expressed confidence that "The International Oil and Gas Exhibition should greatly unite the entire scientific community."

Attendees were then addressed by Aleksey Kosygin. In his speech he presented a brief overview of the achievements of the USSR oil and gas industry in the Ninth Five-Year Plan, emphasized the special significance of fulfilling plan targets in the current Tenth Five-Year Plan, and noted in conclusion that: "The oil and gas industry is assuming greater and greater importance in the world economy and in the development of mankind. Understanding the full importance of future challenges, I would like to hope that in the future, the leading oil and gas powers will work together and help each another in various initiatives." The Soviet prime minister's speech was warmly received by the audience, and set the right tone for the further productive work of the International Oil and Gas Exhibition.

The newspaper *Izvestia* dedicated a review article to the opening of the International Oil and Gas Exhibition in Baku, which it characterized rather expansively: "The exhibition has become one of the links in the chain promoting stabilization and further development of friendly relations between the Soviet Union and countries of the world."

Altogether, more than 2,000 people from 40 countries participated in the oil exhibition. They included representatives of both leading oil-producing powers and developing states who expressed their insistent desire to join the "international oil club."

The exhibition's guests and visitors focused most on the Soviet display, the stands of which were decorated with exhibits presented by leading Russian scientific research institutes. The main organizer of the Soviet display was the USSR Ministry of the Oil Industry. All preparation for the exhibition events and the way they were subsequently carried out were under the personal control of Minister Nikolay Maltsev.

Because of time constraints, the Soviet display emphasized mostly high technology for the oil and gas industry, including a large-scale demonstration of new equipment, high-performance oilfield equipment, apparatus, and tools.

Numerous exhibition visitors focused their attention on the detailed displays of leading industry scientific research institutions: VNIIneft, TatNIPIneft, Giprotyumenneftegaz, and the Siberian Scientific Research Institute of the Oil Industry, which presented its high-efficiency hardware technology and engineering solutions that were a key factor for high rates of Western Siberian oil and gas province development. Among these, specialists singled out: movable masts for new construction, mechanical wrenches of original design that could be disassembled, cable reeling and unreeling systems for tripping operations, electric centrifugal pumps, elevators with changeable bushings, automatic devices for making and breaking sucker rods, and workover swivels, among others.

Moreover, a special stand separately displayed the latest developments in the area of the oil and refining industry that had been built by leading scientific institutions of the USSR Academy of Sciences.

The attention of visitors was also attracted to the interesting display of the Ivan M. Gubkin Moscow Institute of the Petrochemical and Gas Industry.[56]

The leading oil-producing powers, headed by the US, were thoroughly represented by displays at the Baku exhibition. Their presence at the event was largely connected to a renewal of the Soviet-American energy dialog in the fall of 1977, which in turn echoed throughout the world oil community.

The US display was led by J. Wade Watkins, deputy director of the Oil, Gas, and Shale Production Technology Division of the US Department of Energy, cochairman of the Soviet-American Working Group on Scientific and Technical Cooperation in the Oil Industry. In his words: "Such a friendly initiative of the Soviet government should result in a flurry of scientific and technical activity in the production and development of hydrocarbon fields, and also in the technical and technological innovations necessary for dynamic development of the industry." Under the patronage of the US DOE, visitors were shown displays of the DOE's Phillips Petroleum research center (Osage County, Oklahoma), and the Kevany Oil Company (Osage County, Oklahoma), and B&H Oil Company (Nowata County, Oklahoma), which presented the latest development of injecting micelle solutions and polymers. At their exhibits, the Americans also presented brief accounts of work carried out in petroleum geochemistry, formation-pressure maintenance, enhanced oil production, and technology for developing heavy oil and tar fields and for determining basic petroleum properties.

Moreover, numerous prominent American scientists and specialists were delegates at the Soviet exhibition. Among them were the following members of the Soviet-American Working Group on Scientific and Technical Cooperation in the Oil Industry: J. Ball, director of a US Department of Energy research center, T. Donovan, geologist with the central office of the US Geological Survey, V. Robinson, section director at a DOE research center, R. Johansen, director of the oil production section at a DOE research center, L. Schrader, deputy director at a DOE research center, G. Dean, director of the DOE Research Administration, L. Marchant, project director at a DOE research center, George Stosur, director of the DOE Enhanced Oil Production Division, A. Layton, engineer with the DOE Research Administration, V. Heinz, director of the physical sciences section at a DOE research center, and other engineering and technical specialists.

Several international conferences and seminars of great scientific significance were held under the auspices of the exhibition. In the course of their work, Soviet scientists and foreign specialists had creative discussions on subjects of mutual interest, and there was a productive exchange of opinions about future directions of joint scientific and technical cooperation.

Patrice Roi, one of the representatives of the French Ministry of Energy, had an interesting recollection: "It is difficult to convey the delight over what was seen and heard. Here in Baku, an impetus was given for development of the technical and technological future. I believe that, in the very near future, the oil powers will stun the most skeptical of minds with new hydrocarbon production records. Such events will definitely have an effect on mankind's future prosperity." Numerous visitors from Eastern and Western Europe, the Middle East, the US, Canada, and other countries had similar viewpoints.

The International Oil Exhibition in Baku gave Soviet specialists a good opportunity, based on its advanced experience in the world oil and gas business, for productive cooperation in the future, using advanced equipment and procedures for oil production.

The first International Oil Exhibition in the USSR drew around 110,000 visitors, including numerous delegations from foreign countries and Soviet specialists from various regions, providing clear evidence of significant interest in both the achievements of the industry and in the trends for development of oil equipment and procedures.

It is also gratifying that it was in this place, where the history of Russia's oil industry began, that the fine tradition started of Russia regularly hosting one of the largest international specialized exhibition events, the Moscow International Oil and Gas Exhibition, which today is one of the most significant events of its kind for the world business, scientific, and engineering community.

Heading for a Crisis

The Soviet Union entered a period of large-scale structural crisis at the start of the 1970s because its supermonopolized bureaucratic authoritarian industrial system was unable to develop any further or respond to the challenges of modern times.

Over several decades, it became clearly apparent that, while a scientific and technical revolution was under way in the world at large, the USSR's economy was incapable of ramping up to large-scale production and adopting new technologies. The global energy crisis forced the economies of the leading countries of the West to move from an industrial development model to a postindustrial (information-based) model. At this stage, they succeeded in switching rather quickly to energy-saving technologies (these technologies were used to upgrade 66% of the equipment in the US, 70–75% of that in EEC countries, and 82% of that in Japan), as well as high-tech production (microelectronics, computer science, biotechnology, and robotics).

These global changes were obvious, but Soviet Party political leadership, headed by Leonid Brezhnev, having formally declared the main priority of the Ninth Five-Year Plan (1970–1975) and the Tenth Five-Year Plan (1976–1980) to be to move the economy onto an intensive development track, in reality was continuing on a path of extensive industrial economic development using the Stalinist model, with the help of traditional contributing industries, including the oil and gas industry.

However, the physical wear and tear and obsolescence of the plants and equipment made it senseless to increase capital investments in industrial construction from one five-year plan to the next, and expect to see a return within a decade. In the rapidly accelerating scientific and technical revolution, new projects frequently became obsolescent at the design stage. The number of unfinished construction projects increased, and capital was undergoing "necrosis." The mania for projects of gigantic proportion did irreparable harm to the ecosystems of many parts of the country. The resources invested in capital construction brought no return. Whereas in 1970 every ruble invested in capital construction increased production by 1 ruble 39 kopecks, in 1973 this figure was 1 ruble 10 kopecks, and by 1981 it was only 81 kopecks. In effect, the country was steadily going bankrupt.

The structural stagnation in scientific and technical areas and the orientation of gross plan targets toward increasing the production volume led to the manufacture of low-quality products that nobody wanted to buy, which in turn led to overstocks. By the end of the 1980s, warehouses had accumulated products worth 400 billion rubles, which were marked down and written off. At the same time, many other products became scarce, creating enormous lines in stores.

Increased raw material and fuel costs likewise drove up the price of industrial products. The rising prices of farm equipment, fertilizer, and compound feed and the rising costs of farm equipment maintenance and agricultural construction wiped out any gains from the increase in the sales prices of foodstuffs purchased from collective farms. Agricultural production growth rates fell from 21% during the Eighth Five-Year Plan (1966–1970) to 6% in the Eleventh (1981–1985).

Social and state interests began to diverge sharply. Soviet workers increasingly felt alienated from property and the lack of incentives for productive labor made them feel like strangers in their own country and enterprises. Labor productivity declined steadily. Qualified labor lost its prestige. Government agencies thrived on excessive paperwork, exaggerated performance, whitewashing of issues, and downward adjustments of plan targets. Society began to feel a general indignation toward the privileged elite, the ineffective work of the administrative apparatus, and the arbitrariness, irresponsibility, and growing corruption of civil servants.

By the mid-1980s, the Soviet population ranked 77th in the world in per capita consumption. The Soviet economy was generally becoming less and less competitive on the world market, and its share of world trade in 1970–1980 was only 4%.

The Soviet leaders failed to acknowledge the fact that a system of social and economic relationships based on mass standardized production, which deprived workers of creative initiative and favored strong-willed, bureaucratic administration of all economic processes, was no longer able to raise production efficiency or product quality. When the system's development inevitably ran up against the barrier of the new scientific and technical revolution—namely the need to solve the problems of the postindustrial era—the country's Party political leadership could not meet the challenge. What was required of them was a decisive renunciation of the old dogmatic Marxist constructs, a decisive restructuring of the entire socioeconomic system on a new basis, including renunciation of attempts to control everything from the center and a move toward greater individual and group autonomy and intellectuality, putting social and communication ties on an equal footing, intensively sharing diverse information, putting industrial production on an ecological foundation, and much more. The USSR's ruling elite, which consisted mainly of people of advanced age, were bewildered by the global information revolution, as they believed that the introduction of any changes would be destructive to the "sacred cause of socialism."

The attempts of Party political leadership to preserve an imaginary stability in the country only served to aggravate the systemic crisis and further the Soviet Union's consistent and steady lagging behind leading foreign countries, which had confidently set off on the path of postindustrial development. This situation was also intensified by the obsessive striving, on the part of Soviet leaders, to achieve military and strategic parity with the US, and to provide an ever-increasing level of fraternal assistance to countries of the socialist camp and people's democracies, and by the exhaustion of the USSR's financial and material resources, which were rapidly dwindling anyway. Another factor that ultimately led to the country's ruin was the course of Party political leadership that considered support for national liberation movements in most of the Third World a top priority, sending contingents of Soviet soldiers to 36 regional conflicts between 1970 and 1980 and into a bloody, ten-year war in Afghanistan (1979–1989).

During this period, Western Siberia was a kind of hydrocarbon Klondike for the Soviet Union. The global energy crisis of the early 1970s oriented the Soviet economy toward raw materials. It became advantageous simply to sell raw hydrocarbons for hard currency and then to buy everything the country needed, including wheat, consumer goods, and foodstuffs. As a result, 83–85% of Soviet exports consisted of raw materials and semifinished products, and only 15–17% consisted of finished products. Oil and gas pipeline systems to Western Europe were completed in short order (the largest being the Trans-Siberian Urengoy–Pomary–Uzhgorod pipeline), and these carried almost one-third of oil and 75% of natural gas that was produced.

By the second half of the 1980s, the lack of a well-thought-out foreign economic strategy resulted in serious losses. A drop in world fuel prices devalued raw materials, which were the principal component of the Soviet economy. In contrast to the 1970s, this part of the economy was now losing $10 billion a year, while maintaining past volumes of oil and gas exports.

In the Tenth Five-Year Plan (1976–1980), the industry began to experience a steady decline in oil production growth rates. Whereas the annual increase in oil and natural gas liquid production was 35 million tons in 1975, by 1980 it was only 19.4 million tons.

The crisis symptoms in the USSR's oil industry that scientists had warned of earlier began to manifest themselves ever more clearly. However, instead of elaborating and implementing a comprehensive approach to solve the industry's acute problems, the CPSU Central Committee proposed, for the umpteenth time, that Soviet oil workers engage in a "wide expansion of socialist competition to fulfill the assignments of the five-year plan ahead of schedule." Party ideologues felt that slogans of the type used at the 26th CPSU Congress, "The economy must be economical" (which amazed both Soviet and foreign specialists by its inadequacy), together with preparations to celebrate significant dates in Soviet history, would succeed once again at giving people the resolve to fulfill the vital decisions of the Party and government.

Party ideologues even brought up the forgotten "Stakhanov movement"[57] of the 1930s, and printed numerous articles and notes about reviving the glorious labor records of the past; such articles filled the pages of national, local, and large-circulation newspapers. It is hardly surprising that local Party organizations soon gave birth to many different kinds of "oil worker team labor initiatives" under very high-sounding industry slogans: "More oil from each well," "Complete the five-year plan ahead of schedule: one well over the quota every 15 days," "Every well must give a lot of oil," "Give the five-year plan a shock-work finish," etc.

Party officials did not give much thought to the meaning of these initiatives or how everything would be carried out; the main thing was to think up a new movement or initiative that had not been heard of before, and to do so as quickly as possible. A pattern soon emerged: First, a "labor initiative" was put forward, followed by Party influence on the administration of an enterprise to create exclusive "greenhouse" conditions for so-called "beacons of socialist competition." This would be followed by the dispatch of a triumphant report to higher authorities and, as a result, a ceremony would be held to celebrate the receipt of honorary Red Banner awards, high governmental awards, and various other honors.

As for the industry as a whole, the influence of such initiatives on the state of production was clearly negative. What was necessary was the very opposite: a radical reexamination of the former frantic rush strategy of oil industry development. A switch was required, as quickly as possible, from intensive methods of oil production to scientifically-based, efficient methods of operating existing fields and developing new ones. However, this was not done.

Thus, despite the experience of developing the Romashkino oil field and foreign fields, oil production at the unique Samotlor oil field in Western Siberia was stimulated starting from the first days it was developed, a practice unprecedented in the world. Very ambiguous design decisions were implemented, such as rigid three-row systems of production well location, suboptimal initial well spacing, and consolidation of independent development sites, including producing several dozen strata from one well and selective advance exploitation of highly productive strata with extremely high depletion rates from the remaining recoverable reserves. The stimulation of oil withdrawals here did not fit into the traditional understanding of this production process, according to which increases in oil withdrawals are done in such a way to maintain efficient development conditions on the oil fields and prevent reduction of the recoverable reserves of the field over its entire life. At Samotlor oil field, petroleum depletion was accelerated to a simply absurd level, without any reasonable limitations. In 1995, the ratio of water volume injected per ton of oil produced reached 13.23. The rate of depletion of remaining recoverable reserves in the middle of the 1980s was 12–14% for the whole field. The vital decisions carried out on the instructions of Party authorities could only result in the irreversible deterioration of the state of development of the Samotlor oil field. The subsequent steady drop in production there simultaneously meant a reduction of oil production volumes in the whole industry.

Other similar examples could be cited. On the whole, development of other fields in Western Siberia also involved minimizing the width of the strips produced when the pool was sliced up into rows of injection wells, or specifying an overall repeating-pattern waterflooding system from the start of field operation. Field practice involved unjustifiably increasing the volume of injected water, while ignoring the reservoir's energy status. The volume of water injected exceeded not only the volume of oil produced, but it even surpassed the amount of fluids produced. Under these conditions, reservoir pressure exceeded overburden pressure at individual fields, forming uncontrolled artificial cracks with all the attendant consequences.

At the major Talin oil field in Western Siberia, repeating-pattern waterflooding was routinely used from the start of development, with no regard for the geologic and physical structure characteristics of the productive strata. Within five years after drilling began at the field, this led to acute water encroachment, i.e., water cuts of up to 90% with a current oil production of less than 10%.

Oil production enterprises thus lost their sense of moderation about the scale of employing primary contour waterflooding technology, and industry leaders ignored the opinion of leading specialists, who maintained that infill drilling was a necessary precondition to prepare for the waterflooding process. Instead, the predominant idea thrust upon oil workers from above involved the complete depletion of recoverable reserves using a small number of wells, that is, with production wells widely spaced and producing a small quantity of associated water, an approach that had been suggested in the 1950s by academician Aleksandr Krylov (1904–1981).

And so, in accordance with the strong-willed directives of Soviet Party political leadership, in the 1980s Western Siberia was turned into a region where petroleum depletion was stimulated to the maximum extent, in disregard of efficient oilfield development principles and optimal design solutions.

Party decisions also imposed unrelated functions on the oil industry. For example, in carrying out the state foodstuffs program, Soviet oil workers not only had to provide the agricultural industrial complex with fuel, but also create their own subsidiary agricultural complexes to grow grain and raise livestock and poultry. Thus, at the end of the 1970s, the oil industry was operating 48 state farms and subsidiary farms on 697,000 acres of land using more than 10,000 workers. This is a very revealing example of the serious disproportions and distortions of the Soviet economy that ultimately led to its downfall.

On March 3, 1981, the 26th CPSU Congress adjourned after adopting "Basic Directions for USSR Economic and Social Development in 1981–1985 and the Period until 1990." The document planned, by 1985, to bring the production level of oil with gas condensate to 683–712 million tons and build 6,138 miles of oil pipelines and 2,356 miles of petroleum products pipelines. The proportion of wells operated using artificial lift was to be increased to 80%.

At the beginning of the Eleventh Five-Year Plan (1981–1985), the oil industry entered a new stage of development characterized principally by a sharp decline in production growth rates; the first signs had begun to appear of an impending day of reckoning for the subjective and poorly considered decisions of industry policy. As a consequence, starting in 1982 the USSR's annual plans for production of oil and natural gas liquids were no longer met, not once. In 1983, production of oil and gas condensate in the USSR fell to 679 million tons, and the following year it slipped again, to 675 million tons.

After the death of Leonid Brezhnev in November 1982, the top Soviet leadership underwent a series of abrupt changes: leadership of the government was assumed by Yury Andropov (1914–1984), and after his death in February of 1984, by Konstantin Chernenko (1911–1985), whose rule lasted little over a year.

Finally, the April 1985 Plenum of the CPSU Central Committee elected Mikhail Gorbachëv to the highest post in the Party. The country's new leader tried to make a realistic assessment of the country's economic situation. In his speech "The Key Issue of the Party's Economic Policy," he laid special emphasis on the fact that the country had started to feel economic difficulties in the early 1970s, and among their causes he mentioned "the inadequacy of the administrative structure of economic activity, its forms, methods, and very psychology."

It was clear from these words that the country's new leader understood that further development of Soviet society inevitably required renunciation of the Stalinist model of state socialism. However, it turned out that a great deal did not depend on him at all: The direction of subsequent reforms, their results, and ultimately the fate of the USSR as a single state were strictly dependent on many factors, including foreign policy, the alignment of forces in the ruling elite, and in most cases that elite's unwillingness to allow sweeping modernization of the country's sociopolitical and economic system.

Mikhail Gorbachëv immediately focused his attention on the state of the oil industry, which contributed much hard currency to the country's budget. On April 19, 1985, Gorbachëv's eighth day as the head of the government, the CPSU Central Committee and the USSR Council of Ministers adopted a resolution, "On Additional Measures to Retool the Oil and Gas Industry." Four months later, on August 10, 1985 the CPSU Central Committee and the USSR Council of Ministers adopted a resolution, "On the Comprehensive Development of the Oil and Gas Industry in Western Siberia in 1986–1990."

The resolution noted that "in connection with the shift of the bulk of operations in Tyumen Region to districts characterized by more difficult natural climate and geology, with delays in commissioning newly discovered oil fields, oil field electrical supply facilities, and housing associated with facilities intended for social, cultural, and everyday uses, and with existing shortcomings in the organization of the production of oil and petroleum gas, many enterprises of the oil production industry in Tyumen Province have of late not been fulfilling the plan for producing oil and associated petroleum gas." The resolution's directives included enhancing the technical sophistication of production equipment and processes, improving the organization of labor, introducing energy-saving technologies, speeding the processes of drilling wells and putting them into production, and taking more precautions to prevent accidents.

However, it is easy to understand why this resolution did not produce a rapid effect. In 1985, USSR oil production was 656 million tons. Western Siberia's share of that total was 388.8 million tons. Overall, the plan for 1985 was only 94% fulfilled, but Western Siberia was responsible for 34 million tons of the plan's 38-million-ton shortfall. Clearly, the principal breakdown in the government oil production plan occurred in this region.

The reasons for the production plan breakdown, both in the entire industry and regionally, were widely discussed at a series of meetings of the CPSU Central Committee and the Ministry of the Oil Industry and meetings of Party economic activists from oil-producing territories and regions. The main reasons for the plan's failure are those mentioned above: insufficient attention to providing workers with housing and sociocultural facilities, slow rates of new field development, inadequate scope of transitioning flowing wells to mechanized oil production methods, delays in creating capacities to prepare for water injection and in constructing water-intake facilities, aqueducts and oil-gathering mains, and a substantial manufacturing shortfall in supplying oil workers with modern oilfield equipment. Alas, such basic industry problems remained unexamined, and instead, a commitment was made to stimulate oil production in every possible way, thereby undermining the very fundamentals of efficient field development. After all, the rapid depletion of active reserves was naturally lowering the quality of the recoverable reserves remaining on the industry's balance sheet, and consequently lowering the productivity of producing wells. At the beginning of the Twelfth Five-Year Plan (1986), the share of inefficient reserves on the industry's overall balance sheet was 48%; at the beginning of the Tenth Five-Year Plan (1976), it had been 30%. Over this period, the share of inefficient reserves in Western Siberia tripled, from 18 to 54%.

The meetings also did not consider the increasing discrepancy between production volumes and the growth of reserves. From 1971 to 1985, oil production in the Western Siberian oil-producing region grew by a factor of 12.7, while reserves of all categories of petroleum increased by a factor of only 3.1, and active reserves increased by a factor of only 1.8.

According to the government's position, a choice was again made in favor of emergency mobilization for a "further assault on the treasuries of black gold." In short order, the conglomerates Bashneft and Tatneft created their own oil production units in Western Siberia, sent numerous crews of qualified oil workers there, and brought new fields into accelerated development. By 1986, 26 fields had been put into operation, twice as many as in the preceding four years. All of this ensured that the conglomerate Glavtyumenneftegaz would achieve planned daily oil production levels by September of that same year.

It should be emphasized that in 1985, the proportion of Soviet energy resource exports was 52.7%, compared with 46.8% in 1980. And although the physical volume of total oil exports declined somewhat over the period, from 131 million tons to 129 million tons, exports to countries that paid in freely convertible currency increased from 30.2 million tons to 31.9 million tons.

A significant portion of the hard-currency funds received from oil exports nevertheless did not go at all toward purchasing the latest equipment and technology urgently needed to modernize industrial production, but was spent to bolster the Soviet economy, which was in a crisis, and to purchase foodstuffs and consumer goods.

In the words of economist academician Stanislav Shatalin (1934–1997), in the early 1980s the situation had already started to get out of control: "Top leadership made increasingly less effort to make rational decisions about what should be done with the petrodollars that were still flowing into the USSR.... But we macroeconomists knew that the economic situation was steadily deteriorating, that the growth rates of the gross national product and national income were falling, and that the proportion of strong factors in them was decreasing."[58]

In the fall of 1985, however, Saudi Arabia abandoned the OPEC price agreement, causing world oil prices to drop from $29–30 a barrel to $12–15. Thus, the USSR treasury experienced a sharp decrease in freely convertible hard currency revenue. Purchases of feed grain, so badly

315

needed by Soviet animal breeders, reached a minimum. The lack of feed immediately produced a shortage of milk and meat. The food crisis that seized the country quickly threatened to grow into an economic and political one. The situation forced the Politburo of the CPSU Central Committee, headed by Mikhail Gorbachëv, to turn to the leading Western powers for economic assistance, which they gladly offered under certain conditions.

Gorbachëv closed his first year as Party leader with a speech at the 27th CPSU Congress, which opened on February 25, 1986. This was one of those rare cases when the forum and the Party leader himself drew great interest from all strata of society, because everyone was expecting long-awaited changes. As it turned out, much of Gorbachëv's speech described events from the recent Soviet past. The key item was the speaker's confidence in the triumph of communism in the country, and he even repeated Khrushchëv's well-known slogan, "Catch up and overtake," expressed in his description of the grandiose economic frontiers that could be reached by the year 2000. The main stages he laid out for economic and social development, along with projected gross indicators of the USSR's economy for the next 15 years, left the Congress' delegates and the country's population breathless. By the end of the century, the gross national income was expected to nearly double, while doubling and qualitatively transforming production potential. Labor productivity was to grow by a factor of 2.3–2.5, the energy/output ratio of the gross national income was to decrease 30%, while metal consumption was to be halved. The Party leader felt that this meant "an abrupt turn towards intensification of production, and an increase in quality and efficiency."

"Acceleration" was one of the key ideas in Gorbachëv's speech, and it was interpreted in reformist terms. "What do we mean by acceleration?" he asked, and immediately responded: "Above all, increasing the rates of economic growth. But more than that, its essence is in a new quality of growth: intensification of production in every possible way on the basis of scientific and technical progress, structural reform of the economy, effective forms of administration, and organized stimulation of labor."

Mikhail Gorbachëv's speech and the Congress' decisions on the basic directions of national economic development suggested that the USSR could no longer pursue a path of expansion. The Soviet ruling elite explained that the experience of developed foreign countries showed that the new stage of economic development was connected with intensification and the application of new technologies, and that product quality was more important than quantity. However, the ruling elite failed to understand that in the West, postindustrial relations based on new principles had begun to mature, and that new social and technological infrastructure had come about, based on mass computerization, networked communications, and flexible relationships in production.

316

Fulfilling the program prescribed by the Congress for technological modernization of the country's industrial complex would require enormous funds: "It is planned that allocations for reconstruction and technical retooling of production be increased to more than 200 billion rubles in capital investment: more than over the preceding 10 years." But where would these funds come from? Decisions are easy to make, but carrying them out is an entirely different matter; unless proper funding is supplied, decisions will remain on paper, unimplemented—which is exactly what happened.

Because financial resources were not available to solve the problem of modernization, the country's Party political leadership again committed to using the mobilization potential of the Soviet economic and political system, with its mechanism of central planning, whose effectiveness was unquestioned by the ruling elite. And so the Party once again used its traditional mechanism of solving the most important economic tasks, organizing mass campaigns in society under loud, attractive slogans such as: "Accelerate the social and economic development of the USSR," "Restructuring at a march," "The labor energy," "Cardinal reform," etc.

Initially, this strategy worked, both in society in general and in the oil industry in particular. In 1986, the USSR produced 678 million tons of oil and gas condensate, an increase of some 22 million tons over the preceding year. By 1987, oil production had reached the 688 million ton mark, which would be the maximum production level over the entire history of the Soviet state. The increase in production was due mainly to regions of Western Siberia, where 44 new fields had been put into production on an accelerated basis by the end of 1987.

However, the country's Party political leadership, headed by Gorbachëv, was unable to make use of these initial results of successful industry developments in 1986 and 1987, which would have justified the trust and expectations of the Soviet people. Instead of continuing to search for new ways to reform the domestic economy on a market basis, the country's leadership went down the dead-end path of deepening the Soviet economy's direct dependence on hydrocarbon exports and using the hard currency earnings from them to patch the "black holes" in the national economy, all the while supporting the traditional vices of the political leadership, such as its lack of receptivity to the introduction of scientific and technical progress (especially in the area of producing consumer goods), its complete inability to develop high-efficiency agriculture, and its unprecedented squandering of human and material resources. With every passing year, the stagnating and increasingly decrepit Soviet command-administrative system became increasingly hooked on hydrocarbons. Meanwhile, mounting political instability in the country and the aggravation of the world economic situation at the end of the 1980s did little to help the situation in the USSR.

317

Practical realization of the sweeping policy of "restructuring and acceleration" in the absence of the necessary financial and material resources soon began to produce serious shortcomings shortly after the 27th CPSU Congress. Decisive and consistent fulfillment of a modernization program gave way to promulgation of certain half-hearted and contradictory reform measures, a sort of grafting of commodity and financial market elements onto a planned economy (although the mixture of one with the other already existed in practice). However, half-measures such as these merely deepened the crisis.

A product of this liberalization was the economic reform of 1987, which laid out a transition to a mixed economy with market levers of control, but which at the same time also proceeded from the mistaken assumption that it had to be put into motion with cautious intermediate steps. It was assumed that this reform would be based on worker self-government, independence of worker teams on the market, and their financial interest in the fruits of their labor. However, after the reform, worker income remained only indirectly linked to production efficiency, self-government was replaced by the delegation of increased powers to corporate administration and its independence from higher agencies, and the introduction of the commodity and financial market was postponed due to fears of possible protests on the part of the public.

Within the oil industry, problems that had previously been hidden began to surface more persistently, mounting up and ultimately creating a difficult situation in the industry. One of the main reasons was the exhaustion of possibilities for extensive production, primarily in the Western Siberian oil and gas complex. The late formation of a scientifically-based development concept for Western Siberian oil and gas potential affected the region's rates of development, its investment policy, its work planning, and the development of its production infrastructure. Every year, existing imbalances deepened in the region's ability to meet the targets set by the Soviet government with the constantly shrinking financial, material, and technical resources they were given.

In July 1988, a new spiral began in the oil industry's crisis. The depth of the crisis was largely due to a substantial drop in oil production due to the high degree of water encroachment (up to 80% or more) in the highly productive fields being developed. The water encroachment started to become massive, reducing the energy conversion efficiency of the widely-used water injection technology. The volume of water injected and brought to the surface was increasing over time, while the oil content of the produced fluids was substantially decreasing. Water encroachment also worsened and reduced the raw material base and the quality of remaining reserves at fields that were under development. Oil workers were not prepared for this phenomenon, nor could they do anything to arrest the drop in oil production, since the new enhanced recovery technologies widely used abroad had not been adopted in time on an industrial scale at the fields. The orientation toward reckless stimulation of oil production also led to other negative phenomena, since future plans for developing the industry did not duly address such problems as how to create and produce a new generation of equipment and instruments for mechanized production of large volumes of water-cut product from wells, including various models of new downhole pumps and gas lifts; well-head equipment to be used with various methods of well operation; rods, tubing, and packers; and, finally, materials for these purposes that were light, strong, and resistant to corrosion. A serious problem was created by the lack of reliable equipment for developing multizone fields through combined/separate oil production and combined/separate water injection, since production plans to combine up to 20–40 strata into a single site were predicated on that type of equipment.

A serious shortcoming in the industry's activity during that period was the lack of a clear, objective vision of the future. There was no sub-stantiated response to the question of what was in store for the industry over the near term and in the future, or how to prepare for change. This key issue was adversely affected by the monopolization of petroleum science by the dominant scientific school of Academician Aleksandr Krylov, which advanced an original and semitheoretical foundation for the Party political leadership's short-sighted plans to sharply increase oil produc-tion in the country by stimulating production, with minimal outlays.

A serious problem was created in the industry by the widening of the gap between growth of industrial reserves and oil production volume, resulting from the constant reduction in the volume of exploratory drilling. There was also a significant increase in energy consumed by the industry for its own needs, which stemmed from a need to lift larger and larger volumes of water-cut product; this also drove up industry expenses.

Maintaining oil production at the level of 640–650 million tons per year mandated in the Thirteenth Five-Year Plan (1991–1995) required allocating something on the order of 10% of the country's capital in-vestments to the oil production industry—i.e., some 110 billion rubles, which was 50% more than during the preceding five-year plan—but the government no longer had such resources.

Overall, the situation in the oil industry correlated with increasingly acute socialist economic crisis phenomena caused by the command-administrative system, whose role had grown out of proportion over many years, and by the domination of the CPSU in all areas of the country's socioeconomic life.

The "restructuring and acceleration" policy brought about by methods of authoritarian modernization made economic changes irreversible in the USSR—the financial system was undermined, inflation rose rapidly, and the former national economic mechanism was thrown into disarray. Day by day, the country's economic situation rapidly worsened, and the country was moving from commerce to simple bartering. The entire enormous expanse of the Soviet Union began to be ruled by "His Excellency Barter," and in the general population, "financial reform" came down to exchanging large-denomination bank notes in January and watching prices increase significantly in April 1991, clearly demonstrating the inability of Gorbachëv and the Soviet leadership to rescue the economy from this crisis.

In 1991, the US temporarily unfroze its Strategic Petroleum Reserve, and Saudi Arabia quadrupled its oil production. As a result, the world price for "black gold" fell to $8 a barrel. This was a catastrophe for the USSR, as the cost of oil production had by then reached $9 a barrel in parts of Siberia.

In July 1991, Mikhail Gorbachëv sent a letter to the leaders of the G7 countries, asking that he be included as a participant in an upcoming London meeting of participants. The Western leaders invited him to the meeting, but gave no additional money. Even so, the total amount of debt assumed by the Soviet Union by that time had reached $80 billion.

Having lost the ability to purchase food or feed grain for animal husbandry from foreign countries, the USSR was very quickly seized by a food crisis, which quickly grew into a systemic collapse.

The struggle for sovereignty and independence among the union republics, disagreements in the CPSU and among the upper and regional echelons of the ruling elite, and a furious power struggle on all levels led to the end of the Soviet Union as a single state in December 1991. In its place, 15 independent sovereign states formed within the administrative borders of the former government of the Soviet Union.

Under these very difficult conditions, the entire domestic oil community was faced with finding some optimal way out of this complicated situation, so that the industry might quickly recover lost ground and make its own major contribution to the revival and subsequent development of a new Russia.

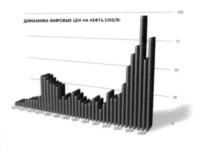

ДИНАМИКА МИРОВЫХ ЦЕН НА НЕФТЬ (USD/B)

The Organization of Petroleum Exporting Countries (OPEC) was established in 1960 to stabilize oil prices. Originally, it included major oil producers in the Middle East (Saudi Arabia, Kuwait, Iran and Iraq) and Latin America (Venezuela). Later, they were joined by several other countries in the Persian Gulf (Qatar and United Arab Emirates), Latin America (Ecuador), a number of African countries (Libya, Algeria, Nigeria and Gabon) and Southeast Asia (Indonesia). In 2008, Russia declared its willingness to become a permanent observer to OPEC. OPEC countries control about two-thirds of the world's reserves, 40% of production and half of global oil exports. However, the volatility of oil prices shows that OPEC cannot always stabilize prices on its own.

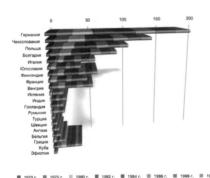

Oil exports from the USSR, by country (1970-1990).

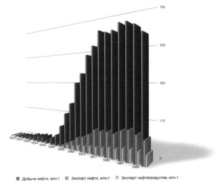

Production volumes; oil and oil product exports from the RSFSR/ USSR (1920-1990).

Signing of a major oil supply contract between Italy and the USSR. Foreign Trade Minister N. S. Patolichev signed for the Soviet Union and ENI head Enrico Mattei signed for Italy (Moscow, 1960). In exchange for oil, the USSR received, in particular, pipes for the construction of the *Druzhba* ["Friendship"] pipeline.

Construction in the early 1960s of the *Druzhba* pipeline through the collective efforts of five countries of the Council for Mutual Economic Assistance (CMEA) solved the problem of supplying Eastern Europe with oil from the Volga-Urals oil and gas region. It remains the largest oil pipeline system in the world.

Nikolay Baybakov (1911-2008): Engineer and oil industry worker widely known for his "Baybakov method" for injecting cement into a water reservoir under pressure. At 29 he became deputy people's commissar of the oil industry of the USSR; in 1944, he became people's commissar, and in 1948 he became the USSR's first minister of the oil industry. He contributed to the emergence of the "Second Baku." He played a major role in the fortunes of F. Salmanov and other well-known members of the oil industry.

Farman Salmanov (1931-2007): Man of the era. Discoverer of oil and gas in Tyumen Region. He fell in love with Siberia and its vast potential as a youth. When the question arose in the late 1950s of suspending the search for oil and gas in Western Siberia, he led an expedition at his own risk and peril from Kuzbass further north to Surgut, where in 1961 he discovered oil deposits and at the same time opened a new chapter in the history of Siberia.

  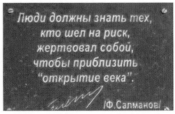

Люди должны знать тех, кто шел на риск, жертвовал собой, чтобы приблизить "открытие века".

Ф.Салманов

Tradition of smearing the first oil.

Interior of accommodations for rotational workers and oil workers' everyday items (1960s-70s).

Western Siberia is a land of strong and ambitious pioneers. Recent decades have ushered in major events. A powerful oil and gas industry has been built along with young northern cities that have become pearls of Siberia and Russia. The region is still a pioneer today: it has become a starting point and model for the dynamic development of other regions of the country.

Langepas, which means "squirrel land" in Khanty, was registered in 1981 as a settlement and became a city of district significance in 1985. The region where only local hunters and fishers once existed is now an industrial center, as well as one of Ugra's most beautiful cultural centers.

 The city of Uray ushered in a new history of Western Siberia when in April 1960 the first industrial oil was produced in Tyumen Region from Well 7 of the Mulyma structure. In 1965 the industrial workers' settlement of Uray became a city of district significance. Fifty years later, the city became the key to Siberian oil, retaining the youthful spirit of a pioneer and becoming one of the most beautiful and comfortable cities in Western Siberia.

The emergence of the city of Kogalym is tied to the discovery of large oil fields in Western Siberia in 1971. The settlement received its official name, Kogalym, in 1976. In 1978, the first ton of "black gold" was produced from Well 7 of Povkh field.

There is good reason for why Siberia is called the storehouse of Russia. But the main wealth of these vast expanses is its dedicated and energetic people. Thanks to them, a beautiful but rugged land has become one of the most dynamically developing regions in the country.

Chapter THREE

The New Russia's Oil

The Thorny Path to a Market Economy

On the evening of December 25, 1991, USSR President Gorbachëv appeared on Soviet television screens and read a strange statement, ending with the words, "In view of the emerging situation with the formation of the Commonwealth of Independent States, I terminate my activity as president of the USSR. I make this decision based on principled considerations." After these words, the red flag was lowered from the flagpole on the main building in the Kremlin and the superpower that was the USSR *de jure* ceased to exist.

On that day, the former Soviet leader merely stated a *fait accompli*, because two weeks earlier, at a meeting in the Bialowieza Forest on December 8, 1991, Boris Yeltsin of Russia, Leonid Kravchuk of Ukraine, and Stanislaw Shushkevich of Belarus had loudly proclaimed the formation of a new entity throughout Soviet territory, the Commonwealth of Independent States (CIS), and stated that "the Soviet Union no longer exists."

From the first days of 1992, the Russian Federation government was faced with the grave consequences of the severe systemic economic and sociopolitical crisis caused by the disruption of economic relations throughout the production chain and the collapse of the financial system, which had struck a serious blow against the Soviet oil and gas industry. A sharp drop in the standard of living, caused by the depreciation of State Savings Bank deposits and business payment delinquencies, was accompanied by failures in the real sector of the economy, which had been inherited from prior years. Furthermore, serious new problems were added to severe economic distortions: chronic lagging of agriculture, light industry, and the food industry, an underdeveloped public service sector and overdevelopment of the military-industrial complex and heavy industry.

The subsequent necessary process of breaking down the command-administrative system and transitioning to the development of a market economy forced the leaders of the new Russia to implement a comprehensive series of critical political, social, and economic transformations. The difficulty of accomplishing this task was formidable, since the USSR's economy had been shaped and operated for seven decades as a "unified economic system," that is, as a single structure with rigid internal division of labor, highly concentrated and narrowly specialized production, and specific technological ties between enterprises regardless of their geographic locations.

The USSR's radical transition to a market economy in the early 1990s began in the context of a catastrophic failure of the administrative mechanism of mandating resource allocations and the resulting complete exhaustion of its ability to continue functioning. The Russian economy had become a complex and unstable system characterized both by an unexpected change in the nature of macroeconomic and microeconomic processes and by a drastic change in the makeup of the factors determining the dynamics and intensities of these phenomena.

During that period, this author worked as USSR first deputy minister of the oil industry, and clearly saw that our industry was under pressure from highly complex problems, including disruption of economic relations, geometric growth in delinquencies, unsupportable burdens of taxes and financing costs, a sharp drop in investments, the appearance and wide prevalence of barter deals, and much more. As professional oilmen, we tried to save the situation, but this proved extremely difficult.

The mechanical, cookie-cutter implementation of theoretical postulates from the Chicago school of economics by members of the young reformers' government headed by Yegor Gaydar, and especially Minister of Fuel and Energy Vladimir Lopukhin, led to the adoption of many contradictory and unjustified financial and administrative decisions for regulating the Russian oil and gas industry. These decisions were largely responsible for the subsequent acute crises in the industry, and most importantly, helped consolidate and promote the "law of the jungle" among entrepreneurs as a unique principle of economic behavior.

As a result, according to a report by the International Monetary Fund (IMF), Russia's real gross domestic product shrank 19% in 1992, and another 12% in 1993. By mid-1994, Russia's total production volume had shrunk by more than half since 1989.

Beginning in 1992, Russia's oil and natural gas production began to fall due to the overall reduction in the country's industrial production and the snowballing of negative phenomena in the industry. A number of critical problems became distinctly apparent: major high-flow production fields that constituted the core of the resource base had largely been depleted; newly-added reserves had sharply declined in quality; funding of geologic exploration had been cut; high-performance technology and equipment for production and drilling were in extremely short supply (most of the hardware was more than 50% depreciated, and 70% of the drilling rigs were obsolete and required replacement); the industry's material, equipment, and financial support had seriously deteriorated; and the shortage of efficient and "green" equipment created an especially acute problem of environmental pollution. That year, the structure of the Russian oil and gas industry comprised nearly 2,000 uncoordinated associations, enterprises, and organizations belonging to the former Soviet industry ministry.

Under these difficult conditions, the Russian government was forced to begin a radical reorganization of the oil industry, inasmuch as it was critical to provide export revenue from the sale of oil, which would support urgent demands for the function of the nation's economy in the transition period.

The reformers initially considered plans for resuscitating several powerful state-owned oil companies within the public economic system. The idea was, essentially, to create some modernized entities borrowed from the previous Soviet economy, adding the elements of a certain financial independence and cost accounting for enterprises.

An alternative program was developed in the oil industry community by this author's colleagues and like-minded people. We came to the conclusion that a radical change was necessary in the approach to oil industry problems (which had never been addressed coherently by the former Soviet government). Under the Soviet system, one ministry was responsible for oil production, another for refining, and a third for petroleum products distribution. In our opinion, the experience of Western oil companies, which combined enterprises of the entire process chain "from the well to the gas pump," should be implemented. In other words, we proposed a strategic course for the creation of major industry corporations. This form of business activity, different and separate from the particular individuals who own it, is acknowledged throughout the world as the most efficient way of organizing enterprise and financial capital. The unique form of financing inherent in corporations, namely the sale of stocks and bonds, can in principle (given a reasonable business organization) overcome the main problem that Russia's fuel and energy industry was facing at the time—a near-total lack of investment. This view was supported by many other heads of Russian oil production enterprises, and ultimately formed the basis for later development of the concept of organizational changes and privatization of the industry's enterprises and organizations.

That same year, the Russian Ministry of Fuel and Energy drafted a concept for organizational changes and privatization of enterprises in the fuel and energy industry, which was based on the following principles: formation of big oil and petroleum products market businesses in the form of vertically integrated oil companies (VIOCs), which would be financially stable and competitive on domestic and foreign markets; preservation of unified process and production complexes for oil production and refining and petroleum products sale; creation of a competitive environment for enterprises performing service functions and for the production infrastructure; state control of industry enterprises during the transition period, provided through direct state capital investment in joint-stock companies; preservation of the integrated trunk pipeline system, with guarantees of free (nondiscriminatory) access for all crude oil and petroleum products producers; procurement of additional funding sources for production through privatization, upgrade of existing production capacity, and construction of new production capacity; and balance between the interests of the federal center and regional authorities. It should be noted that the privatization concept was an attempt to join two incompatible approaches, the first of which put the interests of the work forces at privatized enterprises first, and the second of which prioritized the objectives of public privatization and adherence to the principle of social justice in the distribution of state property.

President Yeltsin initiated the industry's privatization process by Decree 1403 of November 17, 1992, "On Features of Privatization of State Enterprises, Production Associations, and Scientific Production Associations in the Oil and Refining Industry and Petroleum Products Supply and Conversion of These Entities to Joint-Stock Companies." In this decree, oil-industry enterprises subject to privatization under the decree were divided into three groups.

The first group included oil and gas production associations, which were privatized as a unified process complex. Thirty-eight percent interests in these joint-stock companies were restricted to federal ownership for three years and assigned to the state enterprise Rosneft for administration.

The second group included the companies LUKOIL, Yukos, and Surgutneftegaz. The structure of these three companies was defined by a subsequent Russian Federation Council of Ministers decision dated April 22, 1993. These companies included five Tyumen oil production associations, five major refining complexes, and 18 specialized petroleum products supply organizations in the central and northwestern regions, Volga region, and Urals.

According to the charter documents, the oil companies' authorized capital was a 38% stock interest in their subsidiaries. Controlling (49%) interests in the companies themselves were restricted to federal ownership for three years. Twenty-five percent of the stock in each newly-formed joint-stock company was preferred, and common stock was not subject to conversion on subsequent resale. All shares restricted to federal ownership for a particular term were voting shares. Moreover, 40% of the oil company stock was subject to sale at investment auctions for two years on terms set jointly by the Russian Federation State Committee for State Property Management and the Ministry of Fuel and Energy. In addition, foreign investors could not own more than a 15% share of a company's stock.

Management teams for the vertically integrated oil companies were approved by the Russian Federation government. Clearly, the state intended to retain rigid control over the operations of these companies for a certain period.

The third group included companies involved in the transportation of crude oil and petroleum products: Transneft and Transnefteprodukt. Forty-nine percent interests in these companies were restricted to federal ownership for three years.

Several characteristic features of the initial phase (1991–1995) of industry privatization can be identified. The first was the priority given to the political aims of the privatization process and the concomitant ultra-high rate at which it was carried out. The second was the primarily formal nature of privatization (whereby major enterprises were sold for stock) and the low profitability of privatization. And the third was the introduction of a system of privatization vouchers.

Unlike privatization with a developed market economy, the privatization process in Russia and in Eastern Europe encountered a series of obstacles. First of all, the scale of the anticipated transformations was not comparable to similar processes in countries with market economies. There was practically no capital market infrastructure. A sharp drop in production considerably complicated the assessment of the potential of low-profit enterprises. Furthermore, the population was short of funds. These conditions explain the inevitable imbalance between the sale of state property and the need to establish privileges for various population groups (labor, retirees, the unemployed, etc.).

Nevertheless, the radical transformations carried out in the domestic oil and gas industry, which were part of the overall transformation of the Russian economy, are today a shining example of a successful and coherent reform of a key industry in post-Soviet Russia.

As a result of the first phase of privatization, 14 large vertically integrated oil companies, as well as Gazprom Russian Joint-Stock Company and another 250 so-called "independent" companies, all competing with one another, engaged in the production of crude oil and petroleum products in the mid-1990s. The second important phase was the further consolidation of the industry, when the vertically integrated oil companies LUKOIL, Surgutneftegaz, Yukos, Sibneft, Tyumen Oil Company (*TNK*), Sidanco, Tatneft, Bashneft, etc. were formed, which privatized other significant production and refining assets.

President Yeltsin accelerated the vertical integration of privatized companies by a decree dated April 1, 1995, which permitted the incorporation of subdivisions into vertically integrated companies through stock swaps. The subsequent efficient operations of vertically integrated companies during the third phase of the industry's reform, when these companies gained the capacity to independently formulate and implement strategic and tactical market objectives, did much to reverse the alarming trend of sharp decline in oil and natural gas production in the country.

Unlike major Western oil companies, whose vertical integration in the 1960s crossed national boundaries, the Russian VIOCs were created instantly, pursuant to presidential and governmental regulations of the 1990s, at a time when the ambient environment in the global oil business was qualitatively very different and, accordingly, presented more complex problems along the path of its development. In the last decade of the 20th century, the international economic system was entering an age of globalization that encompassed the oil sector as well, so that global oil megacorporations appeared and began to play a leading role in the industry.

However, the Russian oil companies lacked the time to pass through the logical phases for developing vertical integration and gaining the experience to operate in a competitive environment, and so the unsolved problems that had festered since the time of centralized economy, together with the errors committed in the course of privatization, consolidation of assets, and formation of company corporate structures acted as brakes on the path to the development of a major oil business in Russia and its integration into the international oil business. Furthermore, this process occurred under economic conditions that posed a challenge for Russian oil business development, namely, a deteriorating macroeconomic situation associated with a transition to market conditions with an obsolescent business structure, excess capacity, decrepit fixed assets, and falling production due to declining demand for crude oil and petroleum products within the country. Moreover, there was uncertainty during this period regarding how strong a role the state would permit market forces to play.

Nevertheless, it was the market system of control that pulled the oil industry out of the crisis. The industry passed its "strength test" in 1998, when world oil prices fell to $9 a barrel. In that situation, the Russian companies not only did not cut production, but did not freeze their investment programs either. Moreover, the price crisis spurred an explosive growth in production and financial indicators. It forced the companies to sharply increase the efficiency of their operations by cutting costs, expanding sales, and improving the quality of their finished products. The first results of the business restructuring, backed by the favorable price situation of recent years, created a unique opportunity for the Russian oil companies to enter the international capital market. The capabilities of national companies to invest funds in the exploration and development of Russian fields, the production of quality motor fuel, the construction of transportation infrastructure, and the provision of environmental safety also grew.

Thus, with the beginning of the new century, the Russian oil and gas industry became a unique powerful engine for Russian economic growth. Whereas Russia produced 356.4 million tons of crude in 2000, it produced 541.7 million tons in 2006. The efficient operation of Russian vertically integrated oil companies, which now produce 88% of the country's crude oil and petroleum products and control the entire chain of oil production, was a principal result of the organizational restructuring of the Russian oil industry during the transition to a market economy. And not only did the nature and essence of relations among businesses change radically, but a certain specific system of relations between businesses, lawmakers, and government agencies emerged. The political factor has always had a strong influence on the operation of Russian oil and gas companies. Clearly, this influence will continue in the future, and not only because of the industry's huge role in ensuring the socioeconomic stability of Russian society, but also because it is rooted in the very history of the formation of major oil companies in Russia.

With the completion of the organizational phase of Russian VIOC formation, VIOC management faced the question of choosing an effective strategy that would support competitive positions both in Russia and abroad. Incidentally, for a long time, the stated goals of Russian oil companies have not provided a clear idea of their chosen strategies, which is a reflection, on the one hand, of their management's lack of clear ideas on the matter, and on the other hand, of the extreme vagueness of the development goals of their ambient environment. However, the Russian oil companies proceeded to formulate their goals anyway, and these are no different from the strategic goals of leading Western energy corporations, despite their different levels of development and scales of operation.

On the whole, despite the difficult set of problems inherited from the Soviet period, Russia has now managed to create the basis for a new economic system, including a whole series of imperfect, yet still functional market institutions such as private property, convertible currency, a tax system, labor law corresponding to market realities, an elaborate banking system, a securities market regulatory system, and natural monopolies.

In the first decade of the 21st century, all of this has permitted the Russian oil and gas industry, and the entire national economy, to recover fully from the crisis, stabilize the country's financial and foreign trade position, establish stable positive structural shifts in industrial production, and make the transition to sustainable economic growth, providing a steady improvement in the Russian standard of living. According to a World Bank estimate, the oil and gas industry's contribution to Russia's GDP is currently on the order of 25%, with this key industry providing one-third of the nation's industrial production and generating about one-third of all revenue to the Russian Federation consolidated budget and about half the federal budget's revenue from exports and hard-currency income.

The Key to the Treasury of "Black Gold"

The history of our civilization's development has made oil one of the main symbols of the industrial era, and perhaps of the entire 20th century. The change in eras that arrived at the turn of the century, marking the beginning of the "information society," not only failed to reduce the value and importance of "black gold" in the world economy, but on the contrary, raised it to new heights. Moreover, the ever-growing demand for crude hydrocarbons has been forcing scientists and specialists to turn more and more frequently to analyses of remaining crude hydrocarbon reserves. And increasingly, we hear forecasts that global oil reserves are nearing exhaustion.

In late 2007, the documentary film *A Crude Awakening: The Oil Crash,* directed by Basil Gelpke and Ray McCormack, hit the screens of leading Western countries. The film presented a futuristic picture of the world to come after petroleum resources are exhausted, portraying "how our civilization's dependence on oil is colliding with geology." The filmmakers are certain that global oil production has peaked, and a sharp decline will inevitably follow, creating serious problems for our whole civilization.

This view is shared by Zapata George, a leading Western analyst of the energy industry. His website contains a page with the alarming title "Oil Shortage Now!" It is truly an alarming article to read. According to George, our planet passed the peak of traditional oil production in 2005, and the world economy now consumes over 86 million barrels of oil a day, even though it produces less than 85 million barrels. Global oil reserves are declining at about 20 million barrels per month. He predicts a steady rise in the price of oil, which will cause serious problems in the global economy.

We should note that the theory of peak oil production is not new at all, and the earliest version of this point of view dates to the mid-20th century. Its originator, the American geophysicist King Hubbert, predicted in 1956 that peak production in the southern states of the US would occur around 1970, and he was actually proved right. However, his followers tend to forget that he also predicted a global production peak in 1990, which did not happen. Thus, the theory still has many supporters and critics. These include both moderates and radicals, who assert that oil production has not only reached its peak, but has passed it.

The international mass media have had much to say on the subject in the form of various judgments of Russia's approach to the "twilight of the oil epoch," that is, a critical situation with "black gold" reserves in Russian territory. Then again, the first pessimistic forecasts of the approaching exhaustion of Russia's oil reserves appeared in the late 19th century, and the foreign skeptics of the time received a convincing rebuttal from the great Russian scientist Dmitry Mendeleyev, who sent a letter on August 27, 1889 titled "On the Resumption of Rumors of Baku Oil Depletion" to Ludwig Mond, president of the Society of the Chemical Industry in London, and to William Anderson, a department chairman at the British Association for the Advancement of Science, in which he stressed, "The revival of rumors regarding the coming depletion is based partly on a complete unfamiliarity with the phenomena of oil depletion..., and partly on a game of intrigue that spreads rumors for its own purposes."

In the 20th century, the same story was repeated at regular intervals with "expert estimates" made by foreign analysts of the coming exhaustion of Soviet, and later Russian oil. However, these false prophecies were left in ruins by the discovery and development of hydrocarbon resources at the "Second Baku" in the Volga-Urals province, followed by the exploitation of the vast potential of the Western Siberian oil and gas province.

Unfortunately, similar pronouncements can still be heard today. In December 2007, the ranks of "oil pessimists" were joined by the German Institute for Economic Research, whose analysts doubt Russia's ability to meet the world's growing demand for oil and gas. According to the Institute's estimates, Russia accounts for 29% of the European Union's oil imports and a third of its gas imports, but "Russia's existing oil and gas reserves will run out in a decade if their production continues at present rates."[1] The German experts' report states: "Despite the fact that Russia is the world's second largest oil producer, it is only seventh in explored reserves. At the present level of production, these reserves will be exhausted in approximately 22 years."[2] The study's authors claim, "The fact that Russian exports are growing less quickly than provided by its energy strategy does not affect delivery of fuels to Europe over the short and medium term. However, over the long term, shortages could still arise because Europe will be competing with other potential consumers, such as China."[3] In the opinion of these analysts, Russia will experience the anticipated problems with fuels, primarily due to inadequate investment in the energy sector, while foreign capital investments are impeded by "inadequate political conditions."

These pessimistic forecasts can and must be opposed, first of all, by the hard facts, which are stubborn things, as everyone knows. According to the estimate of noted scientist Nikolay Laverov, vice president of the Russian Academy of Sciences, Russia's developed oil reserves total only 16% of those available, and its developed natural gas reserves are only 5%, so a shortage of crude hydrocarbons does not pose a threat to the country at all in the present century. To date, some 3,200 oil and gas fields have been discovered in the Russian Federation, of which only 1,600 are now in development. The other 1,600 have never been developed by anyone, nor have licenses even been issued for their development.

Speaking at a Russian Federation government meeting, Minister of Natural Resources and Ecology Yury Trutnev noted that federal budget investments in geologic exploration had quadrupled from 2004 to 2009, and mineral licensees had quintupled their spending on geologic exploration. In 2005–2007 alone, the country discovered 194 oil and gas fields. In the record year of 2007, 44 oil and gas fields were discovered, two of these in

Eastern Siberia. Thus, 606 million tons of oil were explored, or 20% more than were produced. Moreover, 23 trillion cubic feet (TCF) of natural gas were explored, which is also in excess of production. In addition, the state's annual income from mineral development parcel auctions in the period just ended [2009] has doubled to some 40 billion rubles.

Trutnev also noted that the overall growth of Russian hydrocarbon resources in 2007 alone totaled 7.4 billion tons of coal equivalent (TCE), or 2.4 times more than in 2004, when this indicator stood at 3.1 billion tons. The growth in Category C_1^4 oil reserves just on the Yamal Peninsula was 64 million tons, double the 2006 figure, and gas reserves increased there by 9.8 TCF, 26% more than the prior year. Mineral license income to the state increased 12-fold, and mineral production taxes increased sixfold. Expanded replacement of reserves for the most important types of minerals was assured. Despite the present financial crisis, the Ministry of Natural Resources and Ecology managed to defend the funding of subsurface geologic studies necessary to sustain growth rates in 2010.

The future plans of the Russian Ministry of Natural Resources and Ecology include obtaining geologic, geophysical, and geochemical information on areas of the country totaling 2.3 million square miles in size, while the area covered by a hydrogeologic and engineering geologic study will total nearly 386,000 square miles. Updating of the geologic baseline using modern research methods will improve the accuracy of studies and the efficiency of geologic exploration.

Since hydrocarbons will be the dominant fuel in coming decades, there is an objective need to intensify geologic study and then involve Russia's new major oil and gas provinces in development. For this reason, the Russian government has paid special attention to the following important issues in the course of discussions on replacing the country's crude mineral baseline: improving mechanisms for attracting investments to mineral extraction; stimulating the use of resource-saving technologies and comprehensive use of crude minerals; ensuring the efficient use of funds allocated from the federal budget for subsurface geologic studies and replacement of the crude mineral baseline (including via state procurement of associated activities); linking measures to replace mineral resource reserves with prospects for development of regions and branches of the economy; supporting human resources for geologic exploration; improving geologic environmental monitoring and forecasting of hazardous geologic processes, including earthquakes; and studying the financial and economic feasibility of the proposed steps.

The largest area of promise for such activities is the geologic study of the country's continental shelf. It is in the offshore areas under Russian Federation jurisdiction that the discovery of large and unique crude hydrocarbon fields is considered most likely.

Experience developing the Western Siberian oil and gas province has shown that preparing each new oil-producing region is a long process. Assuming that the geologic study of offshore subsurface resources is intensified quickly, production of crude hydrocarbons on the continental shelf could reach 20% of total crude hydrocarbons produced in the Russian Federation by 2020. The exploitation of offshore subsurface resources will produce a large multiplier effect through the development of related industries, primarily the high-technology areas of machine building and transportation, and will help resolve important issues of energy supply and local employment.

The Russian Federation's continental shelf has an area of 2.4 million square miles. About 1.5 million square miles show promise for oil and gas exploration. Recoverable hydrocarbon resources on the Russian Federation's continental shelf total about 110 billion tons, including over 14.9 billion tons of oil and about 2,578 TCF of gas.

The bulk of the resources (about 66.5%) lie under Arctic shelves (in the Barents and Kara Seas). The degree of exploration of offshore hydrocarbon resources is low, and does not exceed 9–12% in most areas. The area of Russia's expanded continental shelf in the Arctic, beyond the 200-mile limit, could amount to 463,000 square miles, with an inferred hydrocarbon resource potential of 5.4 billion TCE.

So far, more than 20 large promising oil and gas basins have been identified on the Russian shelf, and 36 fields have been discovered, including unique gas fields (Shtokman, Rusanovo, Leningrad) in the Western Arctic and several large oil fields on the northeast shelf of Sakhalin. Moreover, offshore continuations of more than 10 oil and gas fields previously discovered on land have been found.

In December 2007, an office of Gazprom's Scientific and Technical Council and the Coordinating Council for Scientific Research of the Russian Academy of Sciences (RAS) discussed a draft "Program for the Comprehensive Development of Fields on the Yamal Peninsula and in Adjacent Waters." The draft reflected new technologies and technical solutions in the validation of the crude mineral baseline and the geologic exploration, development, and surface construction of fields, the transportation of gas and liquid hydrocarbons from the peninsula, and the refining of liquid hydrocarbons. Special attention was devoted to the environmental component, as the problem of minimizing human impact on the environment is a top priority. In particular, the draft specified the development of processes and special measures to minimize the adverse impact on the troposphere and surrounding territory and the use of closed-loop water-supply systems to prevent surface-water pollution.

One priority of Russian geologists is the discovery of hydrocarbon resources that will subsequently fill the Eastern Siberia–Pacific Ocean trunk oil pipeline. Stratigraphic drilling is proposed to be done in the Krasnoyarsk Territory, Evenk District, of the Sakha Republic (Yakutia), and the Irkutsk Region. In all, seven wells or 79,000 linear feet of hole are to be drilled in just three years.

The Vankor oil and gas field is of particular importance for the economy of Eastern Siberia. In 2007, the growth in recoverable oil reserves at the Vankor field was 200 million tons, and the field's total reserves increased 28 million tons, to 567 million tons. Thus, in terms of oil reserves, the field can be classified as unique. The oil reserve growth constitutes 53% of the total reserve growth for Rosneft.

At present, geologic study is under way within the Yurubchen block of the Yurubchen-Tokhomo oil and gas field, as along with exploration of the Agalya gas condensate field. The Yurubchen block is located in the Baykit District of the Evenk Autonomous District, 93 miles southeast of the town of Baykit. As of January 1, 2005, Category C_1 and C_2 recoverable crude hydrocarbon reserves in these fields amounted to 82.2 million tons and 262 million tons of oil and gas condensate, respectively, as well as 4.5 TCF and 14.4 TCF of gas.

Chayanda field, one of the main fields in Yakutia, contains 44.5 TCF of natural gas reserves. But since its confirmed reserves are only 13.4 TCF, it requires additional exploration. The principal difficulties here stem from the need to exploit oil and gas fields under difficult climatic and mining geologic conditions, where qualitatively new levels of industrial and environmental safety must be assured for exploration and development.

Overall, the extensive lands of Eastern Siberia—from Turukhansk to the Taymyr—exhibited reserve growth of 130 million tons of oil and 1.9 TCF of gas in 2009 alone. Russian geologists continue to work actively, and funding levels for their work match those of the last two years.

Eastern Siberia is expected to become the main resource base for filling the Eastern Siberia–Pacific Ocean (ESPO) pipeline, and special attention is being devoted here to the Talakan, Vankor, and Upper Chona fields. The route of the 2,920-mile long ESPO trunk oil pipeline passes through Tayshet and Ust-Kut, in the Irkutsk Region; Lensk and Aldan, in Yakutia; Skovorodino, in the Amur Region; and Kozmino Bight, in the Maritime Territory.

Construction of the ESPO pipeline began on April 28, 2006. The length of the first stage, from Tayshet to Skovorodino, in the Amur Region, is 1,674 miles. The first oil was pumped into the Eastern Siberia–Pacific Ocean trunk oil pipeline in early April 2008. Near the city of Tayshet, Irkutsk Region, the first completed segment of the Eastern oil pipeline, from the zero mark to mile 148, was tied into the existing Transneft pipeline system and the trunk pipeline began to fill with oil. The beginning of the segment is the tie-in point to the existing Omsk–Irkutsk and Krasnoyarsk–Irkutsk oil pipelines, and the end point is defined as the pig launching unit at Vikhorevka, Irkutsk Region. Construction of most

ESPO pipeline linear facilities was completed in 2009, and late that same year, the Kozmino oil terminal near the city of Nakhodka, the terminal point of the Eastern Siberia–Pacific Ocean pipeline system, was brought online. In November 2009, the first tanker dropped anchor at the new maritime port for loading. During the first phase, the port will receive 33 million tons of crude per year, and there is a real possibility that its capacity will be increased to 55 million tons.

Further development of the ESPO pipeline calls for increasing capacity to 88 million tons of oil per year through phased development and the commissioning of Eastern Siberian fields. In addition, an oil pipeline from Skovorodino to the border of the PRC—a so-called "China Spur"—is planned. The future oil pipeline will integrate fully into the existing Transneft trunk pipeline system, giving Russian oil companies the ability to choose the most efficient routes for transporting crude based on current world competition.

A clear and convincing example of the successful development of the offshore shelf was LUKOIL's placement into service of the Yury Korchagin field in the Russian sector of the Caspian Sea. With Russian Prime Minister Vladimir V. Putin present, the first oil was produced there on April 28, 2010. LUKOIL discovered the field in 2000, and from 2004 to 2009 it invested 34.4 billion rubles in its development. The field's infrastructure consists of an ice-resistant stationary platform (IRP 1) with a drilling system that has a lift capacity of 617 tons for drilling wells as deep as 24,200 feet; an ice-resistant stationary platform (IRP 2) to house 105 personnel, with an independent survival capacity of 15 days; 36 miles of 12-inch diameter underwater pipeline with wall thickness of ⅝ inches; and floating oil storage with capacity of 28,000 deadweight tons. Oil from the field is transported by shuttle tankers with a capacity of 6,000–12,000 deadweight tons.

The first well in the field was drilled for oil; the second, for associated gas that would be used to independently power the facility. A third well injects water to maintain formation pressure. The wells were drilled using a unique Russian design technology: superlong horizontal holes over three miles long. The uniform radial placement of the wells allows for simultaneous penetration of all pay zones. Drilling is monitored in online mode from onshore via a satellite link. During field development, LUKOIL monitored the northern Caspian Sea by satellite. The satellite data reached the company's specialists in near-real time via the LUKOIL–Satellite Images [*LUKOYL–Kosmosnimki*] web service. During the entire study period, monitoring detected no oil pollution within the company's license tracts.

According to reliable estimates, hydrocarbon reserves in the Yury Korchagin field exceed 270 million barrels of oil equivalent (BOE). The planned maximum annual production level is 2.8 million tons of oil and

35 billion cubic feet (BCF) of gas, and by the end of 2010, 330,000 tons of oil will have been produced at the field.

Still, the bulk of the oil reserves (about 70%) are concentrated in the waters of the North Caspian, in Vladimir Filanovsky field, the biggest of those explored in our country by LUKOIL in the last 20 years, while the bulk of gas reserves (about 40%) are in Khvalynsk field. According to preliminary estimates, the recoverable reserves of these fields are 1 billion tons of oil and 27.6 TCF of gas.

The company plans to begin production at Vladimir Filanovsky field in 2012, and by 2015 it plans to produce 13 million tons of oil and 423 BCF of gas per year from its Caspian fields. By 2020, LUKOIL expects to reach a North Caspian production level of 33 million tons of oil and 635–706 BCF of gas.

LUKOIL is also considering the development of the Timan-Pechora oil and gas province, which is viewed as a critical objective in LUKOIL's overall strategic program, because the territory of the Komi Republic alone concentrates the richest reserves of "black gold" in two oil and gas regions: Pechora-Kolva (36%) and Izhma-Pechora (29%). Explored reserves in Categories A, B, and C_1, accounting for hydrocarbons already produced, amount to 1.8 billion tons of coal equivalent (16.2% of the Komi Republic's original resources), including 56% oil and 35% free gas. Preliminary estimates of hydrocarbon reserves are 203 billion TCE, including 70% oil and 23% gas. Currently, the state register of minerals in the Komi Republic lists 137 crude hydrocarbon fields.

LUKOIL's specific work plan is contained in the "Federal Special-Purpose Program for the Comprehensive Development of Oil and Gas Resources in the Timan-Pechora Province Through 2005 and Beyond," which was developed with the company's active participation. Specifically, the company plans to invest 13 billion rubles on geologic exploration alone. Between 2000 and 2007, geologic exploration has resulted in the discovery of nine fields in the Komi Republic and two in the Nenets Autonomous District. In all, the program's implementation will permit the company to increase its oil reserves by about 440 million tons and its gas reserves by 1 TCF over the course of 10 years. Some 30 new fields are expected to be developed in that time, and oil production in 2010 will grow to 33 million tons, as compared with 14 million tons in 2000.

As a clear example of the extent of Russia's vast resources, consider the Nenets Autonomous District, where LUKOIL is developing one of northern Timan-Pechora's biggest fields, South Khylchuyu, where proven oil reserves total over 500 million barrels. The quality of conditioned oil surpasses that of the Russian "Urals" export mixture: its specific gravity is 35.5°API (that of Urals oil is 32.0°API), and its sulfur content is 0.71% (that of the Urals is 1.30%). The project is being developed by the Naryanmarneftegaz joint venture, in which LUKOIL holds a

70% interest and the American company ConocoPhillips holds a 30% interest. In June 2008, construction was completed for Stage One of the South Khylchuyu field. This project includes 32 production wells, an oil conditioning installation with a capacity of 4.2 million tons per year, a system for removing hydrogen sulfide from oil, a tank farm with a total capacity of 1.4 million cubic feet (MMCF), an external delivery pumping station, the 10¾-inch diameter 17.3-mile long Yareyyu–South Khylchuyu high-pressure gas pipeline, a gas conditioning unit with a capacity of 13 BCF per year, a 125-MW generating station, and 178 miles of 220 kV high-voltage lines. In December 2008, construction of Stage Two of the South Khylchuyu field was completed, during which the capacity of the oil conditioning installation was increased by 4.2 million tons per year. A high-pressure compressor station was also built, along with sulfur recycling and storage facilities. The crude produced at the field is transported through a 21-inch diameter pipeline 98 miles in length to the Varandey Oil Loading Terminal, which has a capacity of 13 million tons per year. The terminal is located on the shores of the Barents Sea, and handles 70,000-deadweight-ton tankers that deliver the crude to European and North American markets year round, in part from a floating tank farm in Kola Bay. The target annual oil production level in the field is 8.3 million tons (over 150,000 barrels a day), and is expected to be attained in 2010.

In all, by 2020 LUKOIL plans to commission 60 new crude hydrocarbon fields in the Russian Federation's Northwest Federal District alone.

Traditional Russian oil-producing regions also have good prospects for the discovery of new oil fields. The Western Siberian Province's initial total resources and the status of use of known oil reserves show that the region has enormous potential both for oil production stabilization and even growth. So far, no more than 18.2% of initial total oil resources have been produced. According to Igor Shpurov, general director of the Western Siberian Scientific Research Institute of Geology and Geophysics [ZapSibNIIGG], Western Siberia prospects are linked primarily to pre-Jurassic formations. Discoveries are possible in Neocomian deposits in marginal parts of the Western Siberian oil and gas province, which to date have been studied much less than the central area. Major discoveries are also possible at deeper levels containing oil and gas; this applies primarily to the pre-Jurassic sequence, which is virtually unstudied. It has only been penetrated by fewer than 10% of the exploratory wells drilled in Western Siberia. It is thus possible that the pre-Jurassic sequence will soon be the main source for replacement of the crude mineral baseline. The real path to solving this problem is obvious: the scope and efficiency of geologic exploration must be substantially increased.

Another telling example is the 2008 discovery of a new oil field on the right bank of the Ob, in the Tomsk region. The "black gold" produced from the South Pyzhino well is of very high quality. It has low paraffin content, exhibits low density and viscosity, and is free of sulfur. Furthermore, this well has penetrated at least six thick oil and gas formations. Incidentally, nine new fields have been discovered here in the last three years, and reserve growth has exceeded production by a factor of almost four for the first time in recent years. Geologists call this area the Pre-Yenisey oil and gas subprovince. Three superdeep wells have been drilled here, and further stratigraphic drilling is planned. Sufficient data from drilled wells and seismic exploration are available to confirm the prospects of discovering new hydrocarbon fields, and the results considerably increase the oil and gas prospects of the Pre-Yenisey oil and gas subprovince. At present, license-tract formation is nearing completion.

Yet another example concerns LUKOIL–Western Siberia LLC (a wholly owned subsidiary of LUKOIL), which began drilling the first development well at Pyak-Yakha gas-condensate field (Yamal-Nenets Autonomous District) in April 2009. This is the company's second project, after Nakhodka field, to produce hydrocarbons in the Yamal-Nenets Autonomous District. Medium-term plans call for drilling 55 development wells in this license tract. The proven reserves of Pyak-Yakha field as of the end of 2008 were 70 million barrels of oil and 1.9 TCF of gas. Commercial production at the field is planned for the fourth quarter of 2011. Produced gas will pass through Nakhodka field to the Yamburg gas compressor station, and thence to the Gazprom gas transportation system. Liquid hydrocarbons (oil and gas condensate) will be pumped into the Vankor field oil pipeline (owned by Rosneft Oil Company), for subsequent transmission to the Transneft trunk pipeline system. A 78-mile gas pipeline will be built to Nakhodka field, and a 99-mile pipeline will be built to Vankor field to carry hydrocarbons produced at Pyak-Yakha field.

It is well known that parameters such as well spacing and layout, the existing well utilization rate, the efficiency of the formation pressure-maintenance system, the volume and efficiency of enhanced oil production methods, and the volume and frequency of field studies to monitor development substantially affect oil production efficiency. In this area, enhanced oil production methods, which account for only about 9% of Russia's total annual oil production at the moment, are assuming a special role in stimulating oil production.

In addition, Russia possesses enormous reserves of unconventional crude hydrocarbons. These include bituminous tars and sands, which can do much to compensate for the shortage of conventional fuels. Suffice it to say that within the territory of Tatarstan alone, Russian geologists have discovered 450 natural tar fields, 150 of them within the operational zone of Tatneft, and 12 of these have been prepared for commercial development. By several estimates, natural tar resources in this Russian republic alone may amount to as much as 7.7 billion tons.

On June 7, 2010, we met Tatneft's general director, Shafagat Takhautdinov, in Kazan. In the course of the meeting, we specifically discussed questions of future cooperation between our companies. The head of Tatneft showed great interest in the prompt completion of pilot studies by our subsidiary RITEK on a downhole steam generator for *in situ* heat treatment of high-viscosity crude.

In discussing Russia's supply of oil reserves, one more very valuable crude hydrocarbon must be considered: natural gas. Experts estimate that Russia ranks first in the world in explored natural gas reserves (32%) and provides up to 30% of world natural gas production. The country has 787 discovered fields, of which 352 are in development. The fields under development concentrate 45.5% of Russia's total reserves. Initial total resources of free gas amount to 8,338 TCF, including 5,660 TCF on land and 2,677 TCF on the continental shelf. Explored reserves in Categories A, B, and C_1 amount to 1,652 TCF. Estimated reserves in Category C_2 are 501 TCF. Prospective and inferred resources in Categories C_3 and D, which require confirmation by geologic exploration, are 5,749 TCF. The geographic breakdown of gas reserves is irregular. The Yamal-Nenets Autonomous District in Western Siberia, which contains 15 unique fields with reserves of over 18 TCF each, accounts for two-thirds of explored natural gas reserves. The Volga-Urals region accounts for 130 TCF, or 8%; Eastern Siberia, for 56.5 TCF (3.1%); the Far East, for 49.4 TCF (3%); and the European North, for 17.7 TCF (about 1%). Of the total volume of explored reserves, about 55% (concentrated in the Yamal-Nenets Autonomous District) accounts for purely producer gas.

Another very promising hydrocarbon resource in Russia is methane hydrates. The world's first discovery of free gas under a bed of methane hydrates occurred in 1967, at the Messo-Yakha field in the Yamal-Nenets Autonomous District. Since development began in 1968 using original technology, the field has yielded over 423 MMCF of gas, and since then, over 220 methane hydrate deposits have been discovered. Specialists estimate that natural methane hydrate gas reserves are at least a hundred times greater than in explored gas fields, and Russian scientists believe that research into geologic hydrocarbon pools in the Dolganskoye series will not only eliminate discrepancies in estimating the formation's gas reserves, but permit assessment of possible pools of heavy crude and methane hydrates and the prospects for discovery of oil and gas pools in Lower Cretaceous and Jurassic deposits.

In all, according to current expert assessments, the Russian Federation's present supply of oil reserves would last 36–40 years at current rates of consumption, and that of gas would last 75–80 years. Furthermore, the country has all the prerequisites to further increase oil and gas production volumes over the next 30 years. The country's economic interests will largely be met by further development of the Western Siberian Province, Eastern Siberia, the Timan-Pechora Province, and the continental shelf. These hydrocarbon resources are a valuable heritage of the multi-ethnic Russian nation and the principal reserve for development of the country's crude mineral complex over the medium and long term.

The Investment Climate in Russia

The status and problems of the Russian oil and gas industry steadily remain at the center of attention of leading foreign print and electronic media. These often contain statements that, in the past decade, the government has steadily increased its involvement in the Russian oil and gas industry, which could ultimately end in complete nationalization of the industry. And all this could supposedly lead to an exodus of foreign investors from Russia and a substantial slowdown of investment processes.

As chairman of the Energy Policy Committee of the Russian Union of Industrialists and Entrepreneurs, this author has had to answer questions from Western journalists on numerous occasions on the supposedly forthcoming nationalization of the industry. As this author has emphasized repeatedly, these are unfounded and frivolous opinions, without the slightest basis in fact.

In fact, the Russian oil and gas industry no longer has any state-owned companies in the pure (classical) sense. For example, the state does hold a 50.02% interest in the authorized capital of Gazprom, the leader of the Russian oil and gas industry, which is fourth in the world in market capitalization with $354.6 billion, while the remaining stock is held by a wide range of strategic, institutional, and individual investors, including foreign stockholders with interests amounting to 7.448%. Burckhard Bergmann, chairman of the Board of E.ON Ruhrgas AG, a major German corporation, sits on the Gazprom Board of Directors.

If we look at the ownership breakdown of a key Gazprom subsidiary, Gazprom Neft, we see a similar picture. Gazprom itself holds a 75% stake in the company, while 20% is held by a consortium of the Italian corporations ENI and Enel. The Gazprom Neft Board of Directors includes representatives of foreign stockholders: Marco Alvera, senior vice president for deliveries and portfolio investment development of ENI S.p.A Moscow Milan, and Stefano Cao, ENI senior director for production.

The authorized capital of Rosneft, which the Western media persist in calling "state-owned," is 105,981,778 rubles 17 kopecks (10,598,177,817 shares of common stock) after consolidation of 12 subsidiaries. The government, through Rosneftegaz, owns 75.16% of the company's authorized capital, with the remaining shares held by a broad range of strategic, institutional, and individual Russian and foreign investors. Until recently, the American financial corporation Citigroup held a 110-million-share interest in the company, or about 1% of its stock, based on a market capitalization of about $98 billion. Rosneft's Board of Directors includes Hans-Joerg Rudloff, board chairman of Britain's Barclays Capital, and US citizen Peter O'Brien is a company vice president. Incidentally, data from an independent audit of oil and gas reserves by DeGolyer & MacNaughton showed the company had proven reserves of 2.669 billion tons (17.694 billion barrels) of oil and 27.7 TCF of natural gas per the PRMS classification as of December 31, 2008. Thanks to the large volume and high efficiency of geologic exploration, its proven hydrocarbon reserves increased 2.8% in 2008, to 3.364 billion tons of oil equivalent (TOE), or 22.307 billion BOE.

With respect to the Transneft Pipeline Joint-Stock Company, which is also often characterized as wholly state-owned, it turns out that the state does not hold a 100% interest at all, but 75%, and the remainder of the preferred stock belongs to private stockholders. Transneft's acquisition of Transnefteprodukt, which transports petroleum products within the Russian Federation, is now being finalized.

The above examples clearly show that although the Russian government owns some portion of the total shares of Gazprom, Rosneft, Transneft, and many other companies, this absolutely does not hamper the management of the oil and gas business on market commercial principles and in the interests of product consumers and stockholders.

Idle statements by certain Western media on the reduction of foreign investment activity in the Russian oil and gas industry due to extension of ever-stricter government control over the hydrocarbon assets of Russia's economic growth are equally exaggerated.

The energy policies of leading nations have, above all, always been based on a well-thought-out and intelligent energy strategy that includes both an economic ideology that is distinguished by its long-term sustainability, and specific numeric indicators for fuel and energy industrial development vectors. We should clearly understand, in turn, that only a powerful state with an effective administrative system can support both the normal functioning of a fuel and energy market and the institution of private property in the industry.

Recently, a favorable investment climate for foreign investors has been forming in Russia at an accelerated pace. The Russian government's policy is based on the principle that investments are what the oil and gas industry needs to reach a qualitatively new level.

With clearly defined investment strategies, foreign investments have now become an important component of programs to modernize the Russian oil and gas industry. For example, at its October 11, 2007 meeting, the executive board of Gazprom took special note of the fact that attracting foreign partners to corporate projects can be regarded as an effective mechanism for achieving strategic objectives and, in particular, for reinforcing the vertical integration of the company's business.

Another clear example and a convincing confirmation of the effectiveness of Russian-German energy partnership is the plan to develop South Russian field, which is located in the Krasny Selkup District of the Yamal-Nenets Autonomous District. The development license is held by a Gazprom subsidiary, Severneftegazprom. According to the latest data, the South Russian oil and gas field has Category $A + B + C_1$ gas reserves of 29 TCF and Category C_2 gas reserves of 7.4 TCF. In addition, oil reserves are estimated at 6.3 million tons. Gazprom has used South Russian field to swap assets with BASF and E.ON. Currently, BASF owns an interest amounting to 25% minus one voting share and 10% of the nonvoting stock (one share of preferred stock) in Severneftegazprom, while the Russian company, in turn, has increased its interest in the Russian-German joint venture Wingas GmbH from 35% to 50% minus one share and gained a 49% equity interest in Wintershall, a BASF subsidiary.

Speaking on December 18, 2007 at a gala ceremony marking the beginning of production from the field, Russian President Dmitry Medvedev[5] stressed that, "This is a big undertaking and a very important one for us, essentially representing the development and strengthening of the rise of the Russian North. There is no doubt that the asset swap between the Russian companies, between Gazprom and BASF—and this was the principle on which the project's realization was based—will improve the competitiveness of both companies and strengthen their positions on global markets.... This is a common investment to ensure sustainable energy security for Europe and the flourishing of the entire European continent.... Russia is open to such large and serious business projects, and to bold business initiatives for mutually profitable cooperation." The annual industrial production volume at South Russian field is planned to be 882 BCF of natural gas.

On the Yamal Peninsula, TNK-BP ["Tyumen Oil Company–British Petroleum"] plans to invest about $60 million in the development of Russian fields this year. Oil production has begun, and two wells have been drilled, each producing about 165 tons of oil per day. Another production well is being drilled, and another exploratory well is planned. The field's reserves are 440 million tons; geologic exploration could increase that figure.

Many more examples could be cited from recent times. In Western Siberia, Salym Petroleum Development NV, a joint venture of Shell Salym Development BV and Evikhon (a subsidiary of Siberia Energy), is successfully developing the Salym group of oil fields, which include the

West Salym, Upper Salym, and Vadelyp fields. In 2007, 108 new wells were brought online and 180 miles of rock were drilled at the Salym fields. Daily oil production was 100,000 barrels. Total oil production last year more than doubled as compared to 2006, to 4.7 million tons. The company has not only achieved positive cash flow, but has also become profitable and has begun repaying its stockholder loans. According to its general director, Harry Brekelmans, the company plans to invest $200–250 million to develop the Salym project this year. From the beginning of field development in 2003 to the end of the current year [2009], and taking current-year investments into account, $1.2 billion will have been invested in the project. And by the end of the current decade, the total oil production specified by the technological plan for the Salym Group will exceed 6.6 million tons (about 44 million barrels) per year.

In the same region, the Italian corporations Eni and Enel have invested $852 million to form the joint venture Northern Energy (with 60% and 40% interests, respectively) to buy up some of the production assets of the bankrupt Yukos. In particular, the consortium has acquired the Arktikgaz, Urengoyl Inc, and Neftegaztekhnologiya oil production enterprises, which hold hydrocarbon development and production licenses in the Yamal-Nenets Autonomous District.

Also in Western Siberia in December 2007, the American oil service company Halliburton Co. signed a multimillion-dollar contract with Rosneft to service oil fields in Western Siberia. The American company won an order for hydraulic fracturing at 317 oil wells in the Ob Valley region.

In turn, the American oil services company Weatherford International Ltd. announced the acquisition, in February 2008, of Neftemashvnedreniye (Noyabrsk, Tyumen Region), which specializes in the manufacture of oil and gas production equipment. Neftemashvnedreniye produces flowing-well equipment such as "Christmas trees." This isn't Weatherford International Ltd.'s first acquisition in Russia, either: In late 2007, it acquired a stock interest in Borets, a major Moscow factory, which makes submersible downhole pumps for oil production. It is significant that the American company consistently acquires stock in Russian enterprises that make oil and gas production equipment.

Mention can also be made of the successful activities of Victoria Oil & Gas, a British company with a 74.6% stock interest in Severgazinvest, which is developing the promising West Medvezhye gas-condensate field in the Yamal-Nenets Autonomous District.

An instructive example of foreign investment in Russia occurred on March 21, 2008 in Tyumen, capital of Western Siberia, when Schlumberger formally opened its Siberian Oil Production Training Center, which is designed to train and retrain oil and gas professionals. The Center has no counterpart anywhere in the world, and the 370-acre campus includes a training building, dormitory cottages for students, and a well-equipped area with instructional wells for training in hydraulic fracturing, well servicing, control of drilling systems, etc. The Center can currently accommodate 300 specialists for training. In addition, a training course has been designed to teach safe driving, and a stadium and athletic complex have been built. Construction is actively continuing on the Center's grounds: An area for geophysical research will be built, and three new training wells will be drilled. In all, the leading service company plans to invest at least $100 million in the project. This is but one of the major investment projects by international companies in Russia.

In Eastern Siberia, the joint venture Verkhnechonskneftegaz ["Upper Chona Oil and Gas"], whose stockholders are TNK-BP and Rosneft, is developing the Upper Chona gas-condensate field in the Katanga District, Irkutsk Region. The field is one of the largest in the region, with recoverable Category C_1 and C_2 reserves of 222 million tons of oil and 3.7 million tons of gas condensate. Natural gas reserves are estimated at 4.6 TCF. The company's board of directors includes foreign citizens Gary Jones, Upper Chona project director, and David Jenkins, research director.

It should also be mentioned that on January 15, 2008, a new vertically integrated oil company appeared in Russia, formed under market conditions by the merger of Alliance, a Russian corporation, and West Siberian Resources (WSR), a Swedish firm that operates in three major oil regions of the Russian Federation: Western Siberia (Tomsk Region), Timan-Pechora, and the Volga-Urals region. The merger is of mutual benefit, because it creates a synergy of production and refining capacity. The merged company will have proven and inferred reserves of 484 million barrels of oil, a production volume of 51,000 barrels per day, and a refining volume of 70,000 barrels per day. The company's organization includes 255 retail filling stations and 24 oil tank farms. The merged company's capitalization, according to management estimates, will grow to $2.5 billion, with Alliance's capital estimated at $1.5 billion today and WSR's at $900 million. The merger is expected to more than double the company's net profit and income, especially after commissioning the ESPO pipeline and reconstructing the Khabarovsk Refinery to achieve a refining yield of 93%, which will permit manufacture of Euro-5 fuel and Jet-1 aviation kerosene that could be exported to China and the Asia-Pacific Region, among others.

Another good example of how Western investors firmly believe in the future of the Russian oil and gas industry occurred in early September 2009, when Swiss company Sulzer AG completed building the first enterprise on Russian territory based on the Serpukhov Plant in eastern Russia. The company invested over $8 million in the project, for a plant that specializes in the manufacture of so-called "plates" and "packing"—key components that determine the effectiveness of various chemical assemblies for oil refining and gas processing, petrochemistry, chemistry, and other fields. The new plant will supplement and partially replace established imports of equipment to Russia from other Sulzer AG enterprises in Europe and Asia. In 2008, Sulzer's sales on Russian territory amounted to €15 million. The company's potential and existing clients are in the oil, gas, and chemical industries.

The Russian government continues to systematically implement new steps to improve the investment climate in the Russian oil and gas industry. On December 3, 2007, the Russian president signed the federal law, "On the Amendment of Article 10 of the Russian Federation Law, 'On Minerals,' " which extended the periods for use of the subsurface for geologic study, as reported by the Kremlin press service. The law was adopted by the State Duma on November 16, 2007 and approved by the Federation Council on November 23. It extends the maximum period for use of the subsurface for purposes of geologic study on mineral parcels of inland sea waters, territorial seas, and the continental shelf to 10 years. The previous period had been limited to five years, but analysis and generalization of mineral use practice showed that the term was clearly inadequate for effective performance of geologic studies of the subsurface.

On April 2, 2008, the Russian State Duma adopted the law, "On the Procedure for Effecting Foreign Investments in Business Entities of Strategic Importance for Safeguarding the National Defense and National Security." State Duma Chairman Boris Gryzlov noted the importance of the legislation: "We are introducing a certain element of protection for our strategic industries against the participation of foreign capital and restricting this investment participation, we are raising a barrier in control." Endorsement is required for any deal by which foreign investors would acquire more than 50% of the voting shares that constitute the equity of a commercial partnership (joint-stock company or limited liability corporation) of strategic importance to the defense and security of the state. Deals involving foreign states and international organizations are subject to more stringent requirements. These entities will need to secure endorsement to acquire more than 25% of the stock in a strategic company. The final decision may be made after three months, or a maximum of six. The law does not apply retroactively, but authorities must be notified of ownership shares exceeding 5% of a strategic company. From several initial assessments and comments in the Western media, we can conclude that as expected, foreign investors regard this Russian law more than favorably, because it introduces precise clarity and definiteness for the development and implementation of a foreign business's strategy in Russia.

The Russian business community has not remained aloof to this important activity, and is undertaking the necessary actions. On February

4, 2008 in Moscow, the Russian Union of Industrialists and Entrepreneurs and the Russian Federation Chamber of Commerce and Industry signed a cooperation agreement that specifies an effective partnership for the formation of a favorable business climate and consolidation of the positive reputation of Russian business. The agreement is for four years and anticipates close cooperation in the following major areas: development of a coordinated position on critical socioeconomic issues; development and implementation of steps to protect entrepreneurs' rights and interests; improvement of corporate governance laws and practice; comprehensive strengthening of the public-private partnership; and active development of foreign-trade cooperation and international relations between Russian entrepreneurs and foreign partners and representative organizations of the business community.

Russian Offshore Prospects

From time to time, articles in foreign publications maintain that Russia is imposing unjustifiably rigid constraints on the operation of foreign companies to develop crude hydrocarbon fields on the Russian shelf. In this matter as well, such journalistic claims are far from the truth.

First of all, offshore shelf projects located on Russian territory present a great geologic risk, and there is an objective need here for Russian and foreign companies to work together to study the conditions associated with these projects and to engage in geologic exploration to achieve the desired goal.

Quite a few examples can be cited of the successful operation of Western companies on the Russian shelf. The Sakhalin-1 project, one of the largest involving direct foreign investment in the Russian economy, ranks among the most promising and difficult projects developed by members of many countries in the 21st century. The project involves the development of oil and gas reserves on the northeastern shelf of Sakhalin Island. The project area includes the Chayvo, Odoptu, and Arkutun-Dagi fields. Total recoverable reserves for the project amount to 338 million tons (2.3 billion barrels) of oil and 17.1 TCF of gas. Exxon Neftegaz Limited, an affiliate of ExxonMobil, is the Sakhalin-1 project operator. The Sakhalin-1 Consortium also includes two Russian companies, Sakhalinmorneftegaz-Shelf and RN-Astra, the Japanese company Sakhalin Oil and Gas Development Co., Ltd., and the Indian company ONGK Videsh Ltd. The Sakhalin-1 project is a clear example of the successful realization of a joint large-scale investment program by Russian and foreign companies, achieving on-schedule start of oil production, the timely completion of an export pipeline and terminal, the beginning of oil exports and the early commissioning of an onshore product conditioning complex, a successful

346

production increase to a target level of 37,500 tons (250,000 barrels) of oil per day, and the drilling of record numbers of highly deviated wells. The project now delivers oil to international markets and natural gas to the Russian Far East. Incidentally, Nippon Oil Corp., Japan's biggest refiner, signed a long-term contract in February 2009 to buy Russian crude from Sakhalin fields. Every quarter, it purchases one tanker, or 720,000 barrels, of crude produced by the Sakhalin-1 project. The Japanese company made this decision in order to reduce its dependence on deliveries from the unstable Middle East, and to substantially reduce transportation costs. Previously, Nippon Oil bought 87% of its crude in the Middle East, but deliveries from there take two weeks to reach Japan, as opposed to only four days from Sakhalin. In the opinion of Hirofumi Kawachi, an analyst for the Mizuho Investors Securities Co. consulting firm, "the acquisition of oil from Sakhalin offers a clear advantage in view of its proximity to Japan, because the buyer can save on shipping costs."[6] According to reports in Bloomberg News, all six leading Japanese refineries have made test purchases of low-sulfur Sakhalin crude.

In addition to the Sakhalin-1 project, Rosneft is also realizing second-wave projects such as the Veni block of Sakhalin-3, and has already invited the British corporation BP to participate in a joint venture in the Sakhalin-4 and Sakhalin-5 projects.

Another instructive example occurred in February 2009, in the town of Prigorodny on Sakhalin Island, where a ceremonial opening was held for Russia's first liquefied natural gas processing plant on Sakhalin. The enterprise's launch was marked by the pressing of a symbolic button by the heads of the companies holding stock in the project: Aleksey Miller of Gazprom, Jeroen van der Veer of Royal Dutch/Shell Group, Shoei Utsuda of Mitsui, and Yorihiko Kojima of Mitsubishi. Russian President Dmitry Medvedev participated in the plant opening ceremony, as did representatives of the foreign countries whose companies are involved in the project. Japan was represented by Prime Minister Taro Aso; Great Britain by Prince Andrew, Duke of York; the Netherlands by Minister of Economics Maria van der Hoeven. The Duke of York, in particular, noted that the project would help meet the world's future demand for gas deliveries, and Great Britain regarded Russia "as a sufficiently reliable supplier of energy resources." In turn, Dutch Economics Minister van der Hoeven said that with the opening of this plant, Russia would gain new opportunities to supply energy resources, which would become a major trump card for Russia in the future. "We expect the plant to make it possible in the future to solve many problems, including demand," she said. The LNG plant will process gas produced under the Sakhalin-2 international project. The plant's annual capacity is 10.6 million tons of "blue" fuel. Japanese, American, and South Korean companies have already bought most of the gas for the next 25 years. The liquefied gas will be transported from the plant in tankers holding 635,000 cubic feet (635 MCF) to 5.1 MMCF of gas.

The Sakhalin-2 project is being implemented under a production-sharing agreement (PSA) signed with the Russian Federation in 1994. Sakhalin Energy shareholders are Gazprom (50% plus one share), Royal Dutch/Shell Group (27.5%), and the Japanese companies Mitsui (12.5%) and Mitsubishi (10%). Sakhalin Energy is the project operator.

The total cost of Sakhalin-2 is about $20 billion. The project is developing the Piltun-Astokh and Lunskoye fields, whose recoverable reserves are estimated at 165 million tons of oil and 17.7 TCF of gas.

Another piece of news related to the development of the Sakhalin shelf involves the Russian company Maritime Marine Shipping Line that, three years ago, in collaboration with the Japanese companies Mitsui O.S.K. Lines, Ltd. (MOL) and Kawasaki Kisen Kaisha, Ltd., won a bid to transport liquefied natural gas. In the spring of 2009, Japan successfully completed testing a ship that would carry liquefied natural gas produced under Sakhalin-2 from the Sakhalin terminal at Prigorodnoye. This liquefied natural gas carrier, the *Grand Mereya,* was built at a Japanese shipyard by Mitsui Engineering and Shipbuilding and is designed to carry 5.2 MMCF of liquefied gas. After testing, the ship began operating on a long-term time charter between the MOL/K Line/PRISCO consortium and the Sakhalin-2 project operator Sakhalin Energy.

Active work is going on in other parts of the Far Eastern shelf as well. In 2009, Rosneft began exploratory drilling on the West Kamchatka shelf. This parcel poses quite a challenge, even compared to the Sakhalin fields, as it lies far from supply bases, and moreover, very strict environmental requirements apply. In addition, project challenges include a weak market of regional subcontractors. Difficult production conditions and the difficult process of obtaining all imaginable work permits mean that geologic exploration takes more time. For this reason, the phases of geologic exploration for shelf projects, including the Kamchatka project, will take at least 10 years. In the first phase of geologic exploration off Kamchatka, 2D and 3D seismic exploration has been performed. The process of further geologic exploration will include drilling of several more wells. The city of Magadan has been chosen as the main shore support base to supply these operations.

Rosneft is pursuing a West Kamchatka offshore development project with a Korean consortium, Korea Kamchatka Co. Limited (KKC). The Russian company owns 60% of the project; KKC, 40%. A 50% share of KKC is owned by the Korean National Oil Company (KNOC), while Korea Gas Corp., GS-Caltex Corp., SK Corp, and Daewoo International Corp. each own 10%, and Kumho Petrochemical and Hyundai Corp., 5% each. The project operator and holder of the license for the geologic study of the West Kamchatka license tract is Kamchatneftegaz LLC. The license tract has an area of over 23,000 square miles, and as of 2006, the inferred resources, as estimated by DeGolyer & MacNaughton, were 2 billion tons of oil and 81.2 TCF of gas. Up to $300 million is to be allocated for work on the West Kamchatka shelf in the immediate future; $90 million has been invested since work began on the project. According to expert estimates, development of the Kamchatka shelf will require a total investment of approximately $24 billion.

Geologic and engineering studies have begun in the Lopukhovaya hydrocarbon parcel, located on northern Sakhalin and licensed to Gazprom Neft. Drilling of an offshore geologic exploratory well has already begun on the Tumansky license tract near Anadyr. According to preliminary data, Gazprom Neft calculates the tract's $C_1 + C_2$ reserves to be 35 million tons. It has been deemed advisable to enlist several foreign partners for this tract, and negotiations are now underway.

A good example of international cooperation on the Russian shelf is the involvement of two leading foreign companies, Total (France) and Statoil Hydro (Norway), along with Gazprom, in the development of the enormous Shtokman gas-condensate field, which is located in the central shelf of the Russian sector of the Barents Sea. The licensee is Sevmorneftegaz, a wholly owned subsidiary of Gazprom. According to January 2006 data, Shtokman Category $C_1 + C_2$ reserves approved by the State Commission for Mineral Reserves [*GKZ*] of the Russian Ministry of Natural Resources and Ecology amount to about 130.6 TCF of gas and more than 34 million tons of gas condensate.

On February 21, 2008, Gazprom, Total, and Statoil Hydro formed the Shtokman Development Company, a special-purpose entity to develop Phase One of the Shtokman gas-condensate field. Gazprom's head, Aleksey Miller, was approved as chairman of its Board of Directors. Shtokman Development Company was registered at Zug, Switzerland, and 51% of to the company is owned by Gazprom, 25% by Total, and 24% by Statoil Hydro.

Over the next two years, Shtokman Development Company will work on issues related to field development planning, including preliminary design work. Then, based on studies performed at the design stage, an investment plan will be presented to investors for a decision. The plan will include the necessary costs and investments required to complete the project, as well as a work schedule. This will form the basis for adopting a final investment decision on field development. Several experts estimate the total cost of developing Shtokman Field to be in the range of $43–44 billion. Investment in Phase One of the Shtokman project is estimated at $12 billion. In this phase, production is expected to reach 837 BCF of gas per year, 50% of which is to be delivered to a gas pipeline, and the other 50% sent for production of liquefied natural gas (LNG). The annual LNG output could amount to 8.3 million tons in Phase

One, with expansion to 16.5 million tons in Phase Two and 33 million tons in Phase Three. The gas will be delivered both to Europe and to countries of the Atlantic Basin. Gas pipeline deliveries are scheduled for 2013; those of LNG, for 2014. A site has been selected in the town of Teriberka, Murmansk region, for construction of a plant to liquefy gas from the Shtokman gas-condensate field.

Examples also exist of successful international cooperation in the Russian sector of the Caspian Sea. The British company Timan Oil & Gas plc is developing two blocks, Izberbash 2 and Sulak 4, in the northern part of the Caspian. They have completed 3D seismic exploration, identified prospect structures for drilling, estimated reserves according to Russian standards, and are completing preparation for exploratory drilling.

One more important aspect must be emphasized. The Russian government plans to approve an important document with special environmental requirements applicable to the exploration and development of oil fields in the Caspian zone. A "zero discharge" requirement will apply in the zone of this unique water area, under which no discharges or emissions into the waters will be permitted during oil production. The innovative technology necessary to comply with these requirements has been successfully used by LUKOIL in developing oil fields in the Caspian using the Astra platform, providing convincing evidence that our country is actively seeking to fulfill Russia's obligations under the "Framework Convention for the Protection of the Marine Environment of the Caspian Sea," signed by the Caspian littoral states in 2003. The Convention, which obligates Azerbaijan, Iran, Kazakhstan, Russia, and Turkmenistan to combat pollution of the Caspian and make reasonable use of its resources, entered into force in 2006. Under its provisions, the Caspian littoral states must pool their efforts to restore the natural environment of the Caspian and guarantee its environmental security.

Without a doubt, further research in the Arctic will be an important part of the country's program for industrial development of the oil and gas resources of Russia's offshore shelf. During the first high-latitude deep-water expedition in Russian history, in August 2007, a large volume of scientific research was performed within the scope of the Third International Polar Year, and the Mir deep-submergence vehicles submerged at the North Pole for the first time. Over 15 days, the Rosgidromet [Federal Service for Hydrometeorology and Environmental Monitoring] research vessel *Akademik Fëdorov* ["Academician Fëdorov"] and the Murmansk Marine Shipping Line's nuclear icebreaker *Rossiya* ["Russia"] overcame nearly 2,500 miles of ice in the world's harshest and coldest ocean. During the Arctic 2007 expedition, water, ice, and soil samples were collected in the most scientifically interesting parts of the ocean, over the Lomonosov and Gakkel Ridges and even at the North Pole, which the *Akademik Fëdorov* and *Rossiya* reached on August 1. On August 2, the

Mir 1 and *Mir 2* deep-submergence vehicles worked for almost 10 hours in the ocean depths at the point where the Earth's meridians converge, completing a dive to a depth of about 14,000 feet. A Russian flag made of superstrong metal was planted on the bottom, and a time capsule, the flag of the Third International Polar Year, and a memorial medal were emplaced as well. To a certain extent, the results of the Russian polar expedition to the North Pole should form the foundation for a Russian position when the nationality of this part of the shelf is decided upon by the United Nations.

Surprisingly, several countries of the Arctic region, including Canada, have reacted completely inappropriately to the planting of the Russian flag on the sea floor. In this author's opinion, there should be no grounds for any worry or alarm here. Recall that in 1969, American astronauts planted a flag on the moon, but it is commonly understood that Earth's satellite has not become the property of the US. Moreover, our government has repeatedly stressed that Russia will act in the Arctic only within specific international procedures and through the UN, and will strictly abide by accepted international norms.

A further illustration of the Russian government's constructive position is its approval, on June 16, 2010, of the Russian Geologic Strategy through 2030. Within that framework, the state of knowledge of the continental shelf and inland seas is forecast to grow by nearly double by 2030. (As of today, the shelf is about 42% explored; this figure could grow to 44% by 2012, to 60% by 2020, and to 80% by 2030.) Such progress is made possible by the more rapid introduction of innovative oil exploration and production technologies. The Russian state is prepared to allocate its own money to develop innovative projects, to introduce lease financing of similar initiatives, to offer state guarantees to private investors who make loans for innovative projects, and to subsidize interest rates on commercial bank loans. Financial incentives are also planned using tax benefits for enterprises engaged in innovative activities, and reduced customs duties will be levied on geologic exploration equipment that is unlike any manufactured in Russia. In addition, the Ministry of Natural Resources and Ecology intends to propose steps as early as 2011 to ensure market turnover of mineral prospecting and assessment licenses.

Using the Potential of High Oil and Gas Technologies

The foreign trade press commonly makes rather dubious assessments regarding the low technical and technological level of Russia's oil and gas industry. Sometimes it is even asserted that Russian service companies in the oil and gas industry lag so far behind Western corporations that they will not be able to catch up in the foreseeable future.

On May 20, 2008, at the Standartneftegaz-2008 conference in Moscow on the standardization of oil and gas equipment, Russian oil and gas workers discussed in detail the problem of preparing industry standards. The conference was held to address the urgent need to improve obsolete Russian oil and gas equipment standards and to harmonize them with international standards. The conference examined questions of ensuring equipment safety, which goes a long way toward determining work safety in the entire oil and gas industry. The conference was attended by oil and gas equipment developers, manufacturers, and consumers, as well as by government agencies. A serious positive occurrence noted by participants was the fact that the Russian Federal Agency for Technical Regulation and Metrology [*Rostekhregulirovaniye*] had completed organizing a Technical Committee on Oil and Gas Industry Standardization. The technical committee's primary task is to write new standards in the interests of the industry and to harmonize them with international standards. The Technical Committee on Oil and Gas Industry Standardization is headed by Vlada Rusakova, member of the executive board of Gazprom. Gazprom was responsible for the work of three subcommittees; Rosneft, for that of the subcommittee on oil production. The subcommittee on the development of offshore fields was the responsibility of LUKOIL, and the subcommittee on equipment and materials was the responsibility of the Russian Association of Oil and Gas Equipment Manufacturers. On the whole, the Standartneftegaz-2008 conference was an important step and proposed a set of measures to the government to raise the competitiveness of Russian industrial products for the oil and gas industry.

In turn, the first international forum on "Oil and Gas Service and Equipment: Russian Experience and International Cooperation," which took place in late May 2008 in Tyumen, convincingly showed that the so-called technical and technological backwardness of Russian oil service companies is steadily becoming a thing of the past. While it is true that certain high-tech foreign service companies such as Baker Hughes, Halliburton, Schlumberger, etc., have patents on very efficient technologies that Russian companies do not have, the well-known analytic research company Douglas-Westwood estimates the size of Russia's oil service market in 2007 to have been $12.5 billion, which will increase to $22 billion by 2011, i.e., the market will almost double in three years. Experts estimate that the biggest growth here will be in drilling. Currently, the annual volume of drilling work approaches 32.8 million feet per year, and by 2010 it will exceed 49 million feet. A challenging mining geology makes the current cost of drilling $125 per foot in Western Siberia and $610 in Eastern Siberia. By 2011, the cost of drilling is expected to exceed $150 per foot in Western Siberia and to reach $915 in Eastern Siberia.

Under such conditions, the obvious striving of Western service companies to expand their activity in Russia is readily apparent. For example, in early November 2007, Halliburton Co. closed a deal to acquire the leading Russian drilling company Burservis (Burservice). Simon Turton, Halliburton Country Vice President for Russia, remarked: "Over the past several years, Halliburton has successfully expanded our directional drilling and mud-logging operations in Western Siberia. This acquisition enables Halliburton to expand our operations to serve oil and gas customers in... Russia, thanks to Burservice's outstanding reputation for service quality."[7]

Drilling and capital well rework sectors still overwhelmingly belong to Russian contractors, however. Russia is now creating unique service technologies, which are original process solutions of suitable price and quality.

An example of this occurred in mid-February 2009, at a base on the Upper Salym field near the village of Salym (Khanty-Mansi Autonomous District), where a fundamentally new mobile drilling rig was demonstrated. This was the MBU 3200/200-DER, which was developed by specialists of the Russian company Uralmash Drilling Equipment (Yekaterinburg). The rig's development also involved German engineers, whose participation allowed the new design to take all European requirements for equipment safety and technical characteristics into account.

The mobile drilling rig demonstrated at Salym field has strong competitive advantages. It is a piece of heavy drilling equipment, with a load capacity of 220 tons, capable of drilling to a depth of 10,500 feet. The rig has an adjustable drive and can be operated at an ambient temperature of between −49°F and +104°F. It can also be used for well workover. The rig's basic equipment is broken down into vehicle-mounted subassemblies that are transported to oil fields and assembled using fifth wheel tractors. Other subassemblies and large units are conveyed by general purpose vehicles. The rig's modules include all necessary connections, heating systems, control panels, and electrical equipment, and the equipment is certified to API standards. The new rig has been successfully used by specialists at KCA Deutag, the well-known German drilling contractor.

After the demonstration, leading Russian experts stressed that the production of a new-generation drilling rig meeting international standards was a great victory for Russian mechanical engineers. Its use at Russian fields will undoubtedly raise the technological and commercial efficiency of oil and gas projects, and also ensure the environmental safety of drilling processes. Gazprom's equipment retooling program already contains a line item for the purchase of the MBU 3200/200 DER-M rig, and the first batch of five drilling rigs has already been delivered to replace equipment at the Orenburg gas field.

Another example occurred in February of 2009, when the Russian Hydraulic Machines and Systems investment and industrial group simultaneously won three tenders to deliver pumping and oilfield equipment to

Verkhnechonskneftegaz, operating in Eastern Siberia. The total value of tenders won was around 60 million rubles, in a competition where leading foreign companies also participated in the bidding. During this year, Russian manufacturers supplied oil workers with type *NPV* ("vertical oil booster") high-performance vertical pumps produced by Nasosenergomash, and also modern equipment for a formation pressure maintenance system (manifold subassemblies) and pumping stations.

In 2009, the Russian company Grasis delivered a mobile nitrogen station to Naryanmarneftegaz LLC, a joint venture of LUKOIL and the American company ConocoPhillips. The station is intended to implement an oil-conditioning process at the South Khylchuyu central collection point. The mobile membrane nitrogen station is designed to produce 250 Nm^3/h of 98% pure nitrogen at a pressure of 40 bar.[8] The station is packaged in an enclosure having dimensions of 39 × 8 × 8 feet. Control of the station is as simple and convenient as possible, allowing such equipment to be operated by personnel without requiring special training.

The encouraging prospects of the Russian oil and gas equipment market have helped accelerate integration processes. In March 2009, the Russian Integra group announced the creation of a company to service oil and gas equipment. The new enterprise, called Integra-MashServis, was formed on the basis of subdivisions of Uralmash Drilling Equipment (Yekaterinburg). The new company's main task is to provide a broad range of highly skilled services on an expedited basis in the areas of oil and gas equipment industrial safety expert review, oil and gas equipment examination and technical diagnosis of oil and gas equipment, drilling equipment overhaul, drilling rig and equipment upgrading, and oil and gas equipment servicing.

Integra group management considers the prospects for oil and gas equipment servicing to be very favorable as a market segment. They estimate that around 70% of the active drilling equipment in Russia has become obsolete, and that a significant portion of the growing demand for drilling rigs (the result of increased drilling volume) remains completely unsatisfied. This situation creates great demand, on the part of production companies, for comprehensive service of obsolete equipment, including overhaul and upgrading, provision of spare parts, and maintenance. Demand is also increased by the fact that Russian oil companies are now actively replacing imported field equipment and technology.

Russian products are now finding demand in other countries. Russian oil machine-building enterprises were first able to enter the Central European market in 2009. For example, Korvet (Kurgan) supplied the Serbian company Naftna Industrija Srbije (NIS) with a batch of "Christmas trees" for oil production, equipment that the Serbian company had earlier procured from the American companies Weatherford and Cameron. Moreover, this company also ordered oil producing pumps made by Alnas (part of the Rimera Group), and a contract was signed with the Ozna Group (Ufa) to deliver Impuls units for well flow rate measurement.

On March 25, 2010, LUKOIL-Kaliningradmorneft (a wholly owned subsidiary of LUKOIL) introduced the Yermak, a new Russian drilling rig, at its structural metalwork production plant in Kaliningrad. The Yermak features a unique hydraulic travel system that allows it to move incrementally in all directions and to rotate 360 degrees about its axis. A characteristic of this rig is that it can be used for both development and exploratory drilling. It has a load capacity of 496 tons and can drill down to 21,325 feet. It is equipped with a 2,000-horsepower drawworks, three 1,600-horsepower mud pumps, a 550-ton top drive, and a 1,150-horsepower rotary table. The Yermak drilling rig has been modified to operate under various climatic zones, and in particular, for work under cold Far North conditions and at high temperatures in hot and humid climates.

On the Agenda: Energy Conservation

Foreign media reports sometimes claim that the Russian economy wastes too much energy and, unlike European countries, is very slow at implementing energy conservation programs. This not-so-simple issue also warrants examination.

International Energy Agency data do show that the GDP energy/output ratio in Russia is 2.5 times higher than in the US, and 3.5 times higher than in Great Britain. Even Canada, with its harsh climatic conditions, consumes only half as much energy per unit of production as Russia does.

Unfortunately, 30–40% of the energy resources our country produces are lost in its worn-out utility networks. Ministry of Energy data indicate that Russia does lose around 440 million TCE every year due to the lack of energy conservation.

Today, growth of the country's production and energy capacities requires enormous resources. At the same time, energy shortages in certain regions are due not only to high rates of economic growth, but also to low efficiency in the use of gas, electrical, and thermal energy. This is why increasing the economic efficiency of Russian companies and, consequently, strengthening their competitiveness through the use of energy-saving technologies, production upgrades, and their own R&D in this area are becoming highly relevant subjects. Data from the Russian Center for Energy Efficiency (CENEf) indicate that while the potential growth in the production of energy resources is approximately 110 million TCE, the potential for energy conservation is 408–430 million TCE. The Center's experts concluded that if the margin of energy efficiency improvement in Russia were to be completely exploited, Russia's economy would confidently continue to grow for 80 years, without having to increase energy production and consumption.

In a speech in September 2009, President Medvedev clearly formulated the goal of achieving world energy leadership by introducing new resource-saving technologies based on intense processing of renewable raw materials. Sergey Chemezov, head of the *Rostekhnologiya* corporation, was delegated the task of introducing high-efficiency technologies both in production and in the area of all public utilities on the basis of six key energy efficiency and energy conservation projects: "Count, Save, and Pay," "New Light," "The Energy-Efficient Residential Quarter," "Small-Scale Integrated Power," "Innovative Energy," and "Energy-Efficient Technologies in Government Institutions."

Today, development and implementation of a new energy policy based on the highly efficient use of every ruble invested, is becoming one of the main priorities for taking the Russian economy to a qualitatively new level. This trend is based on increasing the volume of production and the export of fuel and energy resources produced by major Russian companies combined with organizing a broad regional network of autonomous private/municipal fuel and energy conglomerates that produce inexpensive forms of fuel, heat, and electricity and are located as closely as possible both to raw material sources and to consumption locations.

The pressing problems at the current stage of development of Russia's leading oil and gas companies are further growth in capitalization, profitability, and performance of production investments, reduction of expenses at all stages of production processes, and improvement of environmental indicators. In many cases, it is possible to achieve these goals by actively implementing the latest Russian breakthrough technologies to conserve energy resources and high-tech equipment, which have short payback periods. Conserving energy resources, a business necessity for profitability, is now a pressing requirement in light of the constant growth of energy prices and the looming shortage of electrical energy, which are hampering rapid development of most sectors of the Russian economy.

In turn, effective energy conservation, which is a powerful "hidden" investment resource, makes it possible to accelerate the resolution of the most important strategic national problems, such as achieving sustainable GDP growth, increasing national economic competitiveness, and assuring energy security. The international obligations that Russia assumed by signing the Kyoto Protocol and by its impending entry into the World Trade Organization also require increased energy and environmental efficiency in all areas of economic activity.

Currently, the most pressing obstacle to implementing a national energy conservation program for Russia's oil and gas complex is the use of associated petroleum gas (APG). For quite a long time, oil companies considered associated petroleum gas to be a waste product of conditioning oil before it is pumped into pipelines. Nevertheless, a small part of the products extracted from APG is used as an energy fuel to service fields (in mini-generating stations and boiler rooms), and the rest is flared, releasing an enormous amount of carbon dioxide and soot into the atmosphere. According to data of the social organization Ecological Movement of Concrete Actions, in the past year, the volume of atmospheric pollution from flared APG was 12% of the country's total volume of harmful emissions. Meanwhile, if associated petroleum gas were to be collected using gas capture systems, and if compressor stations were built and the APG were to be delivered by special pipelines to gas processing plants, it would be possible to produce many valuable products. In particular, these include dry stripped gas, whose product characteristics are close to natural gas, allowing it to be transported through Russia's Unified Gas Supply System (UGSS) or used to generate electricity. Moreover, APG contains propane, butane, natural gas gasoline and natural gas liquids, which are key raw materials for the gas processing industry.

Russian Ministry of Energy statistics indicate that in 2009, Russian oil companies produced around 2 TCF of associated petroleum gas. The Sibur company, the main processor of associated gas, processed 494 BCF of APG and produced 353 BCF of natural gas liquids. At the same time, the Russian Ministry of Natural Resources and Ecology indicates that every year, companies write off around 47% of associated gas to process losses or use it for field needs, flare approximately 27%, and send only 26% for further processing, i.e., compression and gas fractionation. Today, many oil field license tracts lack metering systems, record-keeping documentation, atmospheric emission monitoring schedules, and a transportation infrastructure that would allow associated gas to be sent to gas processing plants. Independent experts estimate that the average level of APG recovery at Russian flaring systems was around 70–75% in the past year (that is, 25–30% of the APG, or around 530–706 BCF of gas, was flared). Russian Ministry of Natural Resources and Ecology experts have calculated that Russia loses around 139.2 billion rubles every year due to APG flaring alone, although the total benefit from APG processing in the country could amount to 362 billion rubles per year.

According to Sibur company data, only 24% of the total volume of APG produced is now sent for gas fractionation, which involves separating the liquid fraction or natural gas liquids from unstable hydrocarbon gases or condensates. In turn, only 42% of the total volume of associated gas sent for processing comes out as natural gas liquids and liquefied gases, and the remaining 58% is either used as fuel, or is exported and used for the same purpose. It turns out that, after all these transformations, only 10% of the total volume of APG produced in Russia is used to create chemical products with high added value. It can thus be concluded that the volume of APG involved in the production of expensive products in Russia is still too low. Incidentally, the US captures 97% of APG, and Norway completely prohibits flaring of associated gas.

Russia is already taking certain steps in this direction. For example, the long-awaited government decree freeing the price of APG sent to gas processing plants met the approval of the oil and gas community. However, this step fell far short of resolving the problems of the APG market. So far, the economy of projects depends greatly on the price of dry stripped gas, which is regulated by the government and still remains at a low level. To a certain extent, the freeing of the APG price eliminated some investment risks, but it did not in and of itself radically increase the attractiveness of investment in projects. Oil companies still face problems with delivering dry stripped gas separated from APG to the Unified Gas Supply System. Another factor that negatively influences the profitability of projects to collect and transport APG is the enormous distance between the fields developed by oil workers, gas processing plants, and petrochemical plants, which are frequently located in another part of the country. The number of pipelines for transporting gas condensate in Russia are all too few; for example, only a small transport line connects Tobolskneftekhim with the Sibur gas processing plants. For the most part, therefore, natural gas liquids have to be transported in railroad tank cars, and this greatly increases costs.

Unfortunately, there are complex systemic obstacles on the road to an efficient and comprehensive solution of this problem, but it is encouraging that the Russian government is now taking decisive steps to solve them. On February 13, 2008, the Public Council of the Russian Federal Service for Environmental, Technological, and Atomic Oversight approved a new version of a draft Russian government decree, "On Measures to Reduce Atmospheric Air Pollution Caused by Combustion Products of Flared Associated Gas," whose provisions create real incentives for oil companies to develop technologies for collecting APG with the goal of separating valuable petrochemical products. On March 26, 2008, a government committee on the fuel and energy complex met in Moscow and thoroughly examined issues of APG recovery. Proposed measures included: creating an effective gas control system, implementing stricter licensing, and even substantially increasing environmental fines for exceeding limits on atmospheric emissions of harmful substances as a result of flaring gas. The meeting set the clear goal of increasing the volume of associated petroleum gas used to 95% by 2011. Companies that take real steps to utilize APG will receive preferential access to gas transportation networks and energy infrastructure. Duties on the export of propane/butane fractions or liquefied petroleum gas (LPG) produced as a result of processing associated petroleum gas will also be abolished (currently, the export of LPG is subject to a duty pegged to the price of Urals-grade

Russian oil on world markets). Thus, the government is striving to increase the attractiveness of investments in the APG segment in various ways.

Implementing government decisions to increase the efficiency of APG utilization has, in turn, required serious efforts on the part of Russian oil and gas companies to develop and implement their own corporate programs. In particular, starting in 2008, Gazprom expanded its research program to include measures that will allow elaboration of optimal engineering solutions for APG utilization, so as to increase the degree of APG use at the company's fields to at least 95% by 2011. A Gazprom Executive Board resolution dated January 22, 2009, "On the Prospects for Developing and Introducing Gas and Energy Conservation Technologies and Their Influence on Optimizing the Fuel and Energy Balance Sheet of the Russian Federation" clearly confirmed the course that the company had set toward high APG recovery in all corresponding production units. Implementation of decisions that were made included having its subsidiary Gazprom Neft successfully implement its own program, "Utilizing and Increasing the Efficiency of Use of APG." In 2008–2010, this program involves investing 17.6 billion rubles in projects to utilize associated petroleum gas. Of this sum, more than 12 billion rubles will be earmarked for construction of gas collection networks and gas processing capacity, and around 5 billion rubles will be spent on development of its own generating capacity. The remaining 600 million rubles or so will be used to audit existing resources for APG recovery. The company plans to build new gas pipelines from the Yety-Pur, Mereto-Yakha, North Yangtinsky, Chatylkinskoye, Kholmisty, South Udmurt, Ravninnoye, and Vorgenskoye fields, and also from the Urmanskoye and Shinginskoye fields. Moreover, in 2008–2010, Gazprom Neft built four gas-turbine and two gas-piston power stations, and in the past year the company spent more than 5.5 billion rubles to increase the efficiency of associated gas use.

Positive examples set by other companies can also be cited. RN-Purneftegaz (a subsidiary of Rosneft) invested more than 600 million rubles to implement the first stage of an APG recovery program that should increase the company's associated gas recovery to over 90% on the basis of 2010 results. The TNK-BP company invested $2 billion in the construction of a gas collection network and other measures to recover APG, and the average APG recovery level is now greater than 76%. Surgutneftegaz, Tatneft, Bashneft, and many other oil companies are also making determined efforts to achieve high APG recovery figures.

LUKOIL is successfully implementing its "Associated Petroleum Gas Recovery Program for 2007–2016." The program provides for increasing associated gas recovery at company enterprises from 75% to 95% over 10 years. New projects will recover 100% of associated gas. The tentative increase in gas production will amount to more than 198 BCF per year.

In addition, the company is planning to build gas-piston and gas-turbine power stations with a total capacity of more than 400 MW in remote regions that are short of energy. The largest projects will be carried out at the Tevlin-Russkinskaya and Vat-Yёgan fields in the Khanty-Mansi Autonomous District, and also at South Khylchuyu field in the Nenets Autonomous District. The first of these went online in December of 2007, comprising a 72-MW gas-turbine power station at the Vat-Yёgan field. This is the largest facility of its type in the Khanty-Mansi Autonomous District. As fuel, the station uses associated gas produced at the fields of the Kogalymneftegaz oil production enterprise to operate six gas-turbine engines that, in turn, drive six gas-turbine generating units. The design of the gas-turbine engines is based on the gas generator of the aircraft engine installed on Russian Il-96, Tu-204, and Tu-214 airplanes, while the power station's long-service-life power reducer was developed and manufactured by the Kirov-Energomash Plant. Every year, the power station consumes 4.2 BCF of associated petroleum gas that in turn makes production capacity at the Lokosovsky Gas Processing Plant available to process gas from newly opened fields. In August 2008, LUKOIL–Western Siberia brought a new 72-MW power station online at the same Vat-Yёgan field. Earlier, the Perm Motor Works had delivered six GTU-12 gas turbine units to the station; these had been developed on the basis of the fourth-generation PS-90A aircraft engine, which has an efficiency of 33.7%. An agreement is now being implemented to deliver another eight power units for LUKOIL–Western Siberia, under which two power stations having a total capacity of 48 MW will be set up at the Tevlin-Russkinskaya and Pokachёva oil and gas fields. In accordance with the program mentioned above, LUKOIL also plans to build a series of gas energy complexes that will provide a reliable supply of electrical energy for oilfield production facilities and will substantially increase the volumes of associated gas recovered.

In January 2010, the LUKOIL Executive Board approved an "Energy Conservation Program at Company Enterprises in 2010 and the 2010–2012 Period." It presents energy conservation measures for 48 organizations of the LUKOIL Group in such business sectors as oil and gas production in Russia, gas processing, refining in Russia and elsewhere, petrochemistry, supply of petroleum products to Russia and other countries, power generation, and transportation. In particular, the document calls for the optimization of production processes and the introduction of new energy efficient technologies and equipment. In 2010, pilot projects were undertaken to redesign formation pressure-maintenance system pumps, to broadly introduce valve drives in centrifugal and screw pumps, and to supply energy for production based on renewable energy sources and on combined thermal and electrical energy sources. Successful implementation of this conservation program saved LUKOIL around 700 million kWh of electrical energy, more than 320,000 Gcal of thermal energy, and almost 57,000 tons of boiler/furnace fuel equivalent in 2010. In monetary terms, energy conservation measures saved the company on the order of 2.166 billion rubles. In 2010–2012, implementation of the Energy Conservation Program will allow the LUKOIL Group to save more than 2.35 billion kWh of electrical energy, more than 970,000 Gcal of thermal energy, and almost 235,000 tons of boiler/furnace fuel equivalent. In monetary terms, the company plans to save on the order of 9.203 billion rubles over three years.

Oil companies are now faced with a choice: either build their own gas processing plants, or create joint ventures with Sibur, the primary consumer of natural gas liquids recovered from associated gas. It is obvious that creating one's own gas processing capacity is a capital-intensive process requiring large investments to construct pipelines and gas processing plants, and to set up a product processing and resale system, and therefore most Russian oilmen prefer to share the expenses with gas chemists. Experts estimate that Sibur's independent investment projects and joint investment projects with oilmen will allow the holding company to increase its APG processing volume to 777–848 BCF by 2011.

Experts estimate that in 2007, Russian oil companies spent around 20 billion rubles for these purposes, and that another 100 billion rubles of investment would be required over the next two years. On the whole, implementation of corporate programs substantially increase the purposeful use of produced raw hydrocarbons in Russia, minimize environmental limitations, ensure uninterrupted energy supply to oil production facilities, lower tax risks, and increase revenue derived from selling additional volumes of APG and its processed products.

Energy Cooperation in the CIS Framework

A highly successful roundtable dedicated to problems of economic cooperation among CIS member countries was held on June 17, 2010 as part of the annual St. Petersburg Economic Forum. The roundtable participants reiterated that energy is one of the most important areas of economic development for CIS countries and that it plays an enormous role both in ensuring the normal function of all industries and in enhancing the operation of public agencies and the quality of life. The CIS Presidential Council had previously designated energy cooperation as a key area of interaction among CIS member nations on October 10, 2008.

Around the same time, several biased commentaries were once again published in the Western media regarding alleged crises in the CIS, including in the energy sector. But was this really the case?

The experience of leading industrialized countries, in particular of

Western European nations that have made serious efforts in recent years to create competitive energy markets within the European Union, shows that the policy of regionalizing energy markets is viewed as an important prerequisite for the energy industry's successful future development and once again underscores how extremely difficult it is today for one country, even one with a substantial energy resource base, to ensure its energy security when isolated from global integration processes in the fuel and energy sector.

An impartial analysis of the current state of energy cooperation between Russia and two of its CIS partners, Kazakhstan and Azerbaijan, reveals that the energy sector is one of the most significant and promising aspects of their productive cooperation.

As a member of the Foreign Investors Council of the President of the Republic of Kazakhstan, this author can say that successful and mutually beneficial interaction between Kazakhstan and Russia can clearly be seen in several large projects in the energy sector. One area of significant importance in the development of the oil and gas transport infrastructure between the two countries is their participation in the Baltic Pipeline System, which will make it possible to export oil from the Timan-Pechora oil and gas province and the Western Siberia and Volga-Urals regions, along with oil from CIS countries—principally Kazakhstan—via the Baltic port of Primorsk. In addition, the two countries are making joint efforts to efficiently utilize transit potential, in particular by increasing the carrying capacity of the Atyrau–Samara pipeline to 28 million tons of crude per year. Other notable areas of cooperation include a promising oil and gas condensate field within the Kurmangazi structure, which the Kazakh national oil and gas company KazMunayGas is developing jointly with Russia's Rosneft; the organization of parallel operations between the energy systems of the two countries; the establishment of a joint venture on the basis of the Ekibastuz-2 State Regional Power Station; and many other potential business initiatives.

The project to develop the Karachaganak oil and gas field is particularly noteworthy. One of the largest in the world, the Karachaganak field was discovered in western Kazakhstan in 1979. The field covers an area of 173 square miles and has recoverable reserves of 2.4 billion barrels of oil and 16 TCF of natural gas. Field development intensified in 1995 after the Kazakh government signed an agreement on production-sharing principles with British Gas and Agip. In August 1997, Texaco purchased a 20% stake in the project from British Gas and Agip, which now each hold a 32.5% interest in the field. Gazprom transferred its 15% stake in the project to LUKOIL in November 1997. The investors established a joint operating consortium called Karachaganak Integrated Organization (KIO), which is headquartered in Aksay. A final Production-Sharing Agreement (PSA) was signed in November 1997 and took effect on January 27, 1998. The PSA envisions the Karachaganak field being developed over a 40-year period ending in 2038. A total of $160 million was invested in the project from various sources during the project's first, preparatory phase from 1995 to 1997. Phase Two (1998–2003) required $3.5 billion in investment and increased liquid hydrocarbon production to 210,000 barrels per day by mid-2004. By that point, the Karachaganak project was independently generating its own free cash flow. LUKOIL's share in production currently amounts to 15.3 million BOE, but this figure is expected to increase to 22 million BOE by 2010. The project's high level of efficiency can be attributed to the sale of gas condensate via the Caspian Pipeline Consortium (CPC) system following the opening of the 395-mile Karachaganak–Bolshoy Chagan–Atyrau connecting pipeline. Gazprom and the Karachaganak consortium are implementing an agreement in this region to set up a joint venture that would annually ship up to 530 BCF of Karachaganak gas to the Orenburg Gas Processing Plant.

The Turgai Petroleum joint venture, which was set up under equal ownership by LUKOIL Overseas Holding and Canada's PetroKazakhstan, is developing the northern section of the Kumkol field in Kazakhstan's Kyzylorda Region. The field's license area exceeds 57 square miles. Having produced 3.9 million tons of oil and 5.1 BCF of gas last year, the project is already providing a steady supply of crude hydrocarbons. The field has residual reserves of 41 million tons. The 110-mile Kumkol–Jusali oil pipeline has been operating successfully for five years, shortening the western export route by 745 miles and making it possible to export crude hydrocarbons via the CPC system. Facilities have been built to process and treat associated gas, and a gas turbine power unit with generating capacity of 55 MW has also been put into operation. This project allows 6.3 BCF of associated gas to be utilized each year and provides a reliable source of inexpensive electricity for the development of hydrocarbon fields.

According to the agreement between LUKOIL and KazMunayGas, the Russian oil giant has a 50% stake in the PSA for the Tyub-Karagan section in the Kazakh part of the Caspian Sea. This section covers an area of 450 square miles and is located 25 miles northwest of the port of Bautino at a water depth between 23 and 39 feet. The section has projected resources of 472 million TCE, including 357.6 million tons of oil. If commercial hydrocarbons are discovered, total expenditures on both projects could exceed $3 billion.

In addition, KazMunayGas and LUKOIL Overseas Holding set up a joint venture called Atash to drill an exploratory well as part of a contract for the geological exploration of the Atash block, which covers an area of 3,243 square miles and is located 50–53 miles from Bautino at a water depth of 23–115 feet. Atash has projected resources of 274.3 million TCE, including 156.2 million tons of oil. Other promising structures could be discovered in the eastern part of the block following additional exploratory operations.

LUKOIL's works in progress also include projects to develop the Alibekmola, Kojasay, Karakuduk, North Buzachi, and Arman hydrocarbon fields as well as options for the acquisition of two exploratory blocks in the Kazakh section of the Caspian Sea: South Jambay and South Zaburin. These fields have 269.6 million barrels of proven and probable hydrocarbon reserves.

LUKOIL is the driving force in the energy dialogue between Russia and Azerbaijan and has made a significant contribution to several important projects. The Russian oil company's largest project in Azerbaijan is the development of the Shah-Deniz gas-condensate field, which is located offshore about 62 miles south of Baku on the Caspian Sea shelf, at a water depth of up to 1,200 feet. The contract area covers 332 square miles and has recoverable reserves of 22 TCF of gas and more than 110 million tons of gas condensate. Azerbaijan enacted a law on October 17, 1996 ratifying an agreement for the exploration, development, and production sharing of Shah-Deniz field. At present, the international consortium members are BP (the project operator, with 25.5%), Statoil (25.5%), the State Oil Company of the Azerbaijan Republic (SOCAR) (10%), TotalFinaElf (10%), NICO (10%), and TPAO (9%). After acquiring the LUKAgip joint venture in January 2004, LUKOIL Overseas Holding increased its stake in the project to 10%. With the development of the Shah-Deniz field, LUKOIL increased natural gas production in Azerbaijan from 49 MMCF in 2006 to 11.3 BCF in 2009, while oil and gas condensate production grew from 330 tons to 97,000 tons.

Another important project is the development of the potential D-222 Block, a part of the large Yalama area, the most promising structure in the northeastern Caspian Sea, roughly equal parts of which are located in the Azerbaijani and Russian sectors of the Caspian, about 18 miles offshore. The water depth near the structure ranges from 260 to 2,300 feet.

The contract to develop this block was signed on July 3, 1997 and ratified on December 10 of the same year. Investment in the project is estimated at $2 billion. According to our estimates, the block has reserves of roughly 800 million barrels of oil and 1.8 TCF of gas. LUKOIL holds an 80% stake in the project, while SOCAR has a 20% interest. Contractual obligations called for the Russian oil company to drill two exploratory wells in the D-222 block. Drilling of the first exploratory well began in October 2004 and ended in June 2005. Unfortunately, drilling did not reveal any hydrocarbon reserves, although experts are hopeful that a second well will produce positive results.

LUKOIL has also made significant contributions to the development of the Azerbaijani fuel market. In 1995, the oil giant opened the first gas station in Baku that complied with international technical, environmental, and service standards. By 2008, LUKOIL was successfully operating more than 20 gas stations in Azerbaijan, in addition to one of the country's most modern gas tank batteries. The high level of cooperation between Baku and LUKOIL, which has invested more than $1 billion in the Azerbaijan economy, provided an impetus for the Russian company to expand its operations in Georgia and Turkey. LUKOIL currently accounts for a considerable share of the fuel markets of these countries in addition to the bunker business in the Black Sea.

Russia's energy relations with Uzbekistan and Turkmenistan have also been developing productively as of late. On November 29, 2007, LUKOIL Overseas Holding and Uzbekneftegaz commissioned the Hauzak gas field as part of a PSA on the Kandym-Hauzak-Shady-Kungrad project. Hauzak field, which is part of Dengizkul field, is located on the shore of Dengiz Lake in the Bukhara Region in southwest Uzbekistan about 118 miles from the city of Bukhara near the Turkmenian border. The field could have a maximum annual production level of roughly 388 BCF of natural gas (production is expected to peak in 2012–2013), giving LUKOIL one-fifth of overall gas production in Uzbekistan. The project could ultimately result in total output of more than 7 TCF of gas.

Existing intergovernmental agreements between Russia, Kazakhstan, Azerbaijan, Uzbekistan, and Turkmenistan emphasize enhanced cooperation in the oil and gas sector as well as coordination of the fundamental restructuring of their national economies. The key benefit of successful energy cooperation between Russia and its individual CIS partners is the opportunity to achieve total energy self-sufficiency and to substantially expand the export potential of both countries. Other important aspects of such cooperation include the establishment of the appropriate legal frame-work in the partner countries to promote development of trade and economic ties in the energy sector, conditions for free and uninterrupted transit of energy resources, and implementation of coordinated customs, tax, and tariff policies in branches of the energy sector.

Russia and its CIS partners could also enhance cooperation in such promising areas as the more efficient use of transit potential, the development of transportation infrastructure, and the expansion of export opportunities for the shipment of oil and gas resources to third countries. Kazakhstan has started building its segment of the Western Europe–Western China International Transit Corridor (overall length 5,247 miles, including 1,732 miles in Kazakhstan). The Kazakh segment of the corridor will bypass the southern regions of the country and eventually enter Russia at Aktyubinsk. According to the 2007–2011 program for the further development of the Khorgos International Border Cooperation Center (Kazakhstan-China), the Kazakh city of Aqtaw is viewed as a strategic point within the unified transportation and logistics system of the Central Asian Transport and Industrial Corridor, which will connect with the North-South and Transsib transport corridors in central Russia.

Today, both the price structure and the geopolitical structure of the global oil market are changing. Key centers of gravity are currently being set up in Northeast Asia, where multilateral cooperation in the energy sector is set to develop. Under these conditions, Russia, Kazakhstan, and Azerbaijan can play key structural roles in the establishment of multilateral Eurasian energy cooperation. Successful cooperation between these countries in the transportation of oil and gas resources to the West can and should be complemented by the joint export of hydrocarbons to the dynamically growing markets of East Asia—above all, China. It is clear that Russia, Kazakhstan, and Azerbaijan are of strategic importance to China thanks to their enormous hydrocarbon reserves, their close proximity to the Chinese border, and the undeniable convenience of transporting crude hydrocarbons.

The expansion of energy cooperation between Russia and its CIS partners naturally does not bind these countries to any harsh restrictions that infringe on their sovereignty or prevent them from participating in other international oil and gas projects. On April 24, 2008, the Kazakh Parliament ratified an agreement with Azerbaijan that envisions the accelerated creation of a Kazakh-Caspian hydrocarbon transportation system that will provide 25 million tons of oil supplies per year to the Baku–Tbilisi–Ceyhan pipeline system. Tankers will deliver Kazakh oil to Baku from the Port of Aktau.

So-called alternative oil transportation projects (the Baku–Tbilisi–Ceyhan and Odessa–Brody oil pipelines, etc.) have met with a mixed reception in the Russian political and business community. Some experts have gone so far as to call these routes an implicit anti-Russian move by Kazakh and Azerbaijani authorities. In this author's view, however, these projects have several significant and constructive components to intensify mutually beneficial Eurasian cooperation. Kazakhstan and Azerbaijan both have an objective need to build new export oil pipelines outside Russian territory so that they can diversify export flows of crude hydrocarbons and thereby raise the overall level of energy security both within particular regions and in the world as a whole.

The creation of a common energy market in Russia and the CIS will promote the development of mutually beneficial economic relations in the energy sector, saturate the domestic market with inexpensive types of energy resources, cover consumer demand for such products, and expand opportunities to export energy resources to third countries. Some major achievements have been made here. President Medvedev paid his first state visit to the Republic of Kazakhstan on May 22–23, 2008. During talks with Kazakh President Nursultan Nazarbayev, the two leaders confirmed plans to form a joint fuel and energy budget for the period until

2020 as part of strategic bilateral cooperation. On the basis of this budget, the two countries will develop joint approaches to the use and development of an energy resource transportation system. The two countries also have a unified position on the issue of expanding CPC capacity from 35 million tons of oil per year to 74 million tons. The pipeline's capacity is to be increased in two phases prior to 2012. In addition, as part of plans to develop the oil industry, another 19 million tons of Kazakh oil are to be shipped to fill the yet-to-be-completed Burgas–Alexandropol oil pipeline, which will substantially increase crude hydrocarbon supplies to southern Europe. For its part, LUKOIL has announced plans to significantly boost investment in Kazakhstan, and the company's board of directors has set a goal of increasing hydrocarbon production in Kazakhstan to 8.8–11 million TOE per year by 2010.

Who Is Creating the Myth of Russian Energy Expansion?

The European Union currently accounts for 52% of Russian exports, and energy commodities make up the overwhelming majority of this volume. For instance, Russia provides roughly 20% of all primary energy resources consumed by Germany, and more than 35% of the natural gas and over 30% of the oil consumed in Germany comes from Russia.

It is therefore clear why the energy industry has become one of the top priorities of the EU's internal policy and why its relations with Moscow have been pushed to the top of the agenda. At present, Russia is building relations with the EU in the framework of a mutually beneficial energy dialogue which was launched at a summit in October 2001. In practical terms, Russia and the EU have managed to reach an agreement on the cancellation of recommended import limits previously established by the EU for Russia (no more than 30% of energy imports from one external source), to link the subject of the dialogue with a roadmap for achieving their objectives, and to provide an overall assessment of several cooperation projects. Together they set up the Energy Technologies Center, where a promising effort is under way to utilize associated gas, refine heavy grades of crude, build mini-hydropower plants, and use clean coal-burning technology. The Center is to play a key role in the realization of a new Russia-EU joint energy conservation initiative. The first projects of this kind have been implemented in Kaliningrad, Arkhangelsk, and Astrakhan regions.

Unfortunately, however, nettlesome hindrances in the form of artificial barriers have periodically blocked the path to mutually beneficial energy cooperation between Russia and the EU.

On February 5, 2008, US National Security Agency Director John Michael McConnell announced in his annual report to Congress that

Russian energy expansion was occurring at a threatening pace. McConnell argued that Russia, whose financial capabilities were growing as a result of windfall oil revenue, aspired to gain control over the energy resources and the transportation network from Europe to Eastern Asia. He called Moscow's potential economic "threat" one of the most serious challenges for the US and said it was on a par with terrorism, the spread of nuclear weapons, and the vulnerability of computer networks.

It is little wonder that not long after this statement was made one of the most respected US newspapers, *The Wall Street Journal*, published a headline with a free interpretation of his words titled "In Gazprom's Grip."

In the European press, unfortunately, the tone of publications under the general slogan "The Russians Are Coming!" was even more alarming. The European community essentially ignored the Russian government's statements that the use of money from the country's Stabilization Fund and Future Generations Fund was a general strategy for diversifying investments and not an attempt to buy up any strategic assets in Europe. The Western press interpreted Russia's refusal to ratify the Energy Charter as some kind of secret plan to achieve energy dominance throughout the continent. It could very well be said that EU countries had never been so concerned before about the alleged weakening of their energy security because of a growing dependence on crude hydrocarbon supplies from Russia. Even the most common market occurrences, such as Gazprom's hike in natural gas prices for Ukrainian consumers this year, was presented in the EU press as an instrument of harsh political pressure on Kyiv. And all of this was happening despite the fact that Russia had been consistently reproached in the past for selling natural gas to CIS countries at prices that were too low.

Unfortunately, under the influence of a massive media campaign, many people in the EU began to perceive Gazprom and all other Russian companies as foreign policy tools of Moscow and the efforts of these companies to expand business on EU markets as a kind of aggressive foreign economic policy. At the end of 2007, the Hamburg-based Europaeische Verlagsanstalt publishing house released a book by German journalist Gemma Pörzgen titled *Gasprom. Die Macht aus der Pipeline [Gazprom: Pipeline Power]*. This was the first work of this kind in Germany that provoked a mainstream debate about the possibility of foreign state-owned companies having wide access to the economies of EU countries, and it captivated European politicians and businessmen. For Russian readers, this book revealed no secrets or sensational details at all about Gazprom or the "motives" of the Russian energy policy. At the same time, it visibly and vividly illustrated the main stereotypes and perceptions, ingrained in the mass public consciousness of various groups and levels of European society, of how Russian companies purportedly conduct their foreign operations. Unfortunately, the psychology of double standards was strongly reinforced here—the flow of foreign capital into the Russian economy is perceived as a positive development and described as Russia's integration into the global community, while the investments of Russian companies in various industrial branches of other countries are sometimes viewed negatively and labeled as threatening "Russian expansion."

At present, with their energy security under threat, European policy-makers have begun to understand that the position of energy suppliers, particularly Russia, has strengthened to a certain degree, which, in their view, has led to a sharp decline in competition on energy markets, heightened political vulnerability in EU countries and ultimately, led to an undermining of the rule of law. Appeals have been increasingly made in the foreign press for protection from Russian "energy aggression" by any means necessary, which led to a kind of psychology taking hold in the West of rejecting Russian business and prompting growth of protectionist sentiment throughout Europe. It is not surprising that the European Commission last year proposed dividing companies operating on the EU market into production and transportation/distribution divisions—a move that, if approved, would block Gazprom from entering the EU energy distribution market.

It is obvious that the energy policy of leading countries is invariably based on a sound and sensible strategy that includes both an economic ideology distinguished by long-term stability and specific targets for the development of branches of the national fuel and energy industry.

The events of the last decade have shown that the global crude market is susceptible to serious market fluctuations, from $9 per barrel in 1998 to $111 per barrel in March 2008. Prominent experts have voiced the unanimous opinion that energy prices will continue to grow steadily while remaining highly volatile. This will clearly have an inevitable negative impact on the economic development of most countries—both importers and exporters of energy resources. It is therefore extremely important for Russia to maintain stable and long-term relations with its foreign partners, given its current economic structure and considerable dependence on crude commodity markets.

With the acceleration of globalization processes, the world is not becoming simpler, but rather more complicated and tougher. An unbiased observer can see how the sovereignty of individual countries has been destroyed by those hiding behind the slogans of freedom, democracy, and an open society, and sometimes even through the use of force, and also how the policy of protectionism and government intervention in the economy is strengthened under vibrant rhetoric about the freedom to trade with and invest in various countries around the world. Oil and gas interests are also clearly present in many conflicts, foreign policy moves, and diplomatic maneuvering.

Russia strongly rejects accusations from the West that it is using raw materials as a tool of foreign policy pressure. No one can cite a single example of Russia using its natural resources to apply pressure in its foreign policy.

The Russian president and members of various levels of government have stated on several occasions that Russia is not planning to use oil and gas as a political weapon, or to allocate its oil and gas revenue for strategic investments with the aim of taking over any branches of foreign economies. Allegations that Russia has of late been conducting an aggressive energy policy in the global arena have no grounds whatsoever. Global energy security not only implies security of supplies, but also security of demand. This point was noted in the concluding documents of the G8 Summit in St. Petersburg in 2006, which means that this principle is shared by leading industrial powers.

Russia is fully accountable for its ability and responsibility to strictly fulfill its obligations to deliver energy resources to Europe, as well as for the need to reliably guarantee such supplies. Russia is a dependable partner for the entire international community when it comes to addressing global problems, including mutually beneficial cooperation in all areas: security, science, energy, and the climate. Our country is interested in participating very actively in global and regional integration processes; cooperating closely in trade, economics, and investment; and promoting advanced technologies and implementing them in everyday life. All of these activities are in keeping with Russia's strategic goals.

It should be recognized clearly that the international development plans of Russian companies are based on generating business revenue and not on any expansionist political aspirations. They seek to ensure that investors get the biggest return on their company investments in a market environment where competition is very high. When Russian companies have to deal with a "policy of containment," in most cases this means that there is often a hidden desire to subject them to improper laws or unfair market competition. Fears in the EU that the dependence of Western nations on Russian energy supplies is growing too rapidly are entirely unfounded, since Gazprom, LUKOIL, and other Russian companies build relations with their European partners on market principles based on mutually beneficial interdependence. Hence they seek to ensure the same degree of reliable security for crude hydrocarbon supplies to both Western countries and all EU nations. It must be understood that, given the falling production in Western Siberia, the logic of globalization processes suggests that if Russian companies do not start actively investing funds in new oil production regions and implementing projects abroad, Russia's role and influence in ensuring global energy security could decline substantially.

Russia is interested in strengthening global energy security in every way possible, particularly in Europe, and a variety of options for transporting crude hydrocarbons could be of practical value. It is clear that the transportation infrastructure for supplying energy resources to Europe must be expanded. Problems with European energy security can only be effectively resolved if the balance of interests between consumers and producers of energy are considered, along with the interests of transit countries. Therefore, the efforts of all parties interested in such a resolution should be directed towards finding this balance.

As for the problem of diversifying energy supplies to Europe, which has become a hot topic in the EU, it is Russia that is currently working on a practical solution. It is our country that is diversifying oil and gas transit routes to Europe by implementing international projects such as the construction of the Burgas–Alexandropol oil pipeline and the extended South Stream and Nord Stream gas pipelines.

The creation of these new transit routes considerably increases energy security in the EU, strengthens stability, and presents new opportunities for delivery of supplies to European consumers. In addition, the expansion of transportation infrastructure in one country does not mean that Russia's cooperation with other transit nations will be reduced or phased out in any way.

It should not be forgotten that there was a serious battle among European nations to host the new transportation capacity being built by Russia. Indeed, the presence of such facilities on the territory of any country undoubtedly raises its political and economic importance and generates budget revenue, among other things.

On January 18, 2008, Russia, Bulgaria, and Greece signed a trilateral agreement on the creation of an international company to build the Burgas–Alexandropol oil pipeline. Russia's Burgas–Alexandropol Pipeline Consortium LLC (comprised of Transneft, Rosneft, and Gazprom Neft) owns 51% of this new company. Greece's 24.5% stake in the company is divided among a consortium comprising Hellenic Petroleum and Thraki (23.5%) and the Greek government (1%), while the other 24.5% is owned by the Bulgarian design company Burgas–Alexandropol BG, which, in turn, is owned by the corporations Tekhnoeksportstroy and Bulgargaz. Agreements between these companies stipulate that the Bulgarian and Greek governments must provide a favorable tax regime for the international company, while Russia, for its part, pledges to fill the new pipeline with oil. The 177-mile Burgas–Alexandropol pipeline will run through Greece and Bulgaria, and will significantly reduce the volume of crude transported by oil tankers through the congested straits of the Bosporus and Dardanelles. The tentative cost of the project is about €1 billion. The pipeline will be able to handle 17 million tons of crude per year in Phase One, 26 million tons in Phase Two, and 39 million tons in Phase Three, with the possibility of eventually boosting this amount to 55 million tons annually. Experts say the project has a clear economic logic and meets the pressing needs of European nations in accordance with their long-term demand for oil.

Greek Development Minister Christos Folias said that the Burgas–Alexandropol oil pipeline will be highly beneficial to the citizens of Russia, Greece, and Bulgaria in addition to their EU partners. He stressed that "a new era has begun for the three participating countries—an era of economic cooperation, common political strategy, and good neighborly relations.... Hard work is still being done to realize the dream belonging to the people we represent.... The citizens of our countries—in addition to our partners in the European Union—will ultimately be the ones to benefit from these major joint efforts."

The joint implementation, with Russian companies, of energy projects for natural gas transportation is also of paramount importance in ensuring Europe's energy security. It is now obvious that existing pipelines do not have sufficient capacity to handle the new volumes of Russian gas. A framework agreement was signed in 2005 to build the Nord Stream gas pipeline. The shareholders in the project's operating company, Nord Stream AG, are Gazprom (51%), Germany's Wintershall Holding and E.ON Ruhrgas (20% each), and the Dutch company N.V. Nederlandse Gasunie (9%). This gas pipeline will create a completely new route for transporting natural gas, which will not only significantly raise the reliability of fulfilling long-term contracts, but will also diversify gas supplies from Russia to Europe. The entire route of the Nord Stream pipeline was designed so as not to pass through sites at which chemical weapons from World War II are stored. A portion of the proposed pipeline runs along the bottom of the Baltic Sea, and in addition to avoiding chemical weapon storage facilities, the route avoids environmentally sensitive zones, military sites, important navigational routes, and other special areas that are used for economic or recreational purposes. At present, a detailed evaluation of the pipeline's impact on the environment is being compiled prior to the start of construction. The pipeline will be built to the strictest environmental standards, which will ensure the ecosystem of the Baltic Sea is not disturbed. Nord Stream will connect the Russian shore near the city of Vyborg with the German shore near Greifswald. The underwater segment will be about 745 miles long. Construction began on the 570-mile land segment in Russia in December 2005, and construction of the first offshore segment of the pipeline began on April 9, 2010. President Medvedev, German Chancellor Angela Merkel, Dutch Prime Minister Jan Peter Balkenende, and other government officials took part in the ceremony marking the start of construction outside Vyborg. During his speech, Medvedev stressed: "Nord Stream is a key link in ensuring global and European energy security. It is an extremely important and system-wide project in the Russia-EU energy dialogue, as clearly evidenced by its special status as a Trans-European Energy Network."

The project's status as a Trans-European Energy Network dates from December 2000, when the European Commission made the designation, which was reconfirmed in 2006, recognizing Nord Stream as a key project for creating an important cross-border transportation capacity to ensure Europe's sustainable development and energy security.

Phase One of the Nord Stream pipeline, which will have a carrying capacity of 971 BCF of gas per year, is to be put into operation in 2011. The completion of Phase Two construction by 2012 will increase its capacity to 1.9 TCF.

The pipeline subcontractors reflect the broad international nature of this project. Italy's Saipem is laying the offshore pipes, while Europipe produced 75% of the pipes and Russia's United Metallurgical Company manufactured the other 25%. Nord Stream AG invested more than €1 billion in the production of pipe for Phase One of the pipeline. France's EU-PEC PipeCoatings S.A. is handling the logistics of the project, including the pipe wrapping, as well as interim pipe transportation, loading, and storage. These services are worth an estimated €650 million. On June 19, 2010, Gazprom and Gaz de France Suez signed an agreement allowing the French company to join the Nord Stream project with a 9% stake.

The new gas pipeline has considerable importance for reliably meeting the European market's growing needs for natural gas. Forecasts indicate that gas imports to the EU will increase by roughly 7 TCF over the next decade, or by more than 50%. By directly linking the world's largest gas reserves in Russia with the European gas transportation system, Nord Stream will be capable of satisfying approximately 25% of this additional demand for imported gas.

Enhanced cooperation between Balkan countries and Russia in the creation of additional gas transportation corridors will enable this region to fully satisfy its demand for energy resources in the coming years, thus providing stable economic growth. The South Stream gas pipeline, a large-scale joint project between Gazprom and Italy's ENI, will play an important role in this process. Under the project, a gas pipeline will run from Russia to Bulgaria along the bottom of the Black Sea and carry gas through Bulgaria to the rest of southern Europe. One of the biggest advantages of this pipeline is that it will bypass problematic transit countries such as Ukraine and Belarus. The pipeline has a projected carrying capacity of 1.1 TCF of gas per year.

The South Stream pipeline, which is being built by Russia, Italy, Greece, Bulgaria, Serbia, and Hungary, is an extremely important transportation project for southern and central Europe that will provide a strategy for diversifying gas supplies. Total investment in the project is estimated at more than $10 billion. The offshore segment of the gas pipeline will run along the bottom of the Black Sea from the Beregovaya Compressor Station on the Russian coast near the village of Arkhipo-

Osipovka to the Bulgarian city of Burgas. The pipeline will be about 560 miles long and run at a maximum depth of more than 6,500 feet. The land-based segment of the pipeline will consist of two branches. One of them will run southwest, through Bulgaria and Greece and across the Adriatic Sea, to the Italian city of Brindisi, while the second branch will travel northwest through Serbia and Hungary. South Stream AG, an equally owned joint venture set up by Gazprom and ENI and registered in Switzerland in mid-January 2008, will be working on a feasibility study for the pipeline's construction in 2011. Construction is scheduled to be completed in 2013.

At the signing of the project agreement in Sofia on January 18, 2008, Bulgarian Prime Minister Sergey Stanishev said: "Bulgaria's interests in the project have been fully taken into consideration, since the company that is being set up to build and manage the pipeline on Bulgarian territory will have equal 50% ownership by each side.... Bulgaria's involvement in this project will significantly enhance the country's role on the energy map of Europe. And since Bulgaria will own a 50% share, its interests will not be violated under any circumstances, including with respect to receiving dividends."[9]

A Russian-Serbian intergovernmental agreement on oil and gas industry cooperation was signed in Moscow on January 25, 2008, covering, among other issues, the construction of the Serbian segment of the South Stream gas pipeline system. The Serbian segment of the pipeline is to have a capacity of at least 353 BCF of gas per year. In addition, an underground gas storage facility with active capacity of at least 10 BCF is to be built on the basis of the depleted Banatski Dvor gas field 37 miles northeast of the Serbian city of Novi Sad. Serbia will earn some €100–200 million each year solely from the transit of gas across its territory.

Russia and Hungary signed an intergovernmental agreement to cooperate in the construction of the South Stream pipeline in Moscow on February 28, 2008, and Gazprom and the Hungarian Development Bank set up an equally owned joint venture to handle issues related to the pipeline. The Hungarian segment of the pipeline will cost the joint venture about €700 million to build. In a March 10, 2008 interview with *Rossiyskaya gazeta*, Hungarian Minister of Finance Janos Veres stated: "I would single out three important points in regards to the South Stream project. First, with the construction of the new gas pipeline, Hungary will acquire a new route by which it can receive gas. In the past, we received gas from Russia through only one pipeline that transited Ukraine. Now a gas pipeline will run to us from the south, through Serbia. This alone will diversify gas supplies for us, which is something on which our economy greatly depends. It will make gas supplies more secure for us. Second, a segment of the new gas pipeline to Europe will be built on Hungarian territory. Its construction promises to be extremely profitable. A state-owned company is to take part in the project on Bulgaria's behalf, and its capital investments are expected to see a quick return and start generating profit for the treasury. Once the gas pipeline is put into operation, the country will start receiving duties for the transit of gas to Western European nations, which will also contribute to the treasury. Finally, in addition to the gas pipeline itself, the South Stream project envisions the construction of a large gas storage facility on Hungarian territory with capacity to store about 1 billion cubic meters [35 BCF]. An agreement on this issue has been signed. All of this means that, on top of previous volumes, Hungary will receive a substantial amount of new gas for storage in the near future. This, in turn, will only strengthen the country's energy security."

It should be emphasized that, on the whole, the Balkan countries were correct in their decision to step up cooperation with Russian energy companies and in their expectations of receiving real benefits from such cooperation. According to data published by Top Energy (the Balkan dispatch center), gas supplies to the Balkan countries increased 13.2% in 2007, while Bulgaria (Russia's main partner in the region) purchased 4.7% more Russian gas. In addition, a record volume of Russian gas transited Bulgarian territory in 2007.

Gazprom CEO Aleksey Miller and OMV[10] Chairman and CEO Dr. Wolfgang Ruttenstorfer signed a framework agreement in Vienna on April 24, 2010 concerning cooperation in the South Stream project within Austria, where the production rate is to amount to at least 177–353 BCF of gas per year. The document set forth the terms and timeline for Gazprom and the Austrian OMV oil and gas company to complete the Austrian segment of South Stream, and also established the principles and mechanisms by which the two parties will interact during the project's pre-investment phase. In accordance with the agreement, Gazprom and OMV began making joint preparations in 2010 for a feasibility study on the Austrian segment of the pipeline, which will contain a detailed evaluation of all the project's technical, legal, financial, environmental, and economic features and indicators. In addition, the two companies set up an equally owned joint project company that will handle the subsequent design, financing, construction, and use of the Austrian segment of the South Stream pipeline. As part of this project, OMV expects to receive additional natural gas supplies of some 70 BCF on a long-term basis.

Currently, a debate is ongoing in the European press about a few so-called alternative projects for gas supplies to the EU. The most prominent of these projects is Nabucco, which calls for a pipeline to be routed from the Caspian Sea region to Austria via Iran and Turkey at an estimated cost of $6.14 billion. An international consortium led by OMV is to build and operate the gas pipeline. Nabucco's maximum carrying capacity is estimated at 1.1 TCF of gas per year. Turkey, Bulgaria, Romania, Hungary, and Austria have all expressed a desire to take part.

Leading energy experts have given an extremely skeptical assessment of the viability of this project. Commenting on Nabucco, André Mernier, secretary general of the Energy Charter Secretariat, said: "Implementing the project under uncertain circumstances in areas close to the Black Sea region is extremely difficult. In the present situation, it is very hard to predict when the problems of Iran and Iraq will be resolved, and so, given the heightened risk and high costs [of the project], it will be difficult to find companies that will invest in it. In addition, the region does not have sufficient natural gas reserves to implement the Nabucco project."[11] This view was shared by Necdet Pamir, the general coordinator at the Center for Eurasian Strategic Studies, who said: "There clearly is not enough Iranian and Azerbaijani gas to implement the project."[12] Pamir maintains the Nabucco pipeline will not be profitable without Russian and Turkmenian natural gas.

Looking at the situation objectively, it should be noted that Azerbaijan is only planning to reach a production level of 706 BCF of gas per year in 2012, and there is even greater uncertainty surrounding gas supplies from Iran. It appears that the EU has recognized this fact and has gradually begun to push back the schedule for the Nabucco project's implementation, initially until 2011 and then to 2012. In February 2008, the Nabucco Gas Pipeline International consortium postponed the launch of the Nabucco gas pipeline by another year, until 2013. Not long after this, Gaz de France withdrew its bid to take part in the construction of the pipeline.

Ensuring global energy security is a complex and systemic problem that can only be resolved on the basis of close and mutually beneficial international cooperation that considers the interests of both the countries exporting crude hydrocarbons and the countries consuming the energy resources. In this regard, it is clear that a new agreement on Russian-European strategic energy cooperation is long overdue. This could be one of the most important components of a new Russia-EU cooperation agreement. The main issues that should be covered in this new document are: determining a mechanism to make long-term forecasts of energy resource demand so that Russia can coordinate the introduction of new production capacity in addition to infrastructure projects; developing a legal mechanism to ensure Russia and the EU make reciprocal investments in the energy sector; developing framework terms for the sale of energy resources; and defining the main parameters of energy resource transit. There are other issues, of course, including the lifting of unjustified barriers to trade and investment, as well as the assurance of preliminary consultations when a government considers making a decision on the energy sector that affects a partner's interests. Russian oil and gas companies are respectful of EU regulatory laws and have expressed willingness to constructively take part in a discussion of sensible European Commission proposals that raise important issues not only regarding property, but also investment, price policy, and the security of crude hydrocarbon supplies. Moreover, if the parties are able to reach agreement on issues concerning the transit of energy resources and take the balance of interests into account, perhaps a legally-based Transit Agreement could be drawn up and passed as part of a new Cooperation Agreement. Other countries transiting crude hydrocarbons could later join such an agreement.

On the whole, Russia and the EU need more openness and predictability with regard to their national energy strategies, as well as the joint development of common rules and institutions to regulate the energy market. All of this will ultimately and undoubtedly contribute to stronger global energy security and a higher level of transparency and predictability in the global energy market, as it will balance the interests of all parties—energy resource consumers, producers, and transit countries. The implementation of these and other sensible proposals will make it possible to reach compromises on other similar complex issues concerning the sustainable development of the global economy as well as modern civilization.

Is There a Real Alternative to Oil Today?

Along with the problems of the world oil market, one of the most popular subjects discussed in the Russian and foreign media has become the possibility of a rapid reorientation of the world economy toward alternative forms of fuel based on nonfossil raw materials, in particular, the broad use of biofuel. There is no dispute that the development of renewable sources of energy simultaneously reduces the use of conventional sources of energy, and accordingly reduces the release of pollutants into the atmosphere. For example, adding only 10% bioethanol to common gasoline reduces atmospheric emissions from automobiles by 30–50%.

Of late, many different countries of the world are pinning great hopes on alternative sources of energy. Today, many European countries facing an impending energy deficiency have turned to developing an alternative energy system, betting on energy from the sun, wind, water, waves, and tides, as well as the production of biofuel. On the whole, the contribution of alternative energy sources in various European countries ranges from 5% to 10%, although by 2020 the European Union plans to increase its share to 20%, and to 40% by 2030. Japan hopes to produce 1.35% of its electricity from alternative energy sources by 2010, not counting geothermal stations or industrial hydroelectric plants. Egypt expects alternative energy sources to account for 14% by 2020. And so forth.

In 2006, US President George Bush's ambitious national program "20 by 2010" set the country's energy policy the goal of reducing automotive gasoline consumption 20% by 2010. Accompanying this was the loud slogan: "Big corn will replace big oil." And earlier, in 2005, the US Congress passed the Energy Policy Act, which set the goal of increasing bioethanol production from 4 billion gallons in 2006 to 7.5 billion gallons in 2012. Such radical measures are explained by the necessity of reducing dependence on crude hydrocarbon imports and concern for the environment. In October 2007, the US Department of Energy published a progress report on the 20-year plan for strategic scientific research aimed at developing conventional and alternative energy. The original plan, dated 2003, listed 28 key types of research and set priorities and deadlines. The report said that bioenergy research was aimed at studying efficient ways of converting cellulose and other types of plant biomass into sugar, the primary feedstock for biofuel. Since January 2005, the number of operational ethanol production plants in the US has increased from 81 to 129, and another 80 are under construction.

In a speech on March 4, 2008 at the International Conference on Renewable Energy Sources, Samuel Bodman, United States secretary of energy, emphasized that American investment in biofuel energy had already exceeded $1 billion. Among key projects, he singled out $400 million in investments in three bioresource research centers, intended for five years. Moreover, Secretary Bodman mentioned a new joint project between the Department of Energy and the Department of Agriculture to carry out more than 20 studies in this industry at a total cost of $18 million. The main goal being pursued by the US in developing biofuel resources is to reduce the country's gasoline consumption by 20% over 10 years, but making biofuel price-competitive with gasoline by 2012 is also important. All of this, the US administration feels, should substantially reduce harmful atmospheric emissions. Acknowledging that "a great deal remains to be done and this will not be easy," Samuel Bodman expressed optimism about the prospects of this new direction in energy, stating that "the world is on the road to cleaner, more available, and safer energy, and biofuel will play the main role here."

Along with starry-eyed optimism in forecasts about biofuel's prospects in the world media, analytical articles began to appear in which the authors expressed very sober opinions about this issue, emphasizing that massive use of biofuel presented substantial global risks in very different areas and spheres.

A rapid and poorly thought-out transition to biofuel by the leading world powers could have negative consequences for the environment and well-being of the inhabitants of developing countries. A report to the United Nations Economic and Social Commission for Asia and the Pacific (ESCAP) published in March 2008 noted that many countries were, that same year, expecting food products to jump in price partly due to the increased use of grain and sugar cane for production of biofuel. "The rapid increase in the prices of food products will be the main problem this year,"[13] said Shuvojit Banerjee, a representative of this commission. "And since it will apparently be impossible to stop the movement toward increasing biofuel production, the region will have to prepare for a long period of inflation due to higher prices for food products."[14] The commission called on the governments of Asian and Pacific countries to undertake additional measures to protect the poor from economic shock. Along these same lines, P. Chidambaram, India's finance minister, declared that the use of agricultural products for producing biofuel was a blow to the poor, and called this "a sign of perverted priorities in some countries.... This is disgraceful and deserves condemnation."[15]

Recently, the US national program to produce bioethanol from corn has been drawing more and more severe criticism in the press. Experts have calculated that grain ethanol requires a massive amount of agricultural land: replacing just 10% of American motor fuel with alternative biofuel would require a third of all cultivated land to be devoted to grain production. In 2006, 60 million of the 295 million tons of grain harvested were used for bioethanol production. This created obvious imbalances in agricultural production, and grain prices increased 50% over the preceding period. An increasing number of American farmers are taking advantage of government subsidies and planting industrial corn, and this in turn creates a shortage of animal fodder, which inexorably drives up the prices of meat products.

At the same time, whereas in 2005 the average price of a gallon of ethanol decreased from $2.00 to $1.55, the cost of corn, the basic raw material for its production, increased from $1.60 to $3.27 per bushel. Thus, biofuel producers ended up squeezed between decreasing revenue and growing expenses, despite generous federal subsidies on the order of 51 cents per gallon.

At first glance it would seem that massive use of biofuel, if we are to believe the claims of its proponents, should substantially reduce dependence on crude hydrocarbons, and consequently, demand for oil should sharply decrease. However, simple calculations show a different picture. Using current technology to process vegetable and grain crops into biofuel, the amount of energy spent on its production is only slightly less than the amount obtained from its energy content. This is readily apparent from analyzing the value of the EROEI (Energy Return on Energy Invested) coefficient, which reflects the ratio of the energy obtained from a resource to the energy expended for its derivation. (This only applies to industrial energy expenditures; sunlight and photosynthesis do not count.) If the EROEI is less than 1, then energy expenditures are higher than the energy extracted from the resource. Experts estimate that the EROEI for various agricultural crops processed into biofuel ranges from 0.7 to 3.2. Given such EROEI values, it turns out that the more biofuel is produced, the more conventional fuel is needed for its production. It is well known that biofuel production involves the combustion of coal or residual oil (to generate electricity), the use of gasoline and diesel fuel (for trucks and tractors to transport raw materials and finished products), and finally the combustion of natural gas (for heating and hot water supply).

The leading American analyst Jim Puplava claims that producing industrial alcohol from corn is completely inefficient under current conditions: "If we calculate the expense of the natural gas consumed in producing fertilizers, the amounts of fuels and lubricants required to treat crops and gather the harvest, and consider that automobile gas mileage per unit of fuel is reduced by approximately a quarter after switching from gasoline to ethanol, the resulting energy balance is negative."[16]

Neither should the adverse environmental impact be disregarded. According to the authoritative journal *Science*, producing bioethanol releases 179–212 pounds of CO_2 per megajoule into the atmosphere, that is, almost as much as when gasoline is burned (207 pounds of CO_2), which is not at all surprising given the EROEI of bioethanol. Producing bioethanol from vegetable materials also involves the use of sulfuric acid, and so far no one has found a use for the sulfonated lignin byproduct.

To expand their so-called "energy-intensive" plants, American farmers who sell their cereal crops for biofuel production must chop down forests, which decreases biodiversity, impoverishes ecosystems, and results in deforestation, salinization, and subsequent soil erosion.

Other countries attempting to follow the route of accelerated biofuel production have encountered problems similar to those in the US. Along these lines, one widely publicized project that Japan never succeeded in realizing is rather revealing. In the summer of 2008, on the eve of the G8 summit in the vicinity of Lake Toya on Hokkaido, the Japanese government decided to demonstrate to the world its desire to develop alternative forms of fuel in the war on global warming. It was expected that the small island of Miyakojima would become a prototype of the "Japan of the future," where gasoline containing ethanol would be sold. There are 19 filling stations on Miyakojima, and the 35,000 automobiles owned by local inhabitants annually consume 27,550 tons of gasoline. At the same time, the island produces a lot of sugar, and the raw material for its production is very well-suited for producing ethanol. However, preliminary calculations by specialists at major Japanese oil companies, including Nippon Oil Corp., showed that this project would not bring anything but serious losses, and in so doing could seriously damage the reputation of national industry. Thus, the idea of turning the island into a zone completely free of conventional gasoline remained an impossible dream.

At present, biofuel accounts for around 1.5% of total worldwide vehicle fuel consumption. In the foreseeable future, it cannot replace natural oil as a raw material for producing fuel. In its report *World Energy Outlook 2006*, the International Energy Agency emphasized that, even if a full-scale active policy were pursued with very significant investments, biofuel's share could not possibly grow to more than 8–12% by 2030.

Incidentally, in the words of Abdalla Salem el-Badri, secretary general of the Organization of Petroleum Exporting Countries (OPEC), the all-out passion for biofuel could make it harder for cartel members to keep oil production at the former level. OPEC members think that it could seriously reduce investments in oil production, and consequently lead to a new spiral of increases in fuel prices.

Another point of discussion in the Russian and foreign press is what place Russia will occupy in the process of developing alternative sources of energy, since—as is the case with oil and natural gas—it has the lion's share of world reserves of alternative energy potential. And although Russia has large reserves of raw hydrocarbons, it also needs diversified energy sources, including the use of renewable energy resources. Several experts have estimated that Russia's potential reserves of alternative energy sources are around 5.1 billion TCE per year, which is five times the country's consumption of all conventional energy resources. However, the economic potential for their use is negligible so far. The Russian government understands this problem, and soon plans to adopt a federal targeted program to develop renewable energy sources in Russia.

Looking back at history, on October 8, 1975, at a scientific session commemorating the 250th anniversary of the USSR Academy of Sciences, the eminent scientist Academician Pëtr Kapitsa (1894–1984), Nobel laureate in physics, gave a conceptual talk about the future of alternative energy. Proceeding from basic principles of physics, he made logical assessments of wind power, geothermal power, wave power, and hydropower, and proved that using existing technical and technological approaches, all these sources would be unable to provide any serious competition to fossil fuel in the last quarter of the 20th century.

On the whole, it can be firmly stated that the Russian academician's prediction is still valid today. Despite the efforts of the world community to increase the share of alternative forms of energy consumed, conventional energy sources will continue to dominate in the near future. According to estimates given in presentations by leading specialists at the International Alternative Energy Forum held in mid-February 2009 in Verona, Italy, fossil fuels—oil, natural gas, and coal—will continue to account for at least 80% of global energy consumption through 2030. And here the leading world experts were unanimous in their opinions: it will only be possible to speak seriously about developing alternative energy after the costs of producing alternative energy become equal to the corresponding costs associated with conventional sources—that is, no earlier than by the middle of this century.

Conclusion

The period comprising the second half of the 19th and the beginning of the 20th century was a very complex and extremely contradictory one in Russia's history. Russia's successful development as an industrial power was interrupted by World War I, two revolutions, and a Civil War, followed by a period of socialist experimentation. These unique historical events substantially changed the face of the country at a dear price: millions of human lives. The Soviet Union remained a powerful industrial and military power for several decades, and the oil industry has played an extremely important role over its entire history. The close of the 20th century saw the end of the ideological confrontation of the Cold War period, the breakup of the USSR, and its replacement by independent states; these events radically altered the whole world order. Starting in the early 1990s, Russia entered a complex period of economic, social, and political transformation and reorganization of its global and regional strategies.

In late June 2009, the International Energy Conference was held in Vienna; it was organized by the UN Industrial Development Organization (UNIDO), the government of Austria, the International Institute for Applied Systems Analysis, and the Global Forum on Sustainable Energy. Forum participants thoroughly examined the world's energy security problems, the use of existing energy resources, and their impact on the social and economic development of the world's countries. Many speakers emphasized that one of the most important problems of our civilization is ensuring global energy security, i.e., seeking effective ways to create a sustainable and uninterrupted supply of fuel and energy resources to all the world's countries, and to do so at prices acceptable to both consumers and producers of these resources, with minimal damage to the environment, based on a systemic approach and the joint efforts of the world community. And this is the most important key to sustainable economic and social development and political stability, the one that ultimately determines the necessary conditions of humanity's life-support system. In the current situation, responsibility for global energy stability is no longer borne only by governments, but also by leading transnational energy companies. They are the ones who can and must become the backbone of further progressive development of the global economy and observance of the principle of sustainable development in the entire world.

At the same time, certain presentations at the Vienna energy forum set this author's teeth on edge with their ritual phrases about how "energy pressure" from Russia is supposedly growing and how certain "aggressive" actions of Russian companies in Europe must be curbed. Meanwhile, any sensible person today can clearly see that Russia has been a reliable supplier of oil and natural gas to Europe for many decades.

The market economy and democracy are developing in the Russian Federation and will continue to develop—not at all because reformist theoreticians and proponents of the struggle for "virtual" human rights insist on it, but because it is necessary for and beneficial to Russians themselves. Today, Russia is fully capable of influencing the rest of the world with the potential of its ideas, its positive example, moral leadership, objective information, and many other factors. With each passing day, Russia's role and importance in the world will only grow with the new challenges posed by the contradictory and complex processes of globalization, social and natural disasters, unresolved territorial and ethnic religious disputes, the growth of radicalism in the world, and the threats of international terrorism.

Today, each of us has the right to be proud of the history of the Russian oil industry, which is the story of many generations of Russian oil workers—courageous and purposeful people, passionate about their beloved business, who have made an enormous contribution to creating the country's fuel base and strengthening Russia's industrial potential. And now, effective development of the Russian oil and gas industry, the introduction of advanced technology, and the professionalism and experience of industry workers will do much to determine the dynamic, balanced growth of Russia's economy and the increased quality and level of international cooperation in ensuring global energy security.

УКАЗ

ПРЕЗИДЕНТА РОССИЙСКОЙ ФЕДЕРАЦИИ

Об особенностях приватиз....ии преобразования в
акционерные общества государственных предприятий,
производственных и научно-производственных объединений
нефтяной, нефтеперерабатывающей промышленности и нефте-
продуктообеспечения

В целях повышения эффективности работы нефтяного комплекса
Российской Федерации, обеспечения надежного снабжения потребителей
нефтью и нефтепродуктами и в соответствии с Указом Президента
Российской Федерации от 14 августа 1992 г. N 922 "Об особенностях
преобразования государственных предприятий, объединений, организа-
ций топливно-энергетического комплекса в акционерные общества"
п о с т а н о в л я ю:

1. Преобразовать до 31 декабря 1992 г. государственные пред-
приятия, производственные и научно-производственные объединения по
добыче, переработке и транспорту нефти и нефтепродуктообеспечению
по перечням согласно приложениям N 1, 2 и 3 в акционерные общества
в порядке, установленном Положением о коммерциализации государственных предприятий с одновременным преобразованием в акционерные
общества открытого типа, утвержденным Указом Президента Российской

The first page of Russian Federation President Boris Yeltsin's Decree of November 17, 1992, "On Features of the Privatization and Conversion to Joint-Stock Companies of State Enterprises, Production, and Scientific Production Associations in the Oil and Refining Industry and Petroleum Products Supply."

The Caspian Pipeline Consortium's 938 mile trunk pipeline, commissioned in 2001, carries over 33 million tons of oil per year. It is convincing proof of productive international cooperation in providing energy security for Europe.

Today, Western Siberia leads the Russian Federation in recoverable reserves of oil and natural gas, providing most of the production of these types of resources. The region produces three-fourths of Russia's oil and nine-tenths of its natural gas.

Since April 2005, LUKOIL -Western Siberia has been producing the Nakhodka Oil and Gas Field in Yamal-Nenets Autonomous District. The field has $C_1 + C_2$ gas reserves of over 8.8 TCF and C_2 oil reserves of about 9.9 million tons. The peak production volume of 880 BCF of gas and 2.2 million tons of natural gas liquids is to be reached in 2012.

Since July 2008, export shipments of crude oil produced by LUKOIL in the Timan-Pechora Oil and Gas Province have been made continually through the Varandey oil loading terminal with a stationary offshore ice-resistant loading wharf with a carrying capacity of up to 13 million tons of oil per year, located in the Arctic Region on the coast of the Barents Sea.

A certificate from Guinness World Records recognizing Varandey as the most northerly continuously operating oil terminal in the world.

GUINNESS
WORLD RECORDS

CERTIFICATE

The most northerly
continuously operating oil terminal
is the Varandey offshore facility
located 22 km (13.7 miles) off the coast
of Varandey, Nenets Autonomous Okrug,
Russia (69 deg, 03 min and 11 sec N Lat),
and is owned by Lukoil (Russia).
It began operating on 9 June 2008.

GUINNESS WORLD RECORDS

Opening ceremony of the first LUKOIL gas station in New York City, September 29, 2003. Left to right: LUKOIL President Vagit Alekperov; General Director of LUKOIL Americas Corp. Vadim Gluzman; President of the Russian Federation Vladimir Putin; Senator Charles E. Schumer (NY); and Russian Ambassador Extraordinary and Plenipotentiary to the USA Yuri Ushakov.

One of LUKOIL's gas stations in New York City.

Opening ceremony of Hauzak Gas Field in the Bukhara Region, Republic of Uzbekistan in November 2007. Left to right: Republic of Uzbekistan Deputy Prime Minister and Minister of Finance Rustam Azimov; Russian Federation First Deputy Prime Minister Sergey Ivanov; LUKOIL President Vagit Alekperov; and Chairman of the Board of Uzbekneftegaz NHC Nurmuhammad Ahmedov. The field's peak annual production of natural gas, expected in 2012 -2013, will be about 388 BCF.

In August 2008, LUKOIL President Vagit Alekperov and ConocoPhillips President Jim Mulva took part in a solemn ceremony to launch South Khylchuyu Field, located in the Nenets Autonomous District and one of the biggest in the northern Timan-Pechora Oil and Gas Province. The field is being developed by Naryanmarneftegaz LLC, a 70:30 joint venture of LUKOIL and ConocoPhillips.

In September 2009, in the town of Krasnaya Polyana (near Sochi, Krasnodar Territory), LUKOIL opened Russia's first gas station equipped with an independent power supply based on a photoelectric generator with a peak capacity of 9.6 kW.

In September 2006, LUKOIL commissioned the third stage of an oil distribution and loading terminal on Vysotsky Island in the Baltic Sea. The terminal was built jointly with Fluor Corporation, a leading American engineering company. The terminal's design capacity is 12.8 million tons a year, and the total capacity of the tank farm is 16 MMCF.

Yury Korchagin Oil Field in the Russian sector of the Caspian Sea is a harbinger of 21st-century big oil in the region.

European parliamentarians visiting an offshore platform at the D-6 Oil Field in the Baltic Sea were satisfied with the results of the use of "zero discharge" technology, which preserves the region's unique biosphere.

Russian Federation President Dmitry Medvedev discusses the development of the national oil industry with LUKOIL President Vagit Alekperov.

On April 28, 2010, the first oil was produced from Yury Korchagin Oil Field in the Russian sector of the Caspian Sea. Attending the ceremonial opening of the field were, left to right: LUKOIL President Vagit Alekperov; Russian Federation Deputy Prime Minister Igor Sechin; Astrakhan Region Governor Alexander Zhilkin; and Russian Federation Prime Minister Vladimir Putin.

Overview of Major Russian Oil Companies

The natural resources and production, scientific–technical, and human resource potential of the oil sector are Russia's national property. The efficient use of such resources and potential creates the necessary conditions for sustainable national economic development and ensures growth of the people's well-being and standard of living. It is an important source of tax and hard-currency revenue for the federal budget. According to data from the Russian Federal Customs Service, the Russian Federation derived $93.486 billion of oil export income in 2009.

The main center of the Russian oil industry is Western Siberia, which houses 53% of the initial total resources. Other major oil and gas regions are the Volga-Urals region (14.2% of initial total resources), the Far East (over 3%), the North Caucasus (1.6%), and in the near future, Eastern Siberia (10.5%) and the Russian continental shelf (12.4%).

The Russian Federation's production of oil, including gas condensate, was 537.5 million tons in 2008 (99.3% of the 2007 figure), just as the world financial crisis was beginning to expand across the globe. Despite this, however, according to the Federal State Statistical Service, in 2009 the country produced 544.2 million tons of oil, or 1.2% more than in 2008.

As of the end of 2009, the oil sector of the Russian fuel and energy industry included 10 major vertically integrated companies, as well as 160 small and mid-sized oil production companies that together account for about 22 million tons of total Russian oil production. Four Russian regions—the Republic of Tatarstan, the Republic of Komi, the Khanty-Mansi Autonomous District, and the Orenburg Region—are home to 60% of small and mid-sized oil and gas companies. Three-fourths (74.2%) of the oil production volume in this sector comes from three oil regions: the Khanty-Mansi Autonomous District, the Republic of Tatarstan, and the Republic of Komi. Such companies are now developing about a billion tons of recoverable reserves at 250 fields.

These 10 vertically integrated companies account for the bulk (95.9%) of Russian oil production. Among these, the leaders in oil production volume are Rosneft (23.4% of the nation's total production), LUKOIL (18.5%), TNK-BP Holding Company (14.1%), and Surgut-neftegaz (12.7%).

Table 1. Oil Production by Russian Vertically Integrated Companies, 2007–2009, in millions of tons

Oil Company	2007	2008	2009
Rosneft	121.7	125.4	128.2
LUKOIL	100.8	99.4	106.9
TNK-BP Holding Company	76.5	75.8	
Surgutneftegaz	71.1	68.0	65.6
Gazprom Neft and refining subsidiaries	51.6	47.8	
Tatneft	28.5	28.8	28.8
Slavneft	23.0	21.6	20.8
Russneft	15.6	15.7	14.0
Bashneft	13.0	12.9	13.4

Source: RF Central Dispatching Administration of the Fuel and Energy Industry *[TsDU TEK]*.

In 2008, Russian refineries processed 260 million tons of crude hydrocarbons (103.2% of the 2007 level). Overall, oil refined as a share of its production increased to 48.5% from 46.6% in 2007. The crude refining yield in 2008 averaged 72% across Russian refineries, versus 71.6% in 2007. The country produced 39.4 million tons of gasoline (101.8% of 2007), 76 million tons of diesel fuel (104.1% of 2007), and 70.4 million tons of heating oil (101.9% of 2007).

Table 2. Refining Input by Russian Vertically Integrated Companies, 2007–2008, in millions of tons

Oil Company	2007	2008
Rosneft	44.3	54.3
LUKOIL	46.8	48.6
TNK-BP Holding Company	24.1	25.4
Surgutneftegaz	22.0	22.7
Gazprom Neft and refining subsidiaries	25.7	27.3
Tatneft	6.8	6.4
Slavneft	14.0	14.9
Russneft	8.1	8.3
Bashneft (at production facilities of Bashneftekhim, Salavatnefteorgsintez, and other refineries)	21.2	22.5

Source: RF Central Dispatching Administration of the Fuel and Energy Industry *[TsDU TEK]*.

It is clear from the above data that the vertically integrated company **Rosneft Open Joint-Stock Company** now leads the Russian oil industry. It was created in 1993 as a 100% state-owned company. The government planned to privatize the company several times in the 1990s, but a lack of investor interest—a result of the company's difficult straits at the time—repeatedly scuttled such plans. Rosneft's financial position did not begin to improve until after 1998, and rising oil prices on the world market played an important role in the improvement of its economic indicators. Within several years, it regained control over its subsidiaries and began acquiring new assets. A new phase in the company's development began with the bankruptcy of Yukos. In late 2004, Rosneft purchased Yugansk-neftegaz, and in 2007 it acquired most of Yukos's remaining assets. This, in turn, enabled Rosneft to assume first place in Russian oil production and refining and to become a leading player in the petroleum products sales market.

Rosneft is currently on Russia's list of strategic enterprises and organizations. Its authorized capital, after consolidation of 12 subsidiaries, is 105,981,778 rubles and 17 kopecks (10,598,177,817 shares of common stock at a par value of 0.01 ruble per share). The state-owned Rosneftegaz holds 75.16% of Rosneft's stock, while the remainder belongs to a wide range of strategic, institutional, and individual investors. The company's net profit in 2008, calculated by US GAAP standards, declined 13.5% compared to 2007, to $11.12 billion.

Rosneft represents Russia's interests in a variety of international projects, in particular in the project to develop the Kurmangazy structure in Kazakhstan, in the Sakhalin projects, and in the construction of the Burgas-Alexandropol oil pipeline.

The geography of Rosneft's operations in the exploration and production division encompasses all of Russia's major oil and gas provinces: Western Siberia, South and Central Russia, Timan-Pechora, Eastern Siberia, and the Far East. The company is also implementing a series of oil projects outside Russia, in Kazakhstan and Algeria.

The size and quality of its upstream reserves guarantee Rosneft a stable leadership position. The company has 22.3 billion BOE of proven reserves, enough to support it for 26 years. Most of these are conventional reserves, which will allow it to increase oil production volumes efficiently in the near future. Rosneft also has 26.6 billion BOE of probable and possible reserves, a future source to replenish proven reserves. The company does most of its geologic exploration in Russia's most promising oil and gas regions, such as Eastern Siberia and the Far East, as well as on the continental shelves of Russia's southern seas. This affords it access to approximately 53 billion BOE of prospective resources.

Rosneft's oil production segment includes: RN-Yuganskneftegaz, RN-Purneftegaz, RN-Severnaya Neft, RN-Samaraneftegaz, Tomskneft,

Udmurtneft, RN-Sakhalinmorneftegaz, RN-Krasnodarneftegaz, Grozneftegaz, Sakhalin Projects, RN-Stavropolneftegaz, Northern Lights Company, Vankorneft, Rosneft-Dalneft Oil Company, Dagneftegaz, Verkhnechonskneftegaz, and Eastern Siberia Oil and Gas Company.

Rosneft is also one of the leading independent gas producers in the Russian Federation. The company produces over 423 BCF of natural and associated gas per year and has substantial potential for further growth in production due to its unique portfolio of reserves. Rosneft is currently implementing a program to increase its associated petroleum gas utilization to 95%.

Rosneft has seven refineries scattered across Russia, from the Black Sea coast to the Far East. The refineries are advantageously located, considerably increasing the efficiency of petroleum products delivery. Rosneft's refining segment includes: the Angara Petrochemical Company, the Achinsk Refinery, the RN-Komsomolsk Refinery, the RN-Novokuybyshevsk Refinery, the Kuybyshev Refinery, the Syzran Refinery, the RN-Tuapse Refinery, and the Rosneft-Moscow Nefteprodukt Refinery. The company is currently implementing projects to expand and modernize its refineries in order to continue to improve the balance between oil production and refining volumes, and to increase the output of quality products with high added value, meeting the most up-to-date environmental standards.

An important competitive advantage for Rosneft is its proprietary export terminals at Tuapse, De Kastri, Nakhodka, and Arkhangelsk, enabling it to substantially increase the efficiency of crude oil and petroleum products exports. The company is currently implementing comprehensive terminal expansion and modernization programs to bring capacities in line with planned export volumes.

One of Rosneft's strategic objectives is the further development of its proprietary petroleum products retail sales network, which currently includes some 1,700 gas stations in 38 regions of the Russian Federation.

LUKOIL Open Joint-Stock Company is one of the largest international vertically integrated oil and gas companies. The company's principal activities are oil and gas exploration and production, petroleum products and petrochemical production, and end product sale. Most of the company's exploration and production operations take place within the Russian Federation, and its main resource base is Western Siberia. LUKOIL owns modern refineries, gas processing plants, and petrochemical plants located in Eastern and Western Europe, Russia, and other countries of the former Soviet Union. Most of the company's products are sold on the international market. LUKOIL sells petroleum products in Eastern and Western Europe, Russia, other countries of the former Soviet Union, and the United States. In terms of proven hydrocarbon reserves, LUKOIL is the second largest private oil and gas company in the world, with a 1.1% share of total world oil reserves. The company also has a 2.3% share of total world oil production. The company plays a key role in the Russian energy sector, accounting for 18% of total Russian oil production and 19% of total Russian refining. According to data audited by Miller and Lents (US), the company's proven hydrocarbon reserves as of January 1, 2010 amounted to 17.5 billion barrels of oil equivalent, including 13.7 billion barrels of oil and 22.9 TCF of gas. In 2009, expansion of proven reserves through geologic exploration, development drilling, and acquisitions amounted to 782 million BOE, or 95% of its annual production.

LUKOIL's exploration and production division has a high-quality diversified asset portfolio. The company's main oil production regions are Western Siberia, the Timan-Pechora oil and gas province, the Volga region, and the Caspian region. LUKOIL's Russian oil production division includes: LUKOIL-Western Siberia, LUKOIL-Komi, LUKOIL-Naryanmarneftegaz, LUKOIL-Perm, LUKOIL-Kaliningradmorneft, LUKOIL-Nizhnevolzhskneft, LUKOIL-Volgogradneft, and RITEK.

Through a subsidiary, LUKOIL Overseas Holding Ltd., the company also implements oil and gas exploration and production projects outside Russia—in Kazakhstan, Egypt, Azerbaijan, Uzbekistan, Saudi Arabia, Colombia, Venezuela, Côte d'Ivoire, Ghana, and Iraq.

In 2005, when Nakhodka Field came online, LUKOIL began a program under which gas production would grow at accelerated rates, both in Russia and abroad, increasing the share of produced gas to one-third of total hydrocarbon production. The upstream reserves for realizing this program are the fields of the Big Kheta Depression, the Caspian Sea, and the Central Astrakhan field in Russia, as well as the international gas projects at Kandym-Hauzak-Shady in Uzbekistan (where production began in 2007) and Shah-Deniz in Azerbaijan. The leading enterprise in the company's gas processing segment is Permneftegazpererabotka (Perm).

LUKOIL owns modern refining capacity in Russia and abroad. The company's Russian refining segment includes: LUKOIL-Permnefteorgsintez, LUKOIL-Volgogradneftepererabotka (Volgograd), LUKOIL-Nizhegorodnefteorgsintez (Kstovo, the Nizhny Novgorod Region), and LUKOIL-Ukhtaneftepererabotka. The total capacity of its Russian refineries is 49.3 million tons of crude oil per year.

The company's foreign refineries are located in Ukraine, Bulgaria, and Romania, and it also holds a 49% interest in the ISAB refining complex (Sicily, Italy). The total capacity of its foreign refineries is 24 million tons of crude oil per year.

LUKOIL attends carefully to the development of its petrochemical segment, which includes: Stavrolen (Budënnovsk, the Stavropol Territory), LUKOIL-Saratovorgsintez, LUKOR (Ukraine), and Karpatneftekhim (Ukraine).

In 2008, as part of the implementation of its Strategic Development Program for 2008–2017, LUKOIL created a new business division, Power Generation. In addition to the TGK-8 Southern Generating Company acquired in 2008 and proprietary generating stations at a field in Russia, the division includes enterprises that generate electrical and thermal energy in Bulgaria, Romania, and Ukraine. The total electric power generated by division companies was 16.2 billion kWh, and thermal energy generated exceeded 18.1 million Gcal (TGK-8 Southern Generating Company accounted for 90% and 85% of these totals, respectively). Over the long term, the Power Generation division will become an important factor in the company's capitalization growth.

As of the beginning of 2009, the company's sales network operated in 25 countries, including Russia, the former Soviet Union, and Europe (Azerbaijan, Belarus, Georgia, Moldova, Ukraine, Bulgaria, Hungary, Finland, Estonia, Latvia, Lithuania, Poland, Serbia, Montenegro, Romania, Macedonia, Cyprus, Turkey, Belgium, Luxembourg, the Czech Republic, Slovakia, and Croatia), as well as in the United States, and comprised 204 oil tank farm facilities with a total tank capacity of 108 MMCF and 6,748 gas stations (including franchise stations).

The company is confidently building its strategy and production policy on the principles of effective nature and resource conservation, and is actively introducing state-of-the-art technologies to substantially reduce the anthropogenic environmental impacts.

TNK-BP Holding Company Open Joint-Stock Company is one of Russia's leading vertically integrated oil companies. It was formed in 2003 by the merger of the oil and gas assets of the transnational BP in Russia and the oil and gas assets of a Russian consortium of Alpha and Access/Renova (AAR). BP and AAR own TNK-BP Holding Company on a parity basis.

TNK-BP Holding Company incorporates a series of production, refining, and sales enterprises in Russia and Ukraine and employs some 63,000 people.

The company's oil production assets are located mainly in Western Siberia (the Khanty-Mansi and Yamal-Nenets Autonomous Districts and the Tyumen Region), Eastern Siberia (the Irkutsk Region) and the Volga-Urals region (the Orenburg Region). An independent audit of reserves performed by De Golyer & MacNaughton has confirmed that, as of December 31, 2008, TNK-BP's total proven reserves were 10.252 billion BOE, using PRMS (former SPE) criteria, and the reserve replacement ratio was 146%. Using the SEC method and ignoring license expiration dates, TNK-BP's total proven reserves were 8.112 billion BOE, with a reserve replacement ratio of 82%. TNK-BP Holding Company holds about 200 production licenses. Eighty percent of proven reserves are in the company's 20 main fields and about two-thirds of production occurs at 10 main fields.

TNK-BP's oil production division includes: Samotlorneftegaz, TNK-Nizhnevartovsk, Orenburgneft, TNK-Nyagan, NNP, Varyëgannneftegaz, Tyumenneftegaz, Yugraneft, Novosibirsknneftegaz, Rospan International, Orenburggeologiya, and Vanyëganneft.

At present, TNK-BP has refining capacity of 675,000 barrels/day. TNK-BP's refining division includes: the Ryazan Refinery, the Saratov Refinery, and the Nizhnevartovsk and Krasnoleninsk Refineries, both located in Western Siberia. The company also owns the Lisichansk Refinery in Ukraine, which is advantageously located from the standpoint of serving the domestic market as well as making export deliveries through Black Sea terminals.

TNK-BP's retail network includes some 1,400 gas stations in Russia and Ukraine, operating under the TNK and BP brands. The company is among the most important petroleum products suppliers on the Moscow retail market, and is well-positioned on the Ukrainian market.

Surgutneftegaz Open Joint-Stock Company is Russia's fourth-largest vertically integrated company in oil production. Its upstream reserves include mineral licenses in the Western Siberian, Eastern Siberian, and Timan-Pechora oil and gas provinces within the territory of 10 Russian Federation regions. An estimate made per international standards puts the company's recoverable oil and gas reserves at about 2.8 billion TOE.

Surgutneftegaz has 60 organizational units, including six major oil production divisions: Surgutneft, Bystrinskneft, Nizhnesortymskneft, Komsomolskneft, Lyantorneft, and Fëdorovskneft. The company is well-positioned to build wells and develop new fields, having accounted for 20% of the industry's exploratory drilling in 2008. The growth in its C_1 oil reserves in 2009 exceeded 115 million tons, or 171% of its annual oil production volume.

Surgutneftegaz is also a leading independent gas producer. Its assets include one-third of the gas produced by Russian oil companies. The company was an industry pioneer in the creation of a full cycle of gas production, processing, and sale, as well as the gas-fired generation of electricity to supply its own fields and industrial processes.

The main enterprise in the company's refining division is the Kirishinefteorgsintez Refinery (the Leningrad Region), which has transitioned to the manufacture of high-octane gasoline that meets the Euro-4 standard, and continues to manufacture diesel fuel to current European standards.

Surgutneftegaz's retail network includes six petroleum products supply subsidiaries: Kaliningradnefteprodukt, Kirishiavtoservis, Lennefteprodukt, Novogorodnefteprodukt, Pskovnefteprodukt, and Tvernefteprodukt.

In all, Surgutneftegaz employs about 100,000 people.

With every year, **Gazprom Neft Open Joint-Stock Company** confidently increases its pace as it strives to improve its standing among Russian vertically integrated companies. It was founded in 1995 and was originally called "Sibneft." In 2005, Gazprom became the main stockholder in Gazprom Neft, when it acquired 75.68% of the company's stock. Another 20% belongs to EniNeftegaz, which is controlled by Eni (Italy). The remainder of the stock is in public circulation. Gazprom Neft controls 50% of Slavneft and 74.43% of Sibir Energy on an equal footing with TNK-BP Holding Company.

Gazprom Neft operates in Russia's largest oil and gas regions: the Khanty-Mansi, Yamal-Nenets, and Nenets Autonomous Districts, the Tomsk and Omsk regions, and the Krasnoyarsk Territory, as well as areas outside the former Soviet Union, in Serbia and Angola. The company and its subsidiaries currently hold more than 60 field exploration and development licenses, and the proven oil reserves of the company's fields exceed 4.5 billion barrels. Its upstream reserves increase annually due to the acquisition of new assets in Russia and abroad. Today, its proven and probable oil reserves per international Society of Petroleum Engineers (SPE) standards amount to 7.2 billion barrels. Most of Gazprom Neft's oil reserves are at the early stages of development. This is a great plus, affording the company excellent prospects for further growth and development.

The Gazprom Neft Group includes more than 40 oil production, refining, and sales enterprises that are vertically integrated in 18 regions of the Russian Federation and former Soviet Union. Gazprom Neft has a total payroll of more than 48,000 people.

Gazprom Neft's oil production division includes: Gazprom Neft-Noyabrskneftegaz, Gazprom Neft-Khantos, Gazprom Neft-East, Gazprom Neft-Yamal, Gazprom Neft-Sakhalin, Gazprom Neft-Angara, Meretoyakhaneftegaz, NP Ortyagunskoye, Sibneft-Yugra, Archinskoye, Sibneft-Chukotka, Severnaya tayga-Neftegaz, Zapolyarneft, Pechora-Neftegaz, and Shinginskoye.

Gazprom Neft refines over 60% of its crude oil, demonstrating the industry's best production to refining ratio. Gazprom Neft refines its production mainly at the processing facilities of the Gazprom Neft-Omsk Refinery. The company's other refining assets are located in the Moscow and Yaroslavl regions. Gazprom Neft also holds a stock interest in the Moscow Refinery (38.8%).

Gazprom Neft's products are exported to 48 countries and sold throughout the Russian Federation through an elaborate network of proprietary sales enterprises. The company currently operates 812 gas stations in Russia and more than 100 in Kyrgyzstan under the Sibneft brand.

The company's plans, focused on 2020, are aimed at increasing annual oil production to 88 million tons. Gazprom Neft also plans to develop new oil and gas fields, improve its network of proprietary gas stations, and participate in social projects and programs of a regional, national, and international nature.

Tatneft Open Joint-Stock Company's history goes back to before 1950, when a USSR Council of Ministers resolution organized the Tatneft association, consisting of the Bavlyneft and Bubulmaneft oil production trusts, the Tatburneft drilling trust, the Tatneftepromstroy construction and erection trust, and the Tatnefteproyekt design office. Late that same year, oil workers reported production of the millionth ton of Tatarstan oil. Tatneft has been a joint-stock company since 1994. At present, Tatneft is a vertically integrated oil company that produces and refines crude hydrocarbons primarily in the Republic of Tatarstan. The company's main stockholders include Svyazinvestneftekhim (30.44%) and the Bank of New York International (22.99%); 31% of the company's stock is held by the Republic of Tatarstan, which provides appropriate support on the part of regional authorities.

Tatneft holds 109 crude hydrocarbon prospecting and development licenses. Of these, 73 are within the Republic of Tatarstan. Tatneft has four licenses outside the Republic of Tatarstan (one each in the Samara, Ulyanovsk, and Orenburg regions and one in the Nenets Autonomous District). Miller and Lents, Ltd. (US) estimates that, as of January 1, 2008, Tatneft's oil and gas reserves were 6,139,700,000 barrels of proven oil and gas condensate reserves and 2,141,300,000 barrels of probable oil and gas condensate reserves (per the international classification of the SPE and the World Petroleum Congress (WPC)). Tatneft's upstream reserves are among the most complex in the industry, as most fields in Tatarstan are at the stage of declining production. The company's largest field, Romashkino, is 80% depleted. The crude underlying the Republic of Tatarstan is highly dense and sour, and the company's cost of producing oil at its fields is very high.

Tatneft includes nine major oil production divisions: Almetyevneft Oil and Gas Production Administration, Aznakayevskneft OGPA, Bavlyneft OGPA, Dzhalilneft OGPA, Yelkhovneft OGPA, Leninogorskneft OGPA, Nurlatneft OGPA, Prikamneft OGPA, and Yamashneft OGPA. The company is a founding stockholder of several oil production joint ventures, including: Tatoylgaz, Tatekh, KalmTatneft, Okhtin-Oyl, Yambul-Oyl, Tatneft-Samara, Tatneft-Severny, Tatneft-Abdulino, and Tatneft-Tarakal. The main enterprise in Tatneft's refining and processing division is the Tatneftegazpererabotka Administration. The company has a total payroll of more than 100,000 employees. Tatneft's retail network counts over 473 gas stations in 20 regions of Russia and the CIS.

At present, Tatneft is actively building a new-generation major refining complex at Nizhnekamsk, the Republic of Tatarstan, which will refine 15 million tons of oil per year and produce 18 types of refined products, from motor fuels to feedstocks for the production of a wide range of petrochemicals.

Slavneft Open Joint-Stock Company was founded in 1994, based on a Russian Federation Government resolution dated April 8, 1994 and a Belarusian Council of Ministers directive dated June 15, 1994. Slavneft's founders were the Russian State Property Management Committee [Goskomimushchestvo] with an initial equity interest of 86.3% and the Republic of Belarus Ministry of State Property with 7.2%. In November 2002, the Republic of Belarus government sold its interest in Slavneft, and on December 18, 2002, the Russian federal government auctioned off its 74.95% stake in Slavneft. After privatization, Slavneft became a wholly private oil company. As of May 15, 2009, company stock was owned as follows: Invest-Oyl (74.9570%), Stranberg Investments Ltd. (11.5772%), and Select Holdings Ltd. (7.7037%).

At present, the company's vertically integrated structure enables it to support a full production cycle, from field exploration and production of hydrocarbon reserves to their refining. Slavneft holds subsurface geologic study and oil and gas exploration and production licenses to 39 license tracts within the territory of Western Siberia and the Krasnoyarsk Territory. The company's main production unit is Slavneft-Megionneftegaz. Operating at Megion, Agan, and many other fields, the company produces over 1.8 million tons of crude hydrocarbons annually. The produced crude (except the export portion) is sent for refining to the Slavneft-Yaroslavnefteorgsintez, the Slavneft–Yaroslavl Refinery, and the Mozyr Refinery.

The company's principal objectives in the next few years are to implement its new oil production strategy, continue to upgrade its refining capacity and increase its refining volume, restructure its business, create an optimal interactive framework for holding company enterprises, reduce costs, and increase production efficiency.

Russneft Open Joint-Stock Company is also one of the ten largest Russian oil companies. Geographically, Russneft's operations cover the Khanty-Mansi Autonomous District, the Yamal-Nenets Autonomous District, the Tomsk, Ulyanovsk, Penza, Volgograd, Bryansk, Saratov, Kirov, and Orenburg regions, the Krasnodar Territory, the Republic of Udmurtia, and the Republic of Belarus. The company currently has 178 oil and gas fields under development.

In 2008, Russneft increased its crude reserves by more than 22 million tons (a 5% increase over 2007). In Saratov Region, Russneft discovered Luzyanskoye field, and found new accumulations within the Tagr-Yëgan field (the Khanty-Mansi Autonomous District), the Roslavl field (the Khanty-Mansi Autonomous District), the Belokamennoye field (the Saratov Region), and the Gurarinskoye field (the Tomsk Region). According to Miller and Lents (US), Russneft's proven reserves, certified according to international accounting standards, amounted to 1,713.3 million BOE, including 1,562.5 million barrels (235 million tons) of oil and 905 BCF (25 billion cubic meters) of gas. The total recoverable reserves at fields belonging to Russneft Oil Company are 648 million tons of oil and 3 TCF of gas per the Russian $ABC_1 + C_2$ classification.

Russneft has 21 oil production enterprises. The company's Western Siberian Group includes: Varyëganneft, MPK Aganneftegazgeologiya, White Nights, Goloyl Siberian-Texas, Aki-Otyr Oil Company, Chernogorskoye JV, Mokhtikneft, Archneftegeologiya, and West Malobalyk. Its Urals Group includes Belkamneft, Ural Oil, Udmurt National Oil Company, and Udmurt Oil Company. Its Volga Group includes Saratovneftegaz, Ulyanovskneft, Nafta-Ulyanovsk JV, Nefterazvedka, and Penzaneft. Its Central Siberian Group includes Sobolinoye Group and Tomsk Oil.

Russneft's refining division includes: Orsknefteorgsintez, the Krasnodar Refinery–Krasnodarekoneft, Neftemaslozavod, and Slavneftekhim. Russneft's sales network comprises 96 gas stations located in 14 regions of Russia and the CIS. The company has a modern oil-loading terminal in the Bryansk Region with a capacity of up to 7.7 million tons per year. Russneft's total payroll is over 20,000 employees.

The company is trying both to sustain its positive performance of recent years and to make its operation substantially more efficient by introducing advanced technologies and modern oil and gas equipment and by investing in the development of proprietary production facilities.

Bashneft Open Joint-Stock Company rounds out the list of the 10 largest Russian oil companies. Bashneft's history began in 1946, when the Bashkir Petrochemical Integrated Works [Bashneftekhimkombinat] was formed to develop the fields of the "Second Baku." Since 1995, it has been a joint-stock company. In April 2009, Sistema Joint-Stock Financial Corporation [AFK Sistema] completed a deal to acquire controlling stock interests in six Bashkir oil enterprises for $2.5 billion. The company purchased controlling interests in Bashneft, Ufaneftekhim, Novoyl, Ufaorgsintez, the Ufa Refinery, and Bashkirnefteprodukt from Agidel-Invest, Ural-Invest, Inzer-Invest, and Yuryuzan-Invest. Together with its existing holdings, the company then had a 76.52% equity interest in Bashneft, a 65.78% interest in Ufaneftekhim, an 87.23% interest in Novoyl, a 73.02% interest in Ufaorgsintez, a 78.49% interest in the Ufa Refinery, and a 73.33% interest in Bashkirnefteprodukt.

In October 2009, Bashneft formed an oil and gas production operating company, Bashneft-Dobycha. All of Bashneft-Dobycha's stock is held by Bashneft.

At present, Bashneft-Dobycha operates mainly within the territory of the Republic of Bashkortostan, the Republic of Tatarstan, the Orenburg Region, and the Khanty-Mansi Autonomous District. The company's total proven reserves are estimated at 375 million tons. It produces crude oil at more than 160 fields, most of which are nearing exhaustion. The quality of the company's reserves is low; most fields are characterized by high levels of depletion (about 85%), water cuts (up to 90%), and sulfur content (2% or more).

Bashneft-Dobycha includes nine major oil production divisions: Arlanneft, Aksakovneft, Ishimbayneft, Krasnokholmskneft, Oktyabrskneft, Chekmagushneft, Tuymazaneft, Ufaneft, and Yuzharlanneft.

Bashneft delivers most of its crude hydrocarbons (over 60% of oil production) to refineries in Bashkiria, including the Ufa Refinery, Salavatnefteorgsintez, Ufaneftekhim, and Ufaorgsintez.

The leading enterprise in Bashneft's gas processing division is the Tuymaza Gas Processing Plant. In addition, the company also has two oil and gas machine-building enterprises: Neftekamsk Oilfield Equipment Plant (Neftekamsk) and Oktyabrsky Oilfield Equipment Plant (Oktyabrsky).

Bashneft's sales network comprises over 300 gas stations and 60 oil tank farms, which are located in 11 regions of Russia and the CIS. Bashneft has a total payroll of over 67,000 employees.

Over the next several years, the company's will strive to balance development of its production potential and improve the efficiency of its operations using high-performance methods to introduce state-of-the-art technologies to reduce the level of oil production drop-off at depleted fields.

Select Glossary

All-Russian Central Executive Committee of the Soviets of Workers', Soldiers', and Peasants' Deputies (*VTsIK*)—the supreme legislative, directive, and supervisory body of Soviet Russia, operating in the period between the All-Russian Congresses of Soviets. First elected October 25 (November 7), 1917, consisting of 62 Bolsheviks, 20 Left Socialist Revolutionaries, six Social Democrats, and three Ukrainian Nationalists. The first chairman of the *VTsIK* was Lev Kamenev (Rosenfeld) (1883–1936).

All-Russian Extraordinary Commission for Combating Counterrevolution and Sabotage (*VChK*)—a special service for safeguarding the national security of Soviet Russia. Formed December 7 (20), 1917 by a resolution of the Council of People's Commissars. Its jurisdiction encompassed curtailing and preventing crimes against Soviet rule, finding and arresting criminals, investigation, court decisions, and even the execution of sentences. Feliks Dzerzhinsky (1877–1926) was the perennial chairman of the *VChK*.

Artillery Office—Russia's central military institution of the 16th and 17th centuries. The Artillery Office was in charge of specialists in the manufacture of artillery (gunners, fusiliers, gatekeepers), as well as treasury blacksmiths of Russian cities (except lowland, coastal, and Siberian ones). The Artillery Office managed the manufacture, distribution, and accounting of artillery and munitions (the Artillery Court, Ordnance Court, and Treasury "Powder" Mills reported to it), monitored the status of fortifications in most cities, and observed the condition of abatises. Controlled by the boyars (less often by the *okolnichies*) and two chief clerks, it was divided into three desks—city, abatis, and monetary. The Artillery Court was incorporated into the Cavalry Office in January 1678, but became independent again in 1682; in 1701, it formed the basis for the creation of a new central military institution, the Artillery Office.

Bosporan Kingdom—an ancient slave-owning state in the northern Black Sea region in the Cimmerian Bosporus (Kerch Strait), with its capital at Panticapaeum. It was formed about 480 BCE by the merger of Greek cities on the Kerch and Taman Peninsulas, and later expanded along the eastern shore of Maeotis (Maeotian Swamp, Maeotian Lake, modern Sea of Azov) to the mouth of the Tanais (Don) River. After the late 2nd century BCE, it was incorporated into the Pontian Kingdom, later a vassal of Rome. Destroyed by the Huns.

Embassy Office—a central governmental institution of the Muscovite state in the mid-16th to early 18th centuries, created in 1549, charged with conducting relations with foreign states. The Embassy Office was charged with general supervision of the country's foreign policy and all ongoing diplomacy: the dispatch of Russian embassies abroad, the receiving and release of foreign embassies, the preparation of texts of instructions (*nakazy*) to Russian ambassadors and correspondence with them, the drafting of agreements, conduct of negotiations, and—beginning in the early 18th century—appointing and monitoring the actions of permanent Russian diplomatic representatives abroad. The Embassy Office managed foreign merchants during their stays in Russia and all arriving foreigners in general, other than soldiers. In addition, it ransomed and exchanged Russian prisoners, managed newly annexed territories, and dealt with the Don Cossacks and landowning service Tatars of central districts. In the early 18th century, as a result of the reforms of Peter the Great, supervision of foreign relations was transferred from the Embassy Office to the Embassy Chancellery. In 1720, the Embassy Office was abolished and replaced by the Foreign Affairs Board.

Fire worshipers—also called Parsis or Gabrs, were followers of the teachings of Zoroaster who lived in antiquity in Persia, on the Absheron Peninsula, and in northwestern India. They spoke Gujarati.

Icon painter—an artist, usually a member of a monastic order, who specializes in the creation, on the basis of Orthodox canons, of icons for churches and monasteries. An icon is a picture on a wooden board depicting saints and episodes from the Bible. Translated from Greek, "icon" means "image, depiction." In Kievan Rus, icons were called just that— "images." Their ease of placement in a temple, their brightness, and the strength of their colors made icons painted on wood most suitable for decoration of Russian wooden churches. In medieval Russia, icons were treated with great respect as objects of worship. Icons were in every home, and lamps burned before them. Icons were also placed at road forks, wells, hung on gates, and placed at the entrances to cities. Icon painting in Kievan Rus was considered an activity pleasing to God. A true icon painter had to be a righteous man and an outstanding personality— combining the talent of an artist and a knowledge of scripture. Before beginning work on an icon, the artist fasted, bathed the night before, and donned a clean shirt. As he began work, he offered a prayer to God, asking Him to "bless my work."

Joint State Political Directorate (*OGPU*)—a special service for safeguarding the national security of the Soviet Union. Formed in February 1922 by decision of the Politburo of the RCP(b) Central Committee from the former *VChK*, initially designated as the State Political Directorate (*GPU*). With the formation of the USSR in December 1922, it was renamed the Joint State Political Directorate (*OGPU*). Feliks Dzerzhinsky was the chairman of the *OGPU* from 1922 to 1926, followed by Vyacheslav Menzhinsky (1874–1934) from 1926 to 1934.

Khazar Khanate—a state originating in the mid-7th century in the Lower Volga region and eastern part of the North Caucasus as a result of the breakup of the Western Turkic Khanate. In the early 8th century, the Khazars controlled the North Caucasus, the Azov region, and most of the Crimea, as well as the Eastern European steppes as far as the Dnipro [Dnieper], and they warred with the Arabs for the Transcaucasus. Displaced by the Arabs, the Khanate shifted to the Lower Volga. In the late 8th and early 9th centuries, the struggle within the Khazar Khanate intensified, and in the late 9th century the Pechenegs settled on their territory in the Northern Black Sea region and along the Don. In the late 10th century, due to a series of Russian campaigns of conquest, the Khazar Khanate ceased to exist.

Manufacturing and Mining Board—a central governmental industrial institution of the Muscovite state in the early 18th century, founded by Peter the Great's decree of December 23, 1718. This institution supervised all Russian industry, including mining, and was abolished on December 10, 1719 in connection with its reorganization into two new departments, the Manufacturing Board and the Mining Board.

Mining Board—a central governmental ore mining institution of the Muscovite state and Russian Empire in the 18th century, providing supervision of the mining and manufacturing industries. It operated intermittently, from 1719 to 1731, from 1742 to 1783, and from 1797 to 1807. Board operations were governed by the Mining Privilege and the Mining Regulation, as well as special and Senate decrees.

Mining Office—a central governmental mining engineering institution of the Muscovite state in the early 18th century. Formed on August 24, 1700 by a decree of Tsar Peter the Great, it laid the foundation for government administration of mining geology in prospecting for ore and other minerals in various parts of Russia. This institution managed ore prospecting and the training of people versed in mining, concerned itself with the construction of factories, and collected information on metals mined and newly discovered mineral fields. Under its control, iron works were built at Nevyansk, Tagil, Kamensk-Uralsky, and Alapayevsk. Subsequently, the country's need for foreign metal ceased. By the end of Peter the Great's reign, Russia was trading Russian iron and copper abroad. The institution was abolished on December 23, 1718 in connection with its reorganization into a new central industrial department, the Manufacturing and Mining Board.

Order of Lenin—highest decoration of the Soviet Union, instituted April 6, 1930 by resolution of the USSR Central Executive Committee of the Soviets of Workers', Soldiers', and Peasants' Deputies.

Polovtsy—also called Cumans, Kipchaks, and Qypchaqs, spoke a Turkic language and inhabited the South Russian steppes from the western horns of the Tien-Shan to the Danube from the 10th to 13th centuries. They raised livestock and led a nomadic life. From the 10th to 13th centuries, they regularly raided the territory of Kievan Rus. Attacks in the late 11th century were most dangerous. They were crushed and subjugated by the Mongolian-Tatar hordes in the 13th century. Some Polovtsy joined the Golden Horde, while others fled to Hungary. The Russian people's struggle with the Polovtsy tribes was reflected in chronicles and in the monument of Russian literature, *The Story of Igor's Campaign.*

Siberian Office—a central governmental institution of the Muscovite state in the 17th to 18th centuries, separated from the Kazan Palace Office in 1637. It managed administrative, judicial, military, and financial matters, trade, postal services, mining, and other enterprises over the territory of all Siberia, and to an extent, its relations with adjacent countries. This office was reorganized by Peter the Great's decree of December 18, 1708 into the Moscow Chancellery of the Siberian Province, and in 1710 it ceased to exist. Its functions were concentrated in the hands of the Siberian governor and the governor's office in Tobolsk. Due to the declining income received by the treasury from Siberia, the Russian government reinstituted the Siberian Office in 1730 and made it report to the Senate. The newly created institution managed only administrative, financial, trade, and customs matters. The Siberian Office was abolished for good on December 15, 1763, by order of Catherine the Great.

Profiles of Key Historical Figures

CHAPTER ONE: The Russian Empire's "Black Gold"

Alexander I (1777–1825): Russian Emperor (1801–1825). Under the influence of liberal ideas, early in his reign he abolished the use of torture in judicial investigations, gave greater freedom in the performance of rites by religious minorities, permitted the operation of private printers, and encouraged the issuance of liberties to serfs (though only 0.5% of serfs were actually freed). He built new roads and canals in the center of the country and opened universities at Kazan, Kharkiv, Dorpat (Tartu), Vilnius, and St. Petersburg. He also made important changes in the structure of government administration. He expanded the powers of the Senate (1802), replaced the boards with ministries, and instituted the advisory State Council (1810). During the war of 1808–1809, he crushed Sweden, resulting in the annexation of Finland to the empire, and won a war against the Ottoman Empire from 1806 to 1812, capturing Bessarabia and several cities on the Black Sea coast of the Caucasus. In July 1812, Napoleon Bonaparte's army invaded Russia, initiating the Patriotic War of 1812 in which Russia was victorious over the aggressors. Napoleon's new army was crushed by the combined armies of Russia, Prussia, and Austria at the Battle of Leipzig in 1813. After Napoleon's abdication in 1814, Emperor Alexander, along with representatives of Austria, Prussia, and Great Britain, participated in the Congress of Vienna. To keep order in Europe, the Russian and Austrian emperors, together with the king of Prussia, entered into the "Holy Alliance," later joined by most European monarchs. Subsequently, Russia consolidated its positions in the Balkans, continuing to force out the Ottoman Empire. The emperor's sudden death in December 1825 caused an armed uprising by several military units in St. Petersburg, which went down in history as the "Decembrist revolt."

Alexander II (1818–1881): Russian emperor and reformer. He was tutored by the noted Russian poet Vasily Zhukovsky, who inculcated liberal views and a romantic attitude toward life. In 1837, he made a long trip through Russia, and in 1838 another through Western Europe. In 1841, he married the Princess of Hesse-Darmstadt, who took the name Mariya Aleksandrovna. He participated in the affairs of the Empire, becoming a member of the State Council, the Council of Ministers, and the Finance Committee. He assumed the throne on the death of his father on February 19 (March 3), 1855. One of his first signature acts was to forgive the exiled Decembrists, which he announced during his coronation in Moscow on August 26 (September 12), 1856. He ended the Crimean War with England and France by signing a peace treaty in Paris on March 30, 1856. On February 19 (March 3), 1861, he promulgated a manifesto emancipating the peasants from serfdom. This radical reform foreshadowed other equally substantial acts: administrative (a statute on provincial and district land institutions), judicial (public and open trials, independent judges, new court procedures), reorganization of the Military System (in particular, a Charter on Universal Military Service), and a reform of public education. Under his reign, the conquest of the Caucasus was completed. Russia expanded its influence in the east, annexing Turkestan, the Amur Valley, the Ussuri Territory, and the Kurile Islands in exchange for the southern part of Sakhalin. During the American Civil War, he opposed British and French policy, and decisively supported the Union. In 1867, he sold Alaska and the Aleutian Islands to the United States. Despite his liberal reforms, his reign was marked by a growth in the revolutionary movement, and the emperor was the target of several attempts on his life. In 1880 he barely escaped death when terrorists detonated a bomb in the Winter Palace. Members of the People's Freedom movement succeeded in assassinating Alexander II on March 13, 1881.

Alexander III (1845–1894): Russian emperor. He was trained for a military career as he was not the heir to the throne through the line of succession. He became Tsarevich (Crown Prince) in 1865 after the death of his older brother, Grand Duke Nikolay Aleksandrovich, whereupon he began to receive a broader and more fundamental education. In 1866, he married the Danish Princess Marie Sophie Frederica Dagmar (1847–1928), who took the name Mariya Fëdorovna when she adopted the Orthodox faith. The marriage produced six children, including the future last Russian emperor, Nicholas II (1868–1918). Alexander III's political ideal rested on the concept of patriarchal autocratic rule, the inculcation of religious values in society, the strengthening of class structure, and ethnically distinctive social development. The beginning of his rule was characterized by a toughening of administrative and police repressions and censorship. By the mid-1880s, the government had instituted repressive measures to suppress the revolutionary movement, primarily the underground People's Freedom organization. At the same time, it adopted a series of decrees easing the material position of the people and relaxing social tensions. He adhered to strict moral rules, was very devout, distinguished by thrift, modesty, and hostility to comfort, and spent his leisure time within a small circle of family and friends. He took an interest in music, art, and history, and promoted liberalization of exterior aspects of public activity by abolishing genuflection before the tsar, permitting smoking on the streets and in public places, etc. The Russian economic life under Alexander III was characterized by economic growth, which was largely due to a policy of increased protectionism toward domestic industry. The Russian government encouraged growth of big capitalist industry, achieving noted successes. However, the rapid development of industry clashed with archaic sociopolitical forms, the backwardness of agriculture, peasant community, and small landholdings, which did much to prepare the ground for subsequent social and economic crises. Russia's foreign policy under Alexander III was distinguished by pragmatism and an effort to protect the country from involvement in international conflicts. The main result of this policy was a turn away from traditional cooperation with Germany toward an alliance with France, signed in 1891–93. From 1880 to 1890, Russia waged practically no wars, and for this reason, the tsar was called the "Peacemaker." His untimely death in 1894 was caused by nephritis.

Catherine II (Catherine the Great) (1729–1796): Russian Empress (1762–1796). Holds the distinction, among Russian emperors, of the longest life span and longest reign. She proved a wise and energetic monarch; her rule was characterized by an aggressive foreign policy and domestic reforms in the spirit of enlightened absolutism and the French Enlightenment. She reorganized the local administrative system, strengthening the position of the political, judicial, and financial bureaucracy. In 1785, she freed the nobles from mandatory service per the Table of Ranks by signing letters patent granting rights and liberty to the nobility. She waged two successful wars against the Ottoman Empire. In the first, (1768–1774), begun by Turkey, Russia acquired part of the Black Sea Coast near the mouth of the Dnipro [Dnieper]; in the second (1787–1791), these gains were expanded to the Dnister [Dniester] River. In 1783 she annexed the Crimea to Russia. She founded the port cities of Nikolayev, Kherson, Odessa, and Sevastopol along the lengthy Azov-Black Sea coast. Leading Russia's alliance with Austria and Prussia, she participated in three partitions of Poland (1772, 1793, 1795), through which Russia not only recovered the western Russian lands lost in the 13th century, but expanded the territory of the Empire somewhat. The expansion of production, spurred by the empress's manifesto on the freedom of enterprise (1775), promoted the development of trade. The number of factories grew from 663 in 1763 to 1,200 in 1796. The Ural industrial region put Russia in first place in the world in iron smelting (1 million barrels in 1790, 60% more than Great Britain). The Senate of the Russian Empire accorded her the titles "Catherine the Great" and "Mother of the Fatherland." Some historians call her reign the "golden age" of the Russian Empire.

Golovin, Fëdor Aleksandrovich (1867–1937): chairman of the second State Duma in 1907, a lawyer, noted activist of the *Zemstvo* Movement, and one of the founders of the Constitutional Democratic Party. He was born into a well-known noble family. He graduated from the university branch of Crown Prince Nikolay's Moscow Lyceum and Moscow University in 1891. He became a member of the Dmitrev District Council in 1893 before joining the Moscow Province Council from 1898 to 1907 and becoming its chairman in 1904. He was in charge of the Office for District and City Councils from 1904 to 1905. He served as an honorary magistrate. He became a member of Tsar Nicholas II's deputation on June 6, 1905. He was elected chairman of the second State Duma on February 20, 1907 and took active part in its peasant commission. Following the Duma's dissolution in June 1907, he became one of the founders of the Cooperation Society and a member of its executive council. He took part in several large railroad concessions. In 1912, he was elected mayor of Baku, although he was not confirmed as governor of the Caucasus because he belonged to the Cadet Party. During the war of 1914–1917, he took part in the All-Russian Union of Cities and was chairman of the War Victims Aid Association. On March 8, 1917, he was appointed commissar of the Provisional Government over the former Ministry of the Imperial Court and Domains, where he was responsible for former imperial theaters, museums, and other cultural institutions. He remained in this position until October 25, 1917, when he was removed by the new authorities. He served as a member of the All-Russian Committee for Aid to the Hungry in July and August 1921 before working in several Soviet institutions. He was shot in November 1937 as part of mass repressions carried out by the *NKVD*. He was rehabilitated in 1989.

Gubonin, Pëtr Ionovich (1825–1894): noted Russian industrialist, patron of the arts, and privy councilor to the Russian empire. Born in a serf family, he worked land for quitrent starting in 1847, and managed to save the required amount to buy his freedom from serfdom in 1858. Entering the merchant class in Moscow, he began producing various articles from stone. In 1868, he took up railroad construction. His successful projects included the Orël–Vitebsk, Gryazi–Tsaritsyn, Lozovo–Sevastopol, Ural Mining, and Baltic Railroads. In 1871, he became one of the founders of the Kolomna Machine-Building and Kulebaki Mining and Steel Mill Company, one of the leading Russian shipbuilding and steam locomotive manufacturing enterprises. In the late 1860s, he entered the oil business, founding Sakhansky & Co. Partnership to develop the Kerch oil fields. In 1882, he acquired a controlling stock interest in the Russian-American Petroleum Production Partnership, which owned a refinery at Kuskovo outside Moscow. In 1883, he founded the Neft Petroleum Products Production, Transportation, Storage and Trading Partnership, with an authorized capital of 2 million rubles. He was an active member of the Imperial Society of Lovers of Nature, Anthropology, and Ethnography and a contending member of the Russian Technical Society.

Guchkov, Aleksandr Ivanovich (1862–1936): chairman of the State Duma (1910–1911), a noted Russian politician, and leader of the Union of October 17 Party. He was born to a prominent merchant family, and graduated from the History and Philology Department of Moscow University in 1886 before studying at Berlin and Heidelberg Universities in Germany. He was a member of the Moscow City Duma from 1893 to 1897. He worked in the security department of the Chinese Eastern Railway in Manchuria from 1897 to 1899. He fought as a volunteer on the Boer side in the Boer War in South Africa in 1900. He served as director of the Moscow Discount Bank from 1902 to 1908. During the Russo-Japanese War of 1904–1905, he worked at the front as a representative of the Russian Red Cross. In March 1910, he was elected chairman of the State Duma. He spoke out against radical changes to the political system, arguing that they could lead to the collapse of the Russian state. He served as a member of the State Council in 1907 and from 1915 on. He was chairman of the Central Military and Industrial Committee from 1915 to 1917 and a member of the Special Defense Council. He was one of the organizers of the murder of Tsar favorite Grigory Rasputin in December 1916. Along with deputy Vasily Shulgin, he persuaded Tsar Nicholas II to abdicate the throne in February 1917. He served as minister of the military and navy under the Provisional Government from March to May 1917, and was elected in May 1917 to the State Council as a representative of trade and industry. He was one of the organizers of General Lavr Kornilov's coup d'état in August 1917. He was an active member of the White Movement, and emigrated to France in 1919.

Kankrin, Count Yegor Frantsevich (1774–1845): noted Russian public figure, economist, and infantry general (1828). He was one of the biggest financiers in the history of Russia. He was educated at Hesse and Magdeburg Universities, and in 1800, was given the rank of collegiate adviser as an aide to the executive board of the Old Russian Salt Works. In 1803, he was appointed to the Ministry of Internal Affairs as an adviser to the State Economic Expedition. Starting in 1809, he was inspector of foreign colonies of Petersburg Province. His research works on economics attracted the attention of the emperor. In 1811, he was made Actual State Councilor and appointed aide to the Quartermaster General of the War Ministry. During the Patriotic War of 1812, he served as Quartermaster General of the First Western Army, and from 1813, of the whole active Russian army. After hostilities ended, he worked to settle accounts with foreign nations. The former allies and France had initially demanded nearly 360 million rubles of Russia, but through skillful negotiations, Kankrin reduced this amount to 60 million. He became a member of the War Council in 1820, and member of the State Council in 1821. From April 1823 to May 1844, he served as Minister of Finance, and carried out a reform of the monetary system, guilds, and several other important measures to revive the financial system. He was an honorary member of the Petersburg Academy of Sciences and the author of a large number of theoretical works on economics and finance.

Kerensky, Aleksandr Fëdorovich (1881–1970): a noted Russian public figure and politician, as well as prime minister of the Russian Provisional Government in 1917. He graduated from the St. Petersburg University School of Law in 1904, after which he worked as a lawyer's assistant and made friends with members of the Liberation Union, which united the liberal supporters of *zemstvo* [a form of local self-government] and the intelligentsia. He was arrested in December 1905 for the possession of antigovernment leaflets and remained in prison until spring 1906. Not long after his release from prison, he became a popular lawyer and was involved in a number of political trials. In 1912, he was elected to the fourth State Duma from the Labor Group [*Trudoviki*] and became the leader of the faction. An active member of the 1917 February Revolution, he participated in the creation and the management of the Provisional Committee of the State Duma, proclaiming himself a proponent of the democratic republic system. He was deputy chairman of the Petrograd Soviet of Workers' Deputies, joined the Provisional Government, and became a member of the Socialist Revolutionary Party. He was the only member of the Provisional Government to be a part of all its different forms from February until October 1917, successively holding the posts of minister of justice, prime minister, and minister of war and the navy. His inability as head of the government to stabilize the country's situation in the fall of 1917 soon led to his name being associated in the public consciousness with *kerenki*, a type of surrogate money that had no serial number, series, or year of issue and depreciated rapidly. On October 25, 1917, the eve of the October Revolution, he traveled to the front to meet soldiers he had summoned, but they never appeared. He dressed in a sailor's uniform at the Gatchina Palace to escape from revolutionary sailors. In June 1918, he traveled abroad to organize intervention against the Bolsheviks. He lived in France for more than 20 years and worked actively with immigrant organizations. He published the newspapers *Dni* ["Days"] and *Novaya Rossiya* ["New Russia"] and regularly spoke out against the Stalinist dictatorship in the USSR. He moved to the US in 1940 and in 1956 began cooperating with the Hoover Institution on War, Revolution, and Peace at Stanford University, where he was a professor.

Along with Professor Robert Browder, he published three volumes of documents called *The Russian Provisional Government* [*Rossiyskoye Vremennoye pravitelstvo*] in 1961. He is buried in the UK.

Khomyakov, Nikolay Alekseyevich (1850–1925): chairman of the State Duma (1907–1910) and one of the heads of the Union of October 17 Party (Octobrists). He was born to a noble family, and graduated from the Moscow University School of Physics and Mathematics in 1874. During the Russo-Turkish War of 1877–1878, he enlisted in the army as a volunteer and helped liberate Bulgaria from the Ottoman yoke. In 1880, he became the Sychëvka District head and was head of the Smolensk Province nobility from 1886 to 1895. He was appointed director of the Department of Agriculture under the Ministry of Agriculture and State Property in 1896. He served as a member of the Agricultural Council of the Ministry of Agriculture in 1904. He was a member of district congresses in 1904 and 1905 and became a member of the Central Committee of the Union of October 17 Party in 1906. Khomyakov was elected as a member of the State Council from the nobility of Smolensk Province in 1906. He served as a deputy from Smolensk Province in the second and fourth State Dumas and was a member of the office of the parliamentary bloc of the Union of October 17 Party. He was chairman of the third State Duma from November 1907 until March 1910. He served as chairman of the St. Petersburg Club of Public Figures from 1913 to 1915, and took charge of the Russian Red Cross in 1915. Khomyakov was evacuated from the Crimea along with units of the Volunteer Army in 1920, and lived the last years of his life in exile in the Croatian city of Dubrovnik.

Kokorev, Vasily Aleksandrovich (1817–1889): noted Russian entrepreneur, columnist, and business adviser. He became rich early in his business career as a wine tax commissioner, performing the instructions of the Ministry of Finance, and by the early 1860s, his worth had grown to 7 million rubles. In 1870, he founded the Volga-Kama Bank and Northern Insurance Company. He built the Ural Railroad. In 1857, he founded the Transcaspian Trading Partnership, and two years later, built an oil-distilling plant on the Absheron Peninsula. In 1862, the refinery's petroleum products won a silver medal at the London International Exhibition on Industry and Arts. In January 1874, along with entrepreneur Pëtr Gubonin, he created the Baku Oil Company, the world's first vertically integrated company. His last, unrealized project was a plan to establish a Caspian Commercial Bank to finance the oil industry and develop the Transcaspian Territory. He was a gifted writer and a sharp-tongued columnist, and was given the humorous nickname "Foggy Billion" by the press (from the title of an article in which he advocated the abolition of serfdom). Of his articles, printed mainly in *Russky Vestnik* ["Russian

Herald"] of the 1850s and 1860s and in *Russky Arkhiv* ["Russian Archive"] of the 1880s, the best known are: "Economic Collapses," "The Sevastopol Way," "A Look at European Trade," "Thoughts on Russian Domestic Trade," and "Tax Farming."

Lepëkhin, Academician Ivan Ivanovich (1740–1802): noted Russian traveler and naturalist. From 1760 to 1762, he studied at the university of the Academy of Sciences; from 1762 to 1767, at Strasbourg University, earning a doctorate in medicine. In 1771, he was elected academician of the St. Petersburg Academy of Sciences. From 1768 to 1772, he supervised an academic expedition to study the Volga region, the Urals, and northern European Russia; in 1773, he completed a trip through the Baltics and Belarus. He became permanent secretary of the Russian academy in 1783, and produced numerous studies in geography, botany, zoology, Russian philology, etc. He expressed innovative ideas regarding the constant changes in the Earth's surface, the origins of caves, changes in the properties of plants and animals under environmental influences, etc. His principal four-volume work—a description of the 1768–1772 expedition (*Travelogue... Through Various Provinces of the Russian State [Dnevnyye zapiski puteshestviya... po raznym provintsiyam Rossiyskogo gosudarstva*], 1805)—contains extensive material on Russian geography and ethnography.

Mendeleyev, Dmitry Ivanovich (1834–1907): renowned Russian scholar and encyclopedist, chemist, and developer of the periodic table of the elements. He graduated from the Main Pedagogical Institute in 1855, and in 1863, took up the problem of refining and developed and introduced the technology of acid-base purification of kerosene distillate. In 1865, he successfully defended his doctoral dissertation, "On the Combination of Alcohol with Water," and was soon approved for a position as an associate professor, and then a full professor in the Department of Technical Chemistry at St. Petersburg University. From March 1869 through December 1871, he worked out all the critical aspects of the doctrine of periodicity and set the direction for future research in this area. In late 1871, he turned to research on the physics of gases. From 1880 to 1885, he studied problems of the refining of oil, and proposed a principle for its fractional distillation. In 1888, he advanced the idea of underground gasification of coal, and from 1891 to 1892, he developed a technology for making a new type of smokeless powder. In November 1892, he accepted the government's offer of a position as head of the Depot of Standard Weights and Measures (the Main Office of Weights and Measures from April 1893), and did much to promote the development of the metric system in Russia. The scope of the public, scientific organizational, and purely research activities in his life is striking. He made three trips to the Absheron Peninsula, where he studied the state of the oil business. On government assignment, he visited the Don Basin, where he studied the causes of a crisis in the coal industry, participated in a review of the customs tariff, published a substantially revised version of his work, *Principles of Chemistry* [*Osnovy khimii*], designed an icebreaker for high-latitude scientific research, participated in a Ural Expedition, etc. Dmitry Mendeleyev was a member of over 90 academies of science, scientific societies, and universities in various countries. He is one of the founders of the Russian Chemical Society (1868), and was elected its president several times (1883–1884, 1891, 1892, and 1894). The 101st element in the periodic table, mendelevium, bears his name. In 1962, the USSR Academy of Sciences established the Mendeleyev Prize and Gold Medal for the best work in chemistry and chemical engineering, and in 1964 Dmitry Mendeleyev's name was entered on the Science Wall of Honor at Bridgeport University in the US, alongside the names of Euclid, Archimedes, Copernicus, Galileo, Newton, and Lavoisier.

Mordvinov, Count Nikolay Semënovich (1754–1845): noted Russian public figure, economist, and admiral. He was sent to England in 1774, where he spent three years improving his knowledge of the naval arts. He participated in the Russian-Turkish War. In 1792, he was appointed Chairman of the Black Sea Admiralty Board, then a member of the Russian Admiralty Board. He was involved in discussions of critical government issues raised by Emperor Alexander and his closest associates, and with the formation of the ministries in 1802, assumed the post of Minister of Naval Forces. In 1806, he was elected head of the Moscow Home Guard. With the institution of the State Council in Russia in 1810, he was appointed a member and chairman of the Department of the State Economy. In 1818, he was appointed chairman of the State Council's Department of Civil and Spiritual Affairs; he was also a member of the Finance Committee and the Committee of Ministers, and retained these posts during the reign of Emperor Nicholas II. In 1823, he was elected president of the Free Economic Society and held that post until 1840, actively promoting scientific research in the field of economics and finance.

Muromtsev, Sergey Andreyevich (1850–1910): chairman of the first Russian State Duma in 1906 and a professor at Moscow University. He was born into an old aristocratic family and, as a ten-year-old boy, he invented a game of government in which he used sensible management procedures and released his own handwritten newspaper about the life of his father and the surrounding villages. In 1867, he graduated from secondary school with a gold medal and entered the School of Law at Moscow University. After graduating from the university in 1871, he began to prepare for a professorship. He attended lectures at several German universities in 1873 and 1874 to further his education and defended his master's thesis in 1875 before successfully launching a research and teaching career. He took part in the constitutionalist *Zemstvo* Movement. In 1880, he became chairman of the Moscow Law Society and an editor of *Yuridichesky Vestnik* ["Law Herald"]. In 1882, he married Mariya Klimentova (1857–1946), an opera singer and soloist at the Bolshoy Theater. Acting as a writer and public political figure, he sought to protect individuals and society from revolutionary radicalism and the despotism of the authorities. He believed it was necessary to continue the reforms that would lead Russia to a constitutional system in a peaceful and evolutionary way. From 1904 to 1906, he became a recognized authority in constitutional and parliamentary law and began promoting the experience of Western parliaments. He was one of the founders of the Constitutional Democratic Party and a member of its Central Committee. He drafted the Russian Basic Law. Muromtsev was elected to the first State Duma as a deputy from Moscow. Following the Duma's dissolution, he led a session of some Duma deputies in Vyborg. A court sentenced him to three months in prison for signing the Vyborg Appeal on July 10, 1906. Upon release from prison, he continued his research and lectured at Moscow University. The entire progressive community of Moscow turned out for his funeral in early October 1910. *Russkiye vedomosti* ["Russian Gazette"] wrote: "In life, Professor Muromtsev was a historic personality for all Russians and all Europeans because Russia's constitutional history starts with his name."

Nicholas II (1868–1918): the last Russian emperor, who ruled from 1894 through March 1917. His reign came at a time of sharply worsening political struggle in the country, as well as a deteriorating political situation (the Russo-Japanese War of 1904–1905; Bloody Sunday (1905); the Russian Revolution of 1905–1907; the First World War; the February Revolution of 1917; and the October Revolution of 1917). In 1894, he married the German Princess Victoria Alix Helena Louise Beatrice of Hesse-Darmstadt (1872–1918), who took the name Aleksandra Fëdorovna after adopting the Orthodox faith. The marriage produced five children: daughters Olga (1895–1918), Tatyana (1897–1918), Mariya (1899–1918), and Anastasiya (1901–1918); and a son Aleksey (1904–1918), who was heir to the throne. During Nicholas II's reign as tsar, Russia was transformed into an agrarian-industrial country, cities grew, and railroads and factories were built. He supported decisions aimed at the country's economic and social modernization, such as the introduction of the gold ruble, the Stolypin agrarian reform, laws on worker insurance, universal basic education, and religious tolerance. Not a reformer by nature, he was forced to make important decisions that did not conform to his personal convictions. He believed that Russia was not yet ready for a constitution, freedom of speech, or universal election rights. However, when a strong public movement arose in favor of political transformations, he signed the Manifesto of October 17, 1905 proclaiming democratic freedoms. A State Duma established by the tsar's manifesto convened in 1906, suggesting that Russia had begun to transform itself gradually into a constitutional monarchy. But the emperor retained the right to promulgate laws (in the form of decrees), to appoint ministers (including a prime minister) who were answerable only to him, to define the course of foreign policy, and to be the head of the army and navy and the secular head of the Russian Orthodox Church. The turning point in the emperor's fate was August 1914, the beginning of the First World War. In August 1915, during a period of military setbacks, he assumed military command (replacing Grand Duke Nikolay Nikolayevich), after which he spent most of his time at the General Headquarters in Mogilev. The war exacerbated the country's domestic problems, and the tsar and his court began to receive most of the blame for military setbacks and the prolonged military campaign. In late February 1917, unrest broke out in Petrograd, growing into massive demonstrations against the government and the dynasty. Initially, the tsar intended to establish order in Petrograd by force, but when the scale of the disorders became clear, he abandoned the idea, fearing widespread bloodshed. He was convinced that pacifying the country required a change of government. On March 2, 1917, after torturous reflection, he signed his abdication from the throne in the lounge car of his train in Pskov. On March 9, 1917, he and the entire royal family were arrested. They spent the first five months under guard at Tsarskoye Selo, but in August 1917 they were transferred to Tobolsk. In April 1918, the Bolsheviks sent the Romanov family to Yekaterinburg. On the night of July 17, 1918, in the basement of a house in the center of town where the royal family had been incarcerated, they were shot without trial or sentence. In 1997, after many years of investigation of remains found near Yekaterinburg, they were ceremonially interred in the Peter and Paul Cathedral in St. Petersburg.

Nobel, Emanuel (1859–1932): a major oil industrialist, honorary production engineer, commercial adviser, and an actual state councilor. The eldest son of Ludvig Nobel, he was born in St. Petersburg, received his secondary education at the St. Anna School (one of the capital's oldest and most prestigious educational institutions), and then graduated from the Stockholm Institute of Technology. Following his father's death in 1888, he took over the Nobel Brothers Petroleum Production Partnership and remained in charge of the company's operations for almost three decades. Emanuel was awarded the Order of St. Stanislav, third degree, in October 1888 after Tsar Aleksandr III visited the company's oil fields. He became a Russian citizen in 1889. A talented manager who took up his father's baton, he did everything possible to make the Nobel Brothers Partnership a leader not only in the Russian oil industry but on the global market as well, where the Standard Oil Company presented strong competition. The Nobel Brothers Partnership produced 5.4 million barrels of oil and 2 million barrels of kerosene in 1890, exporting more than 1 million barrels of kerosene, or 130% more than the 408,000 barrels shipped abroad in 1887. The company took part in the Chicago World's Columbian Exposition in 1893, where it was awarded a certificate of merit and bronze medal, and also received prestigious honors at international exhibitions in Lyon (1894) and Antwerp (1894). Its achievements received high praise at the All-Russian Industrial and Art Exhibition in Nizhny Novgorod in 1896. Oil fields owned by the Nobel Brothers Partnership produced 9.6 million barrels of oil and 2.5 million barrels of kerosene in 1901, exporting 1.5 million barrels. In 1913, the company produced 7.9 million barrels of crude and refined 6.9 million barrels at its refineries, which produced 2.4 million barrels of kerosene alone. Oil production was under way at 479 drill holes, while oil fields were using 177 steam engines and 131 electric motors. The company had a total of 2,541 workers. The Nobel Brothers Partnership had 43 river boats, 14 schooners, 209 barges, and 1,400 rail cars at its disposal to transport crude oil and petroleum products. Emanuel Nobel initiated the full-scale production in Russia of internal combustion engines designed by Rudolf Diesel, and promoted their widespread use in shipbuilding. He actively participated in public affairs and engaged in charitable activities. He became the permanent St. Petersburg representative of the Congress of Baku Oil Industrialists in 1889. He served as a member of the Council of Trade and Manufactures, deputy chairman of the Anglo-Russian Trade Chamber, and a member of the accounting and loan committee of the St. Petersburg branch of the State Bank. In 1906, he was elected chairman of the provisional council for the organization of congresses for industry and trade representatives. From 1912 to 1916, he served as head of the St. Petersburg Society of Manufacturers and Industrialists. He was awarded the title of honorary industrial engineer. He was one of the founders of a St. Petersburg-based committee to assist young people in attaining moral, intellectual, and physical development (*Mayak*). He regularly made monetary donations to the Institute of Experimental Medicine in St. Petersburg in an effort to prevent epidemics from spreading throughout the country. In 1907, the Baku branch of the Russian Technical Society established a prize in honor of Emanuel Nobel, who represented the third generation of a famous family, in recognition of his contribution to the development of the oil business.

Nobel, Ludvig (1831–1888): a major oil industrialist, inventor, St. Petersburg merchant of the first guild, and an honorary production engineer. He was born in Stockholm. He was educated at home and received practical experience working at his father's company in St. Petersburg. In 1862, he founded his own company where he successfully produced various types of products for the military department. From 1871 to 1875, he took part in the reconstruction and modernization of the Izhevsk Armory and set up large-scale production of modern small arms. He began working in the oil business in 1875. With the help of his older brother Robert, he initially acquired a small refinery on the Absheron Peninsula before later purchasing several oil properties. Nobel was the first Russian oilman who began to search for a fundamental solution to the problem of transporting oil. In 1878, the world's first tanker, the *Zoroastr,* was built on Nobel's design to navigate the Caspian Sea, and the first oil pipeline in Russia was constructed on the Absheron Peninsula. In 1879, Russia's second vertically integrated joint-stock company, Nobel Brothers Petroleum Production Partnership, was established on the core of the family business with capital assets of 3 million rubles. The company's charter was approved on May 18, 1879. The key aspects of the company's strategy were the widespread introduction of scientific and engineering achievements into production and the development of its own transportation and sales infrastructure. The active efforts of the Nobel Brothers Partnership resulted in a definitive breakthrough in freeing the Russian domestic market from imported US kerosene. In 1883, the Nobel Brothers Partnership launched trade operations abroad and formed a foreign sales network: *Deutsch-Russisches Nafta-Import-Gesellschaft* was founded in Germany and *Österreichisches Nafta-Import-Gesellschaft* was established in Austria. Receiving warehouses were set up in Marseilles, Antwerp, Hamburg, Gothenburg, London, and other international ports. Ludvig Nobel took active part in public affairs, and was a member of numerous commissions under the Imperial Russian Technical Society, where his experience was highly sought after. In 1884, he was made a lifetime member of the Imperial Russian Technical Society and an honorary member of the society's Permanent Commission on Technical Education. He was awarded the honorary title of Industrial Engineer by the learned council of the St. Petersburg Institute of Technology for his services to the domestic oil industry. Charitable work was particularly important for Ludvig Nobel. The Aleksandr Nevsky Cathedral, the Roman Catholic Cathedral of the Blessed Virgin Mary, and the Evangelical Lutheran Church were all built in Baku using the company's money. A mosque was built for Muslims in the village of Balakhany, and considerable funds were regularly allocated for the upkeep of the Bibiheybet holy tomb in the village of Shikhovo. For his services to Russia and enormous contribution to the development of the domestic industry, Nobel was awarded the Orders of St. Anna, second and third degree. The Imperial Russian Technical Society held a special session on March 31, 1889 to establish a prize in memory of Ludvig Nobel, which was for many years one of the most honorary distinctions in the engineering community.

Ostermann, Count Andrey Ivanovich (Heinrich Johann) (1686–1747): noted Russian public figure and diplomat. His father was a Lutheran pastor. Ostermann studied successfully at Jena University in Germany, but was forced to flee to Holland after a duel with a fatal outcome. He accepted Vice-Admiral Kornelius Cruys's invitation to enter Russian service. He spoke five languages, learned Russian in a year, and was assigned to the Embassy Chancellery as a translator. Ostermann participated in the Prut campaign in 1711 and successfully conducted peace negotiations. In 1718 and 1719, he participated in the Congress of Aland, which resolved disputes between Russia and Sweden, and in 1721, he helped negotiate the terms of the Treaty of Nystad, ending the Northern War. That same year, he was granted the title of baron "for outstanding labors and fidelity." He took part in the organization of the Board of Foreign Affairs, of which he became vice president in 1723. Thanks to his diplomatic experience and skillful intrigues, he made a successful career in the complex setting of palace coups. After the death of Peter the Great, he joined the Supreme Privy Council. In 1727, after the death of Catherine I, he became a tutor for the future Emperor Peter II. In 1730, after the death of Peter II, he declined to sign the "conditions" restricting the authority of Empress Anna Ivanovna, thereby gaining her sympathy, and on receiving the title of count, he became the actual director of the empire's domestic and foreign policy. In 1734, he was appointed Chancellor of the Russian Empire. During the brief regency of Anna Leopoldovna, he managed to befriend her favorite, Burchard Christoph von Münnich, and gained the title of admiral-general. After a palace coup in 1741, which brought Empress Elizabeth Petrovna to the throne, he was sentenced to death, but the sentence was commuted to permanent Siberian exile in Berëzovo, where he died.

Paul I (1754–1801): Russian emperor (1796–1801), an impulsive and inconsistent ruler of the country who implemented a series of ambiguous reforms. After an attempt to aid the serfs by limiting their servitude (corvée) to three days a week, the emperor granted the nobles new lands, which led to the enslavement of state peasants. He successfully fought the French Directory (the Italian campaign of Field Marshal Suvorov and the Mediterranean victories of Admiral Ushakov in 1798 and 1799), and then in 1801, he formed an alliance with Napoleon Bonaparte and planned a large military expedition to conquer India. He was killed in 1801 as a result of a plot that indirectly involved his oldest son, Alexander, who inherited the throne.

Peter I (Peter the Great) (1672–1725): one of the outstanding government figures of world history, the first Russian emperor, military leader, diplomat, and reformer. He was the son of Tsar Aleksey Mikhaylovich (1629–1676) from his second marriage with Natalya Kirillovna Naryshkina (1651–1694). During his Northern War (1700–1721), he annexed lands to Russia along the Neva River, in Karelia, and the Baltic region that had previously been conquered by Sweden. He carried out reforms of government administration, creating the Senate, boards, and agencies of supreme state control and political investigation. Under his rule, the country was divided into geographic administrative provinces. He used the experience of Western Europe in developing industry, trade, and culture, and conducted a policy of mercantilism (creation of manufacturers, metallurgical, mining, and other factories, shipyards, anchorages, and canals). He supervised the construction of a navy and the creation of a regular army. During his reign, the economic and political status of the nobility was strengthened. He personally led the army in the Azov campaigns of 1695–1696, the Northern War of 1700–1721, the Prut campaign of 1711, the Persian campaign of 1722–1723, and others; and commanded troops at the capture of Noteburg (1702) and at the battles of Lesnaya (1708) and Poltava (1709). He initiated the opening of many educational institutions, the creation of the Academy of Sciences, adoption of a civil alphabet, etc. One of his major achievements was the construction of a new Russian capital at Saint Petersburg. As the creator of a powerful absolutist state, Peter the Great achieved Russia's recognition as a great power by the countries of Western Europe.

Ragozin, Viktor Ivanovich (1833–1901): a noted Russian entre-preneur, inventor, honorary production engineer, and columnist. Hailing from the nobility of the Moscow Province, he completed a course at the Moscow University School of Physics and Mathematics in 1857. While working for various industrial companies in the Nizhny Novgorod Province in the 1870s, he began focusing on oil residues (residual oil), coordinating the organization of their transportation along the Volga River and, most important, studying their chemical properties. He became the first person in Russia to develop and introduce oil lubricant production technology. His method was put to practical use for the first time in 1875 in Nizhny Novgorod and then in Balakhna (Nizhny Novgorod Province), where he built the first refinery specializing in oil lubricants. In 1878, his "oleonaphthas" (as the Balakhna refinery called them) were awarded the gold medal at the Exposition Universelle de Paris. In 1879, he built a large lubricant refinery in the village of Konstantinovo, Yaroslavl Province. In addition to establishing a scientific formulation of oil lubricant production, he set up domestic and export trade. His creative legacy includes several original inventions in the refining industry, including the "universal" differential capacitor, refining machinery, and the "continuous pulverization rectifier." He extensively researched the economic conditions of the Volga Basin's industrial development and published his results in a two-volume work, *Volga* (St. Petersburg, 1880). His study *Oil and the Oil Industry* [*Neft i neftyanaya promyshlennost*] (St. Petersburg, 1884) was widely known. The St. Petersburg Institute of Technology awarded him the title of Honorary Industrial Engineer in 1888 for his outstanding work in oil technology.

Rodzyanko, Mikhail Vladimirovich (1859–1924): a major politician, one of the leaders of the Union of October 17 Party, and chairman of the State Duma (1911–1917). A hereditary nobleman, he graduated from the Page Corps in 1877. He served in the Cavalry Guards Regiment from 1877 to 1882, entering the reserves with the rank of lieutenant, and retired from the military in 1885. He was a district marshal of nobility in the Yekaterinoslav Province from 1886 to 1891. He then moved to Novgorod Province, where he served as a member of the district and provincial council. He was chairman of the Yekaterinoslav Province Council in 1901. From 1903 to 1905, he worked as the editor of *Vestnik Yekaterinoslavskovo zemstva* ["Yekaterinoslav Council Herald"]. He served as deputy from the Yekaterinoslav Province in the third and fourth State Dumas, as chairman of the land commission, and was also a member of the resettlement and local government affairs commissions. He was chairman of the office of the Octobrist parliamentary faction in 1910. Following the resignation of Duma Chairman Aleksandr Guchkov in March 1911, Rodzyanko agreed to be nominated for the post despite the protests of several Octobrist deputies. He was elected as chairman of the third State Duma and then the fourth Duma (where he remained until February 1917). In 1915, he was chairman of the committee that oversaw the distribution of government contracts. He was one of the initiators of the Special Defense Council and served as a council member. He was actively involved in logistical support for the army. He served as chairman of the All-Russian Public Assistance for Military Loans Committee in 1916. He was put in command of the State Duma's Provisional Committee on February 27, 1917 and gave orders to the Petrograd garrison on the committee's behalf. He also called on the residents of the capital to remain calm when the revolution began and conveyed this message to all Russian cities in telegrams. He took part in the Provisional Committee's negotiations with the leaders of the Petrograd Soviet Executive Committee on the makeup of the Provisional Government and was involved in talks with Tsar Nicholas II on his abdication of the throne. He remained chairman of the Provisional Committee in name for only a few more months. During the first days of the revolution he claimed the Committee had supreme authority and tried to prevent the army from being further revolutionized. Following the October Revolution, he left for the Don region in southern Russia and became an active member of the White Movement. He spent the last years of his life in Yugoslavia.

Romanovsky, Gennady Danilovich (1830–1906): a noted Russian geologist, mining engineer, actual state councilor, and professor at St. Petersburg Mining Institute. Romanovsky initiated the introduction of machine drilling in Russia, and supervised deep drilling near Moscow, St. Petersburg, and in the Crimea. He was the inventor of many original drilling tools. In 1865, was the first Russian engineer to travel to the US to learn about the oil business, publishing the results of his trip in the study, *On Mineral Oil Generally and North American Petrol in Particular [O gornom masle voobshche i Severo-Amerikanskom petrole v osobennosti]*. He is known in the scientific community for his research on oil fields of European Russia, and for his many years of labor studying the geology and paleontology of Turkestan, which lasted from 1874 to 1879. His three-volume research work, *Materials for the Geology of Turkestan Territory [Materialy dlya geologiya Turkestanskogo kraya]* won the highest prize of the Imperial Russian Geographical Society, the Konstantin Medal. His studies provided a paleontological basis for understanding the geologic structure of Turkestan and clarified a number of practical issues on the occurrence of various minerals there.

Rychkov, Pëtr Ivanovich (1712–1777): naturalist and researcher of the Volga-Urals region. He was of a merchant family background, and worked with the Orenburg Expedition for over 40 years, rising through the service from ordinary clerk to head of the Main Orenburg Salt Board, and then commander-in-chief of the Yekaterinburg Factory Board. He is known in Russia primarily as a scholar who studied the history, ethnography, and economics of the Orenburg region, as well as the author of the famous studies *Orenburg History [Istoriya Orenburgskoy gubernii]* and *Topography of the Orenburg Province [Topografiya Orenburgskoy gubernii]* (1762). He was an active member of the Free Economic Society and first corresponding member of the Russian Academy of Sciences.

Sidorov, Mikhail Konstantinovich (1823–1887): entrepreneur, Krasnoyarsk merchant of the First Guild, titular adviser, and explorer of Siberia and the Russian North. He was born to a merchant family, and although he did not complete high school, in 1845 he passed an examination for the title of "home teacher" without attending classes. In 1859, he discovered a graphite deposit in the Turukhan Territory near the Kureyka River. In 1860, his expedition discovered gold placers near the Shchugor River. In 1863, together with Major General Pavel N. Volkov and Ust-Sysolye merchant Vasily N. Latkin, he formed the Pechora

Company to develop the natural riches of the Russian North. In August 1868, he successfully drilled the first oil well in the Pechora Territory, near the Ukhta River. He resumed drilling in September 1872, and obtained a small natural flow of oil. He was the only Russian industrialist to exhibit at four World's Fairs: in London (1862), Paris (1867), Vienna (1873), and Philadelphia (1876). He wrote a series of books on the problems of developing the Russian North and Siberia: *Plan for the Settlement of the North Through Industry and Trade and the Development of the Foreign Trade of Siberia* [*Proyekt o zaselenii Severa putëm promyshlennosti i torgovli i razvitii vneshney torgovli Sibiri*] (1864), *The Russian North* [*Sever Rossii*] (1870), *The Larch* [*Listvennitsa*] (1871), *Pictures from the Actions of Peter the Great in the North* [*Kartiny iz deyaniy Petra Velikogo na Severe*] (1872), *The Russian North: On Its Mineral Riches and the Obstacles to Their Development* [*Sever Rossii, o gornykh yego bogatstvakh i prepyatstviyakh k ikh razrabotke*] (1881), *On Oil in the Russian North* [*O nefti na severe Rossii*] (1882), *Studies for Familiarization with the Russian North* [*Trudy dlya oznakomleniya s severom Rossii*] (1882), *On the Richness of the Northern Margins of Siberia and Its Nomadic Peoples* [*O bogatstve severnykh okrain Sibiri i narodov tam kochuyushchikh*] (1882), etc. He participated actively in the Society for the Assistance of Russian Trade Navigation, which awarded him its Grand Gold Medal for many years of indefatigable labor and sacrifices in the exploration of the Siberian sea route and for experiments in marine shipbuilding on the Yenisey, and also for outfitting the schooner *Morning Dawn* for an expedition that came from the Yenisey via the Arctic Ocean with samples of Siberian produce. He was a contending member of the Imperial Russian Technical Society, a permanent member of the Imperial Society of Lovers of Nature, Anthropology, and Ethnography, an honorary member of the Society for the Assistance of Russian Industry, an honorary president of the African Institute in Paris, an honorary member of the Royal Geographical Society in Vienna, and a member of the Bremen Polar Geographic Society. His productive social activities earned him high Russian honors; in 1870 he was "all-mercifully bestowed" the Order of Saint Stanislav, Second Degree, and in 1882, the Order of Saint Vladimir, Fourth Degree. The highest mountain on Spitzbergen Island, in Norway, is named in his honor.

Tenishev, Prince Vyacheslav Nikolayevich (1843–1903): a noted Russian entrepreneur, engineer, ethnographer, sociologist, and philanthropist. He graduated from the Polytechnic Institute in Karlsruhe in 1864 before actively working in business from the 1870s to the 1890s. He was one of the founders of the Bryansk Rail, Iron, and Mechanical Plant (1873) and a member of the St. Petersburg International Banking Council. He owned an electromechanical plant and an electrical appliance sales office in St. Petersburg. He was a member of the directorate of the St. Petersburg Conservatory and chairman of the St. Petersburg branch of the Russian Music Society from 1883 to 1887. He devoted a great deal of time to scientific work. In 1898, he set up the Ethnographic Office, a research center that collected and processed information for his planned work, *The Life of Great Russian Peasant Cultivators* [*Byt velikorusskikh krestyan-zemlepashtsev*]. He developed the "Ethnographic Information Program" about peasants and urban residents of the educated class with the aim of collecting material on actions and behavior. The Tenishev Secondary School was built using his funds and embodied his educational ideas. He actively financed his wife's charitable activities. In 1900, he served as general commissar of the Russian division at the Exposition Universelle de Paris. The tsar granted him the title of "Gentleman in Waiting to the Court of His Imperial Majesty," and the French government awarded him the Order of the Legion of Honor for his enormous personal contribution to organizing and overseeing the work of the Russian exhibition.

Vronchenko, Count Fëdor Pavlovich (1780–1854): noted public figure, financier, and Russian Minister of Finance (1845–1851). He graduated from the School of Law at Moscow University (1801). In November 1810, he became head of the first division of the Chancellery of the Russian Ministry of Finance. In 1819, he became a member of the fifth division of the Chancellery of the Ministry of Finance, then temporary administrator of the third division (lending matters) and member of the Learned Committee of the Ministry of Finance. In 1824, he became director of the Special Chancellery of the Ministry of Finance, and a member of the Secret Committee on Foreign Loans (1828) and the Committee on the Reduction of Bank Interest (1829). He became deputy minister of finance and commander-in-chief of the Corps of Mining Engineers in 1840; in 1841, he was a member of the Committee on Credit Establishment Matters and the Finance Committee. In May 1844, he became administrator of the Ministry of Finance, and from March 1845, minister of finance. He implemented Count Kankrin's monetary reform of 1839–1843 and focused his attention on the development of the manufacturing industry. In 1847, he replaced the tax-farming system in several industries with an excise-farming commission system. In 1850, a new customs rate structure that reduced tariff rates was introduced at his initiative.

Witte, Count Sergey Yulyevich (1849–1915): a distinguished Russian statesman, reformer, minister of finance, chairman of the Council of Ministers, and an actual privy councilor. He graduated from the Novorossiysk University School of Physics and Mathematics in Odessa before working at various positions in the railroad transportation system. During the Russo-Turkish War of 1877–1878, he successfully organized the transportation of troops to the scene of military operations, after which he was appointed director of the maintenance division of the Southwestern Railroad in St. Petersburg. His 1883 book, *Principles of Rail Freight Tariffs* [*Printsipy zheleznodorozhnykh tarifov po perevozke gruzov*], brought him fame among economists and the business community. In 1888, he was appointed director of the Railroad Affairs Department under the Ministry of Finance. Witte was appointed minister of railroads in February 1892, and became minister of finance six months later. With the goals of making Russia an advanced industrial nation, catching up with developed European nations, and gaining a foothold in Eastern markets, he developed conceptual and tactical approaches to the problem of establishing market relations and creating an independent national economy. In an effort to accelerate the country's industrialization and accumulate domestic resources, he proposed actively attracting foreign capital and rationalized that industry needed customs protection from competitors and exports needed encouragement. During his time as minister of finance, Russia attracted more than 3 billion rubles in foreign capital. He linked the modernization of the country's economy to the rapid development of transportation infrastructure. The Trans-Siberian Railway was built at his initiative (1891–1901), and passengers could see the inscription "Forward to the Pacific Ocean" on the rocks that had been cut for the railroad. New towns began to appear (such as Novo-Nikolayevsk, now Novosibirsk) as the construction of this railroad progressed. Western business circles recognized him as one of the creators of the Russian trade and industrial miracle. In August 1903, he was appointed chairman of the Council of Ministers of the Russian Empire. In this role, he continued to implement programs to strengthen Russia's position in the Asian-Pacific region while seeking to counter Japan's aggressive policy in the Far East and pursue a policy of rapprochement with China and Korea. Seeking a quick end to the war with Japan in late May 1905, the Russian tsar sent Witte as ambassador extraordinary to conduct the difficult peace negotiations. On August 23, 1905, he signed the Portsmouth Peace Treaty with Japan. He managed to extract everything he could from the lost war (with the active participation of US President Theodore Roosevelt as a mediator) and was granted the title of count for his efforts. On April 14, 1906, he tendered his resignation, which was accepted by a special writ by the tsar, who awarded Witte the Order of Aleksandr Nevsky with diamonds. He served as chairman of the State Council's Finance Committee until his death, and his work was frequently published in the press. In 1912, he completed his memoir *Recollections* [*Vspominaniya*], which to this day remains a valuable eyewitness account of the turbulent events of the early 20th century.

CHAPTER TWO: Oil in the Land of the Soviets

Aliyev, Heydar Aliyevich (1923–2003): noted Soviet and Azerbaijani politician and public figure. Twice a hero of Socialist Labor (1973, 1983), he was born in 1923 in Nakhchivan City. In 1957, he graduated from the Baku State University Department of History. In 1944, he began working in the state security agencies of Azerbaijan. From 1964 to 1967, he was deputy chairman of the Committee for State Security of Azerbaijan. In 1967, he became chairman of the republic's Committee for State Security [*KGB*]. Two years later, he was elected first secretary of the Central Committee of the Azerbaijan Communist Party. From 1974 to 1979, he served as deputy chairman of the Union Council of the USSR Supreme Soviet. From 1982 to 1987, he was first deputy chairman of the USSR Council of Ministers. From 1987 to 1988, he was government advisor in the USSR Council of Ministers. In 1991, he was elected chairman of Nakhchivan Autonomous Republic Parliament and deputy chairman of the Azerbaijan Parliament. From 1992 to 1993, he headed the New Azerbaijan Party. In 1993, he served as chairman of the Supreme Soviet of the Republic of Azerbaijan, simultaneously serving as acting president of the Republic of Azerbaijan. On October 3, 1993, he became president of the Republic of Azerbaijan. On October 11, 1998, he was re-elected president. He died in the Cleveland Clinic in Ohio on December 12, 2003. He is buried in Baku.

Andropov, Yury Vladimirovich (1914–1984): noted Soviet politician and public figure, and a Hero of Socialist Labor (1974). He was born in 1914 in Stavropol Territory to a white-collar family. He entered the work force in 1930 as a blue-collar worker. In 1936, he graduated from a water transportation technical school and worked as secretary of the Communist Youth League [*Komsomol*] organization of the Volodarsky Shipyard in Rybinsk. In 1937, he was elected secretary, and in 1938, first secretary of the Yaroslavl Regional Committee of the *Komsomol*. In 1940, he was elected first secretary of the Central Committee of the Karelian *Komsomol*. In 1944, he switched to Party work, first serving as second secretary of the Petrozavodsk City Committee, and then, in 1947, as second secretary of the Central Committee of the Karelian Communist Party. In 1951, he transferred to work on the staff of the CPSU Central Committee. From 1953 to 1957, he served as USSR ambassador extraordinary and plenipotentiary to Hungary. In 1957, he became a department head in the CPSU Central Committee. From November 1962 to July 1967, he was secretary of the CPSU Central Committee. In May 1967, he became chairman of the Committee for State Security in the USSR Council of Ministers. From 1982 to 1984, he was general secretary of the CPSU Central Committee. From 1983 to 1984, he was chairman of the Presidium of the USSR Supreme Soviet.

Baybakov, Nikolay Konstantinovich (1911–2008): noted Soviet public figure, doctor of technical sciences (1966), and Hero of Socialist Labor (1981). He was born in the village of Sabunchu in Baku Province to a worker's family. In 1932, he graduated from the Azerbaijan Polytechnical Institute.[1] That same year, he took a job at an oil field in Baku. From 1935 to 1937, he served in the Red Army. In 1937, he became chief engineer and then head of the *Leninneft* trust and head of the *Vostokneftedobycha* oil production association. In 1939, he was appointed head of the Main Administration of the Oil Production Industry of the East in the USSR People's Commissariat of the Oil Industry. In 1940, he became USSR deputy people's commissar, and on November 30, 1944, the USSR people's commissar of the oil industry, and subsequently, minister of the oil industry. In 1955, he became chairman of *Gosplan*. From 1958 to 1963, he was Chairman of the Krasnodar and then the North Caucasus Regional Economic Council. From 1963 to 1964, he served as Chairman (at the rank of minister) of the *Gosplan* state committees for chemistry (March–May 1963), the petrochemical industry (May 1963–January 1964), and the oil production industry (January 1964–October 1965). In October 1965, he became deputy chairman of the USSR Council of Ministers. In July 1978, he became chairman of *Gosplan*. In October 1985, he was appointed government advisor in the USSR Council of Ministers. Baybakov retired in 1988.

Bogdanov, Pëtr Alekseyevich (1892–1939): noted Soviet public figure. Born to a merchant family, Bogdanov graduated from Moscow Higher Technical School[2] in 1909. He participated in the revolutionary events of 1917 and in early 1918, he became the *VSNKh's* authorized representative for nationalization of the chemical industry. From 1919 to 1921, he was chairman of the Council of the Military Industry in the Extraordinary Committee to Supply the Red Army. From 1925 to 1929, he worked in the US as director of the Soviet-American Amtorg Trading Corporation. During Stalin's mass repressions of 1937, he was expelled from the Party, arrested, and sentenced to death. He was rehabilitated in 1988.

Brezhnev, Leonid Ilyich (1906–1982): noted Soviet politician and public figure. He was born in 1906 in Yekaterinoslav Province, Ukraine, to a worker's family. In 1927, he graduated from the Kursk Land Management and Reclamation Technical School. In 1927, he became head of the land department, and then deputy chairman of the Bisert Regional Council (Sverdlovsk District, the Ural region). In 1931, he became deputy head of regional administration in Sverdlovsk. In 1935, he graduated from the Dnipropetrovsk Metallurgical Institute, and then served in the Red Army. In 1936, he served as director of a metallurgical technical school. In May 1937, he was promoted to deputy chairman of the Dniprodzerzhynsk City

Executive Committee. A year later, he headed the Soviet trade department of the Dnipropetrovsk Regional Committee of the Ukrainian CP(b). In February 1939, he was confirmed as secretary of the Dnipropetrovsk Regional Committee of the Party. At the beginning of World War II, he was involved in mobilizing the population into the Red Army and evacuating industry. In mid-1941, he quit his job to join field forces as deputy head of the Political Administration on the southern front, and was given the rank of brigade commissar. In 1943, he headed the Political Department of the 18th Army. In 1944, he was promoted to major general. The following year, just several days after the end of the war, he was entrusted with the post of head of Political Administration of the Fourth Ukrainian Front and participated in the Victory parade in Moscow. In August 1946, he was elected first secretary of the Zaporizhia Regional Committee of the Ukrainian CP(b); in November 1947, first secretary of the Dnipropetrovsk Regional Committee; and in July 1950, first secretary of the Central Committee of the Moldovan CP(b). In February 1954, he became second secretary, and in August 1955, first secretary of the Kazakhstan Communist Party Central Committee. In February 1956, he again became secretary of the Central Committee and a candidate member of the Presidium of the CPSU Central Committee. From 1960 to 1964, he served as chairman of the Presidium of the USSR Supreme Soviet. In 1963, he was again secretary of the CPSU Central Committee. On October 14, 1964, he became first secretary of the CPSU Central Committee, then general secretary of the CPSU Central Committee. Starting in 1977, he was also chairman of the Presidium of the Supreme Soviet. He died November 10, 1982, having lived almost to the age of 76; during his life, he was named Hero of Socialist Labor, Hero of the Soviet Union (four times), and marshal of the Soviet Union. He was awarded the Lenin Prize, the Order of Lenin (eight times), and many other Soviet and foreign honors.

Chernenko, Konstantin (1911–1985): Soviet politician and public figure, and Hero of Socialist Labor (1976). He was born in the village of Bolshaya Tes, Krasnodar Territory, to a peasant family. He graduated from the Higher School for Party Organizers of the AUCP(b) Central Committee (1945) and from the Chisinau (Kishinëv) Pedagogical Institute (1953). In 1929, he began working in the *Komsomol*, government and the Party. From 1941 to 1943, he was secretary of the Krasnodar Territorial Committee, and from 1945 to 1948, the Secretary of the Penza Regional Committee of the Party. In 1948, he became head of the agitation and propaganda department of the Moldovan Communist Party Central Committee. From 1956 to 1960, he was section head of the department of agitation and propaganda of the CPSU Central Committee. From 1960 to 1965, he was head of the secretariat of the Presidium of the USSR Supreme Soviet; and from 1965 to 1976, head of the general department of the CPSU Central Committee. On February 13, 1984, he became general secretary of the CPSU Central Committee, and on April 11, 1984, chairman of the Presidium of the USSR Supreme Soviet.

Chicherin, Georgy Vasilyevich (1872–1936): noted Soviet diplomat. Born to a family of hereditary nobility, he graduated from the St. Petersburg University Department of History and Philology in 1896. In 1904, he joined the Social Democratic movement. From 1904 to 1917, he lived abroad. In August 1917, he was arrested in Great Britain as secretary of the Delegate Committee for Return of Political Exiles to Russia. He was freed in January 1918, at the insistence of the Soviet Russian government, and returned to Petrograd, where he was appointed deputy people's commissar of foreign affairs. In March 1918, he participated in the signing of the Treaty of Brest-Litovsk with Germany. On May 30, 1918, he became People's Commissar of Foreign Affairs. In 1921, he participated in the signing of friendship treaties with Persia, Afghanistan, and Turkey, who were Soviet Russia's first diplomatic partners on equal terms. He led the Soviet delegations to the international conferences in Genoa and Lausanne. From 1925 to 1930, he was a member of the AUCP(b) Central Committee.

Dzerzhinsky, Feliks (1877–1926): noted Soviet public figure and founder of the All-Russian Extraordinary Commission (*VChK*)–Joint State Political Directorate (*OGPU*), the Soviet secret political police. Born into the family of a minor Polish nobleman, he joined the Social Democrats in high school and on Gediminas' Hill in Vilnius he swore to devote his life to the struggle against evil and injustice. He left high school in his senior year to become a professional revolutionary. In 1895, he became a member of the organization "Social Democracy of the Kingdom of Poland and Lithuania," and became a part of its organizational center in 1900. On his initiative, the organization united in 1906 with the Russian Social Democrats while preserving its organizational independence. During the 1905 Russian Revolution, he organized labor strikes and led agitation efforts in the military. From 1907 to 1912, he was a member of the RSDLP Central Committee. Arrested numerous times, he spent a total of 11 years in prison and at hard labor, contracting tuberculosis in the process. He was exiled three times. Freed by the February Revolution of 1917, he joined the Moscow committee of the RSDLP(b). At the 6th Party Congress, he came out in favor of an armed uprising and was elected to the Central Committee, becoming a leader of organizational and military efforts. He participated actively in the 1917 October Revolution, assumed control of the postal and telegraph office, and provided communications to the Smolny Institute. At his initiative, a five-member commission was organized under the Military Revolutionary Committee to Combat Counterrevolution. That commission later became the All-Russian Extraordinary Commission (*VChK*), which was created on December 7 (20), 1917 by the Council of People's Commissars to combat counterrevolution and sabotage. Dzerzhinsky led the *VChK* until his death. Starting in February 1918, the *VChK* became a special government entity that assumed the functions of surveillance, arrest, investigation, the office of the public prosecutor, and the court, as well as that of penal institution, thus carrying out the "Red Terror." While remaining chairman of the *VChK*, and then the Joint State Political Directorate (*OGPU*), from 1919 to 1923 he headed the People's Commissariat for Internal Affairs (*NKVD*), and from 1921 to 1924 he headed the People's Commissariat of Railroads. From 1924 to 1926, he combined his activity in the *OGPU* with leadership of the All-Union Council of the National Economy (*VSNKh*), the central state industrial agency. It was he who signed the Sakhalin oil concession allowing the Japanese to develop oil fields on northern Sakhalin Island. He participated in numerous Soviet committees and societies, was a member of the Presidium of the Society for Studies of Interplanetary Travel, chairman of *VTsIK* committees to improve the life of children and improve the life of workers, and was one of the founders of the Society of Political Convicts and Exiles, and also the sports club *Dinamo*. He died suddenly on July 20, 1926 after delivering a speech at a joint Plenum of the RCP(b) Central Committee and the RCP(b) Central Control Commission. During the Great Terror, all his relatives were victims of Stalinist repression.

Gorbachëv, Mikhail Sergeyevich (b. 1931): noted Soviet politician and public figure, Nobel Peace Prize laureate. He was born in 1931 in the village of Privolnoye, Krasnogvardeyskoye District, Stavropol Territory. In 1955, he graduated from the Lomonosov Moscow State University School of Law. From 1955 to 1962, he worked as department head of the Stavropol City Committee of the *Komsomol*, as first secretary of the Stavropol City Committee of the *Komsomol*, and then as second secretary and first secretary of the Territorial Committee of the *Komsomol*. In December 1962, he became department head for organizational and Party work of the Stavropol Rural Territorial Committee of the CPSU. In September 1966, he became first secretary of the Stavropol City Committee of the Party; in August 1968, he was elected second secretary; and in April 1970, first secretary of the Stavropol Territorial Committee of the CPSU. In November 1978, he went to Moscow and was confirmed as Secretary of the CPSU Central Committee on matters of the food and agriculture industry. In March 1985, he was elected general secretary of the CPSU Central Committee. From March 1990 to December 1991, he was president of the Union of Soviet Socialist Republics. On December 25, 1991, he resigned as president of the USSR. He retired in 1992 and is now president of the Gorbachëv Foundation.

Gubkin, Ivan Mikhaylovich (1871–1939): noted Soviet petroleum geologist, academician of the USSR Academy of Sciences, and author of the groundbreaking work *The Science of Oil* [*Ucheniye o nefti*]. He graduated from the St. Petersburg Pedagogical Institute in 1886. In 1910, he graduated from the St. Petersburg Mining Institute. From 1910 to 1917, he carried out a geological study of the oil-bearing areas of the North Caucasus. He spent 1917 and 1918 on a scientific mission in the US. In 1918, he became deputy chairman of the Main Petroleum Committee and head of the Main Shale Committee. In 1920, he was elected professor of the Moscow Mining Academy. In 1922, he was rector of the Moscow Mining Academy. In 1930, he was director of the Moscow Institute of Oil.[3] In 1930, he was appointed chairman of the USSR Council for the Study of Productive Forces. In 1936, he was elected vice president of the USSR Academy of Sciences.

Kaganovich, Lazar Moiseyevich (1893–1991): noted Soviet politician and public figure, loyal comrade-in-arms of Joseph Stalin, and responsible for mass repressions in the country. He was a participant in the Civil War, and from 1922 to 1925, head of the Organization and Assignment Department of the RCP(b) Central Committee. From 1925 to 1930, he was general secretary of the Central Committee of the Ukrainian Communist Party. From 1930 to 1935, he was first secretary of the Moscow City Committee of the RCP(b). From 1935 to 1944, he was people's commissar for railroads, and from 1939 to 1940, he was also USSR People's Commissar of the Oil Industry. In 1944, he became deputy chairman of the USSR Council of People's Commissars. From 1922 to 1957, a member of the CPSU Central Committee. In June 1957, a Plenum of the CPSU Central Committee decided to remove him from his leading post in the government for "participation in an antiparty group," expelled him from the Party, and sent him to do managerial work in the provinces. His *Memoirs of a Working Class Communist and Bolshevik, a Trade Union and Soviet Government Worker* [*Pamyatnyye zapiski rabochego, kommunista-bolshevika, profsoyuznogo i sovetskogo gosudarstvennogo rabotnika*] was published in Moscow in 1996.

Khrushchëv, Nikita Sergeyevich (1894–1971): noted Soviet politician and public figure, a Hero of Socialist Labor (1954, 1957, and 1961) and Hero of the Soviet Union (1964). He was born in 1894 in the village of Kalinovka, the Kursk Province. He participated in the Civil War, and afterwards was involved in managerial and Party work. In 1929, Khrushchëv enrolled in the Industrial Academy in Moscow, where he was elected secretary of the Party committee. Starting in January 1931, he served as secretary of the Bauman and then the Krasnaya Presnya regional committees of the Party, and from 1932 to 1934, he was second secretary and then first secretary of the Moscow City Committee and second secretary of the local committee of the AUCP(b). In 1938, he became first secretary of the Central Committee of the Ukrainian CP(b) and a candidate member of the Politburo, becoming, a year later, a member of the Politburo of the AUCP(b) Central Committee. During World War II, he was a member of the military councils of the Southwestern Direction and the Southwestern, Stalingrad, Southern, Voronezh, and First Ukrainian fronts. From 1944 through 1947 he worked as chairman of the Council of Ministers of the Ukrainian SSR, and then was reelected first secretary of the Central Committee of the Ukrainian CP(b). In December 1949, he became first secretary of the Moscow Regional Committee and again the secretary of the AUCP(b) Central Committee. In September 1953, he was elected first secretary of the CPSU Central Committee. In 1956, at the 20th CPSU Congress, he delivered a speech in which he denounced Joseph Stalin's cult of personality. Starting in 1958, he was chairman of the USSR Council of Ministers. He continued to hold leadership posts until October 14, 1964, and retired from public life when the October Plenum of the CPSU Central Committee relieved him of Party and government posts "for health reasons." He died September 11, 1971, and is buried in Novodevichy Cemetery in Moscow.

Kirov (Kostrikov), Sergey Mironovich (1886–1934): noted Soviet politician and public figure. He participated in revolutionary actions from 1905 to 1907 in Siberia. During World War I, he headed an underground communist organization in Vladikavkaz. After the February Revolution of 1917, he was a member of the Vladikavkaz Soviet of Workers' and Soldiers' Deputies. Kirov participated in the October Revolution in Petrograd in 1917, and was delegate to the second All-Russian Congress of Soviets. In 1919, he became chairman of the Military Revolutionary Committee of the Astrakhan Province and a member of the Revolutionary War Council of the 11th Army, the southern group of troops of the Red Army. In May 1920, he became authorized representative of the RSFSR to the Democratic Republic of Georgia, and in October 1920, he headed the Soviet delegation at the negotiations to reach a peace treaty with Poland. In July 1921, he became secretary of the Communist Party Central Committee in Soviet Azerbaijan and actively directed work to restore the oil fields on the Absheron Peninsula. In 1926, he became first secretary of the Leningrad Regional Committee of the Party. In 1930, he was elected member of the Politburo of the RCP(b) Central Committee. At the 17th Party Congress in February 1934, he was elected secretary of the RCP(b) Central Committee. He was killed on December 1, 1934, in the building of the Leningrad Regional Committee of the Party. This marked the beginning of the "Great Terror" in the USSR, involving mass repression of all strata of Soviet society.

Kosior, Iosif (1893–1937): Soviet public figure. Born to a worker's family, Kosior participated actively in revolutionary actions in 1917 and in the Civil War from 1918 to 1920. From March 1920 to April 1922, he was commander of the Caucasus Army of Labor, and simultaneously head of *Grozneft* Production Association. In 1928, he became deputy chairman of the *VSNKh*. From 1919 to 1936, he was a member of the RCP(b) Central Committee. During Stalin's mass repressions in 1936, he was expelled from the Party, arrested, and sentenced to death. He was rehabilitated in 1988.

Kosygin, Aleksey Nikolayevich (1904–1980): noted Soviet public figure and Hero of Socialist Labor (1964, 1974). He graduated from the Leningrad Textile Institute in 1932. From 1940 to 1953, he was deputy chairman of the USSR Council of People's Commissars, and from 1943 to 1946, he was also chairman of the RSFSR Council of People's Commissars. In June 1941, he became deputy chairman of the Evacuation Council; from January to July 1942, he was authorized representative of the Leningrad State Committee for Defense. In 1948, he served as USSR minister of finance; from 1949 to 1953, as minister of light industry. From 1953 to 1954, he was minister of consumer goods. From 1959 to 1960, he was chairman of *Gosplan*. In 1964, he became chairman of the USSR Council of Ministers.

Krasin, Leonid Borisovich (1870–1926): noted Soviet politician and public figure and diplomat. Krasin came from a family of minor nobleman and his father was a civil servant on the Tyumen district council. After graduating from a technical high school, he entered the St. Petersburg State Institute of Technology. While a student, he became interested in Marxism and joined the Social Democrats. In 1891, he was expelled from the institute, and arrested and imprisoned the next year. He was then called up for military duty. He was arrested a second time in 1895 and sentenced to exile in East Siberia. After completing his term of exile, he finished Kharkiv Polytechnic Institute in 1900. He worked as an engineer in the oil fields of the Absheron Peninsula. In 1904, Krasin wrote the work *Power Consumption for Petroleum Bailing Using Electric Motorized Bailers* [*K voprosu o raskhode energii na tartaniye nefti zhelonkami pri rabote eletromotorami*], published independently in Baku. In 1905, he went to St. Petersburg and worked as an engineer at *Elektricheskoye obshchestvo 1886 g.* ["1886 Electric Company"], and edited the Party newspaper *Novaya zhizn* ["New Life"]. From 1905 to 1907, he participated actively in revolutionary actions in St. Petersburg and Moscow. From 1908 to 1912, he lived abroad, returning in 1912 to work as director of the Russian department of the German company Siemens-Schuckert, while simultaneously engaging in active underground Party work. From December 1917 to March 1918, he was a member of the Soviet delegation at the negotiations with Germany in Brest-Litovsk. In August 1918, in Berlin, he signed a follow-up agreement to the Treaty of Brest-Litovsk. He was then appointed member of the Presidium of the *VSNKh*, and in November 1918, he became chairman of the Extraordinary Committee to Supply the Red Army and the people's commissar for trade and industry. From March 1919 to March 1920, he was people's commissar for railroads. From 1922 to 1923, he was a member of the Soviet delegations at the international conferences in Genoa and The Hague. In 1924, he was authorized representative of the USSR in France. In 1925, he was authorized representative of the USSR in Great Britain.

Lenin (Ulyanov), Vladimir Ilyich (1870–1924): noted Soviet politician and public figure, organizer of the Bolshevik Party, and founder of the USSR. Born to a noble family, he became interested in Marxism in his youth. In 1891, he passed the examinations of the St. Petersburg University School of Law as an independent study student. He briefly practiced law in Samara, then became a professional revolutionary. In 1895, he united a series of St. Petersburg Marxist and workers' groups into a single organization, the League of Struggle for the Emancipation of the Working Class. In December of 1895, he was arrested and sentenced to exile to the Yenisey Province in Siberia. There he wrote a series of works, including the book *The Development of Capitalism in Russia* [*Razvitiye kapitalizma v Rossii*]. He left Russia on a forged passport, and from July 1900 through April 1917 lived as an émigré in Germany, Great Britain, France, and Switzerland. In 1903, at a conference of Russian Social Democrats in London, Ulyanov, who had assumed the pseudonym Lenin in 1901 after his exile, laid the foundation for creation of the Bolshevik Party and elaborated its first platform and rules. When World War I broke out, he proposed the Party slogan "Make the imperialist war a civil war." With the cooperation of the German authorities, who arranged his free passage through German territory in a sealed railroad car, he returned from emigration with a group of like-minded people through the Baltic states and Finland, arriving in Petrograd in April 1917. At the First All-Russian Congress of Soviets (June 1917), he gave speeches about the war and the relationship to the bourgeois Provisional Government. In July 1917, threatened with arrest, he was forced underground and hid until mid-August 1917 in a shelter of branches near the Razliv railway station close to Petrograd, and then traveled to Finland at the beginning of October. He continued to direct the Bolshevik Party's preparations for an armed coup d'état. At the Second All-Russian Congress of Soviets, which opened on October 25 (November 7), 1917 in Petrograd, he declared the transfer of all power in the capital and the provinces to the Soviets, and gave speeches on peace and land. The Congress accepted Lenin's decrees on peace and land, and formed a workers' and peasants' government: the Council of People's Commissars, headed by Vladimir I. Lenin. Having become head of the government, he directed essentially all aspects of life in Soviet Russia and initiated all major government and Party decisions and measures. Under his leadership, the first constitution of the Russian Socialist Federative Soviet Republic was developed, and in 1922 the Union of Soviet Socialist Republics was created. In May 1922 he fell seriously ill, and among his closest comrades-in-arms a fierce struggle began for "Lenin's legacy," which was decisively won by Joseph Stalin (Iosif Dzhugashvili). In 1924, a sarcophagus with the embalmed body of Lenin was set up in a mausoleum built on Red Square in Moscow.

Lomov (Oppokov), Georgy Ippolitovich (1888–1938): noted Soviet public figure. Born to a merchant family, Oppokov graduated from the St. Petersburg University School of Law in 1913. In his youth, he became interested in Marxism, and participated actively in revolutionary actions from 1905 to 1907 and in the October Revolution of 1917. He was people's commissar for justice in the first Council of People's Commissars. In January 1918, he became deputy chairman of the *VSNKh*. From 1921 to 1923, he was chairman of the Siberian Industrial Office of the *VSNKh*. From 1923 to 1926, he worked as chairman of the USSR *Neftesindikat*. From 1926 to 1929, he was chairman of the *Donugol* ["Don Coal"] Production Association. From 1931 to 1934, he was deputy chairman of *Gosplan*. From 1927 to 1934, he was member of the RCP(b) Central Committee. During Stalin's mass repressions in 1937, he was expelled from the Party, arrested, and sentenced to death. He was rehabilitated in 1988.

Pervukhin, Mikhail Georgiyevich (1904–1978): Soviet public figure, lieutenant general (1944), and Hero of Socialist Labor (1949). In 1938, he became deputy, then first deputy USSR people's commissar of heavy industry. In 1939, he became USSR people's commissar of power plants and the electrical industry. From 1940 to 1944 and again from 1950 to 1955, he was deputy chairman of the USSR Council of Ministers. From 1942 to 1950, he was USSR minister of the chemical industry. From 1952 to 1957, he was a member of the Presidium of the CPSU Central Committee, and from 1957 to 1961, a candidate member of the Presidium of the CPSU Central Committee. In 1953, he became USSR minister of power plants and the electrical industry. From 1955 to 1957, he served as first deputy chairman of the USSR Council of Ministers. From 1957 to 1958, he was both USSR minister of medium machine building and chairman of the USSR Council of Ministers Government Committee for

Foreign Economic Relations. From 1958 to 1963, he served as USSR ambassador to the GDR. Starting in 1963, he worked in leading posts in the USSR Council of National Economy and in *Gosplan.*

Radek (Sobelson), Karl Bernhardovich (1885–1939): Soviet Party figure and journalist. He graduated from the Jagiellonian University in Krakow, Poland, with a major in history, and then studied at Humboldt University of Berlin and the University of Leipzig. In 1902, he joined the Social Democrats, and participated actively in revolutionary actions in Poland from 1905 to 1907. From 1903 to 1917, he worked at a series of Polish, German, and Swiss newspapers. After October 1917, he went to Soviet Russia and was appointed head of the European department in the People's Commissariat of Foreign Affairs. In November 1918, he traveled illegally to Germany to organize revolutionary actions, was arrested, and freed in December 1919. After returning to Soviet Russia, he held a series of leadership posts in Soviet periodicals. In 1927, he was expelled from the Party and sentenced to three years of exile for "anti-Soviet activity." In 1936, he was arrested again and sentenced to 10 years of incarceration, but was killed in prison. He was rehabilitated in 1988.

Rykov, Aleksey Ivanovich (1881–1938): noted Soviet public figure and chairman of the USSR Council of People's Commissars (1924–1930). Born to a peasant family, Rykov studied at Kazan University after graduating from high school. He became interested in Marxism, and was arrested and exiled in 1901. He participated actively in revolutionary actions from 1905 to 1907 and in the October Revolution of 1917. He was people's commissar of internal affairs in the first Council of People's Commissars. From 1918 to 1921 and from 1923 to 1924, he was chairman of the *VSNKh.* In 1921, he became simultaneously deputy chairman of the Council of People's Commissars and of the Council of Labor and Defense. In the late 1920s, he spoke out openly against the use of extraordinary measures to carry out collectivization and industrialization. From 1924 to 1930, he was the chairman of the Council of People's Commissars of the USSR. From 1931 to 1936, he was people's commissar for post and telegraph. During Stalin's mass repressions of 1936, he was expelled from the Party, arrested, and sentenced to death. He was rehabilitated in 1988.

Sedin, Ivan Korneyevich (1906–1972): noted Soviet public figure, Hero of Socialist Labor, (1944), and candidate of technical sciences. Born in 1906 to a Cossack family in the Kuban region, he graduated from Maykop Pedagogical School in 1928. From 1928 to 1931, he worked as principal of an elementary school. In 1937, he graduated from the Dmitry Mendeleyev Moscow Chemical Engineering Institute[4] with a major in production engineering. From 1937 to 1938, he worked in leading posts in industry. From March 1928 to September 1939, he performed Party electoral work in the Tambov and Ivanovo regions. In October 1939, he became first deputy USSR people's commissar of the oil industry. From July 1940 to November 1944, he served as USSR people's commissar of the oil industry. In 1944, he was named Hero of Socialist Labor. From May 1945 to December 1948, he was USSR people's commissar of the textile industry. After 1949, he worked in various posts in industry. From 1959 to 1964, he was deputy director of the Institute of Petrochemical Synthesis of the USSR Academy of Sciences. In 1964, he became director of the Scientific Research Institute for Paint and Varnish Products.

Stalin, Joseph Vissarionovich (Iosif Vissarionovich Dzhugashvili) (1879–1953): noted Soviet politician and public figure, general secretary of the Communist Party of the USSR (1922–1953), head of the Soviet government (1940–1953), and Generalissimo (1945). Under his many years of leadership, the country underwent industrialization and collectivization, experienced the Great Terror and the purges of the 1940s and 1950s, the difficult ordeal of World War II, and the joy of victory over the Nazis in May 1945. He was born in the town of Gori, Georgia, to the family of a poor cobbler. After finishing a church school, he entered a seminary, from which he was expelled in 1899. He then decided to become a professional revolutionary, organized workers' demonstrations and strikes, and disseminated forbidden literature. After the Russian Social Democrats split into Bolshevik and Menshevik factions in 1903, he joined the former, since their political platform more closely met his expectations. In the period between April 1902 and March 1913, he was arrested, imprisoned, or exiled to Siberia seven times, but managed to escape every time. Political obsession and a great capacity for work helped him advance through the Party hierarchy. In 1913, he published his article about Marxism under the pseudonym Stalin. He edited the Party newspaper *Pravda* for some period. From July 1913 to March 1917 he was in long-term exile in Siberia. On March 25, 1917, Stalin returned from exile to Petrograd and resumed his editorial activity. In October 1917, he assumed the post of people's commissar for ethnic affairs in the Council of People's Commissars, the first Bolshevik government. In 1922 he was appointed general secretary of the RCP(b) Central Committee. During this period, this particularly technical post was not especially interesting to the brilliant Party figures such as Leon Trotsky, Lev Kamenev, and Nikolay Bukharin, but it was precisely this position that allowed Stalin to compile a dossier on every influential Party member and made it easy for him to put his people in key posts. Moreover, it was precisely this access to compromising information about leading Party functionaries that played an essential role in his fierce political struggle within the Party for its top post. After Vladimir Lenin died in 1924, Stalin assumed the duties of ideologist for building socialism in one country: the USSR. In 1928, he declared the beginning of collectivization in the government and the First Five-Year Plan for developing the country. In 1934, the USSR entered the period of the Great Terror and of the show trials. Stalin gradually did away with all prominent figures in the communist movement, old Bolsheviks, "heroes of the October Revolution," and the top military leadership. Once the upper echelons of state and Party power had been "renovated," mass repression began against the rank-and-file citizens of the country, affecting all strata of Soviet society. In May 1941, Stalin became chairman of the Council of People's Commissars (the Soviet government), concentrating all political and state power in his own hands. His role in World War II (1941–1945) is viewed as quite mixed. On the one hand, he tried to put off the beginning of the fight with Nazi Germany for as long as possible, understanding the country's unpreparedness for war. But on the other hand, his strategic and tactical miscalculations were largely to blame for the USSR's near defeat in the first months of the war. Victory was achieved over Nazism at the bloody price of 27 million Soviet lives. In the postwar period, despite the devastation in which the Soviet state found itself, he sanctioned the allocation of significant resources to support so-called "people's democracies." At the end of the 1940s, at his initiative, a new wave of repression was begun in the Soviet Union, the best known of which were the "Doctors' Plot," in which doctors were accused of attempting to kill Stalin, and the trial concerning the journals *Leningrad* and *Star* [*Zvezda*], after which figures such as the writer Mikhail Zoshchenko and the poet Anna Akhmatova were subjected to persecution and ostracism from public life. The death of the "leader of the peoples" on March 5, 1953 was a shock to the country's population, many of whom blindly believed that Stalin's rule was unshakable, and even that he was physically immortal. A sarcophagus with Stalin's embalmed body was set up in the mausoleum on Red Square in Moscow. However, three years later, Nikita Khrushchëv began to unmask Stalin's cult of personality at the 20th Congress of the CPSU. In 1961, his body was removed from the mausoleum and buried next to the Kremlin wall. Stalin's name was also removed from the many provinces, cities, enterprises, and institutions of the USSR that had been named in his honor.

Tomsky (Yefremov), Mikhail Pavlovich (1880–1936): noted Soviet public figure. Born to a petty bourgeois family, Tomsky became a blue-collar worker in St. Petersburg at the age of 18. Taking an interest in Marxism, he became a professional revolutionary, participating actively in revolutionary actions from 1905 to 1907 and in the October Revolution of 1917. From 1918 to 1921 and 1922 to 1929, he was chairman of the All-Union Central Council of Trade Unions. In the late 1920s, he spoke out openly against the use of extraordinary measures to carry out collectivization and industrialization. From 1929 to 1930, he was deputy chairman of the *VSNKh*. From 1919 to 1934, he was a member of the RCP(b) Central Committee. In an environment of political persecution and mass repression, and faced with the prospect of inevitable arrest, he committed suicide in 1936.

Trotsky (Bronstein), Lev (Leon; Leyba) Davidovich (1879–1940): noted Soviet Party and public figure, one of the organizers of the 1917 October Revolution, and one of the founders of the Workers' and Peasants' Red Army. Born to a prosperous Jewish family, he was the son of a well-to-do landholder and lessee. He completed the technical high school in Nikolayiv, and in his youth, became imbued with the ideas of the *narodniks* [revolutionary populists]. In 1896 in Nikolayiv, he participated in the creation of the South Russian Workers' Union, which had the goal of politically enlightening workers and struggling for their economic interests. In January 1898, he was arrested and sentenced by a court to four years' exile in Siberia. In August 1902, he escaped exile and left the country on a forged passport in which he wrote the last name Trotsky, which later became his Party pseudonym. He settled in London and became friends with the leaders of the Russian Social Democratic Party. In October 1902, he befriended Bolshevik leader Vladimir Lenin, on whose recommendation he was co-opted into editing the Marxist newspaper *Iskra* ["The Spark"]. He returned to Russia illegally in February 1905, soon after the 1905 Russian Revolution began. He actively engaged in revolutionary propaganda in the press and at workers' meetings. In October 1905, he was elected deputy chairman, and then chairman of the St. Petersburg Soviet of Workers' Deputies and edited its print publication, the newspaper *Izvestia*. He was arrested in December 1905, and in prison, wrote the book *Results and Prospects* [*Itogi i perspektivy*], in which he formulated the theory of permanent revolution. In late 1906, he was permanently exiled to Siberia and deprived of all civil rights. He fled the country while in transit and lived abroad until May 1917. After returning to Petrograd, he joined a group of adherents of the Bolshevik tendency. He severely criticized the Provisional Government and came out in favor of the metamorphosis of the bourgeois democratic revolution into a socialist one. He was arrested and imprisoned. He was accepted as a member of the Bolshevik Party in absentia, as a victim of repressions of the Provisional Government, at the 6th Congress of the Russian Social-Democratic Labor Party (bolshevik) or RSDLP(b) in late July to early August 1917 and immediately elected to its governing body, the Central Committee. He was released on September 2 (15), 1917, and on September 25 (October 8), 1917, elected chairman of the Petrograd Soviet of Workers' and Soldiers' Deputies. He actively supported Lenin's proposal to organize an armed uprising immediately. On October 12 (25), he initiated the creation of a Military Revolutionary Committee to protect Petrograd from counterrevolutionary forces. He headed preparations for the October Revolution and was its actual leader. After the Bolshevik victory on October 25 (November 7), 1917, he joined the first Soviet government as people's commissar for foreign affairs. On March 14, 1918, he was appointed people's commissar for military affairs; on March 19, chairman of the Supreme Military Council; and on September 6, chairman of the Revolutionary War Council of the Republic. He headed efforts to create the Red Army, making energetic efforts to professionalize it by actively recruiting former officers ("military specialists"). He established strict discipline in the army, decisively coming out against its democratization. He employed severe repressive measures, being one of the theoreticians and practitioners of the "Red Terror." In March 1919, he joined the first Politburo of the RCP(b) Central Committee. He was involved in the creation of the Comintern, authoring its *Manifesto*. From March 20 to December 10, 1920, he served as acting people's commissar of railroads, using harsh measures to restore railroad transportation. On his death bed, Vladimir Lenin wrote a letter to the Congress characterizing Trotsky "as the most capable member of the Central Committee, and one of two outstanding leaders." After Lenin's death in January 1924, Trotsky ended up politically isolated among the highest Party and government leaders of the USSR. On January 26, 1925, he was removed from his post as chairman of the Revolutionary War Council and appointed member of the Presidium of the All-Union Council of the National Economy (*VSNKh*), the central state industrial agency. In 1927, he was expelled from the AUCP(b). In January 1928, he was exiled to Almaty, in Kazakhstan, and was deported from the USSR early in 1929 along with his family. He lived as an émigré in Turkey, France, Norway, and Mexico. In 1938, he united a group of his supporters throughout the world to form the so-called Fourth International. He was sentenced to death in absentia in the USSR, and his first wife and youngest son Sergey Sedov were shot in the Soviet Union in 1937. On August 20, 1940, he was fatally wounded by Spanish communist Ramón Mercader, who had become a close associate. Trotsky died the following day, and after cremation was buried on the grounds of his house in Coyoacán, Mexico.

CHAPTER THREE: The New Russia's Oil

Bogdanov, Vladimir Leonidovich (b. 1951): General Manager of Surgutneftegaz. He was born in 1951 in the village of Suyerka, Uporovo District, Tyumen Region. He graduated from Tyumen Industrial Institute in 1973. From 1973 to 1976, he worked as an assistant toolpusher and as a toolpusher at Nizhnevartovsk Drilling Administration 1. From 1976 to 1978, he worked as a production engineer at Surgut Drilling Administration 2. From 1978 to 1989, he was deputy director of a drilling administration at Yuganskneftegaz Production Association. From 1980 to 1983, he was deputy general manager for drilling at Surgutneftegaz Production Association. From 1983 to 1984, he was deputy director for drilling at Glavtyumenneftegaz Association. In 1984, he became head of Surgutneftegaz Production Association, later reorganized as a joint-stock company. In June 1999, he became a member of the presidium of the Political Council of the Yugra Interregional Sociopolitical Association. In October 2000, he became a member of the Russian Government Council on Entrepreneurship. He has been elected several times as deputy to the Khanty-Mansi Autonomous District Duma. He is a member of the Standing Commission on Region Policy, an active member of the Academy of Mining Sciences, and an active member of the Academy of Natural Sciences. He is a corresponding member of the Russian Academy of Technological Sciences. He has been awarded the Order "For Service to the Fatherland," Fourth Degree (1997), and the All-Russian Business Olympus Prize.

Khodorkovsky, Mikhail Borisovich (b. 1963): Russian entrepreneur, and former president of Yukos Oil Company. He was born in 1963 in Moscow, and graduated from the D. I. Mendeleyev Moscow Chemical Engineering Institute in 1986 with a major in production engineering. From 1986 to 1987, he was deputy section head at the Frunze District Committee of the Communist Youth League. From 1987 to 1989, he was director of the Youth Scientific and Technical Creativity Center, later renamed the Interdisciplinary Scientific and Technical Program Center (MENATEP). From May 1989 to 1990, he was chairman of the Executive Board of the MENATEP Commercial Innovation Bank of Scientific and Technical Progress. From 1990 to 1991, he was general manager of the MENATEP Interbank Association. In 1992, he became chairman of the Investment Fund for Assistance to the Fuel and Energy Industry. In March 1993, he became Russian deputy minister of fuel and energy. In September 1995, he became chairman of the Board of Directors of Rosprom. In April 1996, he became first vice president of Yukos Oil Company, and was elected chairman of the Board of Directors three months later. In February 1997, he became chairman of the Executive Board of the management company formed by Rosprom and Yukos to manage the oil company. In 1998, after the reorganization of Yukos, he became chairman of the Executive Board of Yukos-Moscow LLC. He was arrested by Russian law-enforcement agencies in October 2003 after numerous investigations of various Yukos entities and the filing of serious charges against a number of company managers. In November 2003, he voluntarily resigned as head of Yukos. The Russian Attorney General's office charged him with numerous offenses, including fraud and tax evasion. In late April 2005, the Meshchansky District Court in Moscow found the former Yukos head guilty under nine articles of the Russian Federation Criminal Code and sentenced him to nine years incarceration, to be served in a standard prison colony.

Medvedev, Dmitry Anatolyevich (b. 1965): Current president of the Russian Federation. He was born 1965 in Leningrad [now St. Petersburg], and graduated from the School of Law at Leningrad State University in 1987. From 1987 to 1990, while a graduate student at Leningrad State University, he worked as an assistant in the Civil Law Department of that institution. In 1990, he became a candidate of law after defending his dissertation on "Problems in the Exercise of Civil Rights by a State Enterprise." From 1990 to 1991, he was an assistant to the chairman of the Leningrad Council of People's Deputies. From 1991 to 1996, he was a legal expert at the Committee on Foreign Relations of the St. Petersburg Mayor's Office. From 1996 to 1999, he was an assistant professor at Leningrad (later St. Petersburg) State University. In November 1999, he was appointed deputy director of the Russian Government Administration, and on December 31, 1999, he was appointed deputy director of the Russian President's Administration. On June 3, 2000, he was approved as first deputy director of the President's Administration. In October 2003, he was appointed director of the Russian President's Administration. In June 2005, he became first deputy prime minister of the Russian Government. In March 2008, he won a strong victory in the election for president of Russia.

Miller, Aleksey Borisovich (b. 1962): chairman of the Board of Gazprom since May 2001 and candidate of economics. He was born January 31, 1962 in Leningrad [now St. Petersburg], and graduated from the Leningrad Finance and Economics Institute with a major in economics. From 1984 to 1986, he worked as an engineer economist; from 1986 to 1989, as a graduate student; and in 1990, as a junior research associate at the Leningrad Scientific Research and Design Institute for Housing and Civil Construction [*LenNIIproyekt*]. From 1990 to 1991, he worked at the Committee for Economic Reform of the Leningrad City Council Executive Committee. From 1991 to 1996, he worked at the Committee on Foreign Relations of the St. Petersburg Mayor's Office. From 1996 to 1999, he was director for development and investments of St. Petersburg Seaport. From 1999 to 2000, he was general manager of Baltic Pipeline System. In July 2000, he was appointed Russian deputy minister of energy, supervising the ministry's foreign economic activities and international cooperation in the fuel and energy industries. On May 30, 2001, he was elected chairman of the board of Gazprom. In July 2006, he was appointed a member of the Presidium of the RF President's Council for the Realization of Priority National Projects and Demographic Policy; he is a member of the Governing Board of the Russian Union of Industrialists and Entrepreneurs (*RSPP*). He has been awarded the Order "For Service to the Fatherland," Fourth Degree (2006), and Kazakhstan's Order of Dostik, Second Degree, for his contribution to the development of relations between Russia and Kazakhstan (2006). He is married, with one son.

Putin, Vladimir Vladimirovich (b. 1952): noted Russian public figure, President of the Russian Federation (2000–2008). He was born 1952 in Leningrad [now St. Petersburg], and graduated from the School of Law at Leningrad State University in 1975. He holds the degree of candidate of economics. From 1985 to 1990, he served on the USSR Committee for State Security [*KGB*]. In 1990, he worked at Leningrad State University as a vice president for international affairs. In 1991, he became an adviser to the chairman of the Leningrad City Council, then chairman of the Committee on Foreign Relations of the St. Petersburg Mayor's Office. From 1994 to 1996, he was first deputy head of the Administration of St. Petersburg. From 1996 to 1997, he was deputy chargé d'affaires of the Russian Federation President. In 1998, he became first deputy director of the Russian President's Administration. In 1999, he became director of the Russian Federation Federal Security Service and Secretary of the Russian Security Council. From December 1999 to March 2000, he was acting president of Russia. From 2000 to 2008, he served as president of the Russian Federation. In May 2008, he became chairman of the Russian Government [prime minister]. His high confidence rating among the people and favorable competition for Russia on world commodity markets give him, as the most prestigious representative of the government, the ability to successfully promote the rapid development of the nation's economy.

Takhautdinov, Shafagat Fahrazovich (b. 1946): general manager of Tatneft since June 1999 and doctor of economics. He was born in 1946 in the village of Abdrakhmanovo, Almetyevsk District, the Republic of Tatarstan. He graduated from the I. M. Gubkin Moscow Institute of Petrochemical and Gas Industry. His labor biography begins in 1965 with a position as assistant toolpusher at the Almetyevsk Drilling Administration. Subsequently, he rose consistently through the ranks from oil production operator to supervisor of well servicing to shop director. In 1978, he began working as head of the Dzhalilneft Administration, and then as head of the Almetyevneft Oil and Gas Production Administration. In 1990, he became chief engineer and first deputy general manager of

Tatneft. On June 21, 1999, he became general manager of Tatneft. In March 2004, he became a deputy to the third Republic of Tatarstan State Council. He is a member of the Republic of Tatarstan State Council Committee on Ecology, Natural Resources, and Land Use. He has been awarded the Republic of Tatarstan State Prize, is an Honored Worker of the Russian Oil and Gas Industry, an Honored Worker of the Russian Ministry of Fuel and Energy, and an Honored Worker of the Republic of Tatarstan. He has been awarded the Order "For Service to the Fatherland," Fourth Degree, the Order of the Red Banner of Labor, the Order of Friendship, the medal "For Distinguished Labor," and other honors. He is married, with a son and a daughter.

Trutnev, Yury Petrovich (b. 1956): Russian Federation minister of natural resources and ecology since March 2004. He was born in 1956 in Perm, and graduated from Perm Polytechnic Institute in 1978 with a major in mining engineering. From 1978 to 1981, he worked as an engineer and a junior research associate at the Perm Scientific Research and Design Technological Institute of the Oil Industry [*PermNIPIneft*]. From 1981 to 1988, he worked in elective posts in public youth organizations. In 1989, he became deputy general manager of the company *Yevraziya* ["Eurasia"]. From 1989 to 1996, he served as general manager of E.K.S. Limited, and president of E.K.S. International. From 1996 to 2000, he was mayor of Perm. On December 3, 2000, he was elected governor of Perm region. On March 9, 2004, he was appointed Russian minister of natural resources by presidential decree. He is a member of the Russian State Council. He has received the Order of Merit. He is married, with two sons.

Yeltsin, Boris Nikolayevich (1931–2007): noted Soviet politician and public figure, and first president of the Russian Federation. He graduated from the School of Construction at the S. M. Kirov Urals Polytechnic Institute (Sverdlovsk, now Yekaterinburg) in 1955, and worked in his field for nearly 13 years, rising through the ranks of the official hierarchy in the construction industry, from supervisor of a construction trust to director of the Sverdlovsk Home Building Integrated Works. He joined the CPSU in 1961, and began his Party career in 1968 as head of a construction section at the Sverdlovsk Regional Party Committee. He was then elected secretary (1975–1976) and first secretary (1976–1985) of the Regional Party Committee. He worked briefly as head of the construction section of the Central Committee, then was elected secretary of the CPSU Central Committee (1985). In December 1985, he became first secretary of the Moscow City Committee of the CPSU and a candidate for membership in the Politburo of the CPSU Central Committee (1986–1988). In 1987, his political destiny took a major turn: at the October plenary session of the CPSU Central Committee, he delivered a speech demanding more decisive reforms. The resolution of the Party plenary session was to characterize the speech as politically erroneous. From 1987 to 1989, he worked as first vice-chairman of the USSR State Committee for Construction, with the rank of minister. In the first free elections in March 1989, he became a USSR people's deputy, and then chairman of the Construction Committee of the Supreme Soviet. He was elected co-chairman of the Interregional Deputies Group (over 300 USSR People's Deputies), the first parliamentary opposition in many years. In 1990, he was elected chairman of the RSFSR Supreme Soviet, and on June 12, 1991, President of the RSFSR. On December 8, 1991, at a meeting in the Bialowieza Forest in Belarus, the leaders of Russia, Ukraine, and Belarus signed an agreement abolishing the USSR and creating the Commonwealth of Independent States (CIS). On December 25, 1991, the RSFSR was renamed the Russian Federation. By then, the president of Russia had already formed a government, whose actual leader was Yegor Gaydar. In April 1993, Russia held a referendum, in which the majority of the voters supported the president. On December 31, 1999, after State Duma elections were won by the pro-government Unity bloc, he retired. He died on April 23, 2007 in Moscow, and is buried in Novodevichy Cemetery.

Abbreviations

Abbreviation	Russian Expansion	English Expansion
ARWC	*Voyenno-Revolyutsionnyy komitet Armenii, VRKA*	Armenian Revolutionary War Committee
AUCP(b)	*Vsesoyuznaya kommunisticheskaya partiya (bolshevikov), VKP(b)*	All-Union Communist Party (of Bolsheviks)
BCF	—	billion cubic feet
BOC	*Bakinskoye neftyanoye obshchestvo, BNO*	Baku Oil Company
BOE	*barrel neftyanogo ekvivalenta*	barrel of oil equivalent
BOITC	*Batumskoye neftepromyshlennogo i torgovogo obshchestvo, BNITO*	Batumi Oil Industrial and Trading Company
CENEf	*Tsentr po effektivnomu ispolzovaniyu energii*	Center for Energy Efficiency
Cheka	(See *VChK*)	(See *VChK*)
CIS	*Sodruzhestvo nezavisimykh gosudarstv, SNG*	Commonwealth of Independent States
CJSC	*zakrytoye aktsionernoye obshchestvo, ZAO; aktsionernoye obshchestvo zakrytogo tipa, AOZT*	Closed Joint-Stock Company
CPC	*Sovet narodnykh komissarov, SNK*	Council of People's Commissars
ESPO	*(nefteprovod) Vostochnaya Sibir–Tikhy Okean*	East Siberia–Pacific Ocean (pipeline)
GKO	*Gosudarstvennyy Komitet Oborony*	State Defense Committee
GKZ	*Gosudarstvennaya komissiya po zapasam poleznykh iskopayemykh*	State Commission for Mineral Reserves
Glavgaztopprom	*Glavnoye upravleniye po iskusstvennomu toplivu i gazu*	Main Artificial Liquid Fuel and Gas Administration
Glavgeologiya	*Glavnoye geologorazvedochnoye upravleniye*	Main Geologic Exploration Administration

Abbreviation	Russian Expansion	English Expansion
Glavgortop	*Glavnoye gorno-toplivnoye upravleniye*	Main Mining and Fuel Administration
Glavkomneft	*Glavny neftyanoy komitet*	Main Petroleum Committee
Glavneft	*Glavnoye upravleniye po snabzheniyu i sbytu nefti i nefteproduktov*	Main Petroleum and Petroleum Products Supply and Sales Administration
Glavneftedobycha	*Glavnoye upravleniye po dobyche nefti*	Main Oil Production Administration
Glavneftepererabotka	*Glavnoye upravleniye po pererabotke nefti*	Main Refining Administration
Glavneftesbyt	*Glavnoye upravleniye po sbytu i transportu nefti i nefteproduktov*	Main Oil and Petroleum Products Sales and Transportation Administration
GNK	*Glavny neftyanoy komitet*	Main Petroleum Committee
GOELRO	*Gosudarstvennaya komissiya po elektrifikatsii Rossii*	State Commission for Electrification of Russia
Gosbank	*Gosudarstvennyy bank*	State Bank
Goskomimushchestvo	*Gosudarstvennyy komitet RF po upravleniyu gosudarstvennym imushchestvom*	RF State Property Management Committee
Gosplan	*Gosudarstvenny planovyy komitet*	State Planning Committee
Gossnab	*Gosudarstvenny komitet po materialno-tekhnicheskomu snabzheniyu*	State Committee for Material and Technical Supply
GULAG	*Glavnoye upravleniye ispravitelno-trudovykh lagerey, trudovykh poseleniy i mest zaklyucheniya*	Main Administration of Correctional and Labor Camps, Labor Settlements, and Places of Incarceration
GUT	*Glavnoye upravleniye po toplivu*	Main Administration for Fuel
IEF	*Institut ekonomiki i finansov*	Institute of Energy and Finances
IMF	*Mezhdunarodny valyutnyy fond*	International Monetary Fund
IRTS	*Imperatorskoye Russkoye tekhnicheskoye obshchestvo*	Imperial Russian Technical Society
JSC	*aktsionernoye obshchestvo*	Joint-Stock Company
KChNTO	*Kaspiyskoye-Chernomorskoye neftepromyshlennoye i torgovoye obshchestvo*	Caspian and Black Sea Oil Industrial and Trading Company

Abbreviation	Russian Expansion	English Expansion
KGB	*Komitet gosudarstvennoy bezopasnosti*	Committee for State Security
Komsomol	*Vsesoyuznyy leninskiy kommunisticheskiy soyuz molodëzhi*	Communist Youth League
LenNIIproyekt	*Leningradskiy nauchno-issledovatelskiy i proyektnyy institut po zhilishchno-grazhdanskomu stroitelstvu*	Leningrad Scientific Research and Design Institute for Housing and Civil Construction
LNG	*szhizhennyy prirodny gaz, SPG*	liquefied natural gas
MCF	—	thousand cubic feet
MMCF	—	million cubic feet
Neftesindikat	*Vsesoyuznyy neftyanoy torgovoy sindikat*	All-Union Oil Trading Syndicate
NEP	*Novaya ekonomicheskaya politika*	New Economic Policy
NGL	*shirokaya fraktsiya zhidkikh uglevodorodov*	natural gas liquids
Nm³	*normalnyy kubicheskiy metr*	Normal cubic meter
OGPA	*Neftegaz-odobyvayushcheye upravleniye*	Oil and Gas Production Association
OGPU	*Obyedinënnoye gosudarstvennoye politicheskoye upravleniye*	Joint State Political Directorate
OJSC	*otkrytoye aktsionernoye obshchestvo, OAO; aktsionernoye obshchestvo otkrytogo tipa, AOOT*	Open Joint-Stock Company
OSOTOP	*Osoboye Soveshchaniye po toplivu*	Special Council on Fuel
PermNIPIneft	*Permskiy nauchno-issledo-vatelskiy i proyektno-tekhnologicheskiy institut neftyanoy promyshlennosti*	Perm Scientific Research and Design Technological Institute of the Oil Industry
PSA	*soglasheniye o razdele produktsii, SRP*	production sharing agreement
RAS	*Rossiyskaya akademiya nauk, RAN*	Russian Academy of Sciences
RCP(b)	*Russkaya kommunistiche-skaya partiya (bolshevikov) (RKP(b))*	Russian Communist Party (of Bolsheviks)
RGIA	*Rossiysky gosudarstvennyy istoricheskiy arkhiv*	Russian State Historical Archive
ROP	[English]	Russian Oil Products, Ltd.

Abbreviation	Russian Expansion	English Expansion
Rostekhregulirovaniye	*Rossiyskoye federalnoye agentstvo po tekhnicheskomu regulirovaniyu i metrologii*	Russian Federal Agency for Technical Regulation and Metrology
RSDLP(b)	*Russkaya sotsial-demokrati-cheskaya rabochaya partiya (bolshevikov) (RKP(b))*	Russian Social-Democratic Labor Party (of Bolsheviks)
RSFSR	*Rossiyskaya sovetskaya federativnaya sotsialisti-cheskaya respublika*	Russian Soviet Federative Socialist Republic
RSPP	*Rossiyskiy soyuz promyshlennikov i predprinimateley*	Russian Union of Industrialists and Entrepre-neurs
SEVLON	*Severnyy lager osobogo naznacheniya*	Northern Special Purpose Camp
sp.gr.	*ud.v.*	specific gravity
TCE	*tonna uslovnogo topliva*	ton of coal equivalent
TCF	—	trillion cubic feet
TDFR	*Zakavkazskaya demokraticheskaya federativnaya respublika*	Transcaucasian Democratic Federal Republic
TNK	*(OAO) Tyumenskaya neftyanaya kompaniya*	Tyumen Oil Company (OJSC)
TNK-BP	*Tyumenskaya neftyanaya kompaniya–British petroleum, TNK-BP*	Tyumen Oil Company–British Petroleum
TOE	*tonna neftyanogo ekvivalenta*	ton of oil equivalent
Tsentroneft	*Tsentralnoye upravleniye neftyanoy promyshlennosti*	Central Oil Industry Admi-nistration
Tsentrosoyuz	*Tsentralnyy soyuz potrebitelskikh obshchestv Rossiyskoy Federatsii*	Russian Federation Central Alliance of Consumer Societies
TUD	[German] *Technische Universität Dresden*	Dresden University of Technology
Uralneftegazstroy	*Uralskiy trest po stroitelstvu predpriyatiy promyshlennosti nefti i gaza*	Ural Oil and Gas Industry Construction and Erection Trust
VChK	*Vserossiyskaya chrezvychaynaya komissiya po borbe s kontrrevolyu-tsiyey i sabotazhem*	All-Russian Extraordinary Commission for Combating Counterrevolution and Sabotage [also known as *Vcheka*]
VIOC	*vertikalno integrirovannaya neftyanaya kompaniya*	vertically integrated oil company
VLKSM	(See *Komsomol*)	(See *Komsomol*)

Abbreviation	Russian Expansion	English Expansion
VNITON	*Vsesoyuznoye nauchnoye inzhenerno-tekhnicheskoye obshchestvo neftyanikov*	All-Union Scientific Engineering and Technical Society of Oil Workers
VSNKh	*Vysshiy sovet narodnogo khozyaystva*	Supreme Council for the National Economy
VTsIK	*Vserossiyskiy Tsentralnyy Ispolnitelny Komitet*	All-Russian Central Executive Committee
WEA	*Mezhdunarodnoye energe-ticheskoye agenstva, MEA*	World Energy Agency

Conversion Table

Unit of Measure	Metric Equivalent	American Equivalent
	$1°F = 0.556°C$ $T_C = (T_F - 32)/1.8$	$1°C = 1.8°F$ $T_F = 1.8T_C + 32$
	1 mi. = 1.6 km	1 km = 0.62 mi.
arshin	71.12 cm	28 in.
desyatina	1.11 ha	2.75 acres
khalvar	45 kg	99.2 lb.
pood	16.38 kg	36 lb.
Nm³	1 m³ at 0°C and 1 atm.	37.24 SCF at 60°F and 1 atm.
sazhen	2.15 m	7 ft.
TCE	29.3 GJ, 7 Gcal	2.78×10^7 BTU
TOE	41.868 GJ, 10 Gcal	3.968×10^7 BTU
vedro	12.3 l	3.254 gal.
verst	initially, 1.5 km; later 1.06 km	initially, 0.93 mi; later 0.66 mi.

Translator's note: The Russian practice is to measure crude oil and refined petroleum products by weight, e.g., in metric tons. This makes conversion to the American measurement in barrels difficult because the specific gravity of the material can vary.

1 tonne of crude = 264.174/G U.S. gal. = 6.28983/G bbl.,

where G is the specific gravity. A typical result based on a specific gravity in the range of 0.75 to 0.80 would then be:

1 tonne of crude ≈ 330.2 to 352.3 U.S. gal. = 7.86 to 8.38 bbl.

The higher figures (more volume per tonne) correspond to lighter crude (sp.gr. 0.75).

For convenience, at the author's request, we have converted all Russian weight measures of oil to barrels as follows: 1 metric ton = 1000 kg = 7.33 US bbl. This assumes a specific gravity of 0.82.

Notes

CHAPTER ONE: The Russian Empire's "Black Gold"

1. Genesis 11:3 (New International Version). For a comparison of English translations of this verse, see http://bible.cc/genesis/11-3.htm.—*Trans.*
2. *Knowledge.* January 18, 1884, p. 35.
3. White petroleum is created by natural filtration and refinement of crude oil as it seeps to the surface through a unique combination of rock and soil.—*Ed.*
4. Unless otherwise specified, all measurements throughout the text given in tons have been converted from metric tons to US short tons (1 ton=2,000 pounds).—*Ed.*
5. *Azerbaijan International.* Autumn 1998, 6.3, pp. 81-84.
6. Olearius, Adam. *The Voyages and Travels of the Ambassadors Sent by Frederick Duke of Holstein, to the Great Duke of Muscovy, and the King of Persia... Containing a Complete History of Muscovy, Tartary, Persia. And other adjacent Countries... Whereto are added the Travels of John Albert de Mandelslo (a Gentleman belonging to the Embassy) from Persia, into the East-Indies...* Translated from Dutch into English by John Davies. London: Thomas Dring and John Starkey, 1662.
7. *Amoenitatum Exoticarum.* Lemgo, 1712.
8. Today this word means "leukoma," but at the time of the quotation it probably meant "cataracts."—*Trans.*
9. Nikolaev, I. *Irkutsk. Materials on the History of the 17th–18th Centuries* [*Irkutsk. Materialy po istorii goroda XVII-XVIII stoletiy*]. Moscow, 1983.
10. At this stage in history, the *verst* equaled 0.93 miles; later in Peter the Great's time, it took on the more familiar value of 0.66 miles.—*Trans.*
11. The *vedro* was properly a measure of volume, equaling approximately 3.254 gallons. The author's conversion to kilograms implies a specific gravity of 0.82.—*Trans.*
12. The German term *Berg Collegium* was retained in Russian.—*Trans.*
13. Matveychuk, Alexander. "Peter the Great's Plans for Russian Oil." *Oil of Russia*, No. 3, 2010.
14. Ibid.
15. Under the tax-farming system, the government paid a private individual or entity a flat fee in exchange for granting it the right to collect taxes within an area.—*Trans.*

16. This campaign is known in the West as the Russo-Persian War.—*Trans.*
17. Matveychuk, Alexander. "Peter the Great's Plans for Russian Oil." *Oil of Russia*, No. 3, 2010.
18. *The Baku Oil and Local Communities*, ed. Leila Alieva. Baku, Qanun, 2009; see also *Documents on the History of Baku: 1810–1917 [Dokumenty po istorii Baku. 1810–1917]*. Azerbaijan State Publishing House, Baku, 1978. pp. 11–12.
19. Russian State Historical Archives. Fund 271, File 1801.
20. Ibid.
21. *Reports of the Caucasian Archeographic Commission.* Vol. II. Tiflis, 1868.
22. Galagan, A. A. "From the History of the Taxation of the Russian Oil Industry in the Second Half of the 19th Century and Early [in] the 20th Century" *The Eve of the Petroleum Era: Topics in the History of the Oil Industry in Russia and the US from the Second Half of the 19th Century to the Early 20th Century [Predvestiye ery nefti: problemy istorii neftyanoy promyshlennosti Rossii i SShA vo vtoroy polovine XIX – nachale XX vv.].* Moscow, 2003, p. 83; see also *Historical Sketch of the Development of the Mining Business in the Caucasus [Istoricheskiy ocherk razvitiya gornogo dela v Kavkaze].* p. 112.
23. *Acts Collected by the Caucasus Archaeographic Commission [Akty, sobrannyye Kavkazskoy Arkheograficheskoy Kommissii].* Tiflis, 1887. Vol. IX, Doc. 548.
24. Mendeleyev, Dmitry. *Works [Sochineniya].* Moscow, 1949. Vol. X, p. 63.
25. Mendeleyev, op. cit., pp. 253 and 803.
26. Ibid.
27. Mendeleyev, op. cit., p. 830.
28. *On the Exhibit of Manufactured Articles in Moscow in 1865 [O vystavke manufakturnykh prozvedeniy v Moskve v 1865 g.].* St. Petersburg, 1867. p. 151.
29. Krasnodar Territory State Archive. F. 318, D. 780, L. 48.
30. Russia did not adopt the Gregorian calendar until February 14, 1918, so dates in the late 19th and early 20th century are often cited as "Old Style" (following the Julian calendar) or "New Style" (Gregorian) or both. Where two dates are given without mention of style, the later (parenthesized) one is the modern (Gregorian) date.—*Trans.*
31. The State Archives of the Krasnodar Territory. Fund 350, File 264.
32. *Gorny Zhurnal* ["Mining Journal"]. No. 12, 1870, p. 132.
33. The Russian State Historical Archives. Fund 37, File 67.
34. The Russian State Military Historical Archives. Fund 45, File 212.
35. Russians normally use a so-called "patronymic," a middle name based on the father's name.—*Trans.*
36. *In memory of Aleksey Semënovich Doroshenko.* Baku, 1894.
37. The Russian State Historical Archives. Fund 1458, File 1725.

38. *Burlaks* were men who hauled riverboats upstream by pulling them with a rope.—*Trans.*
39. *Zapiski Imperatorskogo russkogo tekhnicheskogo obshchestva* ["Notes of the Imperial Russian Technical Society"]. No. 4, 1876, p. 148.
40. Yefimov, Alexander. "Russian Oil in the Eyes of a Briton." *Oil of Russia*, No. 3, 2005.
41. Ibid.
42. Ibid.
43. Ibid.
44. Ibid.
45. Ibid.
46. Ibid.
47. Ibid.
48. Indisova, Ksenia. "The First Oil Exhibition." *Oil of Russia*, No. 1, 2008.
49. Ibid.
50. Alexeyev, Vadim. "Prologue to the Gasoline Era." *Oil of Russia*, No. 2, 2006.
51. Ibid.
52. Matveychuk, Alexander. "Paris Oil Gambit." *Oil of Russia*, No. 3, 2005.
53. The Russian State Historical Archives. Fund 1458, File 1725.
54. In the early 20th century, *softa-mullah* was the term used for dropout students of Islamic religious schools from southern Persia, which was under strong British influence.—*Ed.*
55. Perschke, Stanislav and Ludwig. *The Russian Oil Industry: Its Development and Current Status in Statistical Data* [*Russkaya neftyana promyshlennost, yeyo razvitiye i sovremennoye polozheniye v statisticheskikh dannykh*]. Tiflis, 1913.
56. This expression refers to Nikolay Gogol's famous novel by the same name, in which landowners inflated the value of their wealth by listing on their property registers the names of serfs who were actually deceased.—*Ed.*

CHAPTER TWO: Oil in the Land of the Soviets

1. *Novaya zhizn* ["New Life"], No. 6 (220), January 9, 1918; see also *Maxim Gorky: Untimely Thoughts. Essays on Revolution, Culture and the Bolsheviks*, ed. Ermolaev. Yale University Press, 1995, p. 125.
2. Lenin, V. I. *Complete Collected Works* [*Polnoye sobraniye sochineniy*]. Moscow, 1969. Vol. 31, p. 357.
3. Lenin, op. cit., 1961, Vol. 34, p. 169.
4. Kondratyev, N. D. *The Grain Market* [*Rynok khlebov*]. Moscow, 1922, p. 124.

5. Lenin, op. cit., 1965, Vol. 50, p. 291.
6. Lenin, op. cit., 1962, Vol. 39, p. 306.
7. Stalin, I. V. *Works [Sochineniya]*. Moscow, 1951. Vol. 4, p. 408.
8. See *Pravda* ["Truth"], No. 3, January 12–17, 1918. p. 1; and Stalin, op. cit., Vol. 4, p. 87.
9. Lenin, op. cit., 1962, Vol. 35, p. 268.
10. *Izvestia Bakinskogo Soveta rabochikh, soldatskikh i matrosskikh deputatov* ["News of the Baku Soviet of Workers', Soldiers', and Sailors' Deputies]. No. 100, May 28, 1918, p. 1.
11. Lenin, op. cit., 1965, Vol. 50, p. 90.
12. *Krasny arkhiv* ["Red Archives"]. No. 4–5, 1938, p. 20.
13. *History of the Communist Party of Azerbaijan [Istoriya Kommunistickeskoy partii Azerbaidzhana]*. Baku, 1958, p. 295.
14. Stalin, op. cit., Vol. 4, p. 127.
15. Turkish and Azerbaijani are closely related, like English and Dutch, but different enough to be considered separate languages.—*Trans.*
16. *Kommunistichesky internatsional* ["The Communist International"]. No. 19, 1921, p. 5009.
17. *History of the Communist Party of Azerbaijan [Istoriya Kommunistickeskoy partii Azerbaidzhana]*. Baku, 1958, p. 397.
18. *History of the Communist Party of the USSR [Istoriya Kommunistickeskoy partii SSSR]*. Moscow, 1968, Vol. 3, p. 520.
19. Lenin, op. cit., 1965 Vol. 51, p. 175.
20. Lenin, op. cit., 1963, Vol. 41, p. 106.
21. Lenin, op. cit., 1963, Vol. 41, p. 119.
22. Russian State Economics Archive. Fund 413, File 251.
23. Lenin, op. cit., 1963, Vol. 42, p. 47.
24. *Kommunisticheskaya Partiya Sovetskogo Soyuza v rezolyutsiyakh i resheniyakh sezdov, konferentsii i plenumov TsK [The Communist Party of the Soviet Union in Resolutions and Decisions of Congresses, Conferences, and Plenary Sessions of the Central Committee]*. Moscow, 1970, Vol. 2, p. 285.
25. Lenin, op. cit., 1963, Vol. 44, p. 255.
26. Russian State Archives of Social and Political History. Fund 17, File 111.
27. Proceedings of the Tenth Congress of the RCP(b). Moscow, 1933, p. 34.
28. Ibid., p. 568.
29. *Leninsky Sbornik [Lenin Miscellany]*. Moscow, Vol. XL, p. 151-152.
30. *Foreign Policy Documents of the USSR [Dokumenty vneshney politiki SSSR]*. Moscow, 1960. Vol. 4, p. 433.
31. Russian State Archives of Social and Political History. Fund 17, File 1225.
32. Ibid., File 232.
33. Ibid., File 225.
34. See *Izvestia* ["News"], May 25, 1922, p. 2.

35. The International Association of Oil Companies in Russia was created in September 1922 at a conference in Paris. Among the participants were 18 oil companies, including: Royal Dutch Shell, Standard Oil Company, Nobel Brothers Petroleum Production Partnership, theFranco-Belgian A. I. Mantashev & Co. Petroleum Industry and Trading Company, and G. M. Lianozov Sons Petroleum Production Partnership. The association was the main proponent of the oil embargo of Soviet Russia.—*Ed.*

36. Shpotov, B. M. "Problems of the Modernization of the Oil Industry in the USSR in the 1920s and 1930s," *Soviet Union's Oil: Topics in the History of the USSR's Oil Industry (1917–1991)* [*Neft strany Sovetov: problemy istorii neftyanoy promyshlennosti SSSR (1917–1991)*]. Moscow, 2005, pp. 223-224; see also *Serebrovsky, A. P. The Oil and Gas Industry in America* [*Neftyanaya i gazovaya promyshlennost v Amerike*]. Moscow, 1925, pp. 329–330.

37. Igolkin, A. A. "Early Lessons of Mutually Beneficial Cooperation." *Oil of Russia*, No. 3, 2004.

38. Serebrovsky, op. cit., pp. 382–285.

39. Lomov, G. I. *In Pursuit of Oil* [*V pogone za neftyu*]. Moscow-Leningrad, 1925, p. 21.

40. From 1905 to 1945, Japan controlled the portion of the island south of 50°N.—*Trans.*

41. Strizhov, I. N. *American Refineries* [*Amerikanskiye nefteperegonnyye zavody*]. Leningrad, 1929.

42. Russian State Economics Archive. Fund 3429, File 5162.

43. Stalin, op. cit., Vol. 12, p. 371.

44. State Industrial Archive of Perm Oblast [GOPAPO]. F. 591, Op. 1, D. 136, L. 71–72.

45. Abaturova, O. A. *The First of the Great Ural Oil* [*Pervenets bolshoy uralskoy nefti*]. Krasnokamsk, 2003, p. 9.

46. State Industrial Archive of Perm Oblast [GOPAPO]. F. 4381, Op. 1, D. 1, L. 17.

47. Russian State Economics Archive. F. 4372, Op. 28, D. 196, L. 59.

48. Since this was a war of survival for the Russians, who lost over 20 million people, they customarily refer to their one-on-one conflict with Germany as the "Great Patriotic War." The term "World War II" would refer more broadly to the conflict among many nations.—*Trans.*

49. "Akten zur Deutschen Auswärtigen Politik 1918–1945," Series C, Band V:2. Göttingen, 1977, document № 490, pp. 793-801.

50. Stalin, I. V. *Speeches at Voters' Pre-Election Meetings in the Moscow Stalin Election District* [*Rechi na predvybornykh sobraniyakh izbirateley Stalinskogo izbiratelnogo okruga g. Moskvy*]. Moscow, 1947.

51. See Mark Frankland, *Khrushchev*. New York, 1967.

52. *Oil and Gas of Tyumen in Documents*. Sverdlovsk, 1971, Vol. 1, p. 190.

53. Ibid., p. 191.
54. Ibid., p. 192.
55. Ibid., p. 253.
56. Now called the Ivan M. Gubkin Russian State University of Oil and Gas.—*Trans.*
57. The Stakhanov movement refers to a widespread movement in the prewar period that encouraged workers, farmers, engineers and others to regularly exceed the established norms of production. The movement was inspired by the exploits of Alexey Stakhanov, a miner at the Central-Irmino coal mine in the Donbass, who on August 30–31, 1935 mined 102 tons of coal in a single shift (five hours, 45 minutes)—more than 14 times his quota. Workers from other sectors of the economy soon followed his initiative and on November 14–17, 1935 the first All-Union Stakhanovite Conference was held in Moscow. The Communist Party emphasized the important role of the Stakhanov movement in socialist construction and awarded substantial monetary prizes to those workers who significantly increased productivity.—*Ed.*
58. Shatalin, S. *An Interrupted Dialog* [*Prervanny dialog*]. Tver, 1998.

CHAPTER THREE: The New Russia's Oil

1. Weekly Report of the German Institute for Economic Research [Deutsche Institut für Wirtschaftsforschung]. No. 49, 2007. p. 746.
2. Ibid, p. 748.
3. Ibid.
4. The Russian system of classification for reserves varies from those used throughout most of the world. Whereas estimates of reserves generally take into account both geological and economic factors, the Russian system is based solely on geological attributes as defined by varying degrees of geophysical and geochemical exploration and analysis.—*Ed.*

Russian	International Equivalent
A	Proved reserves; characteristics of the deposit have been studied in detail; reserves are currently in production
B	Proved reserves; characteristics of the deposit have been studied in detail
C_1	Proved or probable reserves; characteristics of the deposit have been determined by geological exploration
C_2	Probable reserves; preliminary estimates have been made based on general exploration and the characteristics of more developed portions of adjoining deposits
C_3	Prospective reserves; preliminary estimates have been made based on general exploration

D_1	Speculative reserves; resources are presumed to exist based on geophysical and geochemical research in the given region
D_2	Speculative reserves; resources are presumed to exist based on general geophysical and geochemical concepts

5. In 2007, Dmitry Medvedev was chairman of the board of Gazprom and a nominee to succeed Putin as president—*Trans.*
6. See Yamanaka, Megumi. "Nippon Oil Buys Crude From Sakhalin-1 Under Long Term Contract." *Bloomberg Online*, February 18, 2008.
7. See Halliburton press release, dateline Houston, November 1, 2007. http://www.halliburton.com/public/news/pubsdata/press_release/2007/corpnws_110107.html
8. Nm³: normal cubic meters measured at the Russian standard temperature and pressure of 0°C and 1 atm. One Nm^3 = 37.24 SCF at 60°F and 1 atm.—*Trans.*
9. See "Russia signs deal to bring natural gas pipeline through Bulgaria." *The New York Times*, January 18, 2008.
10. Originally *ÖMV* for *Österreichische Mineralölverwaltung* ["Austrian Mineral Oil Authority"].—*Trans.*
11. See "Nabucco trans-Caspian gas pipe project unrealistic - EU official." *RIA Novosti*, October 29, 2007.
12. See "Turkish minister vows to implement gas project bypassing Russia." *RIA Novosti*, May 29, 2007.
13. See McDonald, Joe. "UN Report: Asia Faces Jump in Food Costs." AP news feed, March 27, 2008.
14. Ibid.
15. Ibid.
16. See also David Pimentel and Tad Patzek "Green Plants, Fossil Fuels, and New Biofuels." American Institute of Biological Sciences, Online Publications, November 2006. URL: http://www.aibs.org/bioscience-editorials/editorial_2006_11.html

PROFILES OF KEY HISTORICAL FIGURES

1. Now called the Azerbaijan State Oil Academy.—*Trans.*
2. Now called the Nikolay E. Bauman Moscow State Technical University.—*Trans.*
3. Now called the Ivan M. Gubkin Russian State University of Oil and Gas.—*Trans.*
4. Now called the Dmitry I. Mendeleyev Russian University of Chemical Engineering.—*Trans.*

Selected Bibliography

I. ARCHIVES AND STATE LIBRARIES

Archives of the Russian Academy of Sciences
Central Historical Archives of Moscow
Central State Archives of St. Petersburg
Russian Historical Library
Russian National Library
Russian State Archives of Ancient Documents
Russian State Economics Archives
Russian State Historical Archives
Russian State Library
Russian State Military Archives
Russian State Military History Archives
Russian State Navy Archives
State Archives of the Russian Federation

II. GOVERNMENT DOCUMENTS

Decrees of the Soviet Authorities. Moscow, 1957–1965. Vols. 1–11.
Records of the USSR Supreme Soviet. Moscow, 1936–1991.
The Soviet Communist Party in Resolutions of Central Committee Plenums, Congresses, and Conferences (1898–1986). Moscow, 1980–1986, Vols. 1–11.
USSR Foreign Policy Documents. Moscow, 1957–1970. Vols. 1–12.

III. SELECTED BOOKS, ARTICLES, AND DISSERTATIONS

Abaturova, O. A. *The First of the Great Ural Oil* [*Pervenets bolshoy uralskoy nefti*]. Krasnokamsk, 2003.
Abbasov, M. M. and T. A. Balabanova. *History of the Development of Refining in Saratov Territory: 1882–2003* [*Istoriya razvitiya neftepererabotki v saratovskom kraye: 1882–2003*] Saratov, 2004.
Alekperov, Vagit, ed. *New Russia's Oil: Position, Problems, Prospects* [*Neft novoy Rossii: situatsiya, problemy, perspektivy*]. Moscow, 2007.

Alekperov, Vagit, ed. *Soviet Union's Oil: Topics in the History of the USSR's Oil Industry (1917–1991)* [*Neft strany Sovetov: problemy istorii neftyanoy promyshlennosti SSSR (1917–1991)*]. Moscow, 2005.

Alekperov, Vagit, ed. *The Eve of the Petroleum Era: Topics in the History of the Oil Industry in Russia and the US from the Second Half of the 19th Century to the Early 20th Century* [*Predvestiye ery nefti: problemy istorii neftyanoy promyshlennosti Rossii i SShA vo vtoroy polovine XIX – nachale XX vv.*]. Moscow, 2003.

Baryshnikov, M. N. *The Business World of Russia: Historical-Biographical Fact Book* [*Delovoy mir Rossii: Istoriko-biograficheskiy spravochnik*]. St. Petersburg, 1998.

Belkind, L. L., et al. *History of Technology* [*Istoriya tekhniki*]. Moscow, 1958.

Belorusiyev, V. A., et al. *The Oil Complex of Kuybyshev Oblast (1930s to 1950s): Formation and Development* [*Neftyanoy kompleks Kuybyshevskoy oblasti (30–50-e gg. XX v.): stanovleniye i razvitiye*]. Samara, 2006.

Borozinets, L. G., et al. *History of the Formation and Development of the Oil and Gas Complex in Komi Territory* [*Istoriya stanovleniya i razvitiya neftegazovogo kompleksa Komi kraya*]. Ukhta, 2004.

Dinkov, V. A., ed. *Oil of the USSR (1917–1987)* [*Neft SSSR (1917–1987)*]. Moscow, 1987.

Dyakonova, I. A. *Oil and Coal Energy in Tsarist Russia: International Comparisons* [*Neft i ugol v energetike tsarskoy Rossii v mezhdunarodnykh sopostavleniyakh*]. Moscow, 1999.

Dyakonova, I. A. *The Nobel Corporation in Russia* [*Nobelevskaya korporatsiya v Rossii*]. Moscow, 1980.

Fursenko, A. A. *Oil Trusts and Global Politics: 1880s–1918* [*Neftyanye tresty i mirovaya politika. 1880-e gg. –1918 g.*]. Moscow-Leningrad, 1965.

Fursenko, A. A. *The Rockefeller Dynasty* [*Dinastiya Rokfellerov*]. Leningrad, 1973.

Fursenko, A. A. *Oil Wars (Late 19th to Early 20th Centuries)* [*Neftyanye voyny (konets XIX–nachalo XX v.)*]. Leningrad, 1985.

Gavrilova, N. Yu. *The Social Development of Oil Production Regions in Western Siberia (1964–1985)* [*Sotsialnoe razvitiye neftegazodobyvayushchikh rayonov Zapadnoy Sibiri (1964–1985 gg.)*]. Tyumen, 2002.

Gefter, M. Ya., ed. *Monopolistic Capital in Russia's Oil Industry: 1883–1914. Documents and Data* [*Monopolisticheskiy kapital v neftyanoy promyshlennosti Rossii. 1883–1914. Dokumenty i materialy*]. Moscow, 1961.

Goryunov, S. V. *The Geological Service of Russia: 300-Year Commemorative Monograph and Fact Book* [*Geologicheskaya sluzhba Rossii. K 300-letiyu osnovaniya. Monografiya-spravochnik*]. Moscow, 1995.

Gurevich, Ya. D., et al. *The Oil Industry of the USSR* [*Neftyanaya promyshlennost SSSR*]. Moscow, 1958.

Igolkin, A. A. *The Domestic Oil Industry, 1917–1920* [*Otechestvennaya neftyanaya promyshlennost v 1917–1920 godakh*]. Moscow, 1999.

Igolkin, A. A. *The Soviet Oil Industry, 1921–1927* [*Sovetskaya neftyanaya promyshlennost v 1921–1927 gg.*]. Moscow, 2000.

Igolkin, A. A. *USSR Oil Policy, 1928–1940* [*Neftyanaya politika SSSR v 1928–1940 gg.*]. Moscow, 2005.

Karpov, V. P. *History of the Creation and Development of the West Siberian Oil and Gas Complex (1948–1990)* [*Istoriya sozdaniya i razvitiya Zapadno-Sibirskogo neftegazovogo kompleksa (1948–1990 gg.)*]. Tyumen, 2005.

Kostornichenko, V. N. *Foreign Capital in the Soviet Oil Industry (1918–1932)* [*Inostrannyy kapital v sovetskoy neftyanoy promyshlennosti (1918–1932 gg.)*]. Volgograd, 2000.

Krylov, V. I., et al. *Russia's Oil and Gas Industry: Yesterday, Today, and Tomorrow* [*Vchera, segodnya, zavtra neftyanoy i gazovoy promyshlennosti Rossii*]. Moscow. 1995.

Kuryatnikov, V. N. *The Formation of the Oil Complex in the Ural and Volga Regions (1930s–1950s)* [*Stanovlenie neftyanogo kompleksa v Uralskom i Povolzhskom regionakh (30–50-e gg. XX veka)*]. Samara. 2008.

Lisichkin, S. M. *Historical Sketches of the Development of the Domestic Oil Industry: Pre-Revolutionary Period* [*Ocherki po istorii razvitiya otechestvennoy neftyanoy promyshlennosti. Dorevolyutsionnyy period*]. Moscow-Leningrad, 1954.

Lisichkin, S. M. *Historical Sketches of the Development of the USSR Oil Production Industry* [*Ocherki po istorii razvitiya neftedobyvayushchey promyshlennosti SSSR*]. Moscow, 1958.

Markelova, O. A. *History of Oil Production in Perm Oblast: 1928–2004* [*Istoriya dobychi nefti v Permskoy oblasti: 1928–2004 gg.*]. Perm, 2004.

Matveychuk, A. A. *At the Sources of Russia's Oil Industry* [*U istokov neftyanoy promyshlennosti Rossii*]. Moscow, 2000.

Matveychuk, A. A. *The First Oil Engineers in Russia: Historical Sketches* [*Pervyye inzhenery-neftyaniki Rossii: istoricheskie ocherki*]. Moscow, 2002.

Matveychuk, A. A. and I. G. Fuks. *Sources of Russian Oil: Historical Sketches* [*Istoki rossiyskoy nefti: istoricheskie ocherki*]. Moscow, 2008.

Matveychuk, A. A. and I. G. Fuks. *A Technological Saga* [*Tekhnologicheskaya saga*]. Moscow, 2009.

Matveychuk, A. A. and I. G. Fuks. *The Triumph of Russia's Oleonaphthas* [*Triumf rossiyskikh oleonaftov*]. Moscow, 2010.

457

Mendeleyev, D. I. *The Oil Industry in the American State of Pennsylvania and in the Caucasus* [*Neftyanaya promyshlennost v Severoamerikanskom shtate Pensilvaniya i na Kavkaze*]. St. Petersburg, 1877.

Parkhomenko, V. E. *Dmitry Ivanovich Mendeleyev and the Russian Oil Business* [*Dmitry Ivanovich Mendeleyev i russkoe neftyanoye delo*]. Moscow, 1957.

Pazhitnov, K. A. *Historical Sketches of the Baku Oil Production Industry* [*Ocherki po istorii bakinskoy neftedobyvayushchey promyshlennosti*]. Moscow-Leningrad, 1940.

Pritula, A. F. *The Mining Industry in Grozny and Terek Before Nationalization* [*Groznenskaya i Terskaya gornaya promyshlennost pered natsionalizatsiyey*]. Moscow-Leningrad, 1925.

Ragozin, V. I. *Oil and the Oil Industry in Russia* [*Neft i neftyanaya promyshlennost v Rossii*]. St. Petersburg, 1884.

Serebrovsky, A. P. *The Oil and Gas Industry in America* [*Neftyanaya i gazovaya promyshlennost v Amerike*]. Moscow, 1925.

Sergiyenko, S. R. *The Role of Scientists and Engineers in the Development of Oil Chemistry and Technology* [*Rol russkikh uchenykh i inzhenerov v razvitii khimii i tekhnologii nefti*]. Moscow-Leningrad, 1949.

Simonovich, V. *Oil and the Oil Industry in Russia* [*Neft i neftyanaya promyshlennost v Rossii*]. St. Petersburg, 1909.

Troshin, A. K. *The History of Oil Technology in Russia (17th Century to the Second Half of the 19th Century)* [*Istoriya neftyanoy tekhniki v Rossii (XVII v. –vtoraya polovina XIX v.)*]. Moscow, 1958.

Vakhitov, G. G. *The Oil Production Industry of the USSR and Russia: A Half-Century of Field Development, 1950–2000* [*Neftedobyvayushchaya promyshlennost SSSR i Rossii: poluvekovoy opyt razrabotki mestorozhdeniy v 1950–2000 gg.*]. Moscow, 2006.

Yevdoshenko, Yu. V. *Glory to Russian Oil: Proceedings of the Scientific-Historical Conference on the Role of the Private Entrepreneur in the Development of Russia's Oil Industry in the Second Half of the 19th Century* [*Vo slavu rossiyskoy nefti: materialy nauchno-istoricheskoy konferentsii "Rol chastnogo predprinimatelstva v razvitii neftyanoy promyshlennosti Rossii vo vtoroy polovine XIX v."*]. Moscow, 2006.

Zolotarëv, V. A., A. M. Sokolov, and M. V. Yanovich. *Oil and Security in Russia* [*Neft i bezopasnost Rossii*]. Moscow, 2007.

IV. DATA SOURCES

Compendium of Statistical Data on the Mining Industry [*Sbornik statisticheskikh svedeniy po gornoy chasti*]. St. Petersburg, 1826–1875.

Compendium of Statistical Data on the Mining Industry [*Sbornik statisticheskikh svedeniy po gornoy chast.*]. St. Petersburg, 1876–1913.

Fuel and Energy and the Economy of Russia: Fact Book [*TEK i ekonomika Rossii. Spravochnik*]. Moscow, 2007. Vols. 1–7.

National Economy of the USSR [*Narodnoye khozyaystvo SSSR*]. 1922–1982. Commemorative Issue of the Statistical Almanac. Moscow, 1982.

National Economy of the USSR [*Narodnoye khozyaystvo SSSR*]. Statistical Almanac. Moscow, 1983–1991.

Vestnik TEK ["Fuel and Energy Herald"]: Monthly Information and Analysis Bulletin of the Russian Fuel Energy Complex. Moscow, 2004–2010.

V. WEB SITES

Russian President: www.kremlin.ru

Russian Government: www.government.ru

Russian Ministry of Education and Science: www.mon.gov.ru

Russian Ministry of Energy: www.minenergo.gov. ru

Russian Ministry of Natural Resources and Ecology: www.mnr.gov.ru

Russian Federal Service of State Statistics: www.gks.ru

Russian Federal Archive Service: www.rusarchives.ru

Russian State Library: www. rsl.ru

Scientific Electronic Library: elibrary.ru

Economic History Center, Moscow State University: www.hist.msu.ru.

Other Works by Vagit Alekperov

I. BOOKS

Alekperov, Vagit. *Russian Vertically Integrated Oil Companies: Methodology of Formation and Realization* [*Vertikalno integrirovannyye neftyanyye kompanii Rossii: metodologiya formirovaniya i realizatsiya*]. Moscow, 1996.

Alekperov, Vagit. *Russian Oil: A Top Manager's View* [*Neft Rossii: vzglyad top-menedzhera*]. Moscow, 2001.

II. ARTICLES

Alekperov, Vagit. "In the Name of Universal Energy Security." *Mezhdunarodnaya zhizn* ["International Affairs"] (special issue), April 2010.

Alekperov, Vagit. "Not People for Oil, But Oil for the People." *Rossiyskaya gazeta* ["Russian News"], December 18, 2008.

Alekperov, Vagit. "Russia: New Sources of Growth." *Financial Times*, April 10, 2008.

Alekperov, Vagit. "In the Key Information Sphere." *Oil of Russia*, No. 1, 2008.

Alekperov, Vagit. "Oil: The Blood of War." *Krasnaya zvezda* ["Red Star"], May 5, 2007.

Alekperov, Vagit. "2007: The Year of Deep Conversion." *Rossiyskaya gazeta*, February 9, 2007.

Alekperov, Vagit. "The Main Resource." *Izvestia*, November 17, 2006.

Alekperov, Vagit. "Russia's Competitiveness Will Depend on the Level of Training of Young Specialists." *Parlamentskaya gazeta* ["Parliamentary News"], September 26, 2006.

Alekperov, Vagit. "Always Moving Forward." *Oil of Russia*, No. 4, 2006.

Alekperov, Vagit. "On the Wave of Success." *Neft Rossii* ["Oil of Russia"], No. 7, 2006.

Alekperov, Vagit. "Staying at the Top." *Oil of Russia*, No. 2, 2005.

Alekperov, Vagit. "In Search of Competitive Advantages." *Neft Rossii*, No. 2, 2005.

Alekperov, Vagit. "Government Objectives in the Oil Sector." *Neft Rossii*, No. 6, 2004.

Alekperov, Vagit. "Relying on Advanced Science and Technology." *Oil of Russia*, No. 2, 2004.

Alekperov, Vagit. "Oncoming Traffic." *Sotsialnoye partnërstvo* ["The Social Partnership"], No. 1, 2004.

Alekperov, Vagit. "Our Strategy: Steady Growth Toward the Future." *Neft Rossii*, No. 7, 2003.

Alekperov, Vagit. "A Businesslike Energy Dialogue in Progress." *Oil of Russia*, No. 3, 2003.

Alekperov, Vagit. "The Advantages of Competition." *Oil of Russia*, No. 2, 2003.

Alekperov, Vagit. "The Locomotive of the Russian Economy." *Neft Rossii*, No. 1, 2003.

Alekperov, Vagit. "Oil Potential." *Neft Rossii*, No. 9, 2002.

Alekperov, Vagit. "We Are Responding to the Challenge of the Times." *Neft Rossii*, No. 7, 2002.

Alekperov, Vagit. "Time for Decisive Action." *Oil of Russia*, No. 4–5, 2002.

Alekperov, Vagit. "Working Against the Clock." *Oil of Russia*, No. 1, 2002.

Alekperov, Vagit. "Consolidation is the Way." *Neft Rossii*, No. 1, 2002.

Alekperov, Vagit. "The Interests of the Company and Society Are Congruent." *Neft Rossii*, No. 6, 2001.

Alekperov, Vagit. "The Successor of Western Siberia." *Neft Rossii*, No. 4, 2001.

Alekperov, Vagit. "The Oil Industry Has Recovered." *Ekonomika i zhizn* ["Economy and Life"], No. 4, 2001.

Alekperov, Vagit. "Moving Toward New Horizons." *Oil of Russia*, No. 3, 2001.

Alekperov, Vagit. "Forging Ahead Toward Our Strategic Objectives." *Oil of Russia*, No. 2, 2001.

Alekperov, Vagit. "The Main Problem is a Lack of Investment." *Promyshlenny mir* ["Industrial World"], No. 2, 2001.

Alekperov, Vagit. "Into the Future with Confidence." *Oil of Russia*, No. 1, 2001.

Alekperov, Vagit. "Growth Along All Azimuths." *Neft Rossii*, No. 5–6, 2000.

Alekperov, Vagit. "LUKOIL's Foothold in Siberia." *Oil of Russia*, No. 2, 2000.

Alekperov, Vagit. "A Strategic Policy Is Being Implemented." *Neft Rossii*, No. 2, 2000.

Alekperov, Vagit. "LUKOIL's Northern Route." *Oil of Russia*, No. 1, 2000.

Alekperov, Vagit. "If Not for LUKOIL...." *Vremya MN*, November 5, 1999.

Alekperov, Vagit. "Everything Must Be Considered." *Nezavisimaya gazeta* ["Independent News"], August 27, 1999.

Alekperov, Vagit. "The Caspian: A Gate to the Future." *Oil of Russia*, No. 2, 1999.

Alekperov, Vagit. "The Economy Needs Ecologization." *Neft Rossii*, No. 2, 1999.

Alekperov, Vagit. "To Boldly Enter the 21st Century." *Argumenty i fakty*, January 27, 1999.

Alekperov, Vagit. "LUKOIL and the Regions of Russia." *Oil of Russia*, No. 1, 1999.

Alekperov, Vagit. "Capacity Building." *Sotsialnoye partnёrstvo*, No. 1, 1999.

Alekperov, Vagit. "On the Threshold of the 21st Century." *Neft Rossii*, No. 5, 1998.

Alekperov, Vagit. "Getting a Glimpse of the Future." *Russian Economy*, No. 4, 1998.

Alekperov, Vagit. "Gambling on the Future—Under Any Circumstances." *Sotsialnoye partnёrstvo*, No. 3, 1998.

Alekperov, Vagit. "LUKOIL: Today and Tomorrow." *Oil of Russia*, No. 3, 1998.

Alekperov, Vagit. "We Aren't Politicians, We Are Making Money." *Estonia*, March 19, 1998.

Alekperov, Vagit. "Looking into the Future." *Neft Rossii*, No. 2, 1998.

Alekperov, Vagit. "LUKOIL: Consolidating Power." *Oil of Russia*, No. 2, 1998.

Alekperov, Vagit. "On the Way to the Top of the World." *Oil of Russia*, No. 1, 1998.

III. INTERVIEWS AND PRESENTATIONS

"Responsibility for Energy: Interview with Vagit Alekperov." *Rossiyskaya gazeta*, November 11, 2010.

"Innovations. Oil Horizons: Interview with Vagit Alekperov." *Kompaniya* ["Company"], February 15, 2010.

"We Are a European Company: Interview with Vagit Alekperov." *European Energy Review*, Vol. 2, No. 5, July–August 2009.

"I Have a Strong Soviet Upbringing: Interview with Vagit Alekperov." *Vedomosti* ["Gazette"], September 1, 2008.

"Declining Production Is Already a Trend: Interview with Vagit Alekperov." *Smart Money*, May 12, 2008.

"We Are Turning a New Page in Oil Production: Interview with Vagit Alekperov." *Rossiyskaya gazeta*, June 28, 2007.

"We Are Comfortable in Projects with Government Capital: Interview with Vagit Alekperov." *RBK Daily*, February 26, 2007.

"The Company's Upstream Reserves Allow Us to Look Confidently Toward the Future: Interview with Vagit Alekperov." *Neft i kapital* ["Oil and Capital"], December 31, 2006.

"The Gasoline Is Yours, the Ideas Are Ours: Interview with Vagit Alekperov." *Itogi* ["Results"], November 27, 2006.

"The Chinese Have More Opportunities Than We Do: Interview with Vagit Alekperov." *Vedomosti*, August 31, 2006.

"We Should Be Responsible: Interview with Vagit Alekperov." *Rossiyskaya gazeta*, July 12, 2006.

"We Have Huge Overhauls Underway: Interview with Vagit Alekperov." *Vedomosti*, June 23, 2004.

"LUKOIL: The Caspian Is a Strategic Region: Interview with Vagit Alekperov." *Neft i gaz Kazakhstana* ["Oil and Gas of Kazakhstan"], No. 4–5, 2004.

"LUKOIL: Only Takes Part in Profitable Projects: Interview with Vagit Alekperov." *Biznes and Baltiya* ["Business and the Baltics"], March 19, 2004.

"LUKAgip, Yalama, Zykh-Govsany: Vagit Alekperov's Responses to Questions from the Russian and Azerbaijani Media." *Neftyanyye vedomosti* ["Petroleum Gazette"], February 12, 2004.

"We Are Putting Forward New Initiatives: Vagit Alekperov's Responses to Questions from Kazakh Media." *Neftyanyye vedomosti*, December 11, 2003.

"We Believe in Kazakhstan! Interview with Vagit Alekperov." *Novoye pokoleniye* ["New Generation"], October 20, 2003.

"We Are Interested in Everything in Southern Europe: Interview with Vagit Alekperov." *Kommersant*, September 8, 2003.

"Drawing on the Market and Scientific Achievements: Interview with Vagit Alekperov." *Industriya* ["Industry"], No. 37, 2003.

"God Shorted Us on Climate, But Gave Us Natural Resources: Interview with Vagit Alekperov." *Profil* ["Profile"], No. 33, 2003.

"The Fewer Players, the Better: Interview with Vagit Alekperov." *Neftyanyye vedomosti*, June 27, 2003.

"We Are Ready for Dynamic Development: Interview with Vagit Alekperov." *Izvestia*, June 26, 2003.

"Russia Regains Its Leadership in Oil Production: Interview with Vagit Alekperov." *Interfax*, June 25, 2003.

"LUKOIL in Kazakhstan: A Strategic Alliance: Interview with Vagit Alekperov." *Neftyanyye vedomosti*, June 10, 2003.

"Russia Needs Large, Strong Companies: Interview with Vagit Alekperov." *Bolshoy biznes* ["Big Business"], No. 4, 2003.

"The Advantages of Competition: Interview with Vagit Alekperov." *Izvestia*, March 7, 2003.

"We Are Looking Optimistically Both at the Current Situation and Long-Term Prospects: Interview with Vagit Alekperov." *Neft i kapital*, No. 6, 2002.

"Oil Potential: Interview with Vagit Alekperov." *Izvestia*, June 27, 2002.

"LUKOIL Casts Its Net in the U.S. Gasoline Sea: Interview with Vagit Alekperov." *Amerika*, No. 2, 2002.

"Our Company's Employees Are More Valuable Than 'Black Gold': Interview with Vagit Alekperov." *Komsomolskaya pravda* ["Communist Youth League Truth"], November 27, 2001.

"LUKOIL Won't Pay Any Price, It Will Pay a Reasonable Price: Interview with Vagit Alekperov." *Kompaniya* ["Company"], No. 41, 2001.

"Russian-Arab Cooperation: Borders of Partnership: Interview with Vagit Alekperov." *Arabsky Mir* ["Arab World"], No. 6, 2001, p. 21 [in Russian and Arabic].

"Tested by the North: Interview with Vagit Alekperov." *Neftegazovaya vertikal* ["Oil and Gas Vertical"], No. 5, 2001.

"The Oil Formula: Interview with Vagit Alekperov." *Ekspert* ["Expert"], No. 4, 2001.

"LUKOIL to Implement First Major Russian-Azerbaijani Project: Interview with Vagit Alekperov." *Caspian Energy*, No. 3, 2001.

"The Authorities and Business Should Become Partners: Interview with Vagit Alekperov." *Inzhenernaya gazeta* ["Engineering News"], No. 35, 2000.

"We're Interested in Everything! Interview with Vagit Alekperov." *Vedomosti*, July 5, 2000.

"LUKOIL: The Boundaries of Leadership: Interview with Vagit Alekperov." *Permskaya neft* ["Perm Oil"], No. 9, 2000.

"LUKOIL Needs Money, Not Stock: Interview with Vagit Alekperov." *Vedomosti*, September 13, 1999.

"The Crisis Hasn't Altered Our Plans: Interview with Vagit Alekperov." *Rossiyskaya gazeta*, July 3, 1999.

"Strength Test: Interview with Vagit Alekperov." *Permskaya neft*, No. 3, 1999.

"Oil Giants Employ Slick Moves to Beat Hard Times: Interview with Vagit Alekperov." *Russia Review*, September 11, 1998.

"The Crisis of the Real Economy: Ways Out: Interview with Vagit Alekperov." *Izvestia*, September 11, 1998.

"LUKOIL's Alekperov Expands Firm's Horizons Beyond Russia: Interview with Vagit Alekperov." *World Oil*, No. 1, 1998.

Index

Acknowledgments

The book you see before you is yet another result of my six years' work supervising a creative team of scientists to realize the plan of the Oil and Gas Section at the Russian Academy of Natural Sciences (RANS), which was preparing to publish a scientific historical trilogy: *The Eve of the Petroleum Era* [*Predvestiye ery nefti*] (2003), *Soviet Union's Oil* [*Neft strany Sovetov*] (2005), and *New Russia's Oil* [*Neft novoy Rossii*] (2007), which was to fill in many gaps in the history of the Russian oil industry.

I would like to express once again my gratitude to all the colleagues and collaborators who participated in this project and thereby made a substantial contribution to reconstructing an objective picture of the events of our distant and recent past in this key branch of the Russian economy.

I am especially grateful to Professor Aleksandr Vasilenko, Doctor of Political Science and Academician of the RANS, for his active assistance in the work on this book, which contributed many productive and mature thoughts and ideas.

I am also very thankful to Alexander Matveychuk, Candidate of History and Academician of the RANS, for his valuable advice and recommendations, which proved very constructive in the writing of this book.

I also express my deep gratitude to the following people for their assistance and great help: Professor Gadel Vakhitov, Academician of the RANS and Doctor of Engineering; Professor Aleksey Salomatin, Doctor of History; Boris Shpotov, Doctor of History; Irina Dyakonova, Doctor of History; Yury Zhukov, Doctor of History; Professor Yury Yershov, Doctor of Economics; Professor Vladimir Kostornichenko, Doctor of Economics; Professor Aleksandr Bessolitsyn, Doctor of Economics, Professor Lenfrid Borozinets, Candidate of History; Sergey Dëgtev, Candidate of History; Olga Romanovskaya, Candidate of Engineering; and Mikhail Subbotin, Candidate of Economics.

I would also like to pay due respect in memory of the following project participants, who passed away prematurely in the last three years: Professor Igor Fuks, Academician of the RANS and Doctor of Engineering; Professor Aleksandr Igolkin, Corresponding Member of the RANS and Doctor of History; Professor Vladislav Kashchavtsev, Doctor of Engineering; and historian Valery Osinov.

About the Author

Vagit Alekperov was born September 1, 1950 in Baku, in an oilman's family. His father returned from World War II with a serious wound. After devoting the last eight years of his life fully to the Baku oil fields, he passed on when Vagit was three, leaving his widow Tatyana Alekperova with five children: three daughters and two sons.

Vagit Alekperov entered the work force in 1968 as a laboratory assistant in the hydromechanical laboratory of the Azerbaijan Scientific Research Institute of Oil Production. During his studies at the Meshadi Azizbeyov Azerbaijan Oil and Chemistry Institute, he mastered the occupation of oil and gas production operator. In 1974, on graduating from the institute, he received the specialty of mining engineer in the technology and comprehensive mechanization of oil and gas field development. That same year, he was appointed senior production engineer at Kaspmorneft [Caspian Offshore Oil] Production Association.

In 1979, he moved to Western Siberia and began the "Siberian chapter" of the biography of a young but already highly qualified specialist. He was soon appointed head of an oil and gas production shop at a production association of Surgutneftegaz [Surgut Oil and Gas]. From 1980 to 1983, he headed Surgutneftegaz production associations in the towns of Noyabrsk and Lyantor, Tyumen region. From 1983 to 1985, he worked as head of an oil and gas production administration at Bashneft [Bashkir Oil] Production Association in Kogalym, the Tyumen Region. In 1985, he was appointed first deputy director of Bashneft, responsible for the association's production operations in West Siberia. During this period, he proved himself to be a talented, proactive engineer and a skillful production organizer capable of solving the most difficult problems. In 1987, he was appointed general manager of Kogalymneftegaz [Kogalym Oil and Gas] Production Association. He worked there for three years, after which he was transferred to Moscow to serve as USSR deputy minister of the oil and gas industry, and was later appointed first deputy minister.

During this time, he attentively studied the experience of the world's leading oil companies and concluded that the Soviet Union needed to create vertically integrated joint-stock corporations. Thanks to the insistence of Vagit Alekperov and other like-minded entrepreneurs, the Russian Federation formed the country's first vertically integrated oil company, combining enterprises of the entire production cycle "from well to gas pump."

In 1992, Alekperov was appointed president of the Langepas-UrayKogalymneft [Langepas, Uray, and Kogalym Oil] state oil concern, which later became LUKOIL.

In 1993, Vagit Alekperov became chairman of the Board of Directors and Executive Board of LUKOIL Open Joint-Stock Company and was appointed the company's president.

Today, LUKOIL is one of the largest independent oil companies in Russia, with authorized capital of 21,264,081 rubles and 37.5 kopecks, divided into 850,563,255 shares of common stock. ING Bank (Eurasia) nominally holds 63.3% of LUKOIL's stock, and the American company ConocoPhillips holds a 20% interest in the company.

According to data audited by Miller and Lents, the company's proven hydrocarbon reserves as of January 1, 2010 were 17.5 billion barrels of oil equivalent, including 13.7 billion barrels of oil and 22.9 trillion cubic feet of gas.

In 2009, expansion of proven reserves through geologic exploration, operational drilling, and acquisitions totaled 782 million barrels of oil equivalent, or 95% of annual production volume. LUKOIL remains among the leaders of Russian and international companies in volume of proven reserves.

Vagit Alekperov is a doctor of economics and an active member of the Russian Academy of Natural Sciences. In recent years, he has chaired the Energy Policy Committee of the Russian Union of Industrialists and Entrepreneurs. He has written several monographs, including *Russia's Vertically Integrated Oil Companies* [*Vertikalno integrirovannye neft-yanyye kompanii Rossii*] (1999), and edited the anthologies *The Eve of the Petroleum Era* [*Predvestiye ery nefti*] (2003), *Soviet Union's Oil* [*Neft strany Sovetov*] (2005), and *New Russia's Oil* [*Neft novoy Rossii*] (2007).

He is actively involved in charitable activities. In 2007, he founded the Our Future Foundation of Regional Social Programs.

Vagit Alekperov was awarded the orders "For Service to the Fatherland" (3rd and 4th degrees), "Friendship of Nations," "Badge of Honor," the medal "For Exploitation and Development of the Oil and Gas Industry in Western Siberia," and Azerbaijan's highest state medal, the order Shohrat ("Glory"). He has also been awarded the Russian Federation Government Prize and many honorary titles from a number of Russian and international public organizations.

He is married, with one son.